THE PERMANENT GOETHE

THE PERMANENT GOETHE

Edited, Selected and with
an Introduction by
THOMAS MANN

A PERMANENT LIBRARY BOOK

THE DIAL PRESS
New York: 1948

Designed by Warren Chappell

PRINTED IN THE UNITED STATES OF AMERICA

Acknowledgments

TRANSLATIONS FROM GOETHE have been proceeding for about 175 years. The accumulation, in sheer numbers, is impressive yet some work still remained to be translated even for this selective edition; or existing translations proved too stilted and had to be replaced with new versions. For filling this gap I wish to make grateful acknowledgment to Mr. Stephen Spender for his new renderings of some of the poems; to Mr. Norbert Guterman for his translations of the *Proverbs in Prose*, the *Letters* and the *Essay on Granite*; and to Mr. Isidor Schneider for his translations of the *Proverbs in Rhyme*. To Mr. Schneider also I wish to give thanks for his help in combing through the many existing translations for the most satisfactory renderings. Acknowledgments are also gratefully tendered to Professor Gustav Arlt for his translation of my introduction. Finally I wish to express warm appreciation to the workers of the New York Public Library and the Nicholas Murray Butler Library at Columbia University for their intelligent and courteous services.

THOMAS MANN

April 1948

Table of Contents

Table of Contents

Table of Contents

Introduction

THE CHILD that was born in great labor of an eighteen-year-old mother in a Frankfurt patrician's home on the twenty-eighth of August, 1749, as the clock struck high noon, was livid and appeared to be dead. It seemed not to see the light, it seemed to have no intention of setting out upon a path of life that was to become long and broad, richly strewn with flowers, full of happy labor, rich with human fulfillment, exemplary. It seemed on the point of turning from the womb directly to the earth. Many minutes passed before the grandmother, crouching at the bed-side could call to the moaning woman: "Elizabeth, he's alive!" It was the cry of one woman to another, there, an animal sound, a cheerful, domestic message, nothing more. And yet it should have been addressed to the world, to all mankind. And even today, after two centuries, it holds its full measure of joy and will hold it for ages to come. As long as there is life and love on this earth, as long as life will love itself and not tire of its sweet sorrow nor turn wearily from itself, this cry from the lips of a woman, this unsuspecting annunciation, will ring and resound: "He's alive!"

The man-child who passed the dark portal that day, strangled and inert, was chosen to complete a tremendous span of life. He was ordained to develop incredible perseverance and to lead a life of truly canonical dimensions, to unfold mighty powers of growth and rejuvenation, to fulfill his human destiny completely, to win a majesty of existence before which kings and nations bowed, and whose natural origin he himself at one time, with due solemnity, made the subject of his investigation. Eighty-three

Translated by Gustav Arlt

years had gone by since the summer noon of his birth. Massive segments of history had rolled past him and had assailed his spirit: the Seven Years' War, America's struggle for independence, the French Revolution, the rise and fall of Napoleon, the dissolution of the Holy Roman Empire, the turn of the century with its transformation of the face and atmosphere of the world, the dawn of the bourgeois age, the machine age, the July Revolution. The octogenarian who had outlived everything stands at his desk, hoary and rigid, strange rings of old age around his pupils that lend an almost avian quality to his narrow-set, brown eyes—he stands at the desk of his intentionally uncomfortable study at Weimar in the house that had long since become a shrine to the human urge for veneration, and he writes his last letter, in sclerotic reverie and lucid contemplation, to an old friend, the philologist and statesman, Wilhelm von Humboldt in Berlin:

". . . The best genius is that which absorbs and assimilates every-thing without doing the least violence to its fundamental destiny—that which we call character—but rather improving and enhancing it as far as possible. . . . Through training, instruction, contemplation, success, failure, advancement, hindrance, and ever more contemplation, the organs of man, in their instinctive, free activity, unite the acquired with the innate *to produce a harmonious unity that astonishes the world.*— Faithfully your J. W. v. Goethe."

Grandiose simplicity, simple grandeur of self-evaluation! There is something childlike and something demonic about it, something delightful and awesome at once. Seventeen years earlier, at the age of sixty-six, he had drawn a similar picture of his existence in a poem that touches and shocks the reader like the phrase about the 'astonished world.' He was involved at the time in a belated, artistically opportune, certainly artistically fruitful love affair with a very young, only recently married woman, Marianne von Willemer, the Suleika of the *West-Eastern Divan.* It was not his final passion by any means, however. To that he succumbed at seventy-four, when His Excellency, the ranking minister of the sovereign Duchy of Saxe-Weimar, the world-renowned poet, turned once more into a ballroom lion at Marienbad, where he flirted and loved, billed and cooed, and set his heart upon marrying a seventeen-year-old sprig of a girl. Nothing came of it, for his family presented a united front and the little girl wasn't too anxious either—it must be added, however, *that she never married anyone else.* At any rate, at the age of sixty-six, head over heels

xii

in love and sentimentally loved in return under the eyes of an indulgent husband, he penned these rhymes:

> *This heart only blooms and flowers,*
> *Lives in ever youthful age;*
> *Under snows and misty showers*
> *Aetna's fires seethe and rage.*

> *Like the dawn, you touch with blushes*
> *Yonder mountain's gloomy spire,*
> *And through Hatim's heart there pulses*
> *Breath of spring and summer's fire.*

> *(Nur dies Herz, es ist von Dauer,*
> *Schwillt in jugendlichstem Flor,*
> *Unter Schnee und Nebelschauer*
> *Rast ein Aetna dir hervor.*

> *Du beschämst wie Morgenröte*
> *Jener Gipfel ernste Wand,*
> *Und noch einmal fühlet Hatem*
> *Frühlingshauch und Sommerbrand.)*

Raging Aetna is poetic hyperbole. As I know him, his heart never burned like a volcano for any woman; he was opposed to everything volcanic, even in the field of science. But: "Yonder mountain's gloomy spire"—what majesty lies in this quite unboastful, dispassionately truthful description of his self-esteem! To say of oneself, to have the right to say of oneself: I am like a mighty, towering mountain, awe-inspiring, inaccessible, in its gloomy grandeur, yet tenderly irradiated by a sweetness that does not fear grim greatness but that kisses it, transfigures it, touches it with blushes—the sweetness that is dawn!

For the non-German reader, moreover, the following comment is needed. The structure of the poem demands a rhyme in the third line of the second stanza to the word "Morgenröte." The rhyme-word which the author archly conceals under the Oriental name Hatem, the rhyme-word which the amused and startled ear, however, involuntarily supplies and is expected to supply, is the real name, *Goethe*—

We are confronted by a kind of magnificent Narcissism, a self-repleteness, much too serious, and striving too constantly for self-perfection, intensification, and re-distillation of its ingredients, to merit so trivial a word as vanity—a profound joy in the ego and in its evolution. It is this quality to which we owe *Poetry and Truth*, the best and certainly the most charming autobiography in the world, a novel in the first person, that tells in an inimitably pleasing tone how a genius grows, how good fortune and worth interweave in accordance with some inscrutable dispensation, and how a personality unfolds in the sunshine of higher grace . . . Personality! Goethe called it "the greatest good fortune of mortals," but what it really is, what constitutes it, wherein its mystery lies—for there is a mystery about it—not even he has revealed. With his love for the fitting, the exact word, he was not of the opinion that everything had to be said and explained. It is certain that with this word, this phenomenon, "personality," we leave the realm of the purely intellectual, rational, analyzable and enter the sphere of the natural, the elemental, the demonic, that "astonishes the world" without being subject to discussion.

A few days after Goethe's death Wilhelm von Humboldt, a remarkably clear-sighted person, commented on the strange fact that this man had exerted a mighty influence unconsciously, effortlessly, by the mere fact of his existence. "This," he wrote, "is *entirely separate* from his creative work as a thinker and writer; it lies in his great and unique personality." This sentence makes it clear that the word is nothing but a linguistic makeshift for something that language cannot describe, for an emanation whose sources do not lie in the intellectual but in the vital. Personality, attracting universal attention, exerting universal attraction, must be the result of a particular, intensely powerful but not crude, not simple vitality, compounded of strength and infirmity in proportions and in a process that represents one of the dark, laboratory secrets of nature.

A racial bloodstream courses through the centuries of German life, unnoticed, ordinary; Mother Nature is certainly not pursuing a goal, but in effect there is one: The One. And he will put these words into the mouth of his Iphigenia:

> *A clan does not bring forth a demigod,*
> *Does not produce a monster unforeseen;*
> *Only a line of good or evil men,*
> *Bring happiness or terror in the end.*

(. . . denn es erzeugt nicht gleich
Ein Haus den Halbgott, noch das Ungeheuer;
Erst eine Reihe Böser oder Guter
Bringt endlich das Entsetzen, bringt die Freude
Der Welt hervor.)

Demigod and monster—that is to say, the superhuman. He thinks of the two together, he takes the one for the other and knows that there is always a touch of terror in happiness, a touch of the monster in the demigod. In cool prose he says: "If families exist for a long time then it sometimes happens that just before their extinction they produce an individual who combines and fully expresses the qualities of all his ancestors in addition to their latent and unconsummated tendencies." Neatly formulated, dispassionately didactic, dedicated to the better understanding of man and of nature, thoughtfully deduced from his own superhuman existence. But how did it come about? How did the amalgamation proceed? Quite unostentatiously, quite humbly. Various clans breed and crossbreed, artisans, blacksmiths, butchers. In accordance with the old custom the migrant journeyman marries the master's daughter, the chambermaid from the earl's manor espouses the government surveyor or the county administrator—a harmless potpourri, stirred between birth and death, that looks like nothing important but then, gradually, begins to assume the dignity of property and culture, oppidanism and patricianism, until it eventually produces a city magistrate. So the Lindheimers intermarried with the Textors, a family that had immigrated to Frankfurt from South Germany, and the Textors with the Goethes, whose origin lay to the north, in the region between the Thuringian Forest and the Harz Mountains.

I believe that the Lindheimer blood from the vicinity of the old Roman frontier, where Mediterranean and barbarian bloodstreams had mingled from time immemorial, was the best, healthiest, most decisive element in the nature of the great poet: the heritage of his mother's mother, a Lindheimer by birth, a Textor by marriage, a sturdy, plain, gentle, brown-skinned woman. From her, judging by pictures, he inherited his forehead, the shape of his head and mouth, his Italian eyes and southern complexion; from this side, surely, he had his classical bent, the demand for form and clarity, his spirit, irony, and charm, his peculiar, sometimes critical, sometimes exasperated rejection of the German character.

And yet, at the same time, that German character was a very strong component in the form of the hearty, blunt folk-manner, his inheritance from Hans Sachs and Martin Luther, so that one may well say that such cool and sovereign criticism of things German has never come from a more German spirit, that there has never been a more German anti-barbarism . . .

Biologically the family combination that was to produce the phenomenon, the demi-god, certainly did not look too promising. His paternal grandfather, the tailor Friedrich Georg Goethe, was obviously failing in his faculties as he grew older. Twice married, he had eleven children, most of whom died in infancy. Of the three who survived him the oldest was undoubtedly of unsound mind and died at the age of forty-three, a hopeless idiot. The father of the poet, Johann Kaspar, was the tenth of the eleven children, a belated off-spring of his aging parents. He showed it. A jurist with the purchased title of "Imperial Counsellor," he was a strangely resentful, quarrelsome man, a morose recluse who never practised his vocation, a fanatical amateur collector and insufferable pedant, a querulous hypochondriac whose painful routine was disturbed by the slightest draught of air. Elisabeth, the cheerful daughter of the town magistrate and of Mother Lindheimer, married him when she was only seventeen, exactly half his age. She might have done better, for she spent her best years as nurse to a decrepit tyrant. Her progenitor, Johann Wolfgang Textor, must also have been a "blithe spirit," as Goethe used to call his mother, at least in his youth; that is to say, he seems to have been a Lothario, a reckless petticoat-chaser, who was occasionally caught in the act by irate husbands, but at the same time—strange mixture—he had prophetic powers, the gift of second sight, and in his old age (he died at eighty) he more than made up for the frivolities of his youth in seriousness, taciturnity, sternness, and dignity. His final years were spent in a wheel chair as an imbecile invalid.

Elisabeth, the wife of the Imperial Counsellor, gave birth to six children; four of whom returned to the realm of shadows within a few days. Only one sister, along with Wolfgang, survived infancy, Cornelia, an unfortunate, sullen creature, afflicted with neurotic psoriasis, a frigid, sexless girl, destined to be a nun rather than a wife, as her brother said. Nevertheless she married only to die in childbed, to which she had looked forward with abhorrence. He alone lived, and he lived for all six of them, one might say, although not in the vigor and health that the others had lacked and that he had grasped for himself in metaphysical greed.

One of his grandsons, who were only wisps of men, used to say in melancholy self-derision: "My grandfather was a giant (Hühne) and I am only a little chicken (Hühnchen),"—a clever but totally untranslatable pun. But the giant had his weaknesses. Tuberculosis, latent for years, seems to run through his entire mighty life. As a student in Leipzig, where he overstepped his physical bounds, once in youthful incontinence and once in a fit of melancholy depression, he suffered a hemorrhage and returned home as a broken youth, a total failure in his studies, to his deeply disappointed parents. And at the age of eighty-one, after the death of his unfortunate son, a recurrence of the terrible attack took place. Incredible to relate, with the phlebotomy which the physicians ordered, he lost five pounds of blood—the octogenarian rose from his sick-bed and compensating by "will and character" for the failure of "spontaneously active nature," he completed the fourth act of *Faust*.

Recovered from the lingering illness that had repeatedly brought him to the edge of the grave, the youth—this rearing, kicking thoroughbred colt, this unmatured genius—must have made a mixed impression upon young and old, great and small, an impression that provoked irritated laughter and exerted irresistible charm. We see him at Strassburg, at the age of twenty to twenty-three, where he continues his studies of law amid many fantastically esoteric, poetically esthetic digressions from his prescribed course; we see him again at Wetzlar-an-der-Lahn, with the title of "Licentiate" (or "Doctor") of Laws, ostensibly practicing at the Imperial Supreme Court, but in reality doing nothing except loving, suffering, dreaming, loafing, and letting his spirit grow. And everywhere he provokes annoyed laughter by his mannerisms in dress and behavior, by his insufferable "presumptuosity" and callow immaturity, and everywhere, he also radiates charm by his youthful fire, his scintillating talent, the almost physically palpable, galvanic force of his animal spirits—and all of it tempered by the indescribable naivete and good nature of a nice, perhaps slightly pampered but well-meaning youth.

He was very handsome at that time, a friend of children and of the common people, in other words, of nature. At the same time he was "very flighty and sparrow-like," according to Herder's characterization, "a high-strung young lord with the horribly scraping feet of a cockerel," that is, when he was not submerged in the melancholy depths of lovesickness or uncontrolled Weltschmerz and not experimenting with a knife which he pushed a little deeper into his flesh near the heart every day. "I don't know what kind of attraction I exert upon people," he wrote, "so many of them like me." But this "attraction" must have been at its height when the twenty-six-year-old, already widely known author of magnificent songs, of *Götz von Berlichingen*, of *Werther*, and of a few incredibly novel and gripping fragments of a Faust-poem made his triumphal entry into Weimar as the favorite of the young duke—presumably for a brief visit, actually to spend his life there. Wieland, the tutor of the young princes there, a man of forty-two, was the mouthpiece of the general enthusiasm when he wrote, a few days after the arrival of the guest from Frankfurt: "Since this morning my soul is as full of Goethe as a dew-drop of the morning sun." And in these lines of verse he reveals the full depth of his emotion:

> *With a pair of regal dark eyes,*
> *With magic divinely scintillant,*
> *Able alike to kill and enchant,*
> *He came as a ruler, ready to reign,*
> *A genuine king of the spirit domain.*
> . . . .
>
> *Never before in God's time*
> *Has been seen man so sublime,*
> *In whom all goodness and all might*
> *Of mankind's character unite!*
> . . . .
>
> *Who, by her burden unoppressed,*
> *Holds all of nature in his breast,*
> *Who burrows deep in every soul,*
> *And yet grasps living as a whole,*
> *He is indeed a sorcerer.*
> *Oh, how he plays upon our hearts,*
> *Torments and stabs with gentle darts!*
> *He stirs us with profoundest feeling*
> *And touches us with blissful pain,*
> *Our deepest hidden springs revealing . . .*

This effusive adulation may serve as a measure of the vital magnetism, the blazing spiritual force that must have emanated from this man after he had passed through the colt and sparrow stage, when he began to have a presentiment of the deep and grave import of his mission on earth, when he used his youthful flamboyancy only as a foil to the high spirits of the young sovereign who loved him, while he sought secretly—and successfully—to teach him seriousness, industry, and goodness.

The removal to Weimar and his entry into the service, or rather, the government of the small state, viewed from the outside, was a matter of pure chance—chance, however, that served the inner plan of his life, the decree of that which Goethe called the "leadership from above." For no writer's life and work were ever more closely knit, more inseparably joined, so that his work consisted solely of experience, expression, lyrical confession, while his life served the predestined work. When Goethe, in the mid seventeen-seventies, made the acquaintance at Karlsruhe of Crown Prince Karl August through the mediation of two aristocratic admirers, the Counts Stolberg, he was engaged to Lili Schönemann, the rich and charming daughter of a Frankfurt patrician. Whether the engagement was based on love or infatuation, the happy young fiancé was deeply unhappy in his heart over the untoward folly—untoward as far as his work was concerned—which he was about to commit. He was mysteriously plagued by pangs of conscience over the prospect of civil fixation and marital tranquillization in his life. His conscience urged him— not for the first time—to take flight, and the trip to Switzerland in the company of the two enthusiastic young noblemen was a flight. His heart cried: "I must get out into the world!" and he echoed the cry on paper. But the voice that uttered this cry, along with him or even through him, was the voice of the central figure of his favorite work, his life work, then still in a phase of charming, youthful immaturity but destined to mighty maturity and age; and with this cry it made the author himself the "central figure": It was the voice of Faust who wanted to be led out into the world, into the world of affairs, among other places to the court of a duke. And Goethe arrived at the court of a duke.

Karl August of Saxe-Weimar, so says his biographer, had fallen in love twice on this trip: once with the beautiful Princess Louise of Hesse-Darmstadt and the second time with Dr. Goethe. When they met again a little later in Frankfurt, Karl August was a reigning sovereign and married. He took both of them home with him, his sweetheart and his favorite. In his little capital city and in the villages, hunting-grounds and riding courses nearby he amused himself enormously, sovereignly, and extravagantly with his protégé and heaped upon him confidence, honor, and authority which, in the opinion of his staid old advisors, were quite inappropriate for this inexperienced young man, this socalled "original genius," this recently arrived lawyer and poet from Frankfurt.

It is a matter of record that Karl August did not share their views. "You will agree," he wrote to his grumbling, protesting Prime Minister, a certain von Fritsch, who threatened to resign, "that a man like this could never stand the dull, mechanical work in a government office if he started at the bottom. Failure to use a man of genius in a spot where he can apply his extraordinary talents amounts to misuse." And so he appointed Goethe, at the age of twenty-seven, to the post of Privy Legation Counsellor with a chair and a vote in the cabinet and a salary of 1,200 Talers; and at thirty-three to the post of Minister with the titles of Acting Privy Counsellor and Excellency; and in the same year he prevailed upon the Emperor to raise him to the hereditary nobility— though the latter made no great impression on Goethe, since "we Frankfurt patricians had always considered ourselves peers of the nobility." Moreover he never regarded his elevation as something fantastic or overwhelming, much as it reminds one of Joseph's elevation by Pharaoh. In a little self-analysis he writes: "I have never known a more presumptuous person than myself, and the fact that I say it is proof that what I say is true. I never thought of something to be attained; I always thought I already had it. If someone had placed a crown on my head I would have taken it as a matter of course. But that I always sought by hard work to deserve what I had grasped beyond my powers, to merit what had come to me without my desert, in that respect alone I differed from a true megalomaniac."

Those are not the words of an inordinately ambitious person, of a boaster. They are the words of a naturally favored man, one to whom everything comes of itself but one who is a serious mortal and willing to work to earn his own. Someone who looked at one of his late portraits remarked that this was a man who had suffered much. Goethe replied that he preferred to phrase it more actively and to say: "That's a man who took great pains."

And he truly took great pains as favorite minister and "Second in the Realm," as he called himself once, probably not unmindful of Joseph, as the wise manager and pedagogical Mentor of the Duke and as the soul of the Weimar Government. For ten years, after his boundlessly trusting ruler had also made him President of the Chamber of Deputies, he was the factotum of the little state, "the marrow of things," as someone said in surprise and derision. Meanwhile his fame as an author almost faded while he himself tried to suppress his golden gift, his natural calling. "As far as I am able," he wrote at this time, "I withdraw the water from these fountains and cascades and divert it to the mills and irrigation works." And what are these mills and irrigation works? Excise tax orders, regulations for the cotton industry, military recruitment, building of canals and roads, almshouses, mines and stone quarries, finances, and a hundred other things. In this sacrifice he directed himself fanatically with such slogans as, "Iron patience! Stony persistence!" And he succeeded in many respects, in establishing order and economy in a rather down-at-heels, little, eighteenth century state.

Finally, however, he came to the conclusion: "How much better off I would be if I could forget political quarrels and devote my powers to the sciences and the arts, for which I was born! With reluctance I tore myself from Aristotle to give my attention to leaseholds and public pasturage. I am a private citizen by nature and I can't understand how fate managed to patch me into a government position and into a princely family." And his conclusion is this: "Whoever devotes himself to administration without being a ruling prince, is either a Philistine, a scoundrel, or a fool."

In one of his memorable comments he said: "Whether a man expresses his genius in science or in war or in government, or whether he composes a song, it is all the same; the only thing that matters is that the idea, the formulation, the act must live and continue to live." This is directed against the narrow esthetic concept of genius of his time; it is the word of a man who made no compromises, an integral man, who knew that a great poet is first of all great and only in the second place a poet. And yet it became evident that to regard the object of devoted activity as something immaterial and interchangeable, "a mere parable," was going too far. In time grief and sickness overcome him when Pegasus is forced to turn the mill. Goethe grieved and became ill, he grew tactiturn, he faded physically, and he fled—fled once more, head over heels. Again a seraphically enervating love affair was partly responsible: an affair with a lady of the court, Frau von Stein, a somewhat obscure, strangely ecstatic, not quite wholesome passion, that ruled over a decade of his life, an incredibly protracted, half-mystic surrender which—had it lasted longer, had he not escaped when he did—would surely have done serious harm to his nature, to his earthiness, his autochthonism, without which his creative gift was exposed to the danger of pallid dilution and debilitation.

At the same time it was not entirely unfruitful, this queer passion that probably never flowered into a real love affair. *Iphigenia, Tasso,* even Mignon's ardent songs of longing are its product. And yet, when Goethe says that the chief object of his Italian journey—this hastily planned and secretly executed flight —had been "to cure him of the physical and moral ills that tormented him in Germany," we may connect Charlotte's name with them though he himself was too considerate to mention it.

And so it was Italy next, a two years' vacation under the classical sky, in the midst of a southern people, a period devoted to the contemplation of antiquity and of great art, a cultural experience richer than the polite and chivalrous love affair in Weimar would have afforded him. To grasp the meaning and character of this experience as a whole, this transformation and re-formation, is not easy for us today. Even the literary historians and Goethe-scholars know a good deal less about it than they will admit. It is impossible to feel with him the emotions of happiness, of liberation, of renascence which he expresses in countless exclamations: "I had a second birthday, a true rebirth, on the day when I entered Rome"; "a new youth, a second youth, a new man, a new life"; "I feel changed into the innermost marrow of my bones"—exclamations in many letters, among them those addressed to Charlotte, whom he had left without a farewell. The nature of the affair seems to have been a preordained, intended, existentially necessary and immediate re-integration of his person, of his disparate tendencies, his natural and spiritual, scientific and artistic, sensual and moral tendencies—"definitely, vitally, and coherently," to use his own words. *Totality* is the quality for which he was striving, the word which was constantly on his lips at this time. "Natural history, art, manners, etc. are becoming amalgamated in me. I feel that the sun of my strength is merging." It merged in the contemplation of antiquity which he no longer regards with the eye of the esthete but as a magnificent natural growth, to which he develops a much stronger and at the same time higher and hardier relationship than he had had before, or under the aegis of Charlotte, when it was classicistic rather than classic. The latter had been culture, restraint, civilization, at bottom something quite anti-pagan and anti-natural—while the coalescence and unification of the concepts "antiquity" and "nature" were the essential fruits of his stay in Italy. There, as he said later, "the formerly cramped and constricted child of nature could again breathe the air of freedom."

What the experience of pagan simplicity, of the naturalness of southern folk-life meant to him, can be measured. It meant happiness and totality. "Incidentally," he writes, "I made the acquaintance of happy people, who are happy only because they are whole . . . That quality I too will and must attain . . . I would rather choose death than the life of the past few years." It is incredible that he should write this to Madame von Stein, of all people, who must have read between these lines the rupture in their relations before it took place. Every word that he then wrote is primarily directed against her and her ethereal sphere. "My existence has acquired substance that gives it the necessary weight; I am no longer afraid of the *ghosts* that often used to play with me." What is the opposite of the ghostly? The stable. "Whoever looks around here earnestly with eyes that see must become *stable*, he must acquire a concept of stability more vital than ever before." And his conception of love now became stable, pagan, classical, simple, and "whole," for, to quote the *Roman Elegies*, "Desire followed the glance, enjoyment followed desire." In 1795 the spirituelle Charlotte had to read these words in print. She must have raised her eyes to heaven.

We can only guess and tentatively reconstruct the other factors that contributed to his epoch-making consolidation, to the coming-of-age of his personality: The contact with the Mediterranean character, to which his blood in some manner had an affinity, with the non-German—that had a beneficent, liberating effect on him; with historical greatness—that flattered his instinct for greatness. At any rate, it is fact that Italy put the finishing touches on this urbane genius, this well-bred Titan, this European German, who shows a characteristically German face to the world at large, but a European face to his own nation

And so he returned to the little Thuringian capital at the age of thirty-nine, with the assurance of the Duke that in the future he would have only the honors but not the responsibilities of his high position, that is, that he would have only the general superintendence over theatres and educational institutions, in order to devote himself to his work. A remarkable ruler, this miniature Pharaoh, who had so much of an eye, instinct, and feeling for the singularity of his Joseph. Among the rulers of Germany he is a unique and eternally estimable figure. A pleasant little detail is his order that Goethe, whenever he wished to attend a meeting of the cabinet or the chamber, should be entitled to the seat reserved for the Duke himself. And to think that Goethe, in his capacity as Minister, had reduced the Duke's standing army of six hundred soldiers by two hundred and ninety!

He returned into the midst of petty, esthetically pretentious or crude, narrow-minded, primly gossiping, prudish provincials, while he himself was a changed man, settled, perfected, experienced and self-sufficient, with an established sense of perspective —a lonely man at heart. To reveal himself, to communicate confidentially with others had become very difficult. He was accused of banally conventional behavior, of using stilted expressions, of exhibiting annoying pretensions, of being hard to understand. He no longer had intimate contact with his old friends; everyone felt the chill emanating from him. After a social evening at his house where he temporized by exhibiting sketches, the remark was made: "We all felt decidedly uncomfortable." His magnanimity became condescension, reserved politeness. Schiller, who was scarcely noticed by Goethe during the first winter he spent in Weimar, put it as follows: "He has the talent to captivate people, to make himself agreeable by minor as well as major favors, but he always manages to keep himself aloof. He makes his existence pleasantly felt, but only like a god, without giving any part of himself." This is the comment of a man whose observation has been made more acute by humiliation.

There is Madame Herder, for example, Karoline Herder, the wife of the famous clergyman, philosopher of art, and folksong collector, Goethe's Strassburg mentor, whom he had brought to Weimar as archdeacon of the state church. She remarked: "He wants to have nothing to do with his friends any more. He is no longer of any use to Weimar." She also said in the typical Weimar tone: "Oh, if he could only put a little feeling into his creations, if only that *note of licentiousness* were not always in

evidence, or as he calls it himself, that coquettish manner!" Dear
admirable Karoline! She is quite right. He himself informed his
Egeria of yesteryear, Frau von Stein, that, "My virtues are increasing but my virtue is diminishing." It cannot be said more
tersely or more distressingly. Italy, antiquity, and contact with
great art had not made him more sympathetic. A shocking note
had now been added to the bewildering ones in his character: a
decided sensuality, untempered by the pangs of a Christian conscience, defiant toward its social grimaces; a pagan attitude, in
short, that prompted his well-read friends—and they were all
well-read—to nickname him "Priapus."

He drove his forsaken Iphigenia and Princess d'Este, Madame
Stein, to wild-eyed despair, and all people of standing and morals
to shocked indignation by taking unto his bed and board a very
pretty and thoroughly uneducated little flower-girl, *un bel pezzo
di carne*, Christiane Vulpius by name. It was a liaison of provoking
profligacy, which he legalized only many years later and which
society never forgave him or her. She bore him several children
of whom only one, August, was to reach middle age—a burden
both to himself and to his father, for he was an unfortunate creature, drunken and dissolute, intemperate, brutal, and weak, a
poor desperate soul from the start.

The durable physique of his progenitor went through various
phases whose appearance we know from pictures, sketches, sil-
houettes, and the description of contemporaries. In his youth he
had resembled a dandified Apollo or perhaps rather Hermes
(except for his rather short legs). At the beginning of the century in which he survived a full generation, his body assumed
a ponderous corpulence already burgeoning in Italy. There were
years in which his potentially beautiful face was fat and sullen
with hanging jowls. In his old age, however, his appearance again
approached that of the youth, except that Apollo or Hermes had
turned into Jupiter, a majestic Jupiter, half king and half father,
as Grillparzer said: a marvellous head with a splendid, craggy
brow, surmounted by profuse, well-kept hair that was curled and
lightly powdered daily; a pair of dominating black eyes, flashing
with spirit except when they were veiled with sulky fatigue; very
distinguished, well-chosen clothing, a trifle conservative, even
old-fashioned in style. The stiffness which, as dignified preten-
tiousness, had already marked the youth, became more and more
characteristic of the aging man: a deliberate ceremoniousness, a

crotchetiness, a restrained conventionality, which frequently reduced his conversation to the level of an ordinary, well-educated official, so that many an enthusiastic visitor left the author of *Werther* and *Wilhelm Meister* chilled and disenchanted. His paternal heritage, that of old Johann Kaspar, began to come into spectral prominence: his unbending pedantry, his old-maidish tidiness, also his splenetic collector's mania and his curious bustling busyness. We need not doubt that he was fully aware of this glorified recessivism, that he recognized the old man in himself, and that he smiled to himself with ghostly cheerfulness as he sublimated the father-prototype.

In that period, that is between the ages of seventy and eighty, he was already far more than the author of *Werther* and *Faust*—he had become an almost mythical figure, the leading representative of Occidental culture, and he viewed himself with the eyes of the historian. He was a towering personality of the highest intellectual solemnity, to whom people made pilgrimages from everywhere, from all Europe and even from beyond the ocean—with reverence and often with trembling knees. Those who wore spectacles used to take them off in the anteroom, since it was well known that he hated to look into reflecting glasses. Visitors who had travelled, who had seen or experienced something of interest, were cross-examined. With the command: "Stop, let's go farther into this matter!" he would elicit exact information. He wanted to know everything, he wanted to acquire all facts that others happened to possess. And they were in good hands when he took charge of them. If someone proved especially interesting and useful he was invited to stay to dinner; he was wined and dined to a king's taste and pumped dry. Perhaps he was permitted to see something of the collections with which the elegant house on the Frauenplan, a gift of the Duke, later the Grand Duke, was crammed: copperplate engravings, medals, minerals, antiques. "I possess," said the old man, "the coins of all the popes since the fifteenth century. This collection is essential to the history of art. I know all the engravers. Greek coin engraving of the time of Alexander and earlier has never been equalled." This was only a small province of the empire of learning which he commanded and whose symbols he collected in portfolios, boxes and showcases.

He was one of the most comprehensive, most diversified dilettantes that ever lived, a pan-amateur. Nor was he in the least disturbed when it was suggested to him that with so many interests —physics, botany, osteology, mineralogy, geology, zoology, anatomy, etc., not to mention the fine arts—his real gift, his poetic genius would suffer. "Who can say," was his opinion, "that dilettantism is not poetry and that the essential thing is something quite different, namely *universality?*" He wrote a book on the theory of colors, in the very first draft of which his friend Schiller found "many significant features of a general history of science and of human thought." In fact, the historical portion of the book is, as Goethe had intended, something like a parable of the history of all sciences, a novel of European thought through the milennia.

The tremendous esteem in which the man was held was, of course, primarily based upon the scope and magnificence of his creative writing. It is quite certain, on the other hand, that his amateur interests and scientific "hobbies" contributed largely to his magic fame as a sage and wove an aura of majesty about him that occasionally found expression in epistolary addresses. His French correspondents called him "Monseigneur," a title normally reserved for a prince. An Englishman wrote: "To His Serene Highness, Prince Goethe in Weimar." "That," explained the old gentleman, "is probably because people like to call me the prince of poets." When he had passed away, the Germans—even those who had read none of his works—said to each other: "Have you heard? The great Goethe has died." It sounded almost like "The great God Pan is dead."

He often said that genius required "a solid physical foundation" and he probably had his own in mind. But he also spoke of the "frail constitution of those who accomplish extraordinary things," and again he was thinking of himself when he hinted at the combination of infirmity and tenacity that constitutes the particular vitality of genius. As a matter of fact, even without tangible detriment, it was generally touch and go with his physical condition and from time to time severe illnesses brought him to the edge of the grave: At the age of fifty-two an attack of pustular erysipelas was complicated by paroxysmal coughing, and followed by a long period of nervous debility. Four years later a "pulmonary fever" (pneumonia?), was also accompanied by paroxysms. And there were attacks of gout and of kidney stones that required repeated visits to the Bohemian Spas. In the fall of 1823, when he was seventy-four, he was in a most critical condition, physically weakened and spiritually apathetic. It was the reaction to the ecstacy of Marienbad, the farewell to love, and even if the illness that followed was indefinable, yet it was almost fatal.

In short his affinity with life was frequently endangered and yet he loved to boast of this affinity, he made a great pretense of his ruggedness, played the part of the robust son of the soil, the oak-tree, and often bragged of his durability. His mode of life was lusty. He was a hearty and enthusiastic eater, giving much thought to his appetite, with a special weakness for cake and other sweets. By our standards he could almost be called an alcoholic, for he drank a whole bottle of wine daily at dinner besides several glasses of sweet wine at lunch and after each meal. But that was regarded as moderate in his day. He was in the habit of humorously disparaging the less enduring vitality of others. At the age of eighty-one he said: "I hear that Soemmering (a distinguished German anatomist) died, just a miserable seventy-five years old. People are such cowards, they haven't the courage to hold out any longer than that! How much more commendable is my friend Bentham (the English utilitarian economist), that radical fool! He keeps plugging right along and he is even a few weeks older than I."

From what a curious aristocratism these facetious comments arise; but it is, in all seriousness, an integral element of his self-consciousness. His ridicule of Bentham's "radicalism," which he regards as folly, is also a part of it. His partner in the conversation remarked: "If Your Excellency had been born in England, you would probably have been a radical too and would have campaigned against abuses in government." And Goethe, with the mien of Mephistopheles, replied: "What do you take me for? I should hunt around for abuses and expose them into the bargain—I who would have lived on abuses in England? If I had been born in England I should have been a rich duke, or rather a bishop with an annual income of thirty thousand pounds sterling." He is reminded that he might have drawn a blank in the lottery of life, there are so very many blanks! And Goethe: "Not every one, my friend, is fit to draw the grand prize. Do you think I would have been fool enough to draw a blank?" This is bravado, innate boastfulness, unqualified consciousness of superiority. Incidentally it reveals that he regards his birth and existence in Germany as a misfortune, compared to what he would have been in England. But the important thing is his metaphysical certainty that he would have been well-born under all conditions, a winner of the grand prize, a child of Lady Luck and a great man of the world—and that indignation over the corruption of that world is a matter for the underprivileged.

He was fond of an expression that is logically untenable but sounds grandly self-evident on his lips: he speaks of "innate deserts." What does it mean? That is wooden iron. The deserved is not innate, it is earned, achieved; and that which is inborn is not merited, unless the word is detached from its moral context. But that is exactly what he intends. The expression is a conscious affront to morality, to all legitimate ambition, to all striving, struggling, endeavoring; these are laudable at best but not genteel; and in the final analysis they are hopeless. "One must *be* something," he says, "in order to do something." In other words, merit (and blame) resides in being, not in doing. The important thing is not thinking, saying, or even acting, it is the existential, the substance—so that a person may champion right and yet it will not be right because he is not the right person. He expressed his belief in predestination to natural nobility in many forms, but never better than in this sentence: "I often hear people say, 'If only thinking were not so difficult!' But the unfortunate thing is that no amount of thinking helps one to think; *one must be right by nature* so that all your good ideas stand before you like free children of God and call to you: Here we are!"

Nature. At heart he is not his father's son at all, although to some extent he repeats and transfigures the paternal characteristics; he is in truth his mother's son, the son of Frau Aja, the Lindheimer daughter with the cheerful disposition—and more than that he is the favorite child, the spoiled pet of the great mother, of Mother Nature. He clings to her, he believes in her, he thanks her. From her stems his blithe receptivity, even as a youth, to the philosophy of Spinoza, to which he held to the end. It is the idea of the perfection and indispensability of all existence to which he clings, the concept of a world free from ultimate causes and ultimate designs, a world in which evil has the right to exist side by side with the good. "We are fighting," he declares, "for perfection of the work of art in and of itself. They (the moralists) are thinking of its external effect, which concerns the true artist as little as Nature when she produces a lion or a humming bird." Thus absence of motive in artistic as well as in natural creation is his first axiom, and he regards his innate creative talent as "nothing but nature," the gift of the all-bountiful mother who embraces good and evil alike. His early enthusiasm for Shakespeare has its roots here, and in the far future Goethe's nature-estheticism and antimoralism were to have a profound influence on Nietzsche, the amoralist, who was to go a step farther and pronounce the preeminence of evil over good, its overwhelming importance for the preservation and triumph of life.

In Goethe this conviction is still objective and plastic, it rests in calm, cheerful equilibrium. But just as this deification of nature, this Spinozistic pantheism, is the root of his goodness, his tolerance and conciliatoriness, his willingness to live and let live, so it is also the root of his indifference, his lack of enthusiasm and rapture, for which he was frequently reproached, his contempt for ideas, and his hatred of the abstract, which he regarded as destructive to life. "General ideas and great conceit," was one of his maxims, "always tend to create horrible mischief." This is the motto for his unfriendly attitude toward the French Revolution, which he detested. As a world event it tortured him more than anything else in his life and nearly cost him his talent, and yet he had stood in prophetic touch with its coming—had even helped to prepare for it—in his *Werther*, that sensational product of his youth, whose wild sentimentalism shook the foundations of the old social order.

His attitude toward the French Revolution is a strikingly exact repetition of that of Erasmus toward the Reformation, for which the great Hollander had helped to pave the way and which he then rejected with humanistic disgust. Goethe himself coupled the names of the two great "disturbances" disapprovingly in a famous distich:

> *In these days of confusion Gallicism repels*
> *Tranquil culture, as Lutheranism did in its time.*

Tranquil culture. It was this serenity, this quietism, this anti-Vulcanism that linked him with Erasmus, and this couplet leaves no doubt—if there could be any doubt—what his position would have been in the sixteenth century: it would have been against the revolt of the subject, on the side of the objective power, the Church. And yet he too, like Erasmus, would probably have refused the cardinal's hat that the pope offered to the great Humanist and which the latter rejected with genteel excuses because he wanted to ally himself neither with the old order, in which he no longer believed, nor with the new, which was too unrefined for him. Even Goethe's political Toryism seems to have been a little shaky and unreliable. When, in the year 1794, a certain Freiherr von Gagern issued a proclamation in which he called upon the German intelligentsia to place their pens at the disposal of the "good," that is, the conservative cause—or, to be more exact, to promote a new German confederation to save the country from "anarchy" (today we would call it bolshevism)—Karl August's intimate friend politely thanked the baron for his confidence and regretted that he considered it "impossible to unite princes and writers in a common cause."

This same withdrawal, this same evasion of the demands of both sides, we find in Erasmus also. To compare the two celebrities of their respective periods, to observe the similarity of their conduct with respect to their times, is a most attractive subject. But the comparison is not favorable to the charming satirist who wrote *The Praise of Folly.* Just as his belletristic refinement, his eloquent but thin-voiced intellect suffer by contrast with the weight and forcefulness, the boorish power and mighty plebeianism of his contemporary Luther, so they suffer by contrast with the cultured nature of Goethe. For he was Erasmus and Luther in one person, a combination of the urbane and the demonic, of an appealing grandeur that has never been duplicated in the history of civilization. In him the racially German and Mediterranean-European qualities joined in a completely natural and logical synthesis, a union which is essentially the same as the union in him of the inspired with the intellectual, the esoteric with the lucid, the voice of nature with the polished word, the poet with the prose writer, lyricism with psychology. Thus there is something exemplary about his existence, something that Erasmus with all his princely culture and dignity cannot equal; something that should serve as model for the German, since he fulfilled within himself the ideal of Germanism—and, one might add, the ideal of man.

And yet many of his highly respectable contemporaries suffered, suffered bitterly and resentfully from him: from his "tremendously obstructing power," as Börne expressed it, from his political apathy, from the forcefulness with which his nature opposed the national-democratic idea, the passion of the time. He was opposed to freedom of the press, to freedom of speech, to democracy and constitution. He was convinced that "everything sensible is in the minority" and he was openly on the side of the minister who carried out his plans against the wishes of the people and the king. He certainly felt hearty affection for the individual human, the sight of whose face, he confesses, could immediately cure him of melancholy; but he had little or no humanitarian faith in man, in mankind, in its revolutionary purgation, in its better future. Men cannot be taught reason and justice. There will be no end of wavering, no end of fighting and bloodshed.

If he had only said these things with some pessimism or grief! But fundamentally he was satisfied that it had to be so, for there was little of the pacifist about him. On the contrary, he has a feeling for power, for strife "until one proves his superiority over the other," strongly reminiscent of the word of Wagner's Wotan: "Where forces fearlessly stir, I frankly counsel war." He confesses that it "makes him sad to be on good terms with everybody" and that he "needs anger." That can hardly be called Christian Concord, although it is Lutheran and Bismarckian, too. Much evidence could be adduced of his contentiousness, his delight in "violence and punishment," his readiness to silence adverse opinions by force and "to remove such people from polite society." All that, if one wishes, is only three feet or less removed from the brute—and the same is true, in general, of his realism, his lack of enthusiasm, the sensuality of his nature that made him regard the pillaging of a farm as something actual and calling for sympathy but "the destruction of the fatherland" a mere phrase.

The sad thing and the most grievous for the patriots who were trying to educate Germany to political freedom was the fact that his unassailable greatness lent so much authoritarian weight to his obstructing views. In Germany greatness of itself tends toward undemocratic hypertrophy. There is an abyss between greatness and the masses, a "pathos of distance," to use Nietzsche's favorite expression, that does not exist to this extent elsewhere, in countries where greatness does not create serfdom on the one hand and bloating into absolutistic egotism on the other. There was a good deal of absolutism and personal imperialism in Goethe's majestic old age. This old age pressed heavily on everything that was trying to exist near him, and when he died it was not only a nymphal plaint for the great Pan that was heard but also a very distinct sigh of relief.

If he thought that liberty was not well taken care of in the hands of serfs, he permitted himself all the more of it—unlimited,

xxxii

esthetic superiority but also of the democratically unifying power of Catholicism. "One should really become Catholic," he exclaims, "to share in the existence of the people. To mingle with them as equals, to live with them in the market-place! What miserable, lonely humans we are in our little sovereign states!" And he lauds Venice, as a monument, not to a ruler but to a people. What about his Germanic aristocratism?

What about his Protestant strength of character in the novel *Elective Affinities*, where his surrender to Catholicism is so complete that he creates a saint in the midst of a Protestant community and permits the Lutheran peasants, with pious faith in miracles, to throng to the church where her body lies! At the same time the nature-fatalism of this masterpiece is not Christian at all, especially since it continues into the hereafter, in which, moreover, no one in the book actually believes. The concluding turn about the reluctant lovers who awake together from the sleep of death, is nothing but a conciliatory flourish.

This spirit is not to be pinned down to anything. Subsume him under any category of thought or existence on the basis of incontrovertible evidence, and in the next instant you will hesitate and discover that he is also the opposite. That is characteristic even of his moral attitudes, his position with regard to *time*, for instance. On the one hand he grandly takes all the time in the world, is dilatory, procrastinating, a dawdler who trustfully vegetates; on the other hand he practices a perfect time-cult, guards, hoards, exploits, cultivates the precious gift of time under the motto:

> *My heritage, how splendid, rich, and grand!*
> *My property is time, and time my harvest land,*

and under the second motto, the French proverb, "Time is the only thing which may properly be hoarded." The same quality extends paradoxically into the realm of the artistic, where he represents himself to be the great objectivist, the Apollonian mocker—and at the same time he is the lyricist and confessor, who draws only upon himself, who expresses only himself, and who, by his very Romantic subjectivism, produced the strongest effect in France. He may well be called a confessor, in a strangely radical and penitent sense. For how does he reveal himself? By depicting malefactors and weaklings: the suicide Werther, the traitor Clavigo, the hysterical Tasso, the unprincipled Edward, the downright silly Fernando in *Stella*. One wonders how he had the temerity to scoff at "hospital literature" and to demand Tyrtaean, spirited literature in its stead. He has a hospital of his own—for this is psychology, confession, exposure of all-too-human frailties. Even Meister and Faust fall considerably short of model manhood and impressiveness of character—if anyone should be particularly interested in these qualities.

But if these manifold literary products are not overly masculine (Schiller's are much more masculine), they are *human* in the frankest, most open, most honest sense. Moreover, or perhaps on that account, they bear on every page and at every turn the personal stamp of a charm, the like of which is not easily duplicated throughout the length and breadth of literary creation. As an illustrative example I like to think of his *Egmont*, a play that is open to all kinds of criticism from a dramaturgic and even from a general artistic point of view. Yet its amiable transgressions against all the laws of the theatre harmonize splendidly with the character of its hero—that aristocratically popular, incorrigibly carefree gentleman, a demonically frivolous favorite of gods and men, upon whose person the poet lavishes all his interest and in whom, in my opinion, all specifically Goethean charm culminates: most of all in his rather dispassionate, tenderly condescending, and somewhat self-complacent relation with Klärchen, the little girl of the common people, a true sister of Gretchen, to whom he shows himself one fine day in his Spanish court dress with the Order of the Golden Fleece, merely to enjoy her child-like Ohs and Ahs! Here we have that Narcissism again, an eroticism that finds its ultimate fascination in the visitation of a charming, simple girl by a guest from a strange, glittering world of spirit and love, who finds it all too easy to cut out her upright, middle-class swain and suitor. The guilt feeling of the penitent seducer who has no intention of marrying, who is always in love and never wants to tie himself down, is a part of the picture.

Goethe's love-life is a strange chapter. Acquaintance with his love affairs is a required subject of general education. In Germany, in the old days, one had to be able to enumerate them like those of Zeus. They have become statuettes in the cathedral of humanity, these figures of a Friederike, a Lotte, a Minna, a Marianne; and that may compensate them for the fact that the roving genius who lay at their feet for a time was unwilling to accept the consequences to his life and liberty of his gallant ad-

xxxvi

ventures. It may compensate them for his recurrent inconstancy, for the fact that his wooing was aimless, his loyalty perfidious, and his love a means to an end, a necessity for his work. Where work and life are one, as in his case, those who take only life, human life, seriously, are left in the lurch. But he reprimands them for it. "Werther must—must be!" he writes to Lotte Buff and her fiancé. "You do not feel *him,* you feel only *me* and *your-selves* . . . If you could feel the thousandth part of what Werther means to a thousand hearts, you would not count the costs to yourselves!" Willingly or unwillingly, they all bore the costs.

He wrote poetry from the very beginning: anacreontic, French, playful, talented, and conventional. He developed into a poet at Strassburg under the influence of Herder, in powerfully liberating contact with Homer, with Macpherson-Ossian, with Shakespeare, whom he admired boundlessly all his life and ranked far above himself, with the Bible as a work of literature, and above all with the folksong, in whose dewy freshness, in whose linguistic and rhythmic, emotional strength his lyrics are bathed and purified.

By virtue of his learning, his insight, his critical instinct for what was necessary Herder should have been the chosen leader of the literary revolutionary yearnings that only awaited a crea-tive summons at that time, around 1770, in Germany. But he lacked what his pupil Goethe, only five years younger, possessed: charm, grace, the compelling secret of personality. The younger man in his immaturity had been quite willing to regard himself as a mere satellite of Herder's sun. Now it turned out that the sun around which the intellectual life of Germany was to revolve was Goethe. I believe that Herder sensed it at an early date and never quite overcame his bitterness at the turn of events. It is hard to distinguish the pedagogical element from the rancorous, even from a profound love-hatred, in his attitude toward the pa-tiently devoted boy, in his everlasting barbed mockery and deri-sion; in his raillery at his name which, he used to say, could have been derived from "Kot" (=filth) as well as from "Gothe" (=Goth) or "Gott" (=god); in his caustic comments on the young man's lack of sagacity and good taste, his affectations, and so forth. Finally, in his old age, he completely alienated his great patron by an ill-advised joke about Goethe's somewhat boring revolutionary drama, *The Natural Daughter.* He said: "I really prefer your natural son;" and that brought about the final rupture of their old friendship.

One can hardly conceive today what a sensation, what wild acclaim, was provoked in that springtime of genius, the early days of formal Storm and Stress, by such a poem as "Welcome and Farewell":

> *To horse!—away o'er hill and steep!*
> *Into the saddle blithe I sprung;*
> *The eve was cradling earth to sleep,*
> *And night upon the mountain hung.*
> *With robes of mist around him set,*
> *The oak like some huge giant stood,*
> *While with its hundred eyes of jet*
> *Peered darkness from the tangled wood.*

How new, how bold, how marvellously free, how melodic and picturesque! How the rush of its rhythm blew the powder from the rationalistic wigs! The dramatic tale of *Götz von Berlichingen* had the same effect, that stage-hit in the style of Shakespeare with its teeming tableaus of German antiquity. Frederick the Great called it formless nonsense and rejected it, but throughout the German lands it evoked joy over its cordial affront to musty poetic rules as well as the "national satisfaction," which the autobiographer charmingly depicts in *Poetry and Truth*. Then came the first few scenes of *Faust*, the ink still wet, and it is easy to believe that his friends clapped their hands with joy to see "how the fellow was visibly growing." *The Sorrows of Werther*, however, the epistolary novel, was not a matter restricted to his friends, his coterie, his school; it was not even an internal German affair. The world at once took possession of it and it took possession of the world. The enervating, distracting sentimentalism of the little book, which called forth the shocked disgust of the moralists in spite of its natural sincerity and youthful, transcendental yearning, aroused a storm of boundless approval. It produced a delirium, a fever, an ecstasy that girdled the inhabited earth. It was the spark that fell into the powder keg causing the sudden expansion of dangerous forces that had been awaiting release. We must assume a general state of readiness for the little book. It seemed as though the public in all countries, secretly and without their own knowledge, had been awaiting this very book by an unknown young man from a German Imperial city;

xxxviii

that this book with revolutionary, liberating power emancipated the fettered yearnings of the civilized world. Napoleon, the iron man of destiny, had the French translation in his knapsack through the Egyptian campaign. He claimed to have read it seven times.

Goethe, the author, never experienced another such hurricane of success. His work, the mighty residuum of his life, was never again, as at the start, greeted by mass enthusiasm. The German public maintained a perfectly cool attitude toward his classicistic tendency exemplified in *Iphigenia* and *Tasso*. They did not feel the enchanting, piquant contrast between the classical form and the lyric intimacy and daring of the content.

In its time *Wilhelm Meister*, achieving significant extensiveness and remarkable intensiveness, was a highly successful novel. From the sphere of the highest German culture of the period, the Romantic movement, came the verdict that the French Revolution, Fichte's theory of science, and *Wilhelm Meister* were the three great events of the epoch. But no matter how many literary descendants this classical German novel was to have (its lineage runs down through Stifter and Keller to *The Magic Mountain*), it necessarily ran a poor second to *Werther* in its immediate success.

This was even truer of the mystic, psychologizing novel of the sixty-year-old Goethe, *Elective Affinities*, whose characters are true enough to life and individually convincing, but nevertheless symbols, chessmen evenly grouped and cleverly moved in a profound intellectual game. Still it was this book that gave the incentive for one of the neatest and handsomest characterizations of Goethe's prose. It was written by his friend, the choral director and composer, Zelter of Berlin, immediately after he had read the book: "There are certain symphonies by Haydn whose free and easy movements set my blood into pleasurable agitation . . . I feel the same thing when I read your novels, and I felt it today as I read your *Elective Affinities*. You never fail in your capricious, mysterious play with the things of the world and with the characters whom you move back and forth, no matter how many complications run through it and demand space for themselves. Moreover you have the most suitable *style*, clear as the crystal element, whose nimble denizens swim to and fro, flashing brilliantly or darkly up and down, without ever losing their way or their direction. One could go into rhapsodies over such prose, and I get angry as the devil because I can't write a single line like it." It took a musician to say the right, cheerfully critical word about the precision and elegance of Goethe's prose, its rhythmic magic, a rational magic, the clearest blend of Eros and Logos.

The first edition of the *West-Eastern Divan*, that contains priceless pearls of Goethe's late lyrics, had no sale at all and remained in the stores as waste paper. When he had concluded, though not completed, the second part of *Faust* (for it is incapable of completion), with a touching effort of his failing strength, the old man sealed it up, refusing to communicate "these very serious jests" even to his "gratefully acknowledged friends," let alone to the world at large, during his lifetime. For, he said, "the times are so absurd and so confused that I am convinced my long, honest efforts on behalf of this strange structure would be ill rewarded. It would be driven on to the beach, lie there a wreck, soon to be covered by the drifting sands of the hours." Notice the old man's style which has retained the picturesqueness of youth and has taken on a spectral aura, the moving dignity of aged, gradually fading creative power, already subsiding into eternity.

Incidentally some portions of the second part of *Faust* appeared during Goethe's lifetime. The Helen episode was published and the author was able to read solemn reviews in all the great foreign journals, French, Scotch, Russian. *World literature*—in effect everything that he wrote had long been received and accepted as such by authoritative opinion, and he was the one who created the word. He uttered it half as a fact and half as a demand, in part probably as an expression of his trait of worldwideness, which grew more and more as he became older—quite natural in an author whose career began with a universal success like Werther, but also as an object lesson to his German compatriots. "Instead of restricting himself to himself," he announces, "the German must take the world into himself in order to have an influence on the world . . . For that reason I like to look around in foreign nations, and I advise everyone else to do the same. National literature is not of any consequence now, the epoch of world literature is at hand and everyone must do his share to hasten the arrival of this epoch." How he took the world into himself and in turn influenced the world, what England, Italy, France, Spain, the Far East, America gave him and what, in turn, his work stimulated in the intellectual life of these countries, as well as in the North and East, this systole and diastole has recently been described by the Bernese literary historian Fritz Strich, in a most praiseworthy book, *Goethe and World Literature*, a work of truly panoramic dimensions, which is so highly satisfying because it demonstrates Goethe's Europeanism in its subjectivity and objectivity, in its reception and its transmission.

It is clear that the concept "world literature" was a result of both, that the consciousness of his own culture and indebtedness was not sufficient, but that it required the abundant reaction to his own work to complete the idea. Besides it is simply a word from the vocabulary of *greatness*—the kind of greatness to which the middle-class boy from the Hirschgraben in Frankfurt had been destined to rise, and of which the man of seventy confesses that he had "with difficulty learned to wear it," that is, to seek the field for his effectiveness in wide national and epochal circles. In one of his late aphorisms he says:

> *He whose vision cannot cover*
> *History's three thousand years,*
> *Must in outer darkness hover,*
> *Live within the day's frontiers.*

Of *Faust* Emerson commented: "The remarkable thing about it is the tremendous intelligence. The intellect of this man is such a powerful solvent that past ages and the present, their religions, politics, and modes of thought resolve themselves into their elements and ideas." This "tremendous intelligence," however, this all-encompassing, organizing, and poetically fusing intellect, did not only serve for the synopsis of the past and present. It is just as bold in its feeling for the future, in its previewing and anticipation of things to come, of that which is "timely," and for which "world literature" is only an abbreviation and a symbol. He occasionally described it as "free trade in ideas and emotions," a characteristic transfer of liberal economic ideas to the realm of intellectual life.

This is the nineteenth century, the century of economics and technology, into which the son of the eighteenth century projected himself for a whole generation, and which he "understood" and prophetically proclaimed far beyond the limits of his personal life, beyond the limits of the century itself, down to the post-bourgeois period. It is strange and even moving how the latter years of his life were filled with this death-defying, death-disregarding, vital perception of that which was "timely," that which was in process of preparation, in the moral and in the external, practical sphere, and which everyone, therefore, was in duty bound to accelerate, even at the expense of long cherished but now out-moded ideals. There is indeed much "renunciation" in the novel of his old age, *Wilhelm Meister's Travel Years*, for example, the self-conquest of individualistic humanity for the benefit of humane, pedagogical principles, which really belong to our day rather than his. The book is full of premonitory flashes of ideas that lead far afield from anything that might be called bourgeois humanitarianism, far from the classical and middle-class concept of culture, which Goethe himself had preëminently helped to shape. The ideal of individual universalism is dropped and the age of collectivism is proclaimed. We find in the book the insufficiency of the individual that prevails today: it takes all men to complete the concept of humanity; the single organism becomes a function, his only importance lies in what he is able to achieve for culture as a whole. The concept of the community emerges, the "communal bond," the commonwealth. The Jesuit-militaristic spirit of the "Pedagogical Province," poetically trans-figured though it may be, leaves very little of the individualistic, "liberal," bourgeois ideal.

What an old age! With all his dignity there is nothing of desic-cation, of ossification about it. It is full of sensitivity, curiosity, interest in life, and promotion of new ideas. At the table of this normally stiff and solemn, eighteen-century grand seigneur the conversation finally revolves about steamships, the first attempts with a flying machine, Utopian technological problems and proj-ects, rather than about literature and poetry. And is it any wonder that Faust at the end of his career experiences his instant of highest exaltation in the realization of a utilitarian dream, the draining of a swamp? The old gentleman never tires of discussing the possibilities of connecting the Gulf of Merico with the Pacific Ocean; never tires of imagining the incalculable effects of this project on the entire civilized and as yet uncivilized world. He advises the United States of America to undertake this work and lets his fancy run riot in the visionary description of flourishing ports to spring up on the shores of the Pacific, where Nature had so generously provided spacious roadsteads and harbors. He could hardly wait for these things to become reality—these, and the connecting link between the Danube and the Rhine, an undertaking enormous beyond all expectations, and then another thing, a third, very great thing: the Suez Canal for the English. "To see all these things come true," he exclaimed, "would make it worth one's while to stay on earth another fifty years!"

So his confidence in the future was all-embracing, it covered the entire world. There is something of a grandiose matter-of-factness in this enthusiasm for world-wide technological rationality, a feeling that the ailing world had to be disenchanted and disencumbered from sentimental memories that impeded life and obstructed progress.

> *America, you fare much better*
> *Than this old continent of ours,*
> *No basalt rocks your land enfetter,*
> *No ruined towers.*

The ruined towers and the all-too-venerable petrifactions are the "extinct nonsense" of which he speaks elsewhere, which man must "shun" in order to love life. They are the symbols of sentimental encumbrance, which this poet put almost on a par with destructive stupidity and against which he campaigned from early youth on, in favor of clear common sense. "The human rabble," he says as early as *Wilhelm Meister*, "fears nothing more than common sense; they ought to be afraid of stupidity if they really understood what is terrible. But common sense is embarrassing, therefore it has to be set aside; stupidity is only destructive, and all that you need to do about that is sit and wait."

To sit and wait for destruction without the courage to let common sense have a free hand: has this tendency and this danger to mankind not reached its pinnacle today? Goethe knew it, he saw it grow; and it was this, the power of stupidity, that he opposed with all his greatness—rather than revolution, constitution, freedom of the press, democracy. It is said that his last word before he closed his eyes in final slumber was: "Let more light in!" It is not quite certain. But what he really said, his actual last word, a word against death and for life, is this:

The only thing that counts in the end is progress!

Thomas Mann

California, 1948

POEMS OF YOUTH
AND LOVE

Poems of Youth and Love

TO THE MOON*

Fillest hill and vale again,
  Still, with softening light!
Loosest from the world's cold chain
  All my soul to-night!

Spreadest round me, far and nigh,
  Soothingly, thy smile;
From thee, as from friendship's eye,
  Sorrow shrinks the while.

Every echo thrills my heart —
  Glad and gloomy mood.
Joy and sorrow both have part
  In my solitude.

River, river, glide along!
  I am sad, alas!
Fleeting things are love and song —
  Even so they pass!

I have had and I have lost
  What I long for yet;
Ah! why will we, to our cost,
  Simple joys forget?

*Translated by John S. Dwight

River, river, glide along,
    Without stop or stay!
Murmur, whisper to my song
    In melodious play, —

Whether on a winter's night,
    Rise thy swollen floods,
Or in spring thou hast delight
    Watering the young buds.

Happy he, who, hating none,
    Leaves the world's dull noise,
And, with trusty friend alone,
    Quietly enjoys

What, forever unexpressed,
    Hid from common sight,
Through the mazes of the breast
    Softly steals by night!

PROMETHEUS*

The following poem is part of a fragmentary drama, which Goethe never completed.

Curtain thy heavens, thou Jove, with clouds and mist,
And, like a boy that mows down thistle-tops,
Unloose thy spleen on oaks and mountain-peaks;
Yet canst thou not deprive me of my earth,
Nor of my hut, the which thou didst not build,
Nor of my hearth, whose cheerful little flame
Thou enviest me!

I know of nought within the universe
More slight, more pitiful than you, ye gods!
Who nurse your majesty with scant supplies
Of offerings wrung from fear, and mutter'd prayers,
And needs must starve, were't not that babes and beggars
Are hope-besotted fools!

*Translated by Theodore Martin

4

When I was yet a child, and knew not whence
my being came, nor what before it lay,
Up to the sun I bent my wilder'd eye,
As though an ear were there
To listen to my plaint,
A heart, like mine,
To pity the oppress'd.

Who gave me succour
Against the Titans' over-mastering force?
Who rescued me from death — from slavery?
Thou! — thou, my soul, burning with hallow'd fire,
Hast not thyself alone accomplished all?
Yet didst thou, in thy young simplicity,
Glow with misguided thankfulness to him,
That slumbers on unheeding there above!

I reverence thee?
Wherefore? Hast thou ever
Lighten'd the sorrows of the heavy-laden?
Hast ever stretched thy hand, to still the tears
Of the perplexed in spirit?
Was it not
Almighty Time, and ever-during Fate —
My lords and thine—that shaped and moulded me
Into the MAN I am?

Belike it was thy dream,
That I should hate life — fly to wastes and wilds,
Because the buds of visionary thought
Did not all ripen into goodly flowers?

Here do I sit, and frame
Men after mine own image —
A race that may be like unto myself,
To suffer, weep; enjoy, and have delights,
And take no heed of thee,
As I do!

Johann Wolfgang von Goethe

THE BLISS OF SORROW*

Never dry, never dry,
Tears that eternal love sheddeth!
How dreary, how dead must the world still appear,
When only half-dried on the eye is the tear!
Never dry, never dry,
Tears that unhappy love sheddeth!

THE ROSE**

Once a boy beheld a bright
Rose in dingle growing;
Far, far off it pleased his sight;
Near he viewed it with delight:
Soft it seemed and glowing.
Lo! the rose, the rose so bright,
Rose so brightly blowing!

Spake the boy, 'I'll pluck thee, grand
Rose all wildly blowing."
Deftly overthrowing."
Thus the scheme thy wit hath planned
Spake the rose, "I'll wound thy hand,
O! the rose, the rose so grand,
Rose so grandly glowing.

But the stripling plucked the red
Rose in glory growing,
And the thorn his flesh hath bled,
And the rose's pride is fled,
And her beauty's going.
Woe! the rose, the rose once red,
Rose once redly glowing.

---

*Translated by E. A. Bowring
**Translated by James Clarence Mangan
6

THE SON OF THE MUSES*

Through country and through city
I pipe my homely ditty,
    I weave my cunning rhyme.
I stroll about at leisure,
But always mind the measure;
    With me all goes by time.

I scarce can wait their coming —
The flowers of earliest blooming,
    That first peep out in Spring;
I sing them, though they are not;
If Winter comes, I care not;
    The fond old dream I sing

I sing where no one listens,
Where ice all round me glistens:
    These are the Winter's *flowers!*
And when they melt, I wander
To the planted hillside yonder,
    And still find pleasant hours.

The young folks, met for pleasure,
Move briskly to my measure
    Under the linden tree;
The stupid rustic, grinning,
The starch, prim maiden, spinning,
    Must own my melody.

Wings to my feet ye give me;
O'er hill and vale ye drive me;
    Your darling child must roam.
Say why, ye kindest Muses,
Your wiser will refuses
    To take the wanderer home?

*Translated by John S. Dwight

7

Johann Wolfgang von Goethe

MAY SONG*

How gloriously gleameth
All nature to me!
How bright the sun beameth,
How fresh is the lea!

White blossoms are bursting
The thickets among,
And all the gay greenwood
Is ringing with song!

There's radiance and rapture
That naught can destroy,
Oh earth, in thy sunshine,
Oh heart, in thy joy!

Oh love! thou enchanter,
So golden and bright —
Like the red clouds of morning
That rest on yon height;—

It is thou that art clothing
The fields and the bowers,
And everywhere breathing
The incense of flowers!

Oh maiden! dear maiden!
How well I love thee —
Thine eye, how it kindles
In answer to me!

Oh, well the lark loveth
Its song 'midst the blue;
Oh, gladly the flowerets
Expand to the dew.

*Translated by Theodore Martin

8

And so do I love thee;
   For all that is best,
I draw from thy beauty
   To gladden my breast!

And all my heart's music
   Is thrilling for thee!
Be evermore blest, love,
   And loving to me!

CALM OF THE SEA*

Silence reigns in deepest water,
   Motionless the sea is bound,
And uneasy sees the sailor
   Level smoothness all around.
Not a breath of air will muffle
   Through the stillness of a grave,
Nor the sleeping ocean ruffle
   Gentlest stirring of a wave.

GOOD VOYAGE*

Dispersed are the vapors,
The sky is transparent
And Aeolus loosens
The strings in his hand.
Untied is the zephyr,
At work is the sailor.
Be quick! Be attentive!
The waves we are cutting,
The distance is shortened
And land I espy.

---

*Translated by Paul Dyrsen

Johann Wolfgang von Goethe

GREETING AND DEPARTURE*

My heart throbbed high: to horse, away then!
  Swift as a hero to the fight!
Earth in the arms of evening lay then,
  And o'er the mountains hung the night.
Now could I see like some huge giant
  The haze-enveloped oak-tree rise,
While from the thicket stared defiant
  The darkness with its hundred eyes.

The cloud-throned moon from his dominion
  Peered drowsily through veils of mist.
The wind with gently-wafting pinion
  Gave forth a rustling strange and whist.
With shapes of fear the night was thronging
  But all the more my courage glowed;
My soul flamed up in passionate longing
  And hot my heart with rapture flowed.

I saw thee; melting rays of pleasure
  Streamed o'er me from thy tender glance,
My heart beat only to thy measure,
  I drew my breath as in a trance.
The radiant hue of spring caressing
  Lay rosy on thy upturned face,
And love — ye gods, how rich the blessing!
  I dared not hope to win such grace.

To part — alas what grief in this is! —
  In every look thy heart spoke plain.
What ecstasy was in thy kisses!
  What changing thrill of joy and pain!
I went. One solace yet to capture,
  Thine eyes pursued in sweet distress.
But to be loved, what holy rapture!
  To love, ah gods, what happiness!

---

*Translated by Charles Wharton Stork

THE GODS GIVE EVERYTHING*

The gods give everything, the infinite ones,
To their beloved, completely,
Every pleasure, the infinite ones,
Every suffering, the infinite ones, completely.

NIGHT SONG**

When on thy pillow lying,
   Half listen, I implore,
And at my lute's soft sighing,
   Sleep on! what wouldst thou more?

For at my lute's soft sighing
   The stars their blessings pour
On feelings never-dying;
   Sleep on! what wouldst thou more?

Those feelings never-dying
   My spirit aid to soar
From earthly conflicts trying;
   Sleep on! what wouldst thou more?

From earthly conflicts trying
   Thou driv'st me to this shore;
Through thee I'm hither flying,
   Sleep on! what wouldst thou more?

Through thee I'm hither flying,
   Thou wilt not list before
In slumbers thou art lying:
   Sleep on! what wouldst thou more?

*Translated by Stephen Spender
**Translated by E. A. Bowring

Johann Wolfgang von Goethe

THE LOVED ONE EVER NEAR*

I think of thee, when the bright sunlight shimmers
    Across the sea;
When the clear fountain in the moonbeam glimmers,
    I think of thee.

I see thee, if far up the pathway yonder
    The dust be stirred;
If faint steps o'er the little bridge to wander
    At night be heard.

I hear thee, when the tossing waves' low rumbling
    Creeps up the hill;
I go to the lone wood and listen, trembling,
    When all is still.

I am with thee, wherever thou art roaming,
    And thou art near!
The sun goes down, and soon the stars are coming.
    Would thou wert here!

NOR WILL THESE TEARS BE THE LAST**

And nor will these tears be the last
That scald the heart with no relieving,
Until, unspeakably surpassed,
They still themselves in deeper grieving.

O let me always here and there
Feel this eternal loving,
And let this burning pain creep near
Through nerve and artery moving.

Could I but once be filled with thee
Utterly, thou Eternal One!
Ah, how the long, deep agony
Lasts here, under the sun.

*Translated by John S. Dwight
**Translated by Stephen Spender

GANYMEDE*

Oh, what a glow
Around me in morning's
Blaze thou diffusest,
Beautiful spring!
With the rapture of love, but intenser,
Intenser, and deeper, and sweeter,
Nestles and creeps to my heart
The sensation divine
Of thy fervour eternal
Oh, thou unspeakably fair!
Oh, in this arm
That I might enfold thee!

Alas! on thy bosom
I lay me, I pine,
And thy flowers and thy greensward
Are press'd to my heart.
Thou coolest the fiery
Thirst of my bosom,
Dear breeze of the morn!
Bear'st me the nightingale's
Fond adjuration,
Forth from the mists of the vale!
I come, I am coming!
Where art thou? oh where?

Aloft! thou art there!
See, where they sweep down,
The clouds, how they bend down,
Inclining to answer
The yearning of love!
Come to me! come!
Up to your bosom
Bear me on high!
Embraced and embracing
Up to thy bosom,
All-loving Sire!

Translated by Theodore Martin

Johann Wolfgang von Goethe

FOREVER YOUNG*

So let me look until I grow
And in this white dress still be dressed.
Far from this lovely earth I go
Up there to yonder house of feast.

There I shall have a little sleeping
And then, with new eyes no more blind,
I'll put off this pure covering,
This wreath and girdle leave behind.

And yonder heavenly presences
Ask not which boy, which girl may be:
No wrapping there nor garment is
Round the transfigured body.

True, here I knew not toil nor worry,
And yet I knew sufficient pain.
From grief I became old too early.
Make me forever young again!

TREASURE TROVE**

Through the forest idly,
    As my steps I bent,
With a free and happy heart,
    Singing as I went.

Cowering in the shade I
    Did a floweret spy,
Bright as any star in heaven,
    Sweet as any eye.

---

*Translated by Stephen Spender
**Translated by Theodore Martin

14

Down to pluck it stooping,
   Thus to me it said,
"Wherefore pluck me, only
   To wither and to fade?"

Up with its roots I dug it,
   I bore it as it grew,
And in my garden-plot at home
   I planted it anew;

All in a still and shady place,
   Beside my home so dear,
And now it thanks me for my pains,
   And blossoms all the year.

PRESENCE*

All things give token of thee!
As soon as the bright sun is shining,
Thou too wilt follow, I trust.

When in the garden thou walk'st,
Thou then art the rose of all roses,
Lily of lilies as well.

When thou dost move in the dance,
Then each constellation moves also;
With thee and round thee they move.

Night! oh, what bliss were the night!
For then thou o'ershadow'st the lustre,
Dazzling and fair, of the moon.

Dazzling and beauteous art thou,
And flowers, and moon, and the planets
Homage pay, Sun, but to thee.

Sun! to *me* also be thou
Creator of days bright and glorious;
Life and Eternity this!

Translated by E. A. Bowring

Johann Wolfgang von Goethe

WANDERER'S NIGHT-SONGS*

I

Thou that from the heavens art,
Every pain and sorrow stillest,
And the doubly wretched heart
Doubly with refreshment fillest,
I am weary with contending!
Why this rapture and unrest?
Peace descending
Come, ah, come into my breast!

2

O'er all the hill-tops
Is quiet now,
In all the tree-tops
Hearest thou
Hardly a breath;
The birds are asleep in the trees:
Wait; soon like these
Thou too shalt rest.

WHO YEARNING KNOWS**

Only who yearning knows
Knows my bereavement.

Shut here within my sorrows
Of joyless banishment
I watch a great sky close
There where he went.
Ah, he who loves and knows
Me is now distant.
This burns, the searing grows
Through my heart rent.

Only who yearning knows
Knows my bereavement.

*Translated by Henry Wadsworth Longfellow
**Translated by Stephen Spender

16

THE LIMITS OF MAN*

When the All-holy
Father Eternal,
With indifferent hand,
From clouds rolling o'er us,
Sows his benignant
Lightnings around us,
Humbly I kiss the
Hem of his garment,
Filled with the awe of
A true-hearted child.

For with Gods must
Never a mortal
Measure himself.
If he mount upwards,
Till his head
Touch the star-spangled heavens,
His unstable feet
Feel no ground beneath them;
Winds and wild storm-clouds
Make him their plaything;—

Or if, with sturdy,
Firm-jointed bones, he
Treads the solid, unwavering
Floor of the earth; yet
Reaches he not
Commonest oaks, nor
E'en with the vine may
Measure his greatness.

What doth distinguish
Gods from us mortals?
That *they* before them
See waves without number,
One infinite stream;
But *we*, short-sighted,

---

* Translated by John S. Dwight

One wavelet uplifts us,
One wavelet o'erwhelms us
In fathomless night.

A little ring
Encircles our life here;
And race after race are
Constantly added,
To lengthen the chain
Of Being forever.

MIGNON*

Knowest thou the land where citron-apples bloom,
And oranges like gold in leafy gloom,
A gentle wind from deep blue heaven blows,
The myrtle thick, and high the laurel grows?
Knowest thou it then?
                    'Tis there! 'Tis there!
O my true loved one, thou with me must go!

Knowest thou the house, its porch with pillars tall,
The rooms do glitter, glitters bright the hall,
And marble statues stand, and look each one:
What's this, poor child, to thee they've done?
Knowest thou it then?
                    'Tis there! 'Tis there!
O my protector, thou with me must go!

Knowest thou the hill, the bridge that hangs on clouds,
The mules in mist grope o'er the torrent loud,
In caves lay coiled the dragon's ancient hood,
The crag leaps down, and over it the flood:
Knowest thou it then?
                    'Tis there! 'Tis there!
Our way runs; O my father, wilt thou go?

Translated by Thomas Carlyle

NOBLE BE MAN*

Noble be man,
Charitable and good.
Since that alone
Distinguishes him
From other existences
Which we know well.

Hail to those unknown
Exalted beings
Whom we forbode.
Let man resemble them;
His example teach us
To hold their faith.

For nature remains
Forever unfeeling:
The sun shines down on
Evil and good men
And moon and stars
Glitter on criminals
As on those who are best.

Wind and rivers,
Thunder and hailstones
Rush on their courses
And, hurrying onwards,
They seize on and tear down
One as the other.

Thus also does fortune
Fumble among men,
Now taking the innocent
Curly-haired lad, but
Soon also the bald
Guilt-laden skull.

Translated by Stephen Spender

Johann Wolfgang von Goethe

Each one of us must,
Accepting eternal
Great, iron laws,
Accomplish the circle
Of his existence.

But man and man only
Can do the impossible:
He distinguishes
Chooses and judges.
He can lend lastingness
To the single moment.

He alone may
Reward the good,
Punish the evil
Heal and be saviour
Bind to his uses
The erring, the drifting.

And we pay honour
To the immortal ones
As though they were men,
Who did in their great deeds
What the best, in their small ones,
Do or would do.

The noble man
Be charitable and good!
Be tireless in making
The useful, the right.
Be to us pattern
Of those foreshadowed beings!

DRAMA

Faust

Dramatis Personae

THE LORD
ARCHANGEL RAPHAEL
ARCHANGEL GABRIEL
ARCHANGEL MICHAEL
MEPHISTOPHELES
FAUST
WAGNER *(his friend)*
MARGARET
MARTHA *(her neighbor)*
LISBETH *(her friend)*
VALENTINE *(her brother)*
STAGE MANAGER
POET
JESTER
FROSCH ⎫
BRANDER ⎪
ALTMAYER ⎬ *tavern merrymakers*
SIEBEL ⎪
TITANIA ⎭
OBERON
Students, soldiers, apprentices, servant girls, citizens, peasants, beggars
Spirits, witches, personified figures, bewitched animals, etc.

Faust

Part One

DEDICATION

YOU HOVERING FORMS, are you drawn near again?
   I saw you once with dim and troubled eyes.
Now shall I fix you? Is my heart still fain
   For old enchantments come in later guise?
You throng and press; be sovran, then, and reign,
   As out of mist and murky air you rise.
A magic breath breathes where your cloud-drifts roll,
I feel a gust of youth that rocks my soul.

You bring me visions of a happier day,
   And troops of shadows, I once loved, ascend;
Like some old, half-forgot, half-muted lay,
   First love returns, and many a vanished friend.
Old wounds new-bleed; I hear sad music play,—
   The dirge of life's lost, labyrinthine way;
I name their names, who, mocked by fortune, passed,
In their glad hour, where I must go at last.

They cannot hear the music's after-tone,
   Those souls, for whom my early songs were sung;
All, all that happy fellowship is flown;
   There is no echo now, no answering tongue.
And while I mourn I mourn to men unknown;
   They praise, and with their praise my heart is wrung;
The few that live, whose praise these numbers nursed,
Life's errants are, wide through the world dispersed.

Translated by G. M. Cookson

I feel the stress of a long-dead desire
  For that far spirit-world, solemn and still;
I am the Aeolian harp, the wind-struck lyre
  Whose trembling chords with a faint music thrill;
Weak is this heart, once iron to the fire;
  Thick fall my tears; my very soul is chill;
All I possess seem far-off things to me;
What's vanished is the sole reality.

PRELUDE IN THE THEATRE

MANAGER. POET. JESTER.

MANAGER:
  Time and again you two have stood by me,
  When I was at a loss and things went ill.
  What think you of our prospects, will
  Our venture thrive in Germany?
  I want to please the man in the street;
  And if you ask the reason why,
  Live and let live's the motto he swears by.
  All's knocked together with hammer and nails,
  Planks and joists and posts and rails,
  And everybody expects a treat.
  There sit the public—a full house—
  And cross their legs and arch their brows.
  I know what takes with them, I trust;
  And yet I never was so nonplussed:
  Not that the best is their daily bread;
  But they're confoundedly well-read.
  The trouble is to give them what they want—
  New, entertaining and significant.
  Frankly I like to see them in a row
  Making their way to our small raree-show;
  To watch them puff and pant and squeeze and rock
  Through the strait gate, salvation's narrow-wicket;
  On fine days when it's not yet four o'clock,
  Fighting their way towards the office, jamming
  As people mob the bakers in a famine,
  Ready to break their necks to get a ticket.

25

Only a poet knows the way
To work that miracle; let's see it done to-day.

POET:

Talk not of them! The genial spirit flies
The motley multitude. Cover my eyes,
Let me not see those rocking billows sway,
That swirl of waters that sweeps us away.
Take me to some calm nook by heaven bedewed,
Where poet's pleasures blossom from the sod,
Where Friendship is the heart's beatitude,
Love the fair flower, and the gardener God.
Oh, that what we conceive in silent thought
And scarce dare falter forth with stammering tongue,
Misprized perhaps, perhaps to honour brought,
Should be a morsel to the moment flung.
Slow thrust of root and blade and bud and flower,
And then the perfect bloom, no petal shorn;
The gilt is given to the passing hour,
The gold outlasts ages not yet born.

JESTER:

Ages not born! If that's what I were after,
Poor world, what would become of present laughter?
The people must, can, will, should, laugh. Egad,
I think a proper, jovial-hearted lad
Is by no means small beer. The man that knows
How to communicate his parts, ne'er yet
Needed to think the crowd treads on his toes
Or suffer their caprice to make him sour.
He wants the widest circle he can get
For only that way comes access of power.
So then take courage; give us a masterpiece;
Find room for phantasy with all her choir,
Plain sense, sound judgment, passion, feeling, fire,
But add the foolery, if you mean to please.

MANAGER:

And put in plenty of incident as well;
The public pay to see a spectacle;
Set the threads running, ravel up the clew,
So that they gape and don't know where they are,
And you can reckon on a *succés fou;*
In fact, you'll be extremely popular.

Much for the many! Gorge their appetite;
Each for himself finds something, when all's said;
Give them a feast and all must get a bite,
And everyone go satisfied to bed.
Is it a piece, then give it them in pieces;
That sort of hash is just the thing that pleases,
Staged as a trifle, finished for a toy,
A bagatelle, your lighter hour's employ.
A whole is neither for their hearts or heads;
Besides they're sure to tear the thing to shreds.

POET:

Bad art! But that is no consideration,
Nor what the artist feels for his vocation.
These deft messieurs! I've noticed that you swear by all
Their clumsy shifts; the thing's become proverbial.

MANAGER:

Your grave remonstrance doesn't trouble me.
A man has work; to make a job of it
He uses the correct tools, doesn't he?
Well now, it's soft white wood you've got to split;
Just think a moment whom you're writing for:
If number one comes because life's a bore,
And number two from a too generous table,
And, what's worse, every second auditor
Puts down his paper to take up our playbill;
If they come skipping for a masquerade
And curiosity wings each step they've made,
And if the ladies play to box and gallery
In their best clothes and don't expect a salary—
What are you dreaming in your Muses' grot?
What matter if the house be full or not?
Look at your patrons; look them in the face;
One half are cold, the other a coarse race;
One goes to cards as soon as the play is done;
One takes a romping girl between the sheets:
If there's no more in it than that, my son,
Why vex the Muses on their holy seats?
Go on! Add more to much, and more beside.
You couldn't miss the target if you tried.
Puzzle them; that's the only thing to do;

You can't please when they won't be satisfied.
How now, my poet,—what's the matter with you?

POET:

Go out and get some other menial!
What? Shall a poet prove a criminal,
Fling to the winds, that fools may play their parts,
The highest of all laws, the Rights of Man,
Nature's own birthright? How does he move all hearts?
Subdue all elements? I'll tell you how:
By harmony, the rapt musician
That sits within the poet's musing brow
And sings till the world gives back his song again.
If nature with her calm, indifferent hand
Winds on the eternal spindle strand on strand,
If the harsh chords of multitudinous life,
The universal cry of joy and pain,
Jar one another with unlovely strife,
Who makes division of these jangling strings,
And gives them rhythm till they seem living things?
Who dedicates the individual soul
And to that dominant attunes the whole?
Who looses passion? Who in the still hour
Leads on the evening glow of solemn thought?
Who is it scatters every vernal flower
Along the path of the beloved? Who weaves
The common verdure of unvalued leaves
Into a green wreath for all virtue wrought?
Who keeps Olympus, heals the gods' discord?
Man's power in the poet's might outpoured.

JESTER:

That's how they work, then, those fine powers of yours;
And so the poet's business takes its course
Just like a love intrigue: you meet by chance,
Are rather struck, indulge some dalliance,
And inch by inch are thoroughly let in.
Bliss and more bliss; and then your cares begin;
Rapture, despair; you've scarcely time to glance
Round you, before you've got a whole romance.
That is the tragedy we ought to give.
Grasp the hard facts, the life that all men live
And so few know; it's bound to interest

Wherever handled; have some motley figures;
Variety is what imparts a zest;
No matter if they look a trifle blurred;
A world of error and a spark of truth,—
That's the best tipple toper ever stirred,
And it's what most exhilarates and invigours.
Then you will see the fine flower of youth
Crowding the doors to hear your revelation;
The tender sentimentalist will suck
From you a melancholy delectation;
First one and then another of them gets struck
And all see in it what's in their own hearts.
They laugh, and weep, admire your fine elan,
And are delighted with the showy parts;
Nothing, of course, contents the finished man;
The unformed youngster blesses his good luck.

POET:

Who will restore for me the time
When I was young as they,
And full and freely flowed my rhyme
Like a mountain spring in May?
When earth still wore her virgin veil,
Buds breathed of mystery,
And every flower bloomed for me
That blossomed in the dale.
Then I had nothing, but enough,
A heart in love with truth,
Yet for fond fancies fain.
Give back untamed those impulses,
The deep, the agonizing bliss,
The strength of hate, the power of love,
Give me my youth again.

JESTER:

If you were in a bayonet fight, dear bard,
Or if a lovely lass hugged you too hard,
You'd need your youth; or on the running-track,
The glittering crown in front, you with the pack.
Or after the frenetic waltz, when you
Keep up the fun, drinking the wild night through.
But all the business you've got to do
Is just to sweep the well-accustomed strings

With power and charm; your role is to pursue
A goal you set yourselves, now and again
Indulging some agreeable wanderings.
Play your appointed part, old gentlemen,
And none will honour you the less. Old Age,
Although the proverb says so, doesn't make
Men childish; we are still, in that last stage,
The children that we were at life's daybreak.

MANAGER:

Suppose you finish your dispute:
When are we going to see events?
Some good idea might bear fruit
While you are chopping compliments.
Power doesn't come to those that pause and shrink;
What's all this talk of hitting the right key?
If you're the poets you would have us think,
Assume command of poesie.
You know what's wanted; something strong
That's got a smack in it; fire away,
Mix us a steaming bowl of song.
What's not done now tomorrow's not in your power.
It's wicked to let slip the passing hour:
Be resolute and do the thing you may;
Seize time by the forelock; it can't shirk
And pulls the load because it must.
You know that every kind of work
Is staged in Germany; make use
Of all our scenery; be profuse;
Don't let the wheels and pulleys rust.
The greater and the lesser light
Employ; be lavish with the stars;
Water and fire and mountain height,
Four-footed beast and bird abound;
So, far beyond these narrow bars,
This little painted house of wood,
Step out into the mighty round
Of all God made and found it good.
Travel post haste, but pondering well,
From Heaven across the world to Hell.

PROLOGUE IN HEAVEN

RAPHAEL:

Even as of old the sun's deep chime
Resounds to all the ringing spheres,
And thundering down the path of Time
Tells the forecasted count of years;
Angels his beams with strength array,
Though none his glory may declare;
All things as on the primal day
Are unimaginably fair.

GABRIEL:

And swift and passing swift revolves
The gleaming earth in splendour dight,
And paradisal day dissolves
In deepest shades of shuddering night:
The grey abysses of the world
With foaming seas beat rock-shut bars,
And rocks and seas are onward hurled
For ever with the rushing stars.

MICHAEL:

And stressful storms from land to sea,
From sea to land in roaring strife
Weld one vast chain of mystery,
The girdle of the cosmic life;
Bright death is in the dazzling flame
That rends the thunder's sounding way;
Yet, Lord, Thy harbingers proclaim
The soft procession of Thy day.

ALL:

Angels Thy beams with strength array,
For none Thy glory may declare;
All things as on the primal day
Are unimaginably fair.

MEPHIST:

Your presence, Lord, vouchsafed us once again,
And your most kind inquiry how we do,
The warmth of former welcomes, must explain
Why I appear among your retinue.
Excuse me, the grand style is not my forte,

31

Johann Wolfgang von Goethe

Though all your suite should vote my language low,
And you would laugh my pathos out of court,
Had you not given up laughter long ago.
I cannot talk of suns and universes;
I watch man's ways, his torments and his curses.
Earth's godling keeps the print of the pristine clay,
A quiz as queer as on the primal day.
He would do better to my thinking,
But for that glimpse of Heaven you gave to set him blinking.
He calls it reason, uses it to be
Worse than a beast in bestiality.
Man, by your Highness' leave, the more's the pity,
For all the world is like a long-legged grig,
And flits and hops and dances the same jig,
And pipes in the green grass the same old ditty.
I wish he'd lie there always; no such luck;
Plump goes his nose in every bit of muck.

THE LORD:

Hast thou no more to tell me? Bring'st no news?
Art come on thy old errand, to accuse?
In the wide earth can'st thou find nothing good?

MEPHIST.:

Lord, not a thing; 'tis evil to the core:
Man is so plaguey miserable I could
Find't in my heart to plague the wretch no more.

THE LORD:

Dost thou know Faust?

MEPHIST.:

That wears the doctor's hood?

THE LORD:

My servant.

MEPHIST.:

Serve! I'll take my oath o' that.
But after what a fashion! Meat and wine
Won't serve this gentle, he is grown so fine;
And there's a ferment brewing 'neath his hat
Is like to blow your faithful minion far.
He's only half aware how mad he is.
He pesters Heaven for her fairest star,
And earth for every highest, heavenly bliss.

32

Near or remote, there's nothing give him rest,
Or stills the deep disorder in his breast.

THE LORD:

Perhaps he serves me now in doubt and teen,
But I will lead him where the darkness clears:
The gardener knoweth, when the tree is green,
Blossom and fruit will crown the coming years.

MEPHIST.:

What will you wager? You may lose him yet!
But I must have full leave and ample play
To lead him gently down my broad highway.

THE LORD:

So long as he yet lives on earth, I set
No interdict 'gainst your essay.
Living is strife and striving is to stray.

MEPHIST.:

I thank you. I have always had a dread
Of complicated dealings with the dead.
Give me a fresh, full cheek; I'm never in
When needy corpses knock with knuckle thin.
The cat's way with the mouse I understand.

THE LORD:

Well, then, the thing's committed to your hand.
From that pure fountain whence his being came
Divert his soul, and lead him, if you can,
Down your own path: and then admit with shame
Through every dim and dark and dubious aim
Still on the right road presses the good man.

MEPHIST.:

Excellent: but, I fear, too short a run.
As for my bet, I count the wager won.
But in my triumph you must not protest
If you should see me puffing out my chest.
Dust he shall eat as greedy as hot cakes,
As did my cousin, the distinguished snake.

THE LORD:

Be free there, too: show yourself what you are:
Your tribe have never moved my enmity:
Of all the naughty spirits that deny
The rogue of wit's least troublesome by far.
Too easily a lethargy may creep

33

Over man's powers: soon his sole bliss is sleep.
Such a companion then as you
I'm glad to give him; one that can divert
And stimulate and keep the mind alert,
And must, being devil, be creator, too.
But ye, true sons of God, your joy possess
In everliving beauty's loveliness:
The Power which creates and lives alway
In the mild bonds of Love your Being bind;
And things unstable in their shifting sway
Stablish ye fast by indestructible Mind.
(*The Heaven closes and the Angels disperse*)

MEPHIST.:

At times I like the Ancient's company,
And I am always careful to be civil:
It's nice to think so great a Lord can be
Quite human, chatting with the very devil.

NIGHT

A narrow vaulted Gothic Chamber. FAUST *in restless mood seated in an armchair at his desk.*

FAUST:

Out on't! I've searched philosophy,
Medicine and Law I've sifted in vain,
And (God above!) to Theology
I've given the best of heart and brain.
Pitiful fool! I ponder and pore
And grow no wiser than before.
Ah, but I wear the master's gown,
The doctor's scarlet; up and down
These ten years past with cons and pros
I've led my scholars by the nose.
I see that knowledge exceeds man's art;
That's a fire consumes my heart.
It's true I have more sense than your lettered
Triflers, your coxcombs, laic and priest,
Penman and schoolman; I'm not fettered
By their nice scruples—not the least
Elusive grain of a misgiving.
Hell and the Devil don't frighten me;
But I've paid for that a ruinous fee,
No less than the loss of all joy in living,
Of the dream that knowledge was mine to reach,
The dream that by something I could teach
Men might be profited or bettered.
Silver and gold, God wot, I've none,
And little honour under the sun.
A dog would scorn the life dealt me;
So my days are given to sorcery.
If mind can solve and tongue rehearse
The secrets of the universe—
That then no more my sour sweat flow
As I grind out my dry harangue,
Talking of what I do not know;
But peradventure I may sound
What's clapped within the world's great round;
Behold all procreant powers at work;

35

And quit at last of quibble and quirk
Let all the peddling truck go hang.

O, full, round moon, that thou might'st look
Thy last on so much toil and pain,
That kept me bending o'er my book,
While slow the midnight hours would wane!
Sad mistress, then thou shon'st above
Crabbed script and ponderous tome,
But, oh, among the hills to roam,
Companioned by the light I love!
To float with spirits by mountain-caves
And over the meadows by thy white beams;
To find the peace that my heart craves,
Bathed in the dew of thy healing streams!

Why should I mope in this stony gaol—
Accurséd den of damp and mould,
Where the very heaven's sweet light looks pale
Through painted windows, dusk and old?
Penned in this close, blind, bookish stye
Where the worm gnaws and the dust lies thick,
With smoky manuscripts heaped high
As the gaunt, ribbed roof of blackened brick.
Beakers and boxes, stacked and shelved,
Crucibles, calipers, balances fine—
All the old lumber since Adam delved—
If you call that a world, you may call it mine!

And would'st thou learn why thy heart sinks,
Held in the iron vice of woe!
What incommunicable throe
Thy life-blood's genial current shrinks?
For Nature, warm with living hues,
Where God set man, I taste the breath
Of chymic vapours, charnel dews,
Men's skulls, beast's ribs—the bones of death!

Take wings! Mount, mount, o'er the wide land!
Is not this volume's deep presage,
From Nostradamus' very hand,

Thine all-sufficient equipage?
The stars shall tell thee of their path,
Nature's sweet wisdom make thee whole;
Strong in all strength that Spirit hath
Thy soul shall commune with her soul.
In vain this adust thought would read
The holy symbols: Spirits of air
That hover near me, in my need
Answer,—if ye have heard my prayer!

(*He opens the book and looks at the Sign of the Macrocosm.*)

Ha! At a glance what instantaneous rapture fills
Each pulse, each vein and every part of me!
Joy, sacred Joy, through youth rekindled, thrills,
And makes each nerve a tingling ecstasy!
Was it a God that drew these magic lines
Of might to make my soul's wild storm relent,
And brim me with a measureless content,
When by supreme compulsion of these signs,
The powers unveil that hide sky, sea, and firmament?

Am I a God? Such light breaks through the murk
In these pure contours to the soul's sense lies
All Nature, visibly at work.
Ah, now I grasp the saying of the wise:
"The world of spirits is not shut away:
Thy heart is dead, thy body's bolts fast drawn;
Up, Student, up, and bathe that breast of clay
In the empyreal crimson of the dawn."

(*He gazes at the Sign.*)

All weaves one fabric; all things give
Power unto all to work and live!
Above, below, the star-throng burns,
Still handing on their golden urns,
With benediction in their wings:
Heaven stoops to earth! To heaven earth clings,
And through the vast one harmony rings.

A vision, but no more! O Nature, tell me where
I may possess thee, measurelessly fair?
Where are the breasts, the founts where life is nursed?
On you heaven hangs and earth; towards you we press

37

Our own, run dry or brimmed with bitterness!
Ye flow, ye brim for me,—and yet I thirst!
*(He turns over the leaves impatiently, and see the sign of the
Earth-Spirit.)*
Oh, how unlike that other is this sign!
Spirit of Earth, thou art my nearer kin;
Now my reviving energies begin
To mount in flame, as I had drunk new wine.
Now my high heart confronts the world and dares
All overplus of bliss, beckons all cares;
Let loose the winds; all storms encompass me;
I fear not breaking ship or crashing sea.

Clouds close above—
The moon hides her light—
The lamp is out—
Mists—red rays—flashing—blinding!
A horror from the vaulted roof
Breathes in my face and binds up every nerve!
Spirit that I have called, it is thy breath,
The beating of thy wings!—Appear,
And show thee what thou art!
I feel a rending here
About my heart
And strong convulsions I have never felt!
Take my whole soul! Do with me what thou wilt,
But show—show—show, though thou strike me with death.
*(He takes up the book, and with mystic incantation recites
the spell of the Spirit. There is a tremor of ruddy flame:
the Spirit appears in the flame.)*

SPIRIT:
Who calls?
FAUST *(turning away)*:
Dread apparition!
SPIRIT:
Thou wast strong
To bid me to thee, and hast suckled long
Thy puny being on my bounteous sphere;
And now—
FAUST:
I am afraid to look on thee!

SPIRIT:

>Why, thou didst pant to look upon me—hear
>My voice and see my face. Thy prayers prevail
>And I am come. Why does thy spirit quail,
>O man, much greater than humanity?
>Where is that cry of the soul—the breast that fashioned
>Its world and gave it suck? Where that impassioned
>Being that would be one with shapes of air—
>The Faust whose voice so resolutely rang?—
>That strove toward me, desperate to dare?
>Thou—Whom my breath makes one incarnate pang,
>A writhing worm, thy inmost soul aghast!

FAUST:

>Thou fiery shape, I will not faint my heart:
>I am that Faust—a spirit, as thou art.

SPIRIT:

>In the flux of Being, in the blast
>Of action, I sweep to and fro,
>Hover high and hover low;
>Birth and the grave,
>The vast
>Heave of the eternal wave,
>Warp and woof that is never the same,
>Life that glows and leaps in flame,
>I weave at the roaring loom of the years
>The living garment the Godhead wears.

FAUST:

>Thou busy Spirit, roving air, earth, sea.
>I feel that thou art very near to me.

SPIRIT:

>Thou art like the spirit thou understand'st, not me.

>*(vanishes.)*

FAUST:

>Not thee! Whom then?
>God's image, and too mean to be like thee!

>*(knocking.)*

>Death! It's my Famulus! I know his rap;
>So ends the fairest hour I ever saw;
>This fawning pedant and his clapper-claw
>Shatters my shining vision with a tap!

39

Johann Wolfgang von Goethe

(Enter WAGNER, *in dressing-gown and nightcap, a lamp in his hand.* FAUST *turns to him impatiently.)*

WAGNER:

    Do I intrude? I heard you, and made sure
    You were declaiming a Greek tragedy.
    Nowadays elocution can secure
    Such power, I seized the opportunity.
    Pardon, if I employ a commonplace;
    But a comedian could teach a priest.

FAUST:

    Yes, if the priest is a comedian,
    Which, by the way, is no uncommon case.

WAGNER:

    Ah, behind study-windows, where a man
    Scarce sees the world except upon a feast—
    And then peeps at it through a telescope—
    To teach and lead it seems a forlorn hope.

FAUST:

    You must first feel; under the powerful stress
    Of soul there comes unsought a readiness,
    An ease, that must compel attention. You
    Are always busy with your paste and glue;
    Where others feasted you hash up the scraps;
    Blow your own dust-heap till your thin flame flaps;
    A prodigy to babes—and monkeys, too,
    If you've a taste for their encomiums.
    But as to fusing heart to heart, that comes
    Only when your own fervid heart can pour
    The word of power to energize mankind.

WAGNER:

    Ah, but delivery makes the orator;
    And there I am so very much behind.

FAUST:

    Young man, let perfect candour be your aim;
    Wag me no fool's tongue, Wagner, like a bell;
    With little art good brains, good sense, can frame
    Good matter and deliver it as well.
    If you feel deeply and must say your say,
    What need to hunt for phrases half a day?

Their gold is glitter merely; shreds you twist
Like tinsel-foil to dazzle human kind,
But with no more of life than the shrill wind
That drives through dying leaves autumnal mist.

WAGNER:
Ah, God, there's no finality to art,
And death soon puts the finish to our days;
My efforts often leave me out of heart,
My long research, my critical essays,
The means are so laborious, yet they
Alone can tap the springs that rise so high.
And so before he has travelled half the way
A poor, unlucky devil has to die.

FAUST:
Is sheep-skin then the sacred well
That slakes eternally the sacred thirst?
Your drought will be unquenchable
Except the waters from your own breast burst.

WAGNER:
With all respect, one thing that thirst assuages;
'Tis to take on the spirit of the ages,
See what wise men have thought before our time,
And then to what prodigious heights we have had
    strength to climb.

FAUST:
Prodigious! You may fairly say, star-high!
My friend, times past, remote antiquity,
To us are as a book sealed with seven seals;
And what you call the spirit of the ages
Is just the spirit of our modern sages,
The glass of their own phantasy reveals.
Then there's a howl; one look and out they pour
To see such jumble-bags turned inside-out,
Such garbage-buckets stood at their front door
At best the thing's a high-class knockabout,
With as much sense in all the solemn twaddle
As when one blockhead raps another's noddle.

WAGNER:
But life!—the human heart and mind!—One would
Give much to know a little of all that.

41

FAUST:

Why, yes, as knowledge now is understood,
But who dare give the right name to the brat?
They who had knowledge, and no care to hide
All that they felt and knew from the crass mob—
Their vision and their high heart's passionate throb—
Were always either burnt or crucified.
But we sit late; the night is far advanced;
Friend, we will leave our colloquy awhile.

WAGNER

I could sit here for ever so entranced,
Discourse, and hear discourse, in such a learned style.
I'll come to-morrow; 'twill be Easter Day;
Some further questions you must let me bring;
Study's my passion; I know much; but, pray,
Go on till I have mastered everything.   (*Exit.*)

FAUST:

They only know not hope's evanishment
Who dig and dig the three-times-sifted sand;
Grubbing for buried gold with greedy hand
They find a worm and feel a rich content.

But, oh, listen to this creature's whine
Where the ripe hour of vision came to birth.
And, oh, that for this once my thanks are thine,
Most pitiful of all the sons of earth!
For thou didst snatch me out of my despair
That else had crushed me; when before me swam
That giant apparition of the air,
I dwindled to the puny dwarf I am.

This Me—God's image—drawn in fancy nigh
To that bright mirror where all truth is glassed,
In self-delight, clear as the unclouded sky,
Earth's clayey vesture from my spirit cast;
Higher than angels, human energy
Released to flow in power through Nature's veins,
Create and form and know felicity
As do the gods—how sharp these after-pains!
A voice like thunder spake and silenced me.

Ah, no! It was not given me to mete
My strength with thine: if I had power at all
'Twas to evoke, not hold thee; in that fleet
Moment of time great was I—yet how small!
And with what grim force thou didst thrust me back
On human fate's incalculable track!
Who is my teacher? What shall I ensue,
What shun? Shall that strong thrust direct my way?
Ah, but not suffering only, all we do,
Narrows our path and cramps our blood's free play.

Unwelcome, alien, hostile things intrude
On all of truth and shining excellence;
Then, having this world's treasure, we conclude
Things of more worth are frauds that cheat the sense;
And the loud world with its distracting strife
Benumbs the very nerve of noble life.

Time was when phantasy yet dared to hope,
Winging aloft where loom the eternal verges;
Now is a little space her amplest scope,
Since such brave barks have split shattered by
    time's rude surges.
Care nestled in the brain
Hatches the secret pain;
There, rocking restlessly all peace and all delight she scares:
And ever on her face some new mask wears;
Wife, child, fair house or broad demesne her guise,
Fire, water, dagger, poison-bowl:
The blow unstruck can daunt thy soul;
The loss thou hast not felt Care can eternalize.

I am not like the gods! Too keen that thrust:
I am the worm that burrows in the dust;
And, feeding there, some traveller's footfall
Crushes the worm and gives it burial.

What else but dust my prison makes, and high
Heaped on a hundred shelves my soul besets?
What else this trash whose tinsel takes the eye,
This world of atoms where the grey moth frets?

43

Shall I find here the thing that I have not?
Or haply on a thousand volumes stare
To learn mere misery is most men's lot
And two or three were happy here and there?

Why dost thou grin at me, thou hollow pate?
Why, but that thy poor brain once dreamed like mine,
Sought the high noon and in the grey dusk wandered late
In sorrow searching after Truth's clear shine?
By God, my very tools make mouths at me,
With wheel and cog and ring and cylinder!
Here stands the door and you should be the key;
Troth, though ye have crimp wards the bolt ye cannot stir.
Close still in the broad day
Nature lets none remove her veil; and you
From whose keen wit she shuts herself away
Will never force the lock with lever or with screw.

Ye only stand here, ye quaint instruments,
Because ye stood here in my father's time;
Long as this lamp its sooty vapour vents,
Thou shrivelled parchment, take thy fill of grime.
Better have spent my pittance than enhance
Labour and sweat with its light load; there's none
Is rightful lord of his inheritance
Till what he had is by new toil re-won.
Wealth not employed lays on a heavy weight,
And we can only use what time and the hour create.
Why is it that I fix my gaze just there?
Is there a magnet in that goblet's gleam?
And why this sudden light so sweet and fair,
As when in woods by night soft floats the cold moonbeam?

Thou glass unparalleled, hither to me!
I take thee from thy shelf full reverently,
For skill and science sparkle in thy glow.
Thou dost seal up the precious balm of sleep,
Death's abstract in thy crystal thou dost keep;
To him that made thee now thy favour show!
I see thee and for torment find long peace;
I grasp thee and these restless strivings cease;

My spirit at the flood ebbs swift away;
I am drawn out into the mighty deep,
Below I see the glassy billows sweep,
And to new shores beckons a newer day.

Lightly there glides to me a fiery car;
And I am ready now to take the rein
And on the empyreal highway travelling far
To reach new worlds where effort knows not pain.
To win that life, that bliss of Gods on high,
Thou, worm but now, what grace hast thou, what worth?
Nay, but thou canst, if, fear and doubt put by,
Thou turn thy back upon the sun of earth.
Dare now to rend wide ope the eternal door
That most would hasten by with sidelong gait;
Prove by thine act, what thou didst dream before,
That man's high meed and worth are as the godlike state;
Dare to cast off all fear of that dark pit
Where phantasy its own damnation frames;
On through that gateway, though the mouth of it,
Narrow and near, shall be encompassed with hell's flames!
Pluck up thy heart and with high courage press
Onward, cost what it may; on, on—to nothingness!

Come down, thou phial crystalline,
Out of that ancient case of thine,
Old friend, forgotten all these years.
At feasts of many a vanished day
Thou shon'st; thou mad'st the grave guest gay,
When healths were drunk, and wassailers
Made verse on thy chiselled frieze,
And drained the good wine to the lees.
Thou tell'st of nights when I was young;
But now no neighbour will I pledge,
Nor whet on thee my wit's keen edge;
Here is a juice soon mutes the tongue.
This darker stuff thou dost not scorn;
You that I brewed, my chosen bowl,
In one last draught with all my soul,
As at a solemn feast I drink the rising morn.

Johann Wolfgang von Goethe

(He sets the goblet to his lips. A clash of churchbells and a
choral chant)

CHOIR OF ANGELS: Now is Christ risen!
> Joy from on high,
> Joy upon earth
> Unto man born to die,
> Born to transgression's
> Inherited throe,
> Wound in the trammels
> Of weakness and woe!

FAUST:
> What echoing hum and what clear choral song
> Can so commandingly the cup withdraw?
> Do ye ring in, deep bells, with iron tongue
> So soon the primal hour that the first Easter saw?
> Ye choirs, are ye so quick to chant the comfortable hymn
> Sung at the dark grave once by seraphim—
> The strong assurance of a newer law?

CHOIR OF WOMEN: Faithful and tender
> We laid Him so fair,
> With sandal and cedar,
> With spikenard and myrrh;
> Wrapped in white linen,
> Borne on the bier,
> Here we entombed Him—
> But Christ is not here!

CHOIR OF ANGELS: Now is Christ risen!
> Blessed be they
> That were steadfast to love Him
> And strong to obey;
> In tribulation
> Standing unmoved,
> Healed by His stripes
> And by His death Proved!

FAUST:
> Why have ye sought me out, so sweet, so strong,
> Ye airs of heaven, where in the dust I lie?
> Chime for the weak! To soft hearts chant your song!
> I hear the call ye make but faith gives no reply.
> Faith's dearest daughter is credulity.
> I have no courage now to seek in strife

46

Those worlds whence these glad news wing earthly ground
Yet was my morn of youth familiar with the sound,
And even now it calls me back to life.

There was a time when heaven stooped down to kiss
My brow, when all one Sabbath stillness held;
Then these deep notes in power through all my
    being knelled,
And when I prayed it was a burning bliss.
Strange longings drove me, holy ecstasies,
Through field and forest in my boyish years,
And 'mid a very rain of scalding tears
I felt within me a new world arise.
These notes once ushered in youth's sports and pastimes gay,
With all the frolic gladness of the spring;
Now tender thoughts to me, sweet childish thoughts
    they bring,
And memory at Death's threshold bars my way.
Ring out, sweet songs of Heaven! This vernal rain
Of tears makes the green earth my home again!

CHOIR OF YOUTHS: He is uplifted
                That lay with the dead
                To glory and honour
                And life and Godhead;
                Perfect activity,
                Endless rest!
                Ah, but in sorrow
                We sob on earth's breast!
                He has forsaken us,
                Left us His Cross!
                Master, Thy gain is
                Our measureless loss.

CHOIR OF ANGELS: Now is Christ risen!
                From the womb of decay!
                Break ye your bonds
                And your cords cast away!
                Rejoice and be glad
                And praise Him and live
                In the love that He gave,
                By the love that ye give;
                Feed Him in brotherly

Breaking of bread;
The word that He spake
Through the wide earth spread;
All His bright promises
Hope and declare!
The Master is with you—
The Master is there!

BEFORE THE CITY GATE

APPRENTICES:
Where are you going to?

OTHERS:
Up the hill
To Hunter's Lodge.

APPRENTICES:
We're for the mill.

FIRST APPRENTICE:
The inn by the stream is the place to go.

SECOND:
But not such a pretty walk.

OTHERS:
Hullo!
Where do you think of walking to?

THIRD APPRENTICE:
Oh, of course, I shall go with the rest.

FOURTH:
Why not come up to Burgdorf with me?
There's pretty girls and beer of the best
For a rare old rackety, ranting spree.

FIFTH:
You're much too fond of that kind of racket:
Do you want someone else to dust your jacket?
I've had enough of your deviltry.

FIRST SERVANT GIRL:
No, no: I'll go back straight to town.

SECOND SERVANT GIRL:
He's sure to be under those poplar trees.

FIRST SERVANT GIRL:
Then your luck's up and my luck's down.

You two will walk about as you please
And dance on the green. I don't care a jot
If you enjoy yourself or not.

SECOND SERVANT GIRL:

But he won't be by himself: so there!
He'll bring the boy with the curly hair.

STUDENT:

Gad, how these strapping wenches stride!
Let's go along with them. That's the stuff!
With a pot of strong beer and a pipe to puff
And a girl in her best, I'm satisfied.

YOUNG LADY:

There, look at that! Boys who could get
With perfect ease in the smartest set—
What a shame! They have no manners at all;
They're after the girls from the servants' hall!

SECOND STUDENT (*to the first*):

Wait! There's a pair coming up behind,
Really smart; and one, by the way,
Lives next door. I've a very good mind
To be—well, more than civil some fine day.
Here they are, just strolling on;
But they'll take us with them before we've done.

FIRST STUDENT:

Bother! That's boring: let's make haste;
Wilder birds are more to my taste.
Saturday's girl with her mop and her muddle
Is Sunday's girl for a kiss and a cuddle.

TOWNSMAN:

No, sir, I've no opinion of our Mayor;
He's much too hoity-toity in the chair;
And really what's he doing for the town?
It's getting daily worse, don't you agree?
He's always setting up authority
And we are always putting money down.

BEGGAR (*singing*):

Good gentlemen and pretty ladies
    That are so smart, with cheeks so red,
A trifle for the poor old beggar,
    The poor old man that begs his bread.

49

Just something for the hurdy-gurdy;
　It is a joy to give away;
A day when all the world is happy
　Is the poor beggar's harvest-day.

SECOND TOWNSMAN:
　What I like best on Sunday or a feast
　Is a good talk about war and rumours of war,
　When there's a lot of fighting in the east,
　Say, Turkey—a safe distance from one's door.
　Then at the window with a glass to sip
　One watches glide down stream ship after ship;
　And in such splendid spirits home again
　Blessing the good things peace brings in its train.

THIRD TOWNSMAN:
　Just so! exactly what I like to do;
　If they like cracking skulls and sword and flame,
　It really need not trouble me and you
　So long as things at home are much the same.

OLD CRONE (*to* TOWNSMAN's *daughter*):
　My! but that's lovely! There's a pretty pet!
　You'll make them crazy; Only not so proud;
　I can read fortunes, don't you fret;
　You'll have your will; you needn't wish aloud.

TOWNSMAN'S DAUGHTER:
　Come along, Agatha! By daylight
　I don't consort with witches. By the way,
　Would you believe it? On St. Andrew's Night
　She showed me my true love as plain as day!

SECOND TOWNSMAN'S DAUGHTER:
　And in a bit of crystal she showed mine.
　A soldier with his comrades near as fine.
　I'm on the look out; but do what I can
　Don't seem to come across my soldier man.

SOLDIERS:　　　　Oh, I would conquer
　　　　　　Castle and wall,
　　　　Mistresses fairer
　　　　　　And prouder than all!
　　　　Soldier, be gallant
　　　　　　And fair thee befall!

　　　　Blow, bonny trumpet,
　　　　　　And woo with thy breath,

Blow, bonny trumpet,
  For rapine and death!

There mount the storm-troops!
  There's plunder to seize!
Fine mistress and castle
  Must yield up their keys.

And to whom but bold heroes
  Should fortresses fall?
So away we go marching,
  The soldier-boys tall.

FAUST *and* WAGNER

FAUST:

The streams and running brooks that froze
Spring sets free from their icy gaol:
Hope is green along the vale;
Bald winter, shivering as he goes,
Retires to the rocks and mountain snows.
Ah, the old bandit still can pelt
The lowlands with a few stray shot,
On the green grass a tinkling belt:
But white the sun endureth not;
Now he shapes with plastic stress,
Soon he will quicken with living hues,
And, as he has no flowers, he strews
Those happy people in their gay dress.
Just turn a moment and look down;
There, behind us, lies the town.
Isn't that pretty! Look how they swarm
Through the black, old arch! The sun is warm
And they love to sun themselves: they keep
The feast of the Risen Lord. What then?
They themselves are risen men;
Shake off a kind of deathly sleep,
As out of doors from alley and slum
And forge and mill and bench they come,
From gables and garrets and stifling lanes
And crooked kennels that load them with chains,
Out from the Church's too solemn night

Into the freedom of air and light.
Look, look, what movement! How they throng!
Through gardens and meadows scattering wide:
The river-reaches stretch broad and long:
And a hundred merry pleasure-boats ride!
Look at this last one: what a load!
Enough to sink them; and there on the high
Hill-paths and the climbing mountain road
What a flutter of colour delights the eye!
I can hear already the village hum:
There is the poor man's kingdom come.
What shouts! What laughter frank and free!
Here I'm the man I ought to be.

WAGNER:

This *is* a privilege; sir, I shall treasure
The memory of this walk. But, oh, dear me!
I should be lost alone here; all rough pleasure
Is too much for my sensibility.
Fiddles and ninepins, shouting. I'm afraid
All this to me is a distressing noise;
One would suppose the devil piped and played;
And yet this is their music, these their joys.

PEASANTS *under the Linden. Dance and Song.*

The shepherd he made himself smart for the ball
With jacket and ribbon and nosegay and all;
As spruce as a sprat on a griddle.
Round the linden there wasn't a place to be had,
And all of them danced as if were mad;
    With a snicker-snee
    And a tweedle-dee-dee,
Merrily scraped the fiddle.

He puffed and he pushed and he elbowed the rest,
And then to a pretty young maiden he pressed
And clipped her round the middle:
She turned about, so fresh and smart,
And she said, "Young man, you gave me a start."
    With a tweedle-dee-dee
    "Don't meddle with me,
I'll thank you not to meddle."

But away they went in the thick of the fun,
Right and left they twisted and spun
And the petticoats flew: taradiddle!
They flushed so red and they flushed so hot,
They sat them down in a quiet spot,
    With a snicker-snee
    And a tweedle-dee-dee,
And he held her round the middle.

    "Now don't you be so free with me,
    There's many that take a poor girl on their knee,
    And then their thumbs they twiddle."
But he was so sly that she soon tripped,
And still the fiddle scraped and ripped
    With a snicker-snee
    And a fiddle-dee-dee,
And a la-la-la to the fiddle!

OLD PEASANT:
Doctor, it's very kind of you to come
Amongst us poor folk on a holiday.
So take a pull with me, Sir, of this jug.
Here's wishing it will take your thirst away,
And there's a better toast I'd like to give:
May you, Sir, have as many years to live
As there are drops of liquor in the mug.

FAUST:
With pleasure. Ha! a most refreshing brew,
So here's your healths and my best thanks to you.
             (The PEASANTS *gather round in a circle)*

OLD PEASANT:
Sure, we're all pleased to see you come abroad,
Now that there's feasting and our hearts are glad:
Many's the time when you and yours have been
A great help to us when the times were bad.
There's many here alive and well to-day
Your father rescued lying at death's door
With fever; it was he who stopped the plague
That took off hundreds of us, rich and poor.
You were a young man then, as I recall.
Yet into every stricken house you went

53

When they brought out the dead into the street,
And by God's blessing took no harm at all.
Stern tests you stood, and they all prove
Help to the helper cometh from above.

CROWD:

Cheers for the doctor! God save him,
That when we want him we may have him!

FAUST:

Uncover to Him from whom proceed
Knowledge and skill and help in need.

(FAUST *and* WAGNER *move on*)

WAGNER:

O Sir! What must your feeling be,
Rich in the people's reverence!
Ah, what a happy man is he
Whose talents win such recompense!
Fathers point you out to their sons,
And one cries "Where?" and t'other runs;
The fiddler stops and the dancers are still;
They stand in rows as you climb the hill;
Up go their hats, as high as the tree;
And very soon they'll be down on the knee
As if for the *Venerabile.*

FAUST:

We'll go no farther than that boulder. There
We'll rest a little. Often in time past
Plunged in deep thought I sat here. Strove with prayer
On this grey stone and well nigh swooned with fast.
Rich then in hope and faith I thought to wrest
From the Lord of Heaven deliverance from that pest,
With wringing of my hands and sighs and tears.
Now all those sounding praises in my ears
Hurt worse than scorn and bitter mockery.
Ah, could'st thou look into my secret thought
And see how little son or father wrought
To earn at all their honest eulogy.
My father was a worthy man, whose dim
Intelligence pondered with a profound
Honesty, but, as he might, with freak and whim,
Nature and her inviolable round.
Secluded in his sooty laboratory,

With other adepts in the famous art,
He tried interminable formulae,
For fusing things her mandate holds apart.
Then did the ruddy lion woo and wed
The fair white lily in a bath of lead,
And both were in one bridal chamber stowed,
While at white heat the fuelled furnace glowed.
Then, if the young queen, brilliant as a bride,
Shone in the glass retort, that worked the spell,
The cure was found; of course the patients died,
And no one thought of asking who got well.
So with our devilish boluses and pills
In these green valleys and these quiet hills,
Worse than the plague we raged. Ah, my dear Sir,
Thousands have had the poisonous stuff from me:
They died, and I am left alive, you see
That I may hear men praise the murderer.

WAGNER:
Why worry over little things like these?
Surely as good a man as ever breathed
Does quite sufficient if he practises
With skill and care an art to him bequeathed.
If you revered your father in your youth
'Twas well, sir, to perpetuate his skill;
If you have now more scientific truth,
Some day your son may carry it further still.

FAUST:
Oh, to have hope! Still to confide in her
To lift me from the flood where error flows!
Ignorance is a prompt practitioner,
And knowledge cannot practise what it knows.
But we'll not let these sad thoughts sour
The benediction of this hour.
See how the low sun's crimson glory shines
Soft on the huts among their sheltering pines.
But now he stoops, he sinks, the day is over,
There where he rushes a new dawn will break.
Oh, that I have no wings that I might hover
And follow, follow ever in his wake!
Then in an evening light that never fails,
For me the world one stillness should enfold,

Fire on all summits, peace upon all vales,
And every silvery beck a rill of gold.
No mountains then should bar my godlike flight,
No savage gorges their grim ramparts raise,
But the great sea on my astonished sight
Dawn, with his basking gulfs and glittering bays.
Now the bright god seems hurling from heaven's steep,
And I am driven, like a venturous bark,
Of his eternal splendour to drink deep,
The day before me and behind the dark.
Heaven shines above, below the waters roll.
A dream, and with the dream he, too, is gone.
Ah, not so lightly can the winged soul
Fledge the crass flesh with phantom pinion.
Yet 'tis a native impulse so to dare,
Upward to soar, beat forward with strong wings,
When high above us, lost in the blue air,
His palpitating song the skylark sings;
When o'er the rugged pine-tree fastnesses
The poising eagle spreads his ample vanes
And over level lands and tumbling seas
Toil to their far off home the straggling cranes.

WAGNER:

I've had strange fits that scarcely squared with sense,
But never such an odd experience.
One soon gets tired of fields and trees and brooks,
I never much begrudged the bird his flight:
But intellectual joy is my delight;
I like the printed leaves bound up in books.
Then are dark winter nights both mild and fair,
Life warms the limbs that frost and cold have nipped;
Show me a valuable manuscript,
All heaven steps down beside my study chair.

FAUST:

You only know one impulse; never come
To know the other. But two souls contend
In me and both souls strive for masterdom,
Which from the other shall the sceptre rend.
The first soul is a lover, clasping close
To this world tentacles of corporal flame;
The other seeks to rise with mighty throes

56

To those ancestral meadows whence it came.
If there be spirits, if the air they crowd,
The master-weavers betwixt heaven and earth,
Let them descend out of their golden cloud,
And bear me hence up to a brighter birth!
Ah, were the great magician's mantle mine,
And could it carry me to far off things,
I would not sell it, not for raiment fine,
And all the splendour that apparels kings.

WAGNER:

Oh, don't call up those fiends; it is well known
How floating round the atmospheric zone
In every quarter of the earth they find
A thousand ways to jeopardy mankind.
Out of the north come goblin teeth that bite
With shooting out of arrow-headed tongues,
And from the east the vampires, whose delight
Is shrivelling up and fattening on your lungs.
And when the south has sent his desert ghouls
To roast your brainpan with their burning rays
The west lets loose the swarm that only cools
To drown yourself, your fallows and your leys.
They hear a whisper, they like mischief so;
They come at once for love of trickery,
And when with airs of heaven they seem to blow
They lisp like angels to delude and lie.
Let us be going; earth is gray and whist,
The air grows cool; and slowly sinks the mist.
Why do you stand stock still and stare and stare?
What spell so charms you in the dusky air?

FAUST:

Do you not see that black dog quartering there
Among the young corn and the stubble bare?

WAGNER:

Oh, yes, I saw him long ago; but he
Did not seem of much consequence to me.

FAUST:

Look at him well. What do you take him to be?

WAGNER:

Why, it's a poodle dog. And I presume
He's looking for his master.

FAUST:

Don't you see

Those snake-like circles nearing in the gloom?
If I mistake not as he runs he leaves
A trail of fire that travels in his track.

WAGNER:

For my part I can only see a black
Poodle. I am afraid your sight deceives
You, sir.

FAUST:

I see a sort of running noose,

A magic cord to bind us hand and foot.

WAGNER:

I see he's off and on, uncertain how to choose;
We are both strangers and his master's lost.

FAUST:

The circle narrows; and here comes the brute.

WAGNER:

You see a dog, dear sir, and not a ghost.
He's whining; lying on his belly, too,
Wagging his tail; that's just what all dogs do.

FAUST:

You come with us, my friend; come on!
You shall be our companion.

WAGNER:

They are absurd beasts, poodles; if you stop
They lie and wait; call them and they'll come quick;
They'll bring you anything you've chanced to drop
Or jump into the water for your stick.

FAUST:

You were quite right; there's nothing spectral thin
About the brute, he's just well broken in.

WAGNER:

Train a dog well and every man of sense
Cannot but value its intelligence.
He's worth your kindness; yes, one sees at once
Of all your class he's by no means the dunce.

(They enter the City Gate.)

STUDY

(FAUST *and* POODLE *enter.*)

FAUST:

Deep night lay on grassland and springing corn
As I came through them in that blessed hour
When the true soul within us is reborn
And things not earthly touch us with dread power.
Then all unruly impulses are still,
All violence is curbed;
The love of man can all our being fill,
The love of God reign undisturbed.

Quiet! Stop that infernal to and fro
And sniffing at the threshold. Here, take that,
And lie on it behind the stove's warm glow;
It's my best cushion and shall be your mat.
Outside on the hill-paths 'twas good to see
You run and leap with eager zest:
But now I am your host and you must be
A quiet though a welcome guest.

Ah, when the friendly lamp relit
Burns in our narrow cell;
The heart takes radiance from it,
If there self-knowledge dwell.
Reason begins to speak that long was dumb;
Hope blooms, that long lay dead
And for the living waters yearnings come;
Yea, for life's fountain-head.

Don't snarl, sir; your brute-noises jar
My very soul, that hears within
Notes of diviner origin.
Men's mockery is familiar;
They gird at all they are too dull
To understand, the Good, the Beautiful;
And grunt at all that's hard; but you,
Dumb beast, will you growl too?

I long for inward peace; but, oh,
The bubbling well is wasted at the spring:

Why has the fountain sunk so low
So soon, and left me languishing?
I suffer a perpetual dearth;
Yet is a rich supply unsealed;
We seek for treasure not of earth,
We hunger after truth revealed;
Where burns it with such beauty blent
As shines in the New Testament?
Let me look up the text; I'm stung
By a strong impulse once for all
To take the great original
And turn it simply into our own tongue.

(He opens a volume and sets to.)
"In the Beginning was the Word"—how so?
I'm stuck already. Who can help me? No;
I cannot value the mere word so high:
I see I must translate it differently,
If only the inspiring light were kind.
Well then: "In the Beginning was the Mind."
That first line needs reflection: else my pen
Will skip too glib across the page and scour
Too fast. Does Mind form, work in all things then?
It must run: "In the Beginning was the Power."
Even while I write it something in me says
It will not stand: I do not like the phrase.
Ah, now I have the light that first I lacked;
"In the Beginning was the Creative Act."

If I'm to share my room with you
Stop howling and stop barking too.
I can't keep such a noisy hound;
So you or I must shift our ground.
You have outstayed your welcome: so—
The door is open—out you go!
Eh, but what's that? Has Nature such surprises?
Is't shadow,—substance? Long it grows and fat;
In a tremendous arch it rises!
I swear a poodle never looked like that!
What goblin-ghost have I brought home to-night?
He's like the Nile-horse with red eyes of flame
And fearful jaws that snap and bite.

But I have that will make you tame.
Solomon's Key is the sovran spell
For these cursed demi-spawn of hell.

SPIRITS *(in the passage)*:

Keep off! keep off! By bolts and locks,
There's one of us trapped like a prowling fox.
Ha! Ha! Ha! how the bold heart sinks.
Wow! Wow! Wow! The old hell-lynx.
Let be! Let be! Warily!
Hover high, hover low,
Hither, thither, to and fro!
He will find a way out, by yes and no.
But we must not leave him in such a plight;
So use all your power and all your sleight,
For we owe him many a delicate delight.

FAUST:

It needs but the words of the mighty Four
And the brute will trouble me no more.

Glow, Salamander, glow!
Flow, Undine, flow!
Sylph, in wandering air be found!
Cobbold, dig beneath the ground!

He that knows not
Dry, cold, moist, hot,
And of each the quality
O'er spirits hath no mastery.

Salamander, Salamander,
Pass in fire! Pass in foam,
Undine, Undine!
Sylph, with falling stars go wander,
Deck thee with the meteor's sheen!
But thou helpmate of the home,
Come thou forth! Come forth to us,
Incubus! Incubus!
Bless this dwelling from all harm,
So complete the powerful charm!

What, hump, not one in thee and no harm done?

61

He lies and grins from ear to ear.
Then if the Four thou dost not fear
I'll try thee with the mightier One.
Companion, art thou
A waif of hell?
Behold the Sign to which black angels bow!

Ah, now the bristly hog begins to swell!

Satan's limb,
Dost thou know Him,
The Uncreate,
Unexpressed,
That fills all heaven, Whom guilt and hate
Pierced through the breast?

Behind the stove he skulks,
Blown to a monstrous elephant he bulks!
The whole room fills as if 'twould fleet
Away in mist! Down from the roof,
Down at thy master's feet!
Thou seest my menace is no dream.
I make the fires of heaven hot
To heat thee with a holy heat,
And singe thee horn and hoof.
Tarry not
Till there shine forth the glory of the Trinal Beam,
Of my most potent art the top supreme.
(*As the mist settles* MEPHISTOPHELES *in the garb of a wandering
pedagogue steps out from behind the stove*)

MEPHIST.:
No need to shout so! What's your worship's will?

FAUST:
You were forsooth the kernel in the nut!
A very droll case, called "The Poodle Dog
Transformed"—into a travelling pedagogue.

MEPHIST.:
My homage, sir, and compliments on your skill.
If e'er I sweat so you may call me cut.

FAUST:
Your name?

MEPHIST.:

Why ask it? You were too astute
To set much value on the Word! The show
Of outward things you do not care to know,
And all your study is the Absolute.

FAUST:

Ah, but you gentlemen are apt to advertise
Your nature by your names; as, God of Flies,
Or I could quote you the Destroyer cursed,
Or him that was a Liar from the first.
Then who are you?

MEPHIST.:

Part of the power endued
With malice old yet ever working good.

FAUST:

That's subtle; but what does it signify?

MEPHIST.:

I am the spirit that doth still deny;
And I am right; for everything that is
By rights should topple down to the abyss:
Ergo, 'twere better if nothing had been.
All that you call destruction, evil, sin,
That is the element that I work in.

FAUST:

A part, you said; yet you're a thing entire.

MEPHIST.:

That's modesty: which you must please admire.
If man, the mite infinitesimal,
Takes his mad microcosm for the All,
Part of that part am I, which ere creation's ray
Was all; part of that darkness whence came forth the Day;
That too pretentious particle of light
Which now disputes her rank with Mother Night,
With small success; for all its effort vast
It is immersed in matter and sticks fast.
Matter reflects it, matter it makes fair,
Matter confines its progress everywhere,
And before long, my expectation is,
With matter it will sink to the abyss.

FAUST:

Ah, now I understand your high vocation:

> Failing a general annihilation
> You've taken to the retail line instead.

MEPHIST.:
> And there's but little in it when all's said.
> All that is most opposed to non-existence,
> This—what you call 'em—gross world's crass resistance,
> So far as I have pushed the job, has proved
> A thing by no means easily removed
> By waves, storms, earthquakes, fire, or what you please;
> There is a settled calm on lands and seas.
> And this damned brat, this man-beast and his get,
> Will not be downed; although it's true, I have
> Helped them by mortal millions to the grave,
> New blood, fresh vigour trickles in him yet.
> So it goes on; enough to make one rave.
> The air wafts germs, they wander in the wave,
> Earth breeds them in her myriad furrows sown;
> And they complacently unfold
> In moist and dry and hot and cold;
> Why, but for fire, there's nothing left I care to have
> That I can call my own.

FAUST:
> Thou dost set up thy cold, stark devil's fist
> Against the everlasting reign
> Of power that hath all made and all things blest;
> Thou doublest it in vain.
> Bethink thee of some likelier strategy
> Chaos' incalculable son.

MEPHIST.:
> Well, we must think about it, you and I;
> More when we next meet, which will be anon.
> Permit me for the moment to retire.

FAUST:
> I don't see why you ask me; now we know
> Each other, you are free to come and go.
> There is the window, there's the door.
> Or there's the stove-pipe if you so desire.

MEPHIST.:
> I must admit there is just one thing more,
> That stops my promenade. If't must be told
> It is the Druid's foot on your threshold.

FAUST:

> You find the pentagram an obstacle?
> Why, you ingenious imp of hell,
> How got you in then? What could so impose
> On such a spook as you, you devil's spawn?
> They must go out the way that they slipt in.

MEPHIST:

> Well, look at it! The thing is badly drawn:
> You see, the outside angle doesn't close.

FAUST:

> As luck would have it! You were fairly crept
> Into the snare and pretty near the noose.

MEPHIST.:

> Why, the poor poodle-dog, as in he leapt,
> Gave't not a thought. Now it's the very deuce:
> The devil's in and can't get out again.

FAUST:

> Why not just flutter through the window-pane?

MEPHIST.:

> It is a law for devil and goblin
> They must go out the way that they slipt in.
> Our coming we are free to pick and choose,
> But when we want to be off, we're tied up tight.

FAUST:

> So hell too has its code of civil right;
> I like that; and no doubt it's possible
> To bind you gentry by a solemn pact.

MEPHIST.:

> What's promised that you shall possess in full;
> And not one syllable will we retract.
> But it's a lengthier business than you guess:
> When we meet presently it shall receive
> A full discussion; in all seriousness
> You must permit me now to take my leave.

FAUST:

> Oh, stay a little while and talk; you see
> There are so many things I want to know.

MEPHIST.:

> I'll soon be back; then you can question me:
> But for the moment you must let me go.

Johann Wolfgang von Goethe

FAUST:

I set no snare for you, nor toil, nor gin;
But you obliged me by just walking in:
When you have caught the devil, hold him fast,
Or your first catch is like to be the last.

MEPHIST.:

Well, if it pleases you, I'll gladly stay;
But you must let me while the time away
With pleasant demonstrations of my art.
I stipulate for that.

FAUST:

With all my heart.
Provided it's diverting.

MEPHIST.:

Tut, my friend,
One hour with me will gratify desire
More than the formal year from end to end.
The chants these gentle spirits choir,
The forms that dance to their sweet stops
Are not like magic's mummery.
Sweet odour from their music drops,
And you will lie and lick your chops,
And stretch each nerve in ecstasy.
There needs no overture to bring them in:
We are all met: so let your song begin.

SPIRITS:

Roll, ye vaulted glooms, away!
Dearer than the dawn of day
Through the rifted darkness shine,
Thou profound heaven's hyaline.
Where the hurrying vapours crowd
Little stars peep through the cloud,
Milder suns that lend their light
To make pale noon of earth's midnight.
Children of the spacious sky,
Hither float and wander by,
Stooping as ye go to bless
With aerial loveliness.
Longing follows where ye pass,
With your scarves and fluttering sleeves
Cast a shadow on the grass,

Curtain up the whispering leaves,
Where the thoughts of love are deep
As life's last look and death's last sleep.
Leaf and tendril, vine on vine,
Hanging down their laden stems,
Gushing grapes and foaming wine,
Rippling over pearls and gems;
Till the mountain it forsakes
And the rushing of its rills
Broadens into slumbering lakes,
Gladdening the grassy hills.
And the minions of the air
Drink of joy, and onward fare,
Winging towards the sun's swift sphere,
Toward the islands beckoning bright
That dance upon their waves of light.
There the choral song we hear,
There the whirling dancers see,
Dancing over wood and lea;
Fading, fading, floating free
To the upland lawns and brakes,
Cleaving the crystalline lakes,
Hovering high and hovering far
To that dear, that distant star,
Where Life, Love, Enchantment are.

MEPHIST.:

He is asleep. Well done, ye airy things,
Ye've hushed him sweetly with your warbled strings.
And for this music I'm your debtor. No;
You are not quite the man as yet
To catch the devil and not let him go.
Fool him with visions, drench him in the brine
Of blissful seas whose waves are fancies sooth.
And now, to pass that mystic sign
Before the threshold set,
I want a ratton's nibbling tooth.
That makes but brief demands upon my skill
Hist! There's one scampering to learn my will.

The Lord of Rattons and of Mice
Of Flies and Frogs and Bugs and Lice

Bids you come out and bravely chew
That thing across the threshold through.
Imagine it is daubed with fat:
Ha! Here you are, come pit-a-pat.
Smartly to work then. 'Tis the edge,
Where the sharp apex cuts the ledge,
That bars my way. Just one bite more.
Now, till we meet again, my Faustus, you may snore.

FAUST *(waking up)*:

What, am I duped twice over? Can it be
These airy spirits beckon to betray!
Only in dreams the devil came to me
And a black poodle ran away.

STUDY

FAUST:

Who is that knocking? Come in! Who are you
Must needs disturb my peace again?

MEPHIST.:

It's me.

FAUST:

Come in!

MEPHIST.:

Say it three times.

FAUST:

Come in!

MEPHIST.:

Thanks, that will do
Nicely. Now we shall get on famously.
To get you out of the dumps, you see,
I am come as a man of quality,
My scarlet suit gallooned with gold,
My dandy cloak of silken fold,
Cock-feathers in my hat, an ell of steel,
Sharp as a spit, to dangle at my heel.
Go, make yourself as smart as me;
Then all formalities put by
We'll see what life is, you and I.

FAUST:

What matters it how I am dressed?
This narrow life will be the same.

I am too old to treat it as a jest,
Too young to have given up the game.
What satisfaction can this world bestow?
Thou shalt forego—forego, forego;
That is the everlasting song
That in the ears of all men rings,
That unremitting our life long
Hour after hour hoarsely sings.
With horror I behold the morning break,
And I could almost weep salt tears to see
The day that its appointed course will take
And never grant one single wish to me:
No, not one wish: all promptings of delight
It damns with critical fastidious stare;
Life wears a thousand masks that come to spite
All that I mean to shape of good and fair.
And when the day is over and I creep
Sick, sick at heart, into my lonely bed,
I am denied the common boon of sleep,
Such uncontrollable dreams run through my head.
The god that made this beating heart his own
Searches my soul and stirs its depths profound;
But he's the monarch of an impotent throne
And alters nothing in the world around.
Merely to be is to know all unrest:
I hate my life and reckon death were best.

MEPHIST.:
And yet death never is a welcome guest.

FAUST:
Happy is he, for whom in noonday sun
Of glory, death the bloody laurels binds;
Happy whom, when the maddening dance is done,
Pillowed upon some fair girl's breast he finds.
Oh, to have sunk in such a swooning-fit,
Exanimate by that Great Spirit's might!

MEPHIST.:
Yet there was someone on a certain night
Sniffed a black draught, but wouldn't sample it.

FAUST:
So you're a spy then: that's your pastime.

Johann Wolfgang von Goethe

MEPHIST.:

Oh,
I'm not omniscient; there are things I know.

FAUST:

If in that ghastly tumult a sweet sound,
Dear to me once, could steal my thoughts away,
And, some faint answering echoes in me found,
Could on the muted stops of childhood play;
My curse on every lure and cheating spell
That cabins up the soul in this close cage,
Dungeoned in sorrow's unremitted hell
By glittering fraud and blinding cozenage;
And before all cursed be those lofty aims
That wind the soul in their false, futile coil;
Cursed be all semblances, all forms, all names
That our vexed spirit occupy and foil!
And you, ye hypocrites, ye cogging dreams,
Of never-dying fame, I curse ye now;
Cursed be all chattels, everything man deems
His dear possessions, wife, child, hind and plough!
Accursed be Mammon with his shining hoards,
Whether he tempt to deeds of high renown,
Or with his filthy surfeit blunt the sword
And roll us wallowing on a bed of down.
My blistering curse the grape vine's balm-drop scathe!
A curse on love for better or for worse!
A curse on hope! A curse upon all faith!
And on submission fall my heaviest curse!

SPIRITS *(invisible)*:

Woe! Woe!
Thou hast destroyed
Thy fair world with the blow
Of a mighty fist!
It topples, crashes, ruining down,
For was not he a demi-god that brake it?
We gather up the fragments; in the void
Leave them, and the lost loveliness lament.
Great son of earth, rise up, remake it
More strong
And more magnificent;
Build it again within

Thy breast; and thy new life begin
With a new heart and a new song!

MEPHIST.:

These are some of my small fry,
Imps of precocity;
You hear, they recommend
Pleasure and action. Their large lure
Is the great world: they bid you end
Your solitude, which, slow but sure,
Obstructs the sap, till from disuse
The very senses grow obtuse.
Ah, toy no more with grief; with beak of steel
The vulture gnaws your vitals; think again;
The worst of company can make you feel
You are a man and they are brother men.
Not that you're to rub elbows with the crowd:
I'm no great oneyer; if you'll condescend
To walk the world with me, I shall be proud
To be your man this minute. I'm your friend,
And if you'll have it so will come at call
Your humble servant and your menial.

FAUST:

And what exact return am I to make?

MEPHIST.:

That's so far off the thing may be dismissed.

FAUST:

No, no! The devil is an egoist,
And not so fond of serving for God's sake.
Make your conditions clear beyond a doubt;
When hireless hirelings come, the luck is out.

FAUST:

I'll serve you here, and you shall have my bond;
Save at your beck I slumber not nor slack;
And when we find us in the world beyond
With the like service you shall pay me back.

FAUST:

The world beyond can give me no concern;
When you have made a rubble-heap of this
It will be time the other had its turn.
Earth is the fountain-head of all my bliss,
The sun of earth shines on my miseries.

Once shut of them nothing shall make me stop;
Come what come may, I have no care to learn
If in the future we know hate and love,
Or whether for the spheres that wheel above
There be perhaps a bottom and a top.

MEPHIST.:

If you're of that mind there's no risk: so give
Your bond: and for the days you have to live
Enjoy my arts; for they can make your own
Things man ne'er yet so much as looked upon.

FAUST:

Poor devil! What hast thou to give?
When was the soul that struggles to ascend
A thing that such as you could comprehend?
True thou hast bread by which man cannot live;
And ruddy gold that through the fingers slips
Like quicksilver; you set the ivory spinning
At that queer game where there's no chance of winning;
Yours are the women of the vermeil lips
That in our arms gaze in our rival's eyes,
And yours in honour our lust deifies,
Gone like a falling star. Tempt me with fruits
That rot ere they be crushed; branches that fade,
For ever verdant with insidious shoots.

MEPHIST.:

That's a commission staggers me no whit;
There I am rich, and you shall be obeyed.
But, my good friend, one day you'll want to sit
O'er some good thing, a gourmet nothing loth.

FAUST:

If e'er I wallow on a bed of sloth,
The game is up, and there's an end of me.
If you can lie so well, so well cajole,
That to myself I am what I would be—
In that complacent surfeit souse my soul—
It shall be my last day. Now—will you bet?

MEPHIST.:
Done!

FAUST:

Done! If e'er I cry to the passing hour
"Thou art so beautiful; Oh, linger yet!"

Fasten my fetters; I am in thy power.
Then I will go down gladly to the pit.
Then let the bell toll for my funeral,
Then of thy servitude thou shalt be quit;
The clock may stop, the hand may fall;
For all time's hours for me will have passed away.

MEPHIST.:

Think well: I shall remember what you say.

FAUST:

And you have an indisputable right,
I do not wantonly miscalculate;
Though I stick out for what I deem my dues,
I am a slave, no matter thine or whose.

MEPHIST.:

Then there's no reason why I should not wait
At the high table where you'll be to-night,
When in their robes the new-dubbed doctors dine.
But to make all things sure as life and death,
Just one thing more, please—just one little line.

FAUST:

What, pedant, must it be in black and white?
You never knew a man then, or man's word once passed
Faithful kept? You think my bond mere breath,
Powerless to bind me while my life shall last?
Does not the world with all its streams rage on
And shall a promise keep me from the brink?
And yet we treasure the illusion,
And who is there would care to break the link?
Well for the heart where pure truth keeps the field;
There is no sacrifice then to recall;
And yet a bit of sheepskin signed and sealed
Becomes a sort of bogey to us all.
The word is done to death with a scratching pen,
Vellum and sealing wax are lords of men.
Thou wicked spirit, tell me what's thy will?
It's brass or marble, parchment or foolscap?
A graver's tool, a chisel or a quill?
Make your own choice, for I care not a rap.

MEPHIST.:

What use is this ungovernable flood
Of scalding words? Pray you turn off the tap.

> The bond will do on any crumpled scrap,
> But you must sign it with a drop of blood.

FAUST:

> If that will satisfy you, well and good:
> To any foolery I'll set my hand.

MEPHIST.:

> Blood is a juice of an especial brand.

FAUST:

> Are you afraid I mean to break the bond?
> My sole ambition and my single aim
> Is punctual performance. In my fond,
> My puffed-up pride, I thought me not like you;
> And now I claim no rank but what you claim.
> A Greater Spirit has put me to shame.
> Nature has barred me out; and my thin clew
> Of thought is broken. I have long ago
> Wearied of knowledge. Let us steep the glow
> Of passion in the sensual deeps; and through
> The magic veil unrent things strange and new
> Their unexhausted miracles provide.
> Down with me, down, to time and tide,
> The breakers that roar, the billows that ride;
> Pleasure and pain;
> Success and impotent disdain,
> Assume all shapes and shuffle as they can;
> Restless energy proves the man.

MEPHIST.:

> No metes and bounds apply to you.
> Indulge omnivorous appetite,
> Or snatch a fugitive delight;
> Merely consult your own digestion:
> Only, no shyness; just fall to.

FAUST:

> I tell you pleasure's not in question:
> I am the reeling votary of strife,
> Of joy's most savage pang, hate sick with love,
> And sullen anger that can stab to life.
> The knowledge-fit has left me. There is no
> Ache I will bar my door to: all that's dealt
> The heart of man, all, all that men have felt,
> Shall throb through my heart with an equal throe.

I'll grapple the great deeps, the heights above;
Upon my head be all men's joys and griefs;
So to their stature my sole self shall grow
And splinter with them on the roaring reefs.

MEPHIST.:

Oh, but believe me—and that same hard tack
I've munched and chewed four thousand years at least—
From cradled babe to corpse in coffin black,
There comes a heart-burn from that bitter yeast.
Trust me, this complete whole transcends your mark;
Its ministry is for a God's delight;
His dwelling place is everlasting light;
He has consigned us to the eternal dark,
And you must be content with day and night.

FAUST:

Ah! but I will!

MEPHIST.:

Oh, that is nobly said!
And yet there comes on me a certain dread:
Time is so short, and art, we know, is long.
You should take lessons, for the school is hard.
Why not strike up a friendship with a bard?
The gentleman might saunter back and forth
And drawl his pensive song,
And to your honoured crown all gifts concede;
The lion's courage and the wild-stag's speed,
The Italian's fire, the endurance of the North.
He might perhaps disclose the gentle art
How to betray, though really you're all heart,
And while youth's impulses inflame you still
Only to fall in love on principle.
Were such my friend I'd take him to my bosom,
And I might call him Mr. Microcosm.

FAUST:

And what am I, if my injurious star
Grudges the crown of life, the golden zone,
That all my senses strive to make my own?

MEPHIST.:

Why, when all's done, you are—just what you are.
Clap on your pate cart-loads of crimp horse-hair,
On ell-high heels clump up the stately stair,—

You will remain exactly what you are.

FAUST:

Then I have sweated for a bauble crown,
Snatched vainly at man's intellectual dower;
And now the end has come and I sit down,
I feel within no fountain of new power.
But not one hair's breadth did my soul ascend
Nor by an inch approach that which can have no end.

MEPHIST.:

Why, my dear Sir, you seem to look at things
As most men see them; we'll be better sped,
Or else the joy of living will take wings.
Hang it! You've arms and legs; you've got a head
And other fleshy parts. Suppose I dine,
Then are the viands I've just ate less mine?
Suppose I have six stallions in my stall
Are not their muscles mine? Ain't I a stout 'un
With four and twenty legs to get about on?
Oh, thrust your thinking to the wall,
And see the world with me. I'll tell you this;
A fellow damned in self-analysis
Is like the ass some devil with a string
Led round and round among dry heath and ling.
When just beyond him fair, green pastures lay.

FAUST:

What's the first thing to do then?

MEPHIST.:

Go away;
Forsake this scene of noble martyrdom.
Ah, what a life you led! What a dog's lot,
Boring young men with your endless hum-drum!
Now you can leave all that to neighbour Pot.
No need to crack your joints a-threshing straws.
The cream of all the learning you can spell
You daren't serve up to your Johnny Raws.
I hear one coming up the passage now.

FAUST:

I cannot see him; 'tis impossible.

MEPHIST.:

No, but he's waited long, and you'll allow
Deserves a little comforting, poor chap.

So let me have your gown, give me your cap:
This little masque is fairly staged,
So I will robe me handsomely: we shan't
Be more than a short quarter-hour engaged;
Meantime, do you get ready for our jaunt.

(*exit* FAUST.)

(*In* FAUST's *long gown*) Ah-ha! if only you'll contemn
Reason and knowledge, both of them
Twin peaks of human faculty;
And stare until your eyeballs start
At sorcery's phantasmal art
The lying spirit teaches thee;
Then thou art mine to have and keep.
Destiny gave him at his birth
A forward spirit that must sweep
On and still on till it o'erleap
With headlong stride the joys of earth.
I'll drag him through life's carnival,
Through vacant hours that flag and pall,
He'll be my limpet, cling to me and crawl;
I'll carve him dishes; draw him heady
Drinks that shall mock his lips and fade from sight
The more to whet his monstrous appetite.
Refreshment he shall crave and find no whit:
Why, if he hadn't been the devil's own already,
Someway he must have floundered to the pit.

(*Enter* A FRESHMAN.)

FRESHMAN:

I only came up a few days ago,
And venture, sir, to pay my humble call.
I wished so much to speak with you, to know
One who is mentioned with respect by all.

MEPHIST.:

It's very nice of you to bow so low;
I'm a mere man, like all the rest you see.
Did you look round before you came to me?

FRESHMAN:

Take me, I beg! I've mettle in me, sir;
I'm young, I feel my blood begin to stir;
I've money; my allowance might be bigger,
But still it comes to quite a decent figure.

My mother would scarce part with me; but I
Thirsted for knowledge so insatiably.

MEPHIST.:

Then, sir, you've come to the proper place.

FRESHMAN:

Honestly, I'd as lief go back.
I do not like these musty halls,
I do not like these mouldy walls;
There seems to me no room, no space,
No grass, no trees; all's glum and black;
In lecture-rooms, with pen and ink,
I cannot see nor hear nor think.

MEPHIST.:

Oh, you will soon acquire the knack.
A child won't take the breast at first,
Yet loves at last to slake its thirst.
So with a right good will you'll tug
In a few days at Wisdom's dug.

FRESHMAN:

I'd like to hang there if I may;
But you must first show me the way.

MEPHIST.:

We'll come to that: but now, young sir,
Which is the faculty you prefer?

FRESHMAN:

I want to be a savant: that's my bent:
Study the earth, observe the firmament,
Nature—that is, the natural sciences.

MEPHIST.:

You're on the right track; keep it please:
Avoid the snare of time ill-spent.

FRESHMAN:

I'm all for that; but all the same
Just now and then I'd like to seize
Some freedom, an occasional game,
Say, on a summer holiday.

MEPHIST.:

Use your time well; it runs so swift away.
Now method helps you to economize
Your time. So, dear young friend, I would advise

Logic for you. It disciplines the mind,
Like Spanish boots. And you will find
You get on nicely, if you go
Steady along the path of thought;
Not here and there and to and fro
Like Jack o' Lantern. What was taught
Once at a single stroke, you'll see
Requires a little "one, two, three."
'Tis with the workshop of men's brains
As with a piece of tapestry:
One treadle guides a thousand skeins.
You shoot the shuttle to and fro,
You do not see the thin threads grow,
But a thousand are knit at a single blow.
Philosophy (that here comes in)
Will demonstrate it must be so;
Given the first you get the second,
Then your third and fourth are reckoned.
If the first were not so, and the second so,
The third and the fourth could never have been.
That's much esteemed in all the schools
Though they cut queer figures on weavers' stools.
No man ever wrote of a living thing
Till he'd found its soul. But here's the sting:
You may dissect the parts with your knife,
But where, O where, is organic life?
Encheiresis Naturae, says the chemist,
And himself mocks himself; though how that can be
He hasn't a notion—not the dimmest.

FRESHMAN:
I don't quite grasp that.

MEPHIST.:
Never mind.
We'll make that plain next time, when we
By a simple reduction clear the ground
And classify everything in its kind.

FRESHMAN:
I'm afraid it's very stupid of me:
My head's like a mill-wheel going round.

MEPHIST.:
Then metaphysics; that's a vext

Question you must tackle next.
See that your knowledge is profound
Of what man's brain can never sound;
For you see what a splendid word we've got
For what will go in and what will not.
However, for the next half-year
Method's the thing: and, by the way,
Lectures will last five hours a day;
When the clock strikes you'll be there,
And, of course, you must prepare;
Study your text-book carefully:
Then there's no need to take a look;
You'll spot at once (which matters most),
If he says what's not in the book;
And all the time your pen must fly
As if he were the Holy Ghost.

FRESHMAN:

No need to tell me twice: don't I
Know that it helps prodigiously!
It is such a comfort to take home at night
What you've already got in black and white.

MEPHIST.:

Just so: but choose your faculty.

FRESHMAN:

I don't like Jurisprudence.

MEPHIST.:

Very well;
I can't call your dislike unreasonable.
I know exactly how it stands with Law.
Corpuses, statutes, rights, and equities
Are passed on like congenital disease:
It spreads from place to place, and it can draw
Successive generations in its hearse.
Sense turns to nonsense, bounty to a curse.
A grandson are you? Pity if you are!
A right born with us, grievous to relate,
Seems never the affair of Bench or Bar.

FRESHMAN:

O Lord! I simply loathe Law, at that rate!
If I were your pupil, sir, what luck 'twould be!
I've half a mind to read Theology.

MEPHIST.:

> I would not misdirect you there. A serious
> Flaw in this interesting Faculty
> Is 'tis so difficult not to go astray.
> There's latent poison in it, so to say;
> And that, of course, is highly deleterious,
> Especially when scarce distinguishable
> From wholesome physic. It will be as well
> To hear one master only; swear by the words he teaches;
> In fact confine yourself to words; one goes
> On safely then, till through that door he reaches
> The very temple of all certitude.

FRESHMAN:

> The words denote ideas, I suppose.

MEPHIST.:

> Just so! But never fret yourself; for should
> Ideas be wholly lacking, or you've missed 'em,
> Words just pop in and really no one knows.
> Words are a famous weapon for a fray;
> Words are the bricks with which to build a system;
> You may believe in words through thick and thin,
> No man can take a jot of them away.

FRESHMAN:

> I am afraid I keep you in,
> Asking so many questions; pray
> Answer one more. How about medicine?
> I'm sure you have some striking things to say.
> Three years are such a short time, and, my God,
> The field is so extremely wide.
> One needs some finger post, some guide;
> Then one could comfortably feel his way.

MEPHIST. (*aside*):

> I have had enough of this, ecod!
> Now it's the devil's turn to play.
> (*To* FRESHMAN) The spirit of medicine? Anyone,
> Almost, grasps that with ease:
> Study the great world; when that's done
> Study the little; then let the whole thing run
> Exactly as God please.
> It's useless giving every school a turn;
> You'll only learn what you can learn.

Johann Wolfgang von Goethe

Still he's the proper man who can best seize
The occasion. You seem tolerably well made,
Able to call a spade a spade:
Well, if you have self-confidence
Others will give you theirs.
'Tis of the utmost consequence
To manage women; their fine airs,
Their "Ahs" and "Ohs" and deuce knows what.
All yield to pressure on one spot.
So if you're half-way on to that
You have the whole clutch under your hat.
Put letters to your name, some five or six,
For they are great believers in degrees;
Then you can handle the whole bag of tricks
While other men are scratching their own fleas.
Learn how to feel the pulse; that's done
With a sly glance, a fiery one,
One liberal arm thrown round her waist
To see if she's too tightly laced.

FRESHMAN:

Hullo! that's better! One can see
Exactly where and how and why.

MEPHIST.:

Dear friend, all theory is grey and dry;
But green grows Life's all-golden tree.

FRESHMAN:

I swear the whole thing's like a dream to me!
When may I come again and trouble you?
I want to delve deep down so rich a mine.

MEPHIST.:

Oh, what I can I will most gladly do.

FRESHMAN:

I find it very hard to go away.
But here's my album; do write in it, pray.
A word or two, please; merely half a line.

MEPHIST. (*writes*):

Eritis sicut deus, scientes bonum et malum.

(FRESHMAN *makes a deep bow and exit.*)

Stick to the good old text, follow my aunt the snake,
And when they talk of your likeness to God, you'll

begin to shiver and shake.

(Enter FAUST.*)*

FAUST:

Where shall we go to?

MEPHIST.:

Oh, just where you please.
We'll see the small world, then we'll see the great.
It's knowledge cheaply got; no tiresome fees;
And gusto makes the accomplished graduate.

FAUST:

Only, this long beard won't give me a chance:
It isn't quite the cut for comedy;
'Twill be a nuisance when I pay a call.
In fact I'm hopeless in society;
With other people I become so small.
I shall be always out of countenance.

MEPHIST.:

Oh, my dear fellow, don't you care a pin.
That'll wear off; it's only when we win
Self-confidence the joys of life begin.

FAUST:

How shall we go? Have you a carriage and pair?
Have you a lackey?

MEPHIST.:

No, but I've a cloak,
And that'll bear us bravely through the air.
Only, as it's a trifle bold perhaps,
Don't bundle in a lot of heavy traps.
A puff of hot air, then away like smoke!
Up, up we go! The earth drops down through space;
The lighter load the quicker is the pace,
Hearty congrats! New life, new joys to chase!

Johann Wolfgang von Goethe

AUERBACH'S SHADES IN LEIPZIG

A DRINKING PARTY

FROSCH:

> Not a drop do you drink, not a smile on your faces!
> I'll teach you how to pull grimaces!
> A mouldy lot, like straw in the mire;
> Yet I've seen you blaze like a house on fire.

BRANDER:

> Come to that—you're not much use, I guess;
> Start a rag, or do some beastliness.

FROSCH (*throwing a glass of wine over him*):

> There's both for you.

BRANDER:

> You double-dyed
> Hog!

FROSCH:

> Well, you asked for it, didn't you?

SIEBEL:

> If you pick quarrels we'll pitch you outside.
> A round, a round, with bumpers full!
> Up! Holla-ho! Holla-hulli-hoo!

ALTMAYER:

> For God's sake give me some cotton-wool!

SIEBEL:

> It's only when the plaster tumbles
> You feel how the deep bass roars and rumbles.

FROSCH:

> Right! And outside who makes himself a nuisance!
> A! tara lara da!

ALTMAYER:

> A! tara lara da! Tara!

FROSCH:

> That loosens
> The tongue a bit.
> (*Sings*) Holy, holy, roly, poly,
> Ain't the Roman Empire holy?

BRANDER:

> Oh, blast! Get along

With your beastly, stinking, Political song!
(*Sings*) Lift the latch, the night is still;
You may thank your Maker it isn't your job
To run the holy old thing-um-a-bob.
At least I've something to thank Him for—
I'm not Kaiser or Chancellor!
Now all you fellows are full of dope
We want a head; so we'll choose a Pope;
And you know what a dog he's got to be
Who's hoisted high as Peter's See.

FROSCH (*sings*):
Up! Mistress Nightingale! Fly, fly away!
Fair Mistress Nightingale, kiss my love "good-day!"

SIEBEL:
No, no; no kisses, that won't do.

FROSCH:
Kiss her I will, and be dåmned to you!
(*Sings*) Once in a larder there lived a rat
Lift the latch, my true love wakes.
Let the latch fall, the morning breaks,
Morning breaks behind the hill.

SIEBEL:
Oh, sing away! She's chaste and kind and fair
And all the rest; but I'll have my laugh yet.
She has fooled me and someone will fool her.
I wish she and a goblin were well met
At four cross-roads. I shouldn't care a groat.
He'd teach her how to banter and to flite;
And then some old, horned Brocken billy-goat
Might gallop up and snicker a "good-night."
Upon my soul a man is much too good
For any wench, if he's of flesh and blood.
Oh, yes, I'll blow her kisses, if that means
Smashing her windows into smithereens.

BRANDER:
Silence, gentlemen! Listen to me!
I know something of life, you'll agree.
With so many lovers it seems but right
To sing them a song that'll suit their plight,
And send them to bed with a sweet "good-night."
So here's a new thing and a pretty new thing,

85

And mind you make the chorus ring.
(*sings*) Once in a larder there lived a rat
    That ate all the butter and suet,
And grew such a nice little paunch to pat
    Just as Martin Luther grew it.
So the cook she laid the poison thick,
And then the rat felt very sick,
    As if it was love he had lived on.

CHORUS:
    As if , etc.

BRANDER:
    In and out he flung about,
        He drank up the puddles and slops, sir;
    He bit and clawed through joist and board,
        But nothing the pain would stop, sir.
    He danced and skipped with the sorry stuff,
    And soon the poor devil had had enough,
        As if it was love he had lived on.

CHORUS:
    As if, etc.

BRANDER:
    Then into the kitchen plump he plopped
        Where cookie the fire was poking;
    He writhed, he twitched, he jumped, he dropped,
        And began an awful choking.
    And Jezebel laughed as she turned the roast,
    "Ha! ha! he's given up the ghost,
        As if it was love he had lived on!"

CHORUS:
    As if, etc.

SIEBEL:
How the fools laugh at the silly rot.
A pinch of powder would do for the lot;
Poisoning rats is rather my lay.

BRANDER:
You've a fellow feeling for 'em, eh?

ALTMAYER:
His belly's fat and his hair is thin;
That's the worst of the way he is in.
Really it's not to be wondered at
If he sees himself in the bloated rat.

(Enter FAUST *and* MEPHISTOPHELES.*)*

MEPHIST.:

> I think it's well that you should see
> Something of jovial company;
> Their hearts are so light and they live so gay,
> The whole year round is one holiday.
> Small wit, but plenty of give and take;
> Narrow perhaps, but never stale;
> Just kittens playing with their tail;
> And if at times their heads will ache,
> As long as landlord lets the reckoning run
> They've not a care and any amount of fun.

BRANDER:

> Strangers, travelling somewhere:
> You can see that by their curious air:
> They haven't been here an hour.

FROSCH:

> You're right!
> Ah, Leipzig, Leipzig, my delight!
> Paris is little for moulding men!

SIEBEL:

> Whom do you take the strangers for, then?

FROSCH:

> Leave that to me. I'll find out the truth
> As easy as drawing a child's first tooth.
> Good wine, were they as 'cute as Moses,
> Will coax the little worms out of their noses.
> Devilish well-born, and devilish proud:
> They don't seem to think very much of our crowd.

BRANDER:

> I bet they're cheap jacks.

ALTMAYER:

> Possibly.

FROSCH:

> You wait: I'll twist their tails, you see.

MEPHIST. *(to* FAUST*)*:

> That's characteristic! You should note
> That point; the vulgar are not able
> To spot the devil, even when
> The devil's got 'em by the throat.

FAUST:

    Good evening!

SIEBEL:

    Evening, gentlemen!

          (Sotto voce, looking askance at MEPHISTOPHELES*)*

    Why does the fellow limp?

MEPHIST.:

    Sirs, may we sit

    And join you at your table?

    And as good wine, I suppose, is not on tap

    You shall regale us with your wit.

ALTMAYER:

    You seem to be rather a blasé chap.

FROSCH:

    Just come from Rippach? Couldn't leave its charms?

    Dined with old Jack that keeps the Freshman's Arms?

MEPHIST.:

    Passed him to-day; he rather tried our patience,

    Talking so much about his dear relations,

    And sent no end of messages to you.

                      (bows to FROSCH*)*

ALTMAYER *(sotto voce)*:

    You've got it now; he knows a thing or two.

SIEBEL:

    Distinctly clever; quite a pretty wit.

FROSCH:

    I'll get my own back; just you wait a bit.

MEPHIST.:

    Was that a catch I heard or an old round?

    Something you trolled to which the spirit marches:

    Sung as you sang it, it must really sound

    Magnificent under these echoing arches.

FROSCH:

    You're a performer?

MEPHIST.:

    Oh, dear, no!

    No talent whatever; only great delight.

ALTMAYER:

    Give us a song!

MEPHIST.:

    I'll sing to you all night

If you care to listen half as long.

SIEBEL:

Then give us something that's all the go:
Something quite in the modern vein.

MEPHIST.:

Well, we have just come back from Spain
The lovely land of wine and song.
(*Sings*) There once lived a king in a castle
Who had so large a flea—

FROSCH:

D've hear? The king had a thumping big flea:
Well, every man in his humour, but that wouldn't
do for me.

MEPHIST.:

There once lived a king in a castle
Who had such a thumping big flea
That he loved the little rascal,
Dear as a son was he.
He called for the royal tailor,
And up the tailor rose;
"Measure him for a court-suit, tailor,
Measure him for hose."

BRANDER:

Oh, tell the tailor with my love
That the hose must fit him like a glove;
If they hang in creases about his legs
He'll hang on the gallows as sure as eggs.

MEPHIST.:

So now the flea was tailored
In velvet of the best,
And soon became a gay lord
With a star upon his breast;
Which caused him to determine
To send for his brother fleas,
Till the court was full of vermin
And all became grandees.

Great ladies couldn't sit still,
Great lords gat no ease;
The queen was out of her wits,—still
None durst touch those fleas.

> 'Twas impolitic to scratch 'em
> And treasonable to squeeze—
> But we scratch 'em and despatch 'em
> (If we catch 'em) as we please.

CHORUS:
> Oh, we scratch 'em, etc.

FROSCH:
> Bravo! Bravo! I call that fine.

SIEBEL:
> First catch your flea, and then don't fail
> To nip him 'twixt thumb and finger-nail.

ALTMAYER:
> Hey for freedom, hey for wine!

MEPHIST.:
> I'd drink to freedom, but your swipes
> Are pretty sure to give me the gripes

SIEBEL:
> No more of that!

MEPHIST.:
> I'd give you the toast,
> But I should be sorry to trouble mine host:
> Else I'll draw you wine from the wood
> And you shall sip it in Auerbach's Shades.

FROSCH:
> Give me a rummer; bad or good,
> A noggin's nothing; bring in a pottle;
> I judge the brand when I've emptied the bottle;
> The devil take all niggardly blades.

ALTMAYER (*sotto voce*):
> They're from the Rhineland, I'll bet a penny.

MEPHIST.:
> Bring me a gimlet.

BRANDER:
> What's that for?
> Have you got a barrel of wine at the door?

ALTMAYER:
> There's a gimlet in the landlord's basket.

MEPHIST. (*takes a gimlet*):
> What's your vintage?

FROSCH:

Why does he ask it?
Vintages! Lord, have you got so many?

MEPHIST.:

Choose what you like.

ALTMAYER (*to* FROSCH):

That's sweet on the tongue!

FROSCH:

I'll stick to Rhenish; good old Rhine!
Land of my birth, dear land of wine!

MEPHIST. (*bores a hole in the table in front of* FROSCH):

Now just a drop of wax for the bung.

ALTMAYER:

The fellow's a conjuror.

MEPHIST.:

Now, Sir, you?

BRANDER:

Champagne, no matter what breath blew
The bubbles, so they wink and dance.

> (MEPHISTOPHELES *bores as before; meanwhile the
> holes are bunged with wax.*)

One can't avoid these things, you see;
In matters of taste one must be free;
French and Germans don't agree,
But Germans drink the wines of France.

SIEBEL (*as* MEPHISTOPHELES *approaches*):

Wine—by all means—but not a dry wine;
I prefer something sweet for my wine.

MEPHIST. (*boring*):

Then, Sir, you shall have Tokay.

ALTMAYER:

You want to get the best of us, eh?
You think you can fool the lot.

MEPHIST:

Come! Come! That would be rather too venturesome.
So say what you'll have and in a minute
You'll be drinking my health, or the devil's in it.

ALTMAYER:

I don't care much about the liquor
If you'd fill up a trifle quicker.

Johann Wolfgang von Goethe

MEPHIST.:
> Grapes from the vine.
> Horn from the goat:
> If wine be good
> And a vine be but wood,
> Who says I'm not able
> To spile a table?
> Here's a pretty deep look
> Into Nature's book:
> So, now grace is sung,
> Pull out your bung:
> Run off the wine
> And 'twill jump down your throat.

ALL (*as they draw the bungs the wine they asked for runs out.*)
> O fountain fair that flows for us all!

MEPHIST.:
> Only don't let a drop of it fall!

(They drink repeatedly.)

ALL (*sing*):
> We're all as tight as cannibal kings,
> We're foul as runting swine!

MEPHIST.:
> Look at the vulgar! Are not they
> Delightful in their cups, so frank, so free?

FAUST:
> I think it's time we went away.

MEPHIST:
> No, wait a moment; they'll present
> A noble type of bestiality.

SIEBEL (*spilling some wine, which turns to fire*):
> It's fire! It burns like hell!

MEPHIST.:
> Down, friendly element! This is a touch of purgatory.

SIEBEL:
> What! Wait! My God! Do you know who we are?

FROSCH:
> Don't you do that again!

ALTMAYER:
> O now
> Let him sneak off; let's have no row.

SIEBEL:

    I'll stand no more of his hocus-pocus!

MEPHIST.:

    Pooh! Shut up, old wine tub!

SIEBEL:

    You damned broomstick, you!

    No more o' your cursed jokes!

ALTMAYER (*drawing out a bung from which fire spurts*):

    My God, it's flame!

SIEBEL:

    What! Magic! Stab him! Cut the rogue in two:

    The rascal's any fellow's game!

(They draw their knives and rush at MEPHISTOPHELES.*)*

MEPHIST. (*with solemn gestures*):

    False show,

    Come and go!

    Lying art,

    Charm their eyes and cheat their heart!

               (They stand staring at each other.)

ALTMAYER:

    Where am I? What a lovely scene!

FROSCH:

    Vineyards! What's this then?

SIEBEL:

    Grapes!

BRANDER:

    And green vine leaves!

    Lord, what a bunch; That's beautiful!

(Seizes SIEBEL *by the nose. The others seize each other by the*
        nose and raise their knives.)

MEPHIST. (*as above*):

    Undo their eyes that they may see

    What a merry devil the devil can be.

          (Vanishes with FAUST. *The others separate.)*

SIEBEL:

    What!

ALTMAYER:

    You?

FROSCH:
>Did I give your nose a pull?

BRANDER (*to* SIEBEL):
>Did I tweak yours?

ALTMAYER:
>I say, that was a knock!
>It went right through me, a ghastly shock!
>Give me a chair; I can't stand on my feet!

SIEBEL:
>Why, what the devil's happened? Where's he hiding?
>Let me get at him and I'll strike him dead.

ALTMAYER:
>He rode on a butt of wine; I saw him riding
>Out through the tavern door into the street—
>My feet! My God, my feet are heavy as lead.
>
>>(*Turning to the table*)
>
>It's just worth trying: I could do with a glass.

SIEBEL:
>Why, the whole thing was an infernal cheat.

FROSCH:
>No, there was wine all right, I tasted it.

BRANDER:
>And what about the grapes?

ALTMAYER:
>That was a bit queer;
>Who says miracles don't come to pass?

WITCH'S KITCHEN

>*A low hearth with a large cauldron on the
>fire. Various shapes appear in the steam
>of it. A she-baboon skims the cauldron
>and prevents it from boiling over. The
>male with their young warms himself.
>All sorts of wizard-gear hang from roof
>and walls.*

Enter FAUST *and* MEPHISTOPHELES.

FAUST:
>I hate this sorcery business, to say truth;
>Can this foul beldame give me back my youth?

What do I want consulting an old wife?
Do you pretend the muck that's simmering there
Can put the clock back twenty years of life?
If that's all, you'd best leave me to despair.
Is there no balm in Nature? Can I drain
No draught prepared by spirits wise and sage?

MEPHIST.:

There's a great deal of truth in what you say.
Oh, yes, there is undoubtedly a way,
A natural way, to make you young again;
But it is written in another book
And altogether it's a singular page.

FAUST:

I'll read 't.

MEPHIST.:

You shall, if you will deign to look
You don't need magic, gold or pharmacy.
Go out into the fields and dig the ground.
Hack at it with a hoe. Narrow the round
Of your desires; eat but the simplest food;
Live like a beast with beasts; dung every rood
You reap and never think it robbery.
That's the best way that I can recommend:
Then you'll be young at fourscore years, my friend.

FAUST:

No, I'm not used to that, and it can't be;
I'm not the man to hoe and delve and ditch.
Besides, a narrow life won't do for me.

MEPHIST.:

Then there is nothing for it but the witch.

FAUST:

And why a witch? Why an old crooked crone?
Can't you concoct a nostrum of your own?

MEPHIST.:

Sheer waste of time. I'd undertake to build
Bridges by scores ere one drop were distilled.
It isn't science, nor is't art alone;
It's self-devoted patience that produces
A work like that. Long toils the tranquil mind,
Years must mature the quintessential juices.
It's a concoction of the strangest kind:

As to the recipe, the devil found it;
Only, somehow, the devil can't compound it.

(*Looking at the apes*)

What do you think of the little animals? He
Is her handy-man and Jack of all the trades,
And she's the nattiest of lady's maids.
(*To the apes*) Madam is not at home apparently?

THE APES:

> Slipperty slub!
> Gone for her grub,
> Out through the chimney
> To Satan's pub'!

MEPHIST.:

How long over her cups do you suppose?

THE APES:

As long as it takes us to warm our toes.

MEPHIST.:

What do you think of them? Aren't they ducks?

FAUST:

Ugh! nasty little beasts!

MEPHIST.:

Nasty? Oh, no!
I love a chat with you, don't I, my chucks?
Tell me, ye damned little poppets,
What do ye keep on stirring so?

THE APES:

Stirring gruel of scribblers' soppets.

MEPHIST.:

Then you won't lack customers, my jo!

HE-APE (*coming up coaxingly to* MEPHISTOPHELES):

> O rattle the dice,
> Make me rich quick!
> For the world is cold.
>
> But if I win the trick,
> I shall have gold
> And be witty and wise.

MEPHIST.:

How happy would a monkey be
If he had a chance in a lottery!
(*The* BABY APES *roll up a ball they have been playing with*).

HE-APE:

> That little round
> Is the world so wide;
> It gambols and rambles
> And bumps on the ground.
> It rings as clear
> As a glassy sphere;
> Who will break it in shivers?
> 'Tis hollow inside.
> It trembles and quivers,
> Here dark and there bright.
> I live in the light,
> But, oh, my dears,
> Keep away! Keep away!
> For the ball is clay,
> You'll be dead one day,
> By scissors and shears!

MEPHIST.:

> What's that sieve?

HE-APE (*taking it down*):

> If you came to thieve I should know you at once.
> (*The* HE-APE *runs to the* SHE-APE *and lets her look through it*)
> Look through the sieve!
> If you see a thief
> Name him, you dunce!

MEPHIST. (*going up to the fire*):

> And what's the pot?

HE-APE *and* SHE APE:

> A sot! A sot!
> He can't tell a pot,
> He can't tell a kettle!

MEPHIST.:

> Don't be rude, little man!

HE-APE:

> Take a fan and sit down on the settle!

FAUST (*who all this time has been standing in front of a looking-glass, now near and now a little farther away from it*):

> What's this? What form so heavenly fair
> That's mirrored in the magic glass?
> Love, lend me wings and let me glide through air
> To those green meadows and that flowery grass!

97

If I stand still I see her not;
Let me approach before the moment pass.
Ah, now I see her in a cloudy grot,
The fairest woman form that ever was.
Can woman be so lovely? Why
In her recumbent form does heaven draw nigh?
Is there on earth a thing so fair as she?

MEPHIST.:

Well, naturally, if God took six full days
To make the world, and then cried out *Bravo!*
He must have done it pretty cleverly.
Now look your fill before you go
And, when you're satisfied
We'll find her like somewhere in the world's broad ways.
Lucky the dog that has her for a bride!

(FAUST *continues to gaze in the mirror.* MEPHISTOPHELES *lolls on the settle, playing with a fan.*)

Here I sit like a king on his throne.
A sceptre, a sceptre, but never a crown.

THE APES: (*who have been going through all sorts of fantastic performances, bring him a crown and make a great chattering as they do so.*)

It's not set! It's not set!
It won't do yet!
O pray be so good
As to paste it with sweat
And cement it with blood!

(*They dance round in an ungainly fashion with the crown, break it in two, and jump about.*)

In time, in time!
Bide a wee!
We hear and we see
We can rap out a rhyme.

FAUST (*in front of the mirror*):

A sweet, sweet madness!

MEPHIST. (*pointing to the apes*):

Ay, I'm on the brink!

THE APES:

Let the luck hold
Link upon link,
And before Time grows old
We shall scratch our heads and think.

FAUST (*before the mirror*):
Let's go! My heart's on fire.

MEPHIST.:
Well, but I say
They're honest poets, any way.

(*The cauldron boils over and a great flame roars up the chimney.
The* WITCH *comes down it with horrible yells.*)

WITCH:
Wow! Wow! Wow! Wow!
Damned dog-ape and hellish bitch!
To let the pot boil and scald the witch!
You cursed little cat!
(*Seeing F. and M.*) What's that? What's that?
Who sits in my chair,
And how came you there
Here's aches and here's groans!
Hell burn up your bones!

(*She dips the ladle into the cauldron and scatters fire towards*
FAUST *and* MEPHISTOPHELES *and the* APES, *who begin to
whimper.*)

MEPHIST. (*smashing the pots and pans and glasses with his fan*):
Slash, smash!
There goes your hash!
There go your glasses!
You mother of asses,
While you mump and mime,
I beat out the time.
                    (*The* WITCH *starts back in fury and horror.*)
Thou rib, thou squaw, thou harridan abhorred,
Dost know me now, thy master and thy lord?
What lets me else that I split not thy head,
Strike thee and all thy gabbling spooks stone-dead?
Hast no respect, thou doddering, old splayed wether,
For scarlet doublet or for tall cock's feather?
Do you not see my countenance is the same?
Must I announce myself by my own name?

WITCH:
Oh, Sir, forgive me: I have been too rough.
And yet I do not see the cloven hoof.
And where's your raven? 'Twas a pretty chough.

MEPHIST.:
> This once you shall be quit with a reproof:
> For, after all, it's some time since we met,
> And culture, which beslobbers everything,
> If it goes on, will tame the devil yet.
> The phantom of the north has lost his sting;
> Talons and horns and tail are never seen.
> As for my foot, which I can't do without,
> Why, it's a drawback,—socially I mean;
> And so, like young bloods, at my lady's rout,
> I wear false calves whenever I go out.

WITCH *(dancing)*:
> 'Odsbones! If this don't make me vain!
> Here's Squire Satan come again!

MEPHIST.:
> Woman, you let my name alone!

WITCH:
> Why? What harm has your name done?

MEPHIST.:
> Damned to old hornbooks, and the Gothic letter:
> Though for all that mankind don't seem much better.
> The Evil One is gone; but that don't cure all:
> Singular once, the Devil now is plural.
> Call me my lord; that'll be the best plan:
> Who's gentle if I'm not a gentleman?
> I think you know my blood is of the best;
> But if you doubt, old gal, here is my crest.

> *(Makes an indecent gesture.)*

WITCH *(laughs immoderately)*:
> Ha! Ha! that's you,—that's just like you!
> Blackguard you were and always will be, too.

MEPHIST *(to* FAUST*)*:
> Lay hold on that, friend; that'll make her itch,
> If ever you should want to charm a witch.

WITCH:
> Good, now, what is't you gentlemen require?

MEPHIST.:
> Why just a rummer of your famous stuff:
> Only be sure the liquor's old enough;
> For when 'tis well racked you get twice the fire.

WITCH:
>With all my heart; I've got a little bottle.
>Sometimes I take a drop to wet my throttle.
>It's lost its stink; so if he's at that pass
>I shall be glad to let him have a glass.
>*(In a whisper)* Is he prepared? 'Twill get into his head,
>Else: and in half an hour he'll be dead.

MEPHIST.:
>Oh, he's my friend, 'twill do him good; 'oddsfish!
>I'll gladly stand him the best brew you've got;
>So draw your circle, chant your gibberish,
>And when you've finished fill him up a tot.

(WITCH *draws a circle with uncouth gestures and places strange-looking objects in it. Meantime, the glasses ring, the kettles sing to a kind of tune. Then she brings a big book, and stands the* APES *in a circle to serve as a lectern and light it with their torches. She beckons* FAUST *to come to her.)*

FAUST *(to* MEPHISTOPHELES*)* :
>No! tell me what this means; this madman's draught,
>These crazy antics: I've run through before
>All these absurdities; I know the craft;
>And, on my life, I'll deal in it no more.

MEPHIST.:
>O, rubbish! that's her fun; don't be
>So desperately in earnest: hocus-pocus!
>Ain't she a doctor? Don't the faculty
>Ape her example? Else their stuff would choke us.
>>>*(Shoves* FAUST *into the circle.)*

WITCH *(declaiming with great emphasis)*:
>Take a pen,
>Turn one into ten;
>Never mind two;
>Even three,
>Then you'll be
>Rich as a Jew.
>Cast four
>Out o' door.
>Take your slate,
>Write five and six;
>Sure as my thumb pricks
>That's seven and eight,

> And the sum is done,
> And nine is one,
> And ten is none
> And that's the witch's one-times-one.

FAUST:
> The woman's in a fever.

MEPHIST.:
> Oh, there's more;
> I know the book; it's full of jingling rhymes:
> I've idled over it so many times;
> Wise men and fools—I have seen the thing before—
> Will take flat nonsense for deep mystery.
> The art, my friend, is at once old and new;
> Times do not alter in the least degree;
> With three and one and one and three
> All propagate the cult of the untrue.
> So they sit gabbling on their learned stools;
> Who'd be at pains to meddle with the fools?
> Mere jargon; but, when nothing else is taught,
> Men think the balderdash is food for thought.

WITCH:
> The might and light
> Of knowledge bright
> When a thousand errors masked it,
> If you don't think,
> Come in a twink,
> Although you never asked it.

FAUST:
> The gabbling crone! What is this rant?
> It makes my head ache, like the chant
> Of twenty thousand lunatics.

MEPHIST.:
> My trusty Sibyl, cease your hymn:
> Pour out your drink and mind you mix
> A stiff glass; fill it to the brim.
> It cannot hurt my worthy friend.
> He is a man of infinite scope,
> A very graduate in dope,
> And about drinks he knows no end.

(The WITCH *with elaborate ceremony fills a goblet with the liquor
which burns with a thin flame as* FAUST *raises it to his lips.)*

MEPHIST.:

>Down with it! Down with it! That's what gives
>Warmth to the heart and quickens desire.
>Are you and the devil as thick as thieves
>And you afraid of a spurt of fire?
>*(The* WITCH *breaks the magic circle and* FAUST *steps out.)*
>Now come away! You can't stop here.

WITCH:

>I hope, sir, that'll set you right.

MEPHIST.:

>And if I can do you a kindness, my dear,
>Speak to me on Walpurgis Night.

WITCH:

>Here's a little song you may care to sing;
>I warrant you'll find it a marvellous thing.

MEPHIST.:

>Just come at once and follow my lead:
>A nice profuse sweat is what you need,
>Till you're drenched right through with the stuff, like a sop.
>You'll soon learn how to prize noble leisure
>And fill your belly with wanton pleasure
>When little Cupid begins to hop.

FAUST:

>Just let me take one last look in the glass:
>That woman form was so divinely fair.

MEPHIST.:

>No, no; I'll show you one that will surpass
>Her and all else,—solid, not empty air.
>*(To himself)* Why, with this liquor in your guts, my boy,
>You'll see in every wench Helen of Troy.

A STREET

FAUST. MARGARET *passing by.*

FAUST:

>My charming young lady, where do you roam?
>Take my arm, and I'll see you home.

MARGARET:

>I'm not a young lady, and I've no charm,
>And I can get home without your arm.

>*(Exit)*

FAUST:

>By heaven, she was a lovely child!
>I never saw the like of her:
>So modest! Oh, so undefiled!
>And yet she'd rather a saucy air.
>Memory, while Time runs, will trace
>Those lips' ripe curve, that glowing face:
>Then, suddenly, the downcast look!
>My heart of hearts its impress took!
>How curt she was! How quick she passed!
>Oh, this is ecstasy at last!

(Enter MEPHISTOPHELES*)*

>Look here, you'll get that girl for me.

MEPHIST.:

>Which girl?

FAUST:

>She's just gone by.

MEPHIST.:

>Oh, she!
>She's been confessing to the priest
>Her manifold transgressions; I
>Slipped up and sat in a chair close by.
>The whitest lambkin since the Fall,
>And went to confession for nothing at all.
>I've no power over her, not the least.

FAUST:

>She's fourteen years old if she's a day.

MEPHIST.:

>Ah, little Jack Lecher, what's that you say?
>You fancy every flower's for you,
>And all the honours of the spring
>To cull, and sip their honey-dew:
>And yet it's not always an easy thing.

FAUST:

>Now, Mr. Methody, mind your cue,
>And you can leave the law to me.
>Now listen, I tell you candidly
>I'll have that morsel of Eve's flesh;
>To-night I'll have her,—so warm, so fresh,
>Or we part when twelve strikes, you and I.

104

MEPHIST.:

And what if the business go awry?
Fourteen days would be almost too short
To find a good opportunity.

FAUST:

Fourteen days! Give me seven hours!
I should need no devil's magic powers
To seduce a little thing of her sort.

MEPHIST.:

Spoken like a Frenchman. But don't be
So shockingly out of temper with me.
Why such hot haste to enjoy her? Wait;
The pleasure isn't half so great
As if you fooled her with trinkets and trash
And filled her noddle with balderdash,
And made her your own little popinjay:
In Italian stories that's always the way.

FAUST:

I do not need a stimulant.

MEPHIST.:

But now, bar all humbug and cant,
She's but a pretty child; don't go so warm
To work; you can't take her by storm.
Lull her suspicions, and then betray.

FAUST:

Get me something of hers I can keep,
Show me the room where she lies asleep;
Fetch me her handkerchief, bring me
The garter buckled round her knee.

MEPHIST.:

Well, to show you my heart is in it,
I'll put you out of your pain straightway.
There's no reason why you should lose a minute;
I'll take you to her room to-day.

FAUST:

And shall I see her?—have her?

MEPHIST.:

No;
She'll be with a nice old neighbourly crone.
You meanwhile can sit alone
And feed on the hope of joys to come;

And think how soon you'll feel the glow
Of her bodily presence, her breath's perfume.

FAUST:

Can we go now?

MEPHIST.:

It's early yet.

FAUST:

She must have a present; and that you can get.

(*Exit*)

MEPHIST.:

Presents! That's prompt! I think he'll win her:
Presents? I know many a spot
Where buried treasure's to be got:
I must look about me, as I'm a sinner.

EVENING

A small, clean room. MARGARET *binding up her hair.*

MARGARET:

I'd give something if I knew
Who the gentleman was to-day;
A gallant certainly, that must be true,
And by his look an aristocrat;
He wouldn't have been so bold but for that.

(*Exit*)

(*Enter* MEPHISTOPHELES *and* FAUST)

MEPHIST.:

In with you quietly; tip-toe in.

FAUST (*after a moment's silence*):

Have the kindness to let me be.

MEPHIST (*peering about*):

Not every girl keeps the place so trim.

FAUST (*looking round*):

Welcome, sweet twilight, that dost weave thy dim
And dusky veil in this calm sanctuary!
And thou, sweet pain, sick love, that languishest
Upon the dew of hope, torture my breast!
Oh, how the soul of quietude breathes here!
What order! What tranquillity!
What opulence in penury!

In a poor cell what sacred cheer!
>   *(Throws himself into a leather chair near the bed.)*
Oh, take me in your arms, you antique chair,
That in old days so oft held joy and pain!
What troops of children with their sunny hair,
Have hung about you like a golden chain!
Perhaps my love for some new Christmas-toy
Came here to thank her grand-dad; her young joy
Kissed his thin lips and crushed a childish cheek
On his lean hand so tremulous and weak.
Dear girl, thou breath'st on me the very soul
Of thy content, thy manage, thy control,
That like a mother every innocent day
Bid thee to thy delightful tasks; to lay
The spotless cloth and at thy busy feet
Sprinkle the sharp, clean sand, so crisp and neat.
Dear hand! A goddess' hand to me!
Thou mak'st a heaven of poverty!
And here!
>   *(He lifts a bed-curtain)*

O terror! O delight!
I could stay here hour after hour!
Here with soft dreams of infant slumber light,
Nature, thou didst unfold my angel-flower!
Here lay the child; here the warm-breathing life
Filled her soft bosom; and while yet she knew
Love's tenderest texture only, not love's strife,
God's perfect image grew.
And thou, what brought thee here? What deep unrest
Is this within? What mean'st thou? What can lay
This heavy inhibition on my breast?
Faust, thou art not what thou wert yesterday.
What mists are these? Can this be magic ground?
I came because I felt the savage throes
Of appetite, now in Love's dreams I am drowned;
Are we the sport of every wind that blows?
And if this very moment she came in
How then would'st thou do penance for thy sin?
Thou swaggering Jack, where is thy giant lust?
Melt at her feet; go, grovel in the dust!

Johann Wolfgang von Goethe

MEPHIST.:

> Make haste! I see her coming down below.

FAUST:

> Let's go away. I'll not come back.

MEPHIST.:

> No, no:
> But here's a jewelbox I got somewhere;
> A tidy weight; you put it in her drawer;
> And it'll turn her pretty head, I swear.
> I popped some little things in it before
> For someone else: but there; it's all the same;
> Children are children and a game's a game.

FAUST:

> I don't know. Shall I?

MEPHIST.:

> Why do you ask?
> Would you like to keep it? Then spare the sweet light
> The indecency of your gross appetite,
> And save me grubbing further at my task.
> You're not a miser, are you? This is rich;
> Tickles my scalp and makes my fingers itch—
>> *(He puts the box in a drawer and locks it again.)*
> Now then, away with you—to train
> The sweet child in the way you'd have her go!
> And, there are you, about as bright a swain
> As if 'twas dunce's hall on lecture day,
> And your glum physics and philosophy gray
> Had come to life and grinned at you a-row.
> Away! Away!
> Out you go!
>> *(Exeunt)*

(Enter MARGARET *with a lamp.)*

MARGARET:

> It's close and stuffy in the room;
>> *.   (opens a window)*
> Yet out of doors the air is fresh.
> What can be the matter? I'm sure I don't know.
> I wish my mother would come home.
> I'm queer as if I had got goose-flesh;
> And I am a goose to be frightened so.
>> *(She begins singing while she undresses.)*

There dwelt a King in Thule old
  Was faithful unto death—
His sweetheart gave him a cup of gold,
  Gave with her dying breath.

He loved it more than all his pride,
  He drained it to his love
At every feast, and wept and sighed
  Whene'er he drank thereof.

And when he came to die, each fair
  Town in his realm he told,
And left them to his royal heir;
  But not the cup of gold.

He sat at meat in his father's hall,
  With his bold knights drank he,
Where stands with battlement and wall
  The castle by the sea.

The wassail King he raised him up
  And drank down life's last glow;
Then flung afar the holy cup
  Into the waves below.

He saw it plunge, he saw it drink
  And sink in the deep, deep sea;
His eyes began to pale and sink,
  And then no more drank he.

*(She opens the drawer to put away her clothes and sees the jewel-
box.)*
How strange! How came that box in my drawer?
I'm sure I locked it. What can be inside?
Oh, it must be a pawn my mother took.
A key, with a little ribbon prettily tied.
I think I'll open it! What's this? Oh, look!
I've never seen such lovely things before!
Jewels! Why a great lady would look fine
In these on Court days! How does the chain suit me?

Who *is* the owner of such finery?
> (*Puts the jewelry on and goes to the looking-glass.*)
The ear-rings! Oh, I do wish they were mine!
Oh, yes! They would make such a difference!
Good looks and youth are nice, but they
Are treated as nothing out of the way;
Nobody thinks them of consequence;
If people praise they pity, too, I'm sure.
For when all is told
All hangs on gold,
It is so wretched to be poor!

A PROMENADE

FAUST *pacing to and fro in thought.*
Enter MEPHISTOPHELES
MEPHIST.:
> By despised love! By all the fires that singe
> Sick souls in hell. Who'll teach me how to swear?
> I would I knew an oath that's wickeder!

FAUST:
> What is the matter? What's given you such a twinge?
> I never saw such a face.

MEPHIST.:
> Man, man, if I
> Were not the devil I'd give myself up to him.

FAUST:
> Why,
> Have you gone cracked? And yet your rage and wrath
> Suit you; they're quite according to your cloth.

MEPHIST.:
> Just think of it! The things we got for Gretchen,
> What must that damned priest do but come and fetch 'em!
> Mother saw them, mother felt a pang,
> A kind of privy squeamishness. Oh, hang
> The woman! Hang her! She's a nose like a cook;
> She's always snuffling in her cursed prayer-book
> And sniffing every knick-knack, till she's plain

Whether the thing be sacred or profane:
As for our jewelry, the merest squint
Told her there's not a deal of blessing in't.
"Child," cries she, "what comes by stealth
Corrupts the soul and injures the health.
We'll give it God's Mother who always sends
Heavenly manna to make amends."
Maggy pulled a wry face, of course;
She reckoned she'd got a real gift-horse,
And he could hardly lack God's grace
Who brought such a gift to so humble a place.
But mother sent for the priest; he came,
He saw and soon got the hang of the game.
One demure glance, then instantly,
"Quite right! Quite right! The victory
To him that overcomes," quoth he.
"The Church has an excellent stomach to stuff,
She swallows broad acres and doesn't feel queer:
Dear women, believe me, she can't have enough;
She's your only digester of stolen gear."

FAUST:

Why, as to that there's not much to choose
Between holy Church and Kings and Jews.

MEPHIST.:

So he sweeps up buckle and ring and chain
As if they had been so many toadstools,
With no more thanks as out he struts
Than if they had given him a basket of nuts,
And, of course, a word on heavenly gain,
Which greatly edified the fools.

FAUST:

And Gretchen?

MEPHIST.:

She's all restlessness;
Doesn't know what she wants; her head
Is full of trinkets night and day,
And of the donor, it needn't be said.

FAUST:

Poor child! I'm sorry for her distress.
Get some more and a better set.

111

MEPHIST.:
>Oh, that to your honour is mere child's play.

FAUST:
>And mind you're careful what you get.
>Hang on to the neighbour, by the way.
>None of your devil's slops, just see
>You get her handsome jewelry.

MEPHIST.:
>Your worship may rely on me.

(Exit FAUST*)*

>Bang go sun and stars above
>To please a wench when a fool's in love.

THE NEIGHBOUR'S HOUSE

MARTHA:
>God forgive my husband, say I;
>He's treated me downright shabbily!
>Gone off as slick as ever you saw
>And left me here to lie in the straw!
>I never troubled him day or night,
>And God's my witness I loved him all right.

(Weeps)

>P'r'aps he is dead!—well, at that rate,
>I wish I'd his death certificate.

MARGARET:
>Mrs. Martha!

MARTHA:
>What is it, Gretelkin?

MARGARET:
>You can't think what a fever I'm in.
>A box, an ebony box, in my drawer
>With lovelier things than there were before!

MARTHA:
>Don't let your mother know, dear! God bless her,
>She's sure to go and tell her confessor.

MARGARET *(puts them on)*:
>Just look at them! Look, for goodness' sake!

MARTHA:
>Well, you are in luck and no mistake!

MARGARET:

    I shan't dare to wear them when I go out walking,
    Or in church either, or folk'll be talking.

MARTHA:

    But you can often step over to me
    And put 'em on like—quietly.
    You can walk for an hour before the glass
    And so we'll have our bit o' fun.
    And when there's a holiday they'll pass;
    You can show them to people one by one;
    The little chain first, then the pearls in the ear
    Mother won't see them, never you fear,—
    Or we'll tell her fibs if she's a bother.

MARGARET:

    But who can have brought two caskets like these?
    I can't help feeling there's something queer.

                             (A knock)

    Oh, God! supposing that's my mother!

MARTHA *(peeping through the casement curtain)*:

    It's a strange gentleman. Walk in, please!

                      (Enter MEPHISTOPHELES*)*

MEPHIST.:

    I must ask you ladies to excuse me,
    Coming with no one to introduce me.

        (Steps back respectfully before MARTHA.*)*

    Mrs. Martha Schwerdtlein—I came to inquire
    For a lady of that name.

MARTHA:

    That's me.
    What does the gentleman desire?

MEPHIST. *(in a whisper)*:

    Hush! it's enough that I know you. I see
    You have distinguished company.
    Pray pardon me—if it's not too soon,
    I'll come again this afternoon.

MARTHA:

    Child, there's a compliment he's paid ye:
    Lord, Lord, he takes you for a lady!

MARGARET:

    I *am* a child and as poor as can be

And the gentleman's much too kind for me:
All this finery isn't mine.

MEPHIST.:

Oh, it's not the finery; it's the fine
Manners you have, it's that keen way
You look at one. I'm glad I may stay.

MARTHA:

Well, and what have you brought, kind sir?

MEPHIST.:

Bad news, I'm afraid; but you mustn't bear
Me ill-will for that: your husband's dead,
And sent you a message from his death-bed.

MARTHA:

Dead? There's a true heart gone! But there!
I shan't live long; I'm beginning to fail.

MARGARET:

Dear Mrs. Martha, don't despair!

MEPHIST.:

Well, shall I tell you the whole sad tale?

MARGARET:

I hope I shall never love; in faith
I think such a loss would be my death.

MARTHA:

Tell me all about how he died.

MEPHIST.:

He lies in Padua, beside
St. Antony, in holy ground
Where the lodging is cool and the sleep is sound.

MARTHA:

Have you brought nothing else?

MEPHIST.:

Oh, yes, I bring
A message; you're to have them sing
Three hundred masses for him; else my pocket
Is—er—quite empty.

MARTHA:

What's that? Not a thing?
Not a little keepsake or a locket,
That any journeyman chap stows in his kit
And 'ud sooner beg and starve than part with it?

MEPHIST.:

    I'm very sorry, madam; yet

    He'd no extravagance to deplore:

    His faults were a source of the greatest regret,

    And his ill-luck of a good deal more.

MARGARET:

    How sad, that men are so unfortunate!

    I will say requiems for him, that I will.

MEPHIST.:

    You already deserve the married state;

    You're young, but oh, so amiable!

MARGARET:

    No, I'm not old enough.

MEPHIST.:

    For a husband? No;

    But you may very properly have a beau.

    It's one of heaven's best gifts to hold such charms

    As yours, my little darling, in one's arms.

MARGARET:

    It's not the custom here.

MEPHIST.:

    Custom or none,

    I can assure you the thing is done.

MARTHA:

    Go on telling me.

MEPHIST.:

    I stood by his death-bed:

    'Twas better than a dung-heap—rotten straw.

    And yet he died a Christian; and he saw

    There were some other items to be paid.

    "I am a monstrous wretch," I heard him groan,

    "To leave my wife, throw up my honest trade!

    That is enough to kill me, that alone,

    I hope she will forgive me ere she dies."

MARTHA:

    Dear man, I have forgiven him long ago.

MEPHIST.:

    "Only, God knows, she's more to blame than me."

MARTHA:

    Out on it! What a parcel of black lies!

    With one foot in the grave!

Johann Wolfgang von Goethe

MEPHIST.:

    Ah, I could see,
Come the last gasp, he didn't seem to know
What he was saying; very far away!
"Never," says he, "a bit of holiday;
Never an hour to stretch myself at ease;
But getting children's bread till I was sick,
And you may lay she cut it pretty thick,
And not a crust did I ever eat in peace."

MARTHA:

    So he'd forgot my love and his troth plight
And all the hugger-mugger day and night?

MEPHIST.:

    No! That remained a tender memory.
I heard him say, "The time we put to sea
From Malta I prayed with prodigious zeal
For wife and children; which helped us a deal;
For heaven was kind and sent along a Turk,
Chock with the Sophy's treasure in her hold.
We laid aboard, and soon had made short work
And I'd my proper portion of the gold."

MARTHA:

    What? Where's that? Did he bury it in the ground?

MEPHIST.:

    Who knows where the four winds have blown it to?
A pretty lady took him in her care
At Naples as he chanced to ramble round,
A stranger in the land without a friend;
And was so tender to him and so true,
I warrant your good man remembered her
Until at last he made a blessed end!

MARTHA:

    The dirty blackguard, robbing child and wife!
To think that all his want and misery
Could never check him in his scandalous life!

MEPHIST.:

    Ah, well, you see, it brought him to his grave.
If I were you I'd mourn him decently
A twelvemonth: and in the meantime you'll save
Appearances and have sufficient leisure
To look around and find another treasure.

116

MARTHA:

Ah, God, another treasure like my first
I'll never find in this world, I'm afraid.
He was the sweetest donkey ever brayed,
And had no fault; unless it be a vice
To suffer from a thirst for foreign drinks,
And get in tow with every foreign minx,
And keep on rattling those accurséd dice.

MEPHIST.:

Oh, you'd have jogged along all right
If he'd seen your slips in that light.
Why, if such easy terms will do
I'm ready to swap rings with you.

MARTHA:

Oh, now the gentleman's having his fun.

MEPHIST. *(to himself)*:

I think it's time to cut and run,
Or she'll make the devil keep his word.

(To GRETCHEN*)*:

How goes your heart, my little one?

MARGARET:

Oh, sir, I don't know what you mean.

MEPHIST. *(to himself)*:

Ah, what a child! What an innocent bird!
(Aloud) Good-bye, ladies!

MARGARET:

Good-bye!

MARTHA:

Not yet.
Just tell me this; I want some proof
Where, when, and how my precious pet
Died and was buried. I have been
A friend of order from my youth;
I'd like to see my man's decease
Printed in this week's gazette.

MEPHIST.:

Out of the mouths, ma'am, of two witnesses
Shall be established all truth.
I have a friend, who is rather a swell,
He'll take you before the judge. So then,
Shall I bring him here?

117

MARTHA:
    Do, if you please.

MEPHIST.:
    And will the young lady be here as well?
    He's really one of the best of men;
    A man that has travelled and so on,
    And to ladies a perfect paragon
    Of chivalry.

MARGARET:
    How I shall blush!

MEPHIST.:
    Oh, pardon,
    You need not blush before a King.

MARTHA:
    Then we'll expect him in the garden,
    Behind my house this evening.

STREET

Enter FAUST. MEPHISTOPHELES.

FAUST:
    What news?   Have you met with success?
    Will all be in working order soon?

MEPHIST.:
    Bravo! The fire's still going strong?
    Gretchen is yours before very long;
    In fact you shall see her this afternoon
    At Goody Martha's; how I bless
    That woman! She's a perfect boon
    And born to be a procuress.

FAUST:
    Good.

MEPHIST.:
    But there's something we're asked to do.

FAUST:
    Well, one good turn deserves another.

MEPHIST.:
    We've got to prove that our dear brother
    Departed, that's her lord, has laid
    His most unruly members where
    Padua sheds a holy shade.

FAUST:

Upon my word, that's clever of you!
We shall have to make a journey there.

MEPHIST.:

Sancta simplicitas! Simply swear;
Why need you know if it is true?

FAUST:

If that's all, I'll not touch your plan.
O, what a saint! Think of it, man!

MEPHIST.:

Why all these years since you were born
How many false oaths have you sworn,
First about God, whom you defined,
The world and all that moves therein,
Then man, and the throb of heart and mind—
Haven't you lied through thick and thin?
Look deeper; put what you said to the touch;
Then own, at least beneath your breath,
You know about all this as much
As you do about Mr. Schwerdtlein's death.

FAUST:

You are a liar and a casuist!

MEPHIST.:

Oh, if it went no deeper, yes!
But when to-morrow comes, confess
You'll fool poor Gretchen. How you'll twist
The name of honour! How you'll press
That point, and promise love till death,
And swear she's cherished in your soul!

FAUST:

And so she is.

MEPHIST.:

Good—very good!
And beautiful! Eternal faith,
Eternal love, unconquerable
Desire that casts off all control.—
Will they be from the heart as well?

FAUST:

Stop that! They will!—
Oh, if I would,

But cannot, utter this intense
Tumult that my whole soul convulses;
And if I range the world of sense
And summon up all eloquence,
Then call this glow of fiery pulses,
A constant flame that cannot die,
Eternity, eternity—
Is that no more than a devilish lie?

MEPHIST.:

I'm right, all the same.

FAUST:

Listen to me—
And spare my breath; he that will have his way
And won't take nay
Will have his way.
Come, all this chatter fills me with disgust;
Yes, you are right—and right, because I must.

GARDEN

MARGARET *on* FAUST'S *arm.* MARTHA *and*
MEPHISTOPHELES *walking up and down.*

MARGARET:

I feel you are only sparing me, Sir,
But you lower yourself and make me confused.
A gentleman that's a traveller
Takes things as they come and is soon amused.
With fresh experiences every day
You can't find much in what I say.

FAUST:

One look, one word of yours is of more worth
Than all the wisdom of the earth.

(*Kisses her hand.*)

MARGARET:

O please don't trouble! Please don't kiss my hand!
It's such a horrid one, so rough, you see.
I do a lot of work, you understand.
Mother is very strict with me.

(*They pass on.*)

MARTHA:
> And so you're always moving on from place to place?

MEPHIST.:
> Business and duty, Madam, are the goad:
> At times farewells are very hard to face;
> We suffer, but we have to take the road.

MARTHA:
> Oh, there's no harm in a young Devil-may-care
> Gadding about the world; it's not so gay
> To creep into your grave a bachelor;
> That never did a man good any day.

MEPHIST.:
> A terrifying prospect—though I dare
> Hope not a near one.

MARTHA:
> Still you'd best beware,
> Dear Sir; you'd better think of it before.
>
> *(They pass across.)*

MARGARET:
> Yes, out of sight is out of mind!
> You're naturally polite and kind,
> But you've heaps of friends, and by and by
> You'll feel they've got more sense than I.

FAUST:
> Dearest and best one! What's called sense
> Is often rather vanity and shallowness.

MARGARET:
> How can that be?

FAUST:
> Oh, that simplicity does not know its worth!
> That virtue lives in ignorance
> Of its own self. The meek of earth.
> The humble, all fair gifts—

MARGARET:
> Think of me only
> A little tiny moment. I shall have all
> My life to think of you.

FAUST:
> You're often lonely?

MARGARET:
> Oh yes, our home is very small:

121

And yet we have to see to it.
We keep no maid. I cook and sweep and knit
And sew and run about from morn to night.
And mother will have everything just right.
Not that she need be so particular;
We could be easier than most folk are;
Father left property, quite a tidy bit,
A house and garden near the city gate.
I have not had such a busy time of late;
My brother's gone for a soldier, and we lost
My little sister; she was a great care
To me; I had so much to do:
But I loved doing it: it never crossed
My mind to think it hard, she was so dear.

FAUST:

An angel from above
If she took after you.

MARGARET:

I brought her up and she returned my love:
We buried father before she was born,
And we thought mother wouldn't live; she lay
So utterly forlorn.
But gradually got better day by day;
But had no strength to nurse her little daughter;
And so I brought her up alone
On milk and water,
And she became my very own.
First in my arms I held the child,
And in my lap she crowed and smiled,
Then got a big girl and began to crawl.

FAUST:

You must have found in it a pure delight!

MARGARET:

But there were times that tried
My strength; her cradle used to stand at night
Beside my bed, and if she stirred at all
I'd wake and feed her, lay her by my side,
Or, if she cried,
Walk her about. So soon as morning came
There was the washing, and the fire to light,

And then the market; every day the same.
You can't be always in a cheerful mood,
But you sleep well and you enjoy your food.

(They pass across.)

MARTHA:

It's we poor women come off second best;
There's no converting bachelors.

MEPHIST.:

Oh, ma'am, Only a woman like you, I protest,
Could make me something better than I am.

MARTHA:

Tell me, dear Sir, has none such crossed your path?
Have you had no attachment?

MEPHIST.:

We are told
A faithful wife beside her husband's hearth
Is of more worth than pearls and minted gold.

MARTHA:

I mean to say, have you never felt a passion?

MEPHIST.:

I am always treated in the kindest fashion.

MARTHA:

But seriously, I meant.

MEPHIST.:

Frivolity is out of favour with your sex.

MARTHA:

Dear me! You do not understand!

MEPHIST.:

That's most vexatious!
At least I'm certain you're extremely gracious.

(They pass across.)

FAUST:

Dear little angel, you knew me at once
When I came into the garden just now?

MARGARET:

Didn't you see my downcast look?

FAUST:

And you have forgiven the freedom I took
When you came from Church; gross insolence
That you repelled, you well knew how?

MARGARET:

    I was upset,—and naturally;
    It had never happened to me before—
    None could say anything bad about me.
    I thought to myself, "Oh, can it be
    There was something in my behaviour,
    Something too forward and too free?
    It seemed to strike him at once I was
    Just a poor girl he could treat offhand."
    Yet somehow, almost before I knew,
    Something here I don't understand,
    Took your part. What could I do?
    I was so angry with myself because
    I was not angrier with you.

FAUST:

    Darling!

MARGARET:

    Wait! Wait!

(She plucks an aster and begins pulling off the petals one by one.)

FAUST:

    What's that, then! A nosegay?

MARGARET:

    No, it's a game.

FAUST:

    A game?

MARGARET:

    Please go away: You'll only laugh.

FAUST:

    What are you whispering, sweet?

MARGARET:

    He loves me—he loves me not—

FAUST:

    Heaven's in that face! There all things holy meet!

MARGARET *(goes on)*:

    Loves me—not—loves me—not—*(pulling the last leaf with
        pure and innocent joy)*
    He loves me!

FAUST:

    Yes, my child; let the flowery syllables
    Be to you as the utterance of gods.

He loves you! Do you understand
What that means? He loves you!

(*He seizes both her hands.*)

MARGARET:

This is too much!

FAUST:

Don't tremble. Let my eyes speak; my hands'
Pressure tell you what never can be told.
To give one's whole self and to feel
Ecstasy which must last for ever;
For ever. The end would be despair.
No! No end! No end!

(MARGARET *presses his hands, frees herself, and is gone. He
stands a moment in thought, and then follows her.*)

MARTHA (*coming forward*):

It's getting night.

MEPHIST.:

Yes: time for us to go.

MARTHA:

I'd ask you to stay longer, but, dear me,
It's such a wicked place! It's just as though
No one had nothing else to do but be
Spying upon their neighbours. Folk will talk
Be you never so careful. Where's our pretty pair?

MEPHIST.:

Flown away yonder, up the garden walk,
Like butterflies all on a summer's day.

MARTHA:

You know I think he's quite took up with her.

MEPHIST.:

And she with him. So runs the world away!

A LITTLE SUMMER HOUSE

MARGARET *comes running in, hides behind the door, puts her
finger to her lips, and peeps through the crack.*

MARGARET:

Ah, here he comes!

Johann Wolfgang von Goethe

FAUST:

    Rogue! What a tease you are!
    I've got you! *(Kisses her)*

MARGARET *(kissing him)*:

    Dear, take my whole heart.

                    MEPHISTOPHELES *knocks at the door.*

FAUST *(stamping)*:

    Who's there?

MEPHIST.:

    Friend!

FAUST:

    Beast!

MEPHIST.:

    It's fully time to say "Good-bye."

MARTHA:

    Yes, sir, it's getting late.

FAUST:

    Oh, but mayn't I just see you home?

MARGARET:

    My mother would—Good-bye!

FAUST:

    Am I to go? Good-bye!

MARTHA:

    Adé!

MARGARET:

    Adieu! But not for long.
    You'll come soon, will not you?

              (Exeunt FAUST *and* MEPHISTOPHELES.*)*

    He's wonderful! He's wise, he's good!
    What thoughts he carries in his head!
    I blushed all over where I stood.
    Stammering "yes" to all he said.
    I am so ignorant, and he—
    I can't think what he sees in me.

FOREST AND CAVERN

FAUST *alone.*

FAUST:

Spirit sublime! thou gavest, gavest all
I ever asked. Thou didst not show for naught
Thy lineaments to me in flame of fire.
Thou gav'st me sovran Nature for my realm,
Girt me with power to feel, enjoy her. Not
A visitant accost with cold amaze,
But graced with access to her secret heart,
Where I might look as friend on loving friend.
Thou causest to pass by me rank on rank
All that has life; tell'st me the silent trees
My brethren are, the waters, the wide air.
And when the tempest roars and forests crack—
When some tall giant crashing through the pines
Fells his huge peer, and knaps enormous boughs,
And with its fall the hill peals muffled thunder,
Thou hid'st me safely in the caverned rock;
There shew'st me my own self, until the deep
Mysteries and marvels of my heart lie bare.
And at the rising of the lustrous moon
Come floating on her beams from walléd cliffs,
From dripping woods, all silvered with soft light,
The plastic visions of the antique world,
To temper the stern joy of musing thought.

Oh, now I know nothing that men attain
Can be without a flaw. To ecstasy,
That drew me on, near and more near the gods,
Thou couplest the companion, never now
To be abjured; though, cold and insolent,
He can debase me in my eyes, and with
A breath degrade to nothing all thy gifts.
He blows a lawless fire that ceases not
To rage within me for one form most fair.
Desire still thrusts me madly to delight,
And in delight I languish for desire.

Enter MEPHISTOPHELES.

Johann Wolfgang von Goethe

MEPHIST.:

Will you soon have done with this life of yours?
It can't go on contenting you.
Once in a way you may try it, of course;
And then it's time for something new.

FAUST:

I wish you would find a better employment
Than spoil a good day by worrying me.

MEPHIST.:

Come, come! *I'd* leave you to your enjoyment,
But you're not talking seriously.
A comrade so crank and crazy and cross
I should scarcely think an irreparable loss.
My hands are full; you needn't suppose
What you'll have and what you will not
Is a simple matter to plan and plot,
As plain as the tip of your worship's nose.

FAUST:

That's just the right tone. You seem to be sore
That I don't thank you for being a bore.

MEPHIST.:

Poor son of earth, what would have been
Your life if I'd not graced the scene?
I cured you of your fancy hash,
Your physics metaphysical,
And but for me the wretched trash
Had trundled you off this earthly ball.
Why like an owl, then, do you squat
Moping in caves and clefts and clinks,
Your gruel what the puttock drinks,
The dank moss eaves and the drip of stones?
A pretty pastime! I'll tell you what
It seems to me that you've still got
A touch of the doctor in your bones.

FAUST:

Can you understand why I roam the rough
Rocks and the solitary place?
Oh, you are a devil that's devil enough,
Could you guess their power, to grudge me the grace.

MEPHIST.:

A more than earthly satisfaction!
Night,—dew,—the stony mountains for your bed;
Earth, ay, and Heaven, in rapturous interaction
Coupled with you; puffed cheeks and swelling head,
The port and stature of a full-blown god;
The thrust of feverish anticipation,
Urging you in your grubby way to prod
The pith and marrow of the osseous earth.
Then that divine sensation,
The pigmy quickening with a giant birth,
When you can feel the six days of creation
All at one time in your own peevish breast:
The deuce knows what of magisterial zest;
The ecstasy of love that overflows
The universal All; the child of Time,
Earth's son, clean vanished; then the true sublime,
The last and loftiest initiation—

(*He makes a gesture.*)

How done I dare not say—by way of close.

FAUST:

Faugh!

MEPHIST.:

Does that strike you as atrocious taste?
Well, you've a moral right to be put out.
One has no business to outrage chaste
Ears with what chaste hearts cannot do without.
It's not a great indulgence, after all,
The unction of a little graceful fiction;
Only I fear 'twill soon begin to pall:
Why, even now you're overdriven again;
A little more of this incessant friction,
'Twixt fear and horror you'll become insane.
No more of that. Your charming pet
Sits still at home—feels so confined,
So caged, so sad; she cannot get
Your worship's image from her mind.
Her love for you is strong as fate;
And yours began at such a rate
It was enough to drown the wench;

Small brooks soon brim with melting snow,
And her poor heart got such a drench
That now your little rill's sunk low.
If I were you, my noble lord,
I should resign my forest-throne,
Give the young monkey her reward
For all the wondrous love she's shown.
The sad hours scarcely move at all;
She watches the clouds as they float on high
Far away over the city wall.
"Were I a birdie," that's her cry
All day long and half the night.
Mostly sad, but sometimes bright;
Whiles she has no tears left to weep;
Whiles she'll be quiet; but, wake or sleep,
In love, in love, oh, fathoms deep!

FAUST:
    You viper! Oh, you viper!

MEPHIST. (*aside*):
    Quite! I think he's found my teeth can bite.

FAUST:
    Get thee behind me! Cease to profane
    Her beauty with your breath; never again
    Call up desire till I madly pine
    For her sweet body pressed to mine.

MEPHIST.:
    What's to be done, then? She's a fear
    You're fled away; and so you are
    Or halfway to it.

FAUST:
    I am near, near her, and were I never so far
    I cannot lose her or forget.
    I envy the Body of the Lord
    The touch of her lips.

MEPHIST.:
    She *is* adored! That's famous, my dear Sir! And yet,
    I envy you rather for your twin roes
    A-browse where the lily garden blows.

FAUST:
    Out of my sight, you bawd!

MEPHIST.:

 Oh, very good!
 You call me hard names and I laugh. God made
 Lasses and lads; and quickly understood
 All secrets of the honourablest trade,
 Down to producing opportunity.
 Only, you musn't give up. It's agony,
 Sheer agony! You're for your minion's bower,
 Not death or nearly so.

FAUST:

 What's heaven in her arms? What were the bliss
 Of her warm breasts and her enamoured kiss?
 Do I not everywhere and every hour
 Feel all that she must undergo?
 Am I not outlawed, without hearth or home,
 Aimless and restless as nought human is,
 The roaring cataract that leaps in foam
 From rock to rock, greedy for the abyss?
 Quite from my course she dwells apart;
 The sensual slumbers still in her fond heart,
 Poor simple child! Safe in her tiny cot,
 Her lodge on some green garden plot,
 Some shelf of Alpine ground.
 Her small world compassed in its narrow bound,
 And all her first
 Beginnings of housewifely ministry.
 And I, of God accursed,
 'Tis not enough for me
 To shatter rocks; but I must undermine
 Her sweet tranquillity.
 O hell, this sacrifice is thine!
 Shorten my anguish, devil! What must be
 Let it come quickly; and the blow
 That wrecks her life, wreck mine,
 And both together sink to the gulf below!

MEPHIST.:

 All foam and fury and fire once more!
 Go in and comfort her, you dunce!
 Poor Simple Simon cannot find the door
 And thinks, of course, the end must come at once.

Well, here's a health of sterling pluck!
You're a passable devil when you are game;
But of all poor sinners, the tam'st of the tame
Is a devil down on his luck.

GRETCHEN'S ROOM

GRETCHEN *alone at her spinning wheel.*

My peace is gone,
    And my heart oppressed;
Nevermore, nevermore,
    Shall I find rest.

The world without him
    Would bitter be;
Life without him
    Were death to me.

Surely my senses
    Grow wildered and dim,
I am so mad
    For the love of him.

My peace is gone,
    And my heart oppressed;
Nevermore, nevermore
    Shall I find rest.

I wait at the window
    For him to come;
To find him I wander
    Away from my home.

His gallant looks,
    His step so free;
In the glance of his eye
    What majesty!

He smiles—he speaks;
   What enchantment is his!
The touch of his hand,
   And, oh, his kiss!

My peace is gone,
   And my heart oppressed;
Nevermore, nevermore,
   Shall I find rest.

I am woe to follow
   When he is gone;
I am woe to clasp him
   My love, my own.

I would kiss him and kiss him
   With my last sigh,
And then with his kiss
   I would lie down and die!

MARTHA'S GARDEN

MARGARET:
   Will you tell me something, Henry?
FAUST:
   If I can.
MARGARET:
   It's about religion. You are a good man;
   That is, you've a good heart. But somehow there
   You seem to be different; you don't care.
FAUST:
   Dearest, don't raise these questions now. You feel
   A goodness in me towards you; I would seal
   My passion with my blood, and none can say
   I ever took his faith or Church away.
MARGARET:
   But that's not right at all; one must believe.
FAUST:
   Must one?

MARGARET:

    I have no influence over you;
    I wish I had. About the Sacrament—
    You do not care enough.

FAUST:

    Oh, yes I do.

MARGARET:

    And yet I notice that you don't receive.
    Yes, it's a very long time since you went
    To mass or knelt at the confessional.
    Do you believe in God?

FAUST:

    Dear, who can say
    "I do believe?" Ask a philosopher,
    Question a priest, and you will find that all
    Their answers are but throwing words away,
    And ring like mockery to the questioner's ear.

MARGARET:

    And so you don't believe?

FAUST:

    You must not give that meaning to my words, sweet one.
    Who has named Him or known Him?
    Do I believe in him?
    Who that has sense dare say
    "I don't believe in Him?"
    The All-Enfolder,
    The All-Upholder,
    Does not He fold, uphold
    Himself,—you,—me?
    Is not the dome of heaven there?
    Is not the stable earth beneath?
    Do not the everlasting stars uprise
    With lovingkindness in their eyes?
    Do I not look in yours?
    Do you not feel the sacred Whole
    Throb through your soul?
    Does it not weave its mystery,
    Visibly, invisibly
    About you everlastingly?
    Open your heart until

That vastness fill
Your breast; then call it what you will,
Joy, Love, Felicity, God;
There is no name that I dare give;
Feeling is all—the heart by which we live.
The name is sound and smoke
Clouding the light of heaven.

MARGARET:

That's very good and beautiful; it's even
Much what the priest said, though he spoke
Not quite as you do.

FAUST:

It's what all hearts say
In every land where sun and starlight shine,
All in their several languages; then may
Not I say so in mine?

MARGARET:

Ah, as you put it, that sounds fine;
But there's a twist in it all the same;
You're not a Christian except in name.

FAUST:

My darling child!

MARGARET:

It makes me weep to see the company you keep.

FAUST:

How?

MARGARET:

Why, the man who's always about with you.
I hate him! yes, with my whole soul I do!
I can't remember in all my life
Anything that cut me so like a knife
As his repulsive face.

FAUST:

My pretty pet, don't be afraid of him.

MARGARET:

To have him near
Is quite enough to put me in a fret,
Though as a rule I don't think I'm severe.
But though I long to see you ever so
I dread that man; and what is more, I know—

I'm certain—he's a villain. Mark my words!
And God forgive me if I'm wrong.

FAUST:

My dear, there have to be this sort of queer old birds.

MARGARET:

They're not for me, then. Why, he can't look in
Without a sort of supercilious grin,
Half out of temper, too. And one can see
He doesn't care a rap for nobody:
It's written on his forehead, in his whole
Life he could never love a single soul.
Your arm about me makes me feel how good
Love is, how free; sometimes I could
Yield myself utterly.
But when he's there it simply stifles me.

FAUST:

What a foreboding little soul it is!

MARGARET:

I cannot help't; I'm not my own mistress
When he's about; the sound of his footfall
Can make me feel I don't love you at all.
Besides with him by I could never pray.
And that's a thing that eats my heart away.
And you, too, Henry, surely you feel this?

FAUST:

It's a dislike, child; it's just prejudice.

MARGARET:

Now I must go.

FAUST:

Ah, will there never be
One little hour vouchsafed to you and me
When on your bosom I shall lie at rest,
My soul with your soul, my breast on your breast?

MARGARET:

Oh, if I slept alone, this very night
I'd draw the latch; but my mother sleeps light,
And if she caught us 'twere the death of me.

FAUST:

My angel, that's no obstacle at all.
Here is a phial; if you'll just drop three

Drops in her drink, the veil of sleep will fall
And Nature breathe on her peaceful repose.

MARGARET:

There's nothing I'd not do for you, God knows.
I only hope 'twill do no harm to her;
It isn't dangerous?

FAUST:

Darling, if it were, could I suggest it?

MARGARET:

Oh, my love, my love,
I look on you and feel a force above
My feeble will; I am so utterly
Yours, I have done so much for your dear sake,
There's little you could ask or take
That I should have the power to deny.

(*Exit*)

(*Enter* MEPHISTOPHELES.)

MEPHIST.:

Well, has the monkey gone?

FAUST:

Spying again?

MEPHIST.:

Yes, and caught one thing pretty plain;
The doctor being catechized!
Hope it will do him good. You'd be surprised
To see what a point the little things make
To know if you're pious, whether you take
The good old road for old sake's sake.
If he's as meek as all that comes to,
Say they, he'll be pretty soon under our thumbs, too.

FAUST:

You horror, don't you see
That in the sweet serenity
Of faith, which is her sole joy, she,
Saint that she is, is troubled and tossed
With dread she must hold her lover for lost?

MEPHIST.:

You pious wanton, why
It's your own nose she's leading you by!

FAUST:

You mocker, half hell-fire, half dung!

MEPHIST.:

> And then she's great at phrenology.
> When I'm about she's all unstrung,
> Doesn't know how she feels, not she!
> And that's the humour of the play.
> Behind my mask she's got well in.
> Detects a genius or a jinn,
> Why not the devil, eh?
> But what of to-night?

FAUST:

> What of to-night?

MEPHIST.:

> Oh, your delight is my delight!

AT THE WELL

GRETCHEN *and* LISA *with pitchers.*

LISA:

> Heard about Barbara?

MARGARET:

> No, I've not.
> I only see people once in a way.

LISA:

> Well, Sibyl told me about it to-day.
> She's made a fool of herself. That's what
> Comes of aping her betters, the minx.

MARGARET:

> What do you mean?

LISA:

> Oh Lord, it stinks!
> She's stuffing two when she eats and drinks!

MARGARET:

> Oh!

LISA:

> I don't care: it serves her right.
> She shouldn't have clung to the chap so tight.
> Such walking out as never was seen
> And dancing with him on the green.
> She must always be the one to shine,

And he getting round her with tarts and wine.
Vain of her looks, but never thought
'Twas a shame to take the presents he brought.
Such kissing there was and tickling and all,
But you see the flower had to fall.

MARGARET:
Poor thing!

LISA:
You pity her a deal.
When one of *us* sat at the spinning wheel
Mother wouldn't let us out of her sight;
But she and he got a bit too sweet;
On the bench outside, in the passage at night,
I guess they passed the time all right;
Now she'll do penance in a white sheet.

MARGARET:
Of course, he'll marry her.

LISA:
He'd be a proper fool. The lad is smart!
He's had what he wanted, and now he's free
To look about for another sweetheart.
For the matter of that he's gone away.

MARGARET:
That's bad!

LISA:
If she got him she'd rue the day.
They'd trample her wedding-wreath on the floor,
Would the boys; and throw down chaff at her door.

(*Exit.*)

MARGARET (*going home*):
Ah, once I thought I'd a right to rail
At a poor girl for being frail;
I used to think no words too strong
When other people had gone wrong.
I made it out as black as could be,
But nothing was black enough for me.
I crossed myself with such an air;
Now in my sin I'm naked and bare.
Yet all that brought me to this pass
How good and, oh, how sweet it was!

Johann Wolfgang von Goethe

CLOSE

An image of Our Lady of Sorrows in a niche in the wall. There are flower-vases in front of it.

GRETCHEN (*putting fresh flowers in the vases*):
Ah, bow thy head
Queen of Sorrows, shed
The light of thy countenance on my sore need!

The sword is in thy side,
On thy Son crucified
Upward thou gazest, while thy heart-drops bleed.

Yea, to the Father thou dost lift thine eyes
And He receives thy sighs,
For thou art one with Him in thy sore need.

Who is there knows,
Who feels these throes
That rack me flesh and bone?
How the heart within me faileth,
How it trembleth, how it aileth,
Thou knowest, thou alone.

All ways to me are dreary,
My heart is weary, weary,
Would God that it might break!

Weeping, weeping, weeping,
Alone, yet in me sleeping,
The child of my heart-ache.

The flower pots at my window
Were wet, but not with dew,
When in the early morning
I picked these flowers for you.

The early light came creeping,
And on my chamber lay,
But I sat weeping, weeping,
Long before the day.

Help me! Save me! Shield me
From shame and misery!
Queen of sorrows, yield me
Thy comfort or I die!

NIGHT

The street in front of GRETCHEN'S *door.*

VALENTINE, *her brother, a soldier.*

VALENTINE:
    When I sat drinking with my mates
    And they used to talk of their Bessies and Kates,
    And every fellow as proud as Punch
    Swore his girl was the pick of the bunch,
    And hammered and clamoured and filled up his can,
    And elbows jogged till good liquor ran;
    I used to sit as mum as a ghost
    And listen to all their blather and boast,
    And then I'd stroke my beard and stand
    With a smile on my lips and a glass in my hand,
    And say, "Take your choice; they're all of 'em fetching.
    But show me a girl in all the land
    That's fit to look at my sister Gretchen,
    Or give her a cup of water to drink."
    Then the toast went round with a clink-clank-clink;
    And some of 'em cried "What's wrong with that!
    She's the pride of her sex!" And the swaggerers sat
    And said not a word. And now—I could knock
    My brains out; all the rascals mock
    And sneer and flout me to my face.
    I'm like a schoolboy in disgrace;
    Every chance word makes me sweat.
    I could smash the lot of them, and yet
    I don't see how I can give 'em the lie.

    Who's this comes marching along so sly?
    There's a pair; if he's one, so God me shrive,
    He shan't get out of this alive.
             (*Enter* FAUST *and* MEPHISTOPHELES)

FAUST:
    Look how the cresset-lamp that's always lit
    Sends from the window of the sacristy
    An upward beam; pale at its edge, above

And all around is darkness; I'm like it;
So does my soul's black night encompass me.

MEPHIST.:

And I am like a pussy cat in love
Climbing a fire-escape, picking his way
Along the walls. There's valour in me; I
Could pick a pocket or a quarrel. Why
Do my pulses beat? It's the bonny tune they play
For the high revels of Walpurgis Night.
That'll come on the morn's morn, as they say;
Then there's some sense in not sleeping a wink.

FAUST:

And is the treasure coming into sight?
There's something there that seems to glance and blink.

MEPHIST.:

Don't be a fidget; I shan't keep
You waiting long; give the pot a cant
And up she comes. I lately took a peep;
'Twas full of lion-thalers of Brabant.

FAUST:

Are there no pretty trinkets, never a ring
For my love's finger, bright as her golden curls?

MEPHIST.:

Oh, certainly I did see some such thing:
I think it must have been a rope of pearls.

FAUST:

That's good; I hate to go and bring
Nothing to please her.

MEPHIST.:

We won't quarrel,
And you needn't make a grievance of that:
Why should your bliss be tit for tat?
Now that the stars are shining above
You shall hear a masterpiece; I'll sing
A little song with an elegant moral
The better to fool your lady love.

(Sings to the guitar.)

What are you doing, Katie dear,
When the light of the morning begins to peer,
Here at your lover's door?

Have nothing to do with him, Katie dear!
He'll let you in a maid, but alack,
You won't be a wife when you come back,
And you won't be a maid any more.

Have a care, sweet lass,
If it comes to pass,
Good-night! So do not linger!
Love's a thief, and his bliss is
A stealing of kisses,
So all pretty misses,
First see you've a ring on your finger.

VALENTINE (*coming forward*):
Whom are you piping to? God's light!
You bawdry ratcatcher! Out of my sight,
Damned instrument! And devil take the singer!

MEPHIST.:
Now, look at that! He's broken my guitar!

VALENTINE:
I'll bash your head in!

MEPHIST.:
Doctor, here you are!
Look sharp now! Don't throw up the sponge!
Stick to me close and we'll soon make short work.
Just do as I. Get out your toasting-fork.
Now, sir, I'll do the parrying, you may lunge.

VALENTINE:
Then parry that!

MEPHIST.:
Why not!

VALENTINE:
And that!

MEPHIST.:
Thank you!

VALENTINE:
My hand is crippled! I can't make this out!
Am I fighting the devil?

MEPHIST.:
Run him through!

VALENTINE:
O God! (*Falls*)

MEPHIST.:

 A cripple he is, the lout!

 We'd best clear out: do you hear that hullabaloo?

 They're crying murder. I can square

 The watch, but not the Lord High Justicer.

(Exeunt.)

MARTHA (at her window):

 Come out! Come out!

GRETCHEN (at hers):

 O bring a light!

MARTHA:

 Such swearing and tearing; There's been a fight.

THE CROWD:

 There's a man killed.

MARTHA (coming out):

 Have the murderers run?

GRETCHEN (coming out):

 Who has been killed?

THE CROWD:

 Your mother's son.

GRETCHEN:

 God Almighty!

VALENTINE:

 I'm dying! That's soon said,

 And it won't be much longer before I'm dead.

 Why do the women howl and shriek?

 Listen, while I have strength to speak.

(They gather round him.)

 Gretchen, you're young and you've not much sense;

 And now you've gone wrong. You've made

 A mess of your life past praying for.

 So I'd like to tell you in confidence,

 Since you're no better than a whore,

 You'd better take to the trade.

GRETCHEN:

 Brother! O God! How can you talk so?

VALENTINE:

 Just leave the Lord God out of this show.

 What's done can never be undone.

 No; you'll go on as you've begun.

 First you had one of 'em on the sly;

144

There'll be plenty more coming on by and bye;
When you've had a dozen between the sheets,
After that you'll be on the streets.
Shame's like a love-child; when it's born
It's hidden decently from sight;
Ay, over head and ears are drawn
Curtains and coverlids of night:
And some would be glad to put it away.
But soon it gets to be big and tall,
Naked and unashamed before all.
But broad noon can't give it grace;
The more it looks on the light of day
The more repulsive grows its face.

I tell you that the time's not far
When you'll be known for the trull you are,
And honest men your touch will shun
As they flee from plague-struck carrion.
And if they look you in the face
You'll feel the heart within you quail;
You'll wear no more a gold necklace
Nor kneel down at the altar-rail.
And when the dancers take the floor
You'll not be merry any more,
But creep into some noisome cave
With beggars and blind and lame and halt,
Taking my curse with you down to your grave
Though God in Heaven forgive your fault.

MARTHA:
Commend your own soul to God's grace.
Will you die with curses on your lips?

VALENTINE:
Would I could lay on you with whips
You skinny hag! You procuress!
And if I could the deed would win
Pardon for me for every sin.

GRETCHEN:
O, Brother! This is the torment of hell!

VALENTINE:
Stop crying, will you? When you fell

145

From virtue, that drove through my breast
The keenest, heaviest stroke of all.
But now in death I hear God's call,
And He will give an honest soldier rest.

CATHEDRAL

GRETCHEN *in the crowd. Service going on.*
Organ and choir. An EVIL SPIRIT *behind*
GRETCHEN.

EVIL SPIRIT:

Gretchen, do you remember
When you were innocent
And used to trot to Church,
Thumb your little prayer-book,
Lisp your little prayers,
Half a child at play,
Half with God in your heart?
It's different now, isn't it, Gretchen?
What are you thinking of now?
There's a crime on your conscience, isn't there?
P'r'aps you're praying for the soul of your mother
Whom you sent to long, long penal pangs.
There's blood on your threshhold now.
—And in your womb
Something begins to stir.
It's misery,
And you are its mother, Gretchen.

GRETCHEN:

Oh! Oh! If only these thoughts would leave me!
They come and go
But I can't put them away.

CHOIR:

Dies irae, dies illa
Solvet saeclum in favilla.

(*The organ peals.*)

EVIL SPIRIT:

Do you hear that, you
Child of wrath?
It's the trump of doom!

146

The graves yawn!
And the ashes of your heart,
Raised up to trembling life,
Are cast to the torment of everlasting fire!

GRETCHEN:

Let me get out!
The organ stifles me;
The chant tears at my heart-strings!

CHOIR:

Judex ergo cum sedebit,
Quidquid latet apparebit,
Nil inultum remanebit.

GRETCHEN:

I can't get my breath!
Oh, these pillars! This dark roof!
I'm in a dungeon!
They'll crush me! Air!

EVIL SPIRIT:

You can't hide yourself.
Sin and shame are never hidden.
Air? Light?
Pain! Pain!

CHOIR:

Quid sum miser tunc dicturus,
Quem patronum rogaturus,
Cum vix justus sit securus?

EVIL SPIRIT:

Angels of Light
Turn away their faces;
They that have kept themselves pure
Will not give you their hands.
Pain! Pain!

CHOIR:

Quid sum miser tunc dicturus?

GRETCHEN:

Neighbour, your smelling salts!

(*Faints*)

147

Johann Wolfgang von Goethe

WALPURGIS NIGHT

The Hartz Mountains. The Country around
Schierke and Elend.

MEPHIST.:

You would give something for a broomstick, eh?
A stocky billy-goat's the mount for me.
The path we're taking, it's a good long way.

FAUST:

Oh, if my legs are working lustily
This knob-stick's all I want. Who would curtail
Our jaunt? To thread this labyrinthine vale,
Then climb those rocks, with their eternal fall
Of mist-hung waters, makes such wanderings sweet.
The spring has touched these birches; soon the tall
And gloomy pines will feel her gentle heat;
And shall our pulses know no quickening beat?

MEPHIST.:

Can't say I feel it. It's much more like dead
Mid-winter with me; I'd love frost and snow.
The moon's a nasty, melancholy red;
It's not full yet, and comes up late and slow,
Like broken glass. An execrable light!
One keeps on running against rocks and trees.
Confound! Will you allow me, if you please,
To call a Will-o'-the-Wisp? That one shines bright.
Hey, friend! We want you. Will you kindly stop?
Why do you waste your lantern on the night?
Just be so good as show us to the top.

WILL-O'-THE-WISP:

It isn't natural: but I daresay
My great respect for you will steady me.
We generally take a zig-zag way.

MEPHIST.:

He wants to be like men! Fiddle-dee-dee!
Just go straight on, you little gad-about!
None o' that flickering! Or I'll blow you out.

WILL-O'-THE-WISP:

Oh, I can see you're master over us.
I'll very gladly light you on your way.
Remember the whole hill's bewitched to-day,

148

And if your guide's an *ignis fatuus*,
You mustn't grumble if you're led astray.

FAUST, MEPHISTOPHELES, WILL-O'-THE-WISP (*Part Song*):

We wander along magic ways
Into a world of dream
Would you have your meed of praise,
Lead us quickly by your beam
To the upland waste and wide.

The trees behind each other glide,
The lofty cliffs stoop low,
The rocks thrust out a stony snout,
I can hear them snort and blow!
Brook and trickling runnel flow
Over pebbles, under grasses.
Hist! a breath, a murmur passes!
Is it music? Is't love's sigh,
Heaved for happy days gone by,
Fond hope pledging absent lover?
Like a tale of long ago
Echo answers dreamily.
Here they come: Hu-hu! Schuhu!
Devil-bird and jay and plover,
Have they all kept wide awake?
Salamander, is that you
Dragging through the thorny brake
Your swag belly and lean shanks?
Every root's a knotted snake
From the soft and sandy banks,
From the stony fissures slid,
Dragons that for us unwind
Serpent coils of phantom kind.
Dead trees that have shed their bark
Come to life and like a squid
Feel to nd us in the dark.
Mice among the moss and ling,
Motley hosts, straked, spotted, pied,
Swarms of fire-flies on the wing
To haunt and dazzle and misguide.
Tell me, do we stand or go?
Boulder, crag, and forest spin;

There are mouths that gape and grin,
And the marsh fires burn and grow
Bigger as they fade and glow.

MEPHIST.:

You hold on to my lappet tight.
Here's a sort of half-way height.
You'll see, and it's really a wonderful show.
The Hill of Mammon all a-glow.

FAUST:

Astonishing! a reddish light like dawn
Glooms with a glimmering flare along the ground;
Where the ravines and rocky chasms yawn
It rolls and tumbles to the abyss profound.
Here it's a cloud of steam and there it trails
Long swaths; the gauzy mist its light exhales;
Then it becomes the merest thread, and there
Leaps like a fountain in the enchanted air.
A whole broad tract is branched with its bright veins,
And all of them along the valley run,
To meet where that curved coign its course contains,
A hundred affluents gathered into one.
Here in a flight of drifting sparks it plays,
Like golden sand in glittering handfuls cast.
But look how the whole mountain is ablaze,
Its bastions and its towers and ramparts vast.

MEPHIST.:

Lord Mammon's courtesy; hasn't he lit
His palace nobly for the holiday?
You are in luck to have got a glimpse of it:
I hear the rowdy guests coming this way.

FAUST:

It's the wind's mad bride, I hear her ride!
That was a regular thump on my back!

MEPHIST.:

Find a rib of rock and in you pack,
Or you'll be pitched down the mountain-side.
The night is overcast with cloud.
Do you hear the forests crack?
The frightened owls flit through the trees
And in the evergreen palaces
The pillars split and are bowed.

Branches are shattered and grind and scrape
And mighty tree trunks moan,
The roots are wrung and they gasp and gape,
And root and branch and stem and stone
Are tossed to the precipices,
While down the glutted gorges blown
The storm-blast howls and hisses.
Do you hear these voices in the air?
Near and far and everywhere,
The roaring song of the witches rolled
Over the hills and the mountains old?

CHORUS OF WITCHES:

Heigh for the Brocken! Apace, apace!
The corn is green and the stubble dry.
That's the holy meeting place,
There Sir Urian sits on high.
Hie over stock and hie over stone!

A VOICE:

Old Baubo's coming on alone.
She squats on the back of a grunting sow.

A VOICE:

Make way! Make way—with mop and mow!
Duchess Baubo's our leader now,
A prime fat pig with mother astride
And after her all the witches ride.

A VOICE:

Which way came you?

A VOICE:

By Ilsen Crag.
I saw the screech-owl on her nest:
As I peeped in she glared and hissed.

A VOICE:

Why do you ride so fast, you hag?
Go to hell with your headlong pace.

A VOICE:

She's plucked my beard and scarred my face,
I'm bleeding!

CHORUS OF WITCHES:

On! Apace apace!
The road is broad, the way is long,
And are not we a ranting throng?

The besom tickles, the dungfork pokes,
Mother bursts and baby chokes.

WARLOCKS (*semi-chorus*):

We crawl along like creeping snails,
These women ride like blazes.
Oh, when it's a race for the devil's pales
They lead by a thousand paces.

WARLOCKS (*semi-chorus*):

A thousand paces! Oh, we're not
So careful to measure the ground.
A woman rides and her pace is hot,
Man takes it at a bound.

VOICES (*above*):

Follow, follow, faithful flocks,
From the lake among the rocks!

VOICES (*below*):

We are struggling towards the height,
We have bathed and washed us white;
But ours is the eternal doom
Of a dead and childless womb.

BOTH CHORUSES:

The wind is still, the stars rush by,
The weary moon is glad to die,
The screeching of the eldritch quire
Scatters sparks of blazing fire.

VOICE (*below*):

Wait for me! I can't be left!

VOICE (*above*):

Who calls out of the rocky cleft?

VOICE (*below*):

Stop and take me with you! Stop!
I've been climbing three hundred years,
And yet I cannot reach the top.
I want to be among my peers.

BOTH CHORUSES:

Take a stick or take a stock
Take a he-goat of the flock,
Take a fork—if you can't climb
To-night you're damned to the end of Time.

NOVICE (*below*):

Here I come trotting, trip, trip, trip;

But the rest of the crowd have given me the slip;
At home I've the fidgets, and here I find
They've gone ahead and left me behind.

CHORUS OF WITCHES:

Lay ointment to the witch's lip,
With a rag for a sail sit in any old trow,
It'll carry you as good as a ship;
You'll not fly at all if you don't fly now.

BOTH CHORUSES:

When we're near the mountain top,
Like a flight of corbies down you drop;
Cover the heath and cover the heather
With your rag-tag witches huddled together.

(*They alight.*)

MEPHIST.:

They push and shove and fidget and yell,
They hiss and whirl and dance and babble,
They stink and fizzle and burn like hell
A regular witches rabble.
Stick close to me, or you'll lose yoursel'.
Where are you?

FAUST:

Here!

MEPHIST.:

Oh, there you are!
Already carried pretty far.
I must assert my rights. Make way!
Squire Voland comes! Sweet hags! Hey! Hey!
Doctor, catch hold! We'll clear this lot
At a jump, you and I. It's a bit too hot
Even for me. I see something bright
In the bushes there,—an odd kind of light.
I've a fancy to see what it may be,
So come along and slip in with me.

FAUST:

Spirit of Contradiction! Still, you're right;
Show me the place and there I'll take my station;
It's the Brocken and this is Walpurgis Night,
Yet we preserve a splendid isolation!

MEPHIST.:

Aren't the flames pretty among the scrub?
They're a sociable lot, and this is their club.
We're not singular, you see,
There's others like their coterie.

FAUST:

I think the top would be better fun,
With clouds of smoke and fiery rain;
The people flock to the Evil One;
There's a good many dark things there made plain.

MEPHIST.:

And much that's dark made darker again.
Let the great world roar and rant its fill;
You and I will just keep still.
Men in all ages, you may be sure,
Model the mass in miniature.
There are naked young witches and elderly hags
Who've the sense to wrap up their wrinkles in rags.
Be nice to them, won't you, for my sake;
It's a screaming farce and you'll laugh till you ache.
They've struck up a tune! What a damnable din!
They know no better, that's all you can say.
One soon gets used to it—come along in,
You follow me, I'll show you the way,
And knit our agreeable bond anew.
There's no lack of space here; what say you?
You can scarcely see from end to end.
A hundred fires along the level;
Jigging and jabbering and boiling and roasting,
Quaffing and daffing and ogling and toasting!
What could be better than this, my friend?

FAUST:

What's your office? Do you propose
To make your bow as warlock or devil?

MEPHIST.:

I'm rather well versed in incognitos,
But here there's no need for dissimulation.
Orders are worn on a great occasion.
I haven't a garter to buckle my knee,
The hoof's my badge of nobility.
Do you see that crawling snail? With his quaint,

Querying horns he knows I'm no saint:
He's nosed me out, the inquisitive imp;
Here I'd be known in any attire,
So let's go on from fire to fire:
You're the wanton and I'm the pimp.
          (*To a group seated round dying embers.*)
Why at the end, old gentlemen? If you
Had been in the thick of it I should have cried
Bravo! Your place is among youth's roystering crew;
You're lonely enough by your own fireside.

GENERAL:
          Put not your trust in any tribe or race:
          Look what we've done for them! Yet in mere truth
          They don't know gratitude. The populace,
          Like women, keep their patronage for youth.

MINISTER:
          Wrong triumphs now and justice goes to the wall:
          A fig for the new times! Give me the old.
          When we were absolutely all-in-all,
          That in my judgment was the age of gold.

PARVENU:
          Who calls us blockheads—says we were above
          Doing at times the thing that we ought not?
          But now that the whole world is on the move
          There's no security in what we've got.

AUTHOR:
          I can't think what's the matter with literature.
          They never publish a work of merit.
          Why are young people so dreadfully cocksure?
          Teach your grandfather! That's the new spirit.

MEPHIST. (*who suddenly looks very old*):
          Now when for the last time up this hill I go
          Men seem like ripe fruit rotting on the trees,
          Ready for doom: if my small keg's run low,
          The world's a-tilt and life's wine on the lees.

WITCH (*hawking curios*):
          Kind gentlemen, don't turn your backs,
          Such a chance doesn't come every day;
          So take a good look at my little knick-knacks,
          I've all sorts of things in my tray,
          (The world cannot show such another),

And all have done some deed of guilt;
Not a dagger but's splashed with blood to the hilt,
Not a cup but has poured some fiery draught
To poison a man and a brother.
Not a trinket or toy of the jeweller's craft
But made lovesick women forlorn;
Not a scabbarded sword but was handled to hack
A friend or a foe when he turned his back,
Or break an oath deep-sworn.

MEPHIST.:

You quite mistake the time of day.
The past is dead and buried, too:
If you want to make your business pay
You must show us something new.

FAUST:

I shall lose myself if I don't take care.
This really is something like a fair!

MEPHIST.:

It's a crush, it's a rush to get up above.
You're shoved along, though you think you shove.

FAUST:

Who's that?

MEPHIST:

Look well, but you'd better beware:
That's Lilith.

FAUST:

Who's she?

MEPHIST.:

Old Adam's first wife.
But be on your guard as you value your life,
There's death in her long bright hair.
That's her garb and that's her caul,
And the youth that is wound in the golden snare
Shall live and die her thrall.

FAUST:

There's an old carline with a young witch:
You can see they have run the rig.

MEPHIST.:

Why, of course, to-night we all of us itch.
Come along! They've begun a new jig.

FAUST (*dancing with the young one*):
> I saw a vision in the night;
> An apple-tree appeared to me;
> And on it hung two apples bright;
> They shone so fair I climbed the tree.

GOOD-LOOKING WITCH:
> You've had a fancy for apples since
> Eve took a bite of the fragrant quince
> And sinned the sin without pardon.
> I'm really delighted that still unblighted
> They grow in my little garden!

MEPHIST.:
> A naughty dream once came to me.
> I thought I saw a cloven tree;
> The fruit was hard and the rind was split,
> And yet I'd a fancy to taste of it.

OLD WITCH:
> My compliments to you, Sir Knight,
> Of the cloven hoof! If you don't mind
> Shrunken fruit and shrivelled rind,
> You're very welcome to take a bite.

MR. SPOOKBOTHAM:
> You rascals, what do you mean? Oh this beats all!
> How do you dare to dance with such abandon
> When it's been proved by methods hypercritical
> That spirits haven't got a leg to stand on?

THE PRETTY WITCH (*dancing*):
> What is the fellow doing at our ball?

FAUST (*dancing*):
> Oh, he's ubiquitous! The great critic,—
> Pronounces judgment if you give a kick;
> Hop on one toe and he must have his word;
> If he can't crab you, why you haven't stirred;
> What makes him furious is to see us move.
> If you went rambling round in the old groove,
> As he does in his damned old donkey mill,
> He'd say you were quite right to stand stock still:
> It is the only possible position,
> Especially if you asked his permission.

Johann Wolfgang von Goethe

MR. SPOOKBOTHAM:

    Are you still there? This is preposterous!
    Vanish! The problem's been cleared up by us!
    Devils don't care if things are not *en règle*.
    We are so brainy, yet there are spooks at Tegel.
    I thought I'd made a clean sweep of illusions;
    But what a mess! A perfect cataclysm!

GOOD-LOOKING WITCH:

    Well, then, just stop making yourself a nuisance.

MR. SPOOKBOTHAM:

    Soi-disant thinkers, spirits of the abysm,
    If there is one thing I despise, it
    Is intellectual despotism,
    Especially as I can't exercise it.

                    (They go on dancing.)

    I can do nothing with them. Let them wag;
    I've got my volume of travels,
    And they'll come in handy as a gag,
    Ere my last jaunt, to silence bards and devils.

MEPHIST.:

    Do you know what he does when he's got the hump
    And wants to cool his gizzard?
    He'll just go and squat in the nearest ditch.
    When the leeches have had a good go at his rump
    He'll be cured of his hypercritical itch,
    And he won't look much like a wizard.
    Where's your partner that sang so sweet
    As you two danced on nimble feet?

FAUST:

    Oh, she danced north and she danced south,
    But a little red mouse popped out of her mouth.

MEPHIST.:

    That's right. It's a shepherd's holiday
    And you mustn't be meticulous.
    As long as the little mouse wasn't gray
    To worry is truly ridiculous.

FAUST:

    Then I saw—

MEPHIST.:

    What?

MEPHIST:

    Mephisto, do you see
    A pale fair girl standing far off, alone?
    She moves so slow, she moves so mournfully,
    There must be gyves about her feet; and yet
    I have a solemn feeling she's my own
    Poor sullied flower, my simple Margaret.

MEPHIST:

    Oh, stop all that! It does no good.
    She is a lifeless spectre, thin as air;
    They're ill to meet; they freeze the blood
    And almost turn a man to stone.
    You've heard of the Medusa's stare?

FAUST:

    Her eyes are like the eyes of the dead
    That none has closed with love's last kiss.
    That is the bosom that pillowed my head:
    That is the body of my bliss.

MEPHIST.:

    You fool, it's all a fake,—phantasmal show;
    Why, everybody thinks that she's his jo.

FAUST:

    Oh, rapture, mingled with most sick surmise!
    I cannot turn away from those sad eyes.
    She wears a throat-band like a scarlet braid
    About her neck, no thicker than a blade.

MEPHIST.:

    Quite right. I see exactly what you see.
    Sometimes she'll carry her head under her arm.
    Well, Perseus chopped it off for her, didn't he?
    Illusion seems to have a curious charm
    For you. Let's climb this hillock anyway.
    Vienna's famous park is not more gay.
    And if my eyesight isn't getting queer
    I see before me a real theatre.
    What's on?

A SUPER:

    They're ready to begin the play;
    A new piece; this will be the seventh and the last
    Performance; that's the usual number here.
    Author a dilettante, and the caste

All dilettantes. I must disappear,
If you don't mind my vanishing away, sir,
For I'm a dilettante curtain-raiser.

MEPHIST.:
Well met on the Blocksberg, then, with all my heart.
It's just the place for dilettante art.

WALPURGIS NIGHT'S DREAM,
or
OBERON AND TITANIA'S GOLDEN WEDDING

INTERMEZZO

MANAGER:
Mieding's sons, you may rest a spell;
To-day there's no scene-shifting;
A mountain old will serve us well,
And a valley with low mists lifting.

HERALD:
Fifty years of married life,
Then comes the golden wedding:
But the sterling gold is love without strife,—
No tears unwept or shedding.

OBERON:
Spirits all about us be,
Lest such a day be slighted;
For the King and the Queen of Faërie
Are now again united.

PUCK:
Here comes Puck and skims the ground,
In his quaint figures whisking,
But a hundred follow with leap and bound
For fun and frolic frisking.

ARIEL:
Ariel's song is heard in air,
Like dew with heaven's light on it;
And he can charm the hearts of the fair
And the frumpy old maid in her bonnet.

OBERON:
Married folk by us he taught
How to live single-hearted:

If you'd love as couples ought
You must first be parted.

TITANIA:

If he look cold and she's a scold,
Take them both by the scruff in a trice, Sir!
Send her to the South to stop her mouth
And him to the Arctic ice, sir!

ORCHESTRA (*fortissimo*):

Neb of gnat and snout of fly,
With all their generation;
Frog on bough and grasshopper's cry,
That's the orchestration!

SOLO:

Here comes the pipes, as like as you please
To the bubbles an urchin blows.
You can hear them sniff, you can hear them sneeze
As if they'd a cold in the nose.

SPIRIT (*taking shape*):

Puttock's paunch and spinneret,
With little wings to row 'em.
If it isn't a full-sized insect yet
It's a perfect little poem.

A LITTLE COUPLE:

Through the honey-dew balm and breath of flowers
You hop high but keep much where you were.
We're rather fatigued with admiring your powers;
You never will wing blue air.

INQUIRING TOURIST:

There's meaning in these maskers; I'm
The butt of their derision.
God Oberon! Is this the time
Or place for such a vision?

ORTHODOX:

No claws, no tail! Let all the geese
In Weimar hiss and snivel,
King Oberon, like the gods of Greece,
Is nothing but the devil.

NORTHERN ARTIST:

I interpret this stuff as a sketch in the rough,
In a small sort of way it supplies a

Pleasant evening's recreation while I have in preparation
My *Italienische Reise.*

PURIST:

I'm sorry I came; they fill me with shame
And disgust; I never saw louder
Wantons than these; not a witch, if you please,
Except two, has the taste to wear powder!

YOUNG WITCH:

Your powder and your petticoat
Are for old frights de rigueur:
So I sit naked on my goat
And show my pretty figure.

MATRON:

I won't soil my lips with answering your quips;
Good manners are not quite forgotten:
But I think it my duty to wish your ripe beauty
May hang on the tree till it's rotten.

CONDUCTOR:

Neb of gnat and snout of fly,
On the nude you seem to fatten.
Frog in bower and grig on flower,
Will you kindly attend to my baton.

WEATHERCOCK (*turning in one direction*):

What women! Lovely as a bride,
Or I'm an ignoramus;
These gilded youths in all their careless pride
Are certain to be famous.

(*Turning in the opposite direction.*)

If the earth don't open and swallow the brutes,
The pit and the people in it,
I'm perfectly ready to take off my boots
And jump into hell this minute.

XENIES:

We are feeble things on insect wings
But that never yet dismayed us,
For we're pert little nippers and carry sharp clippers
As Satan our poppa bade us.

HENNINGS:

They throng and they press and their simple address
Is clearly designed to disarm you:

So when the thing's done they'll say it was fun
And they never intended to harm you.

MUSAGETES:

I'd rather ramble where witches gambol,
It's the thing my fancy chooses;
It's more my line than leading the Nine,
For I'm not much account with the Muses.

CI–DEVANT GENIUS OF THE AGE:

Catch hold of my coat; if a man's worth a groat,
He always knows how to class us;
This noble elevation provides grand accomodation,
Like the crown of the German Parnassus.

INQUIRING TOURIST:

Who's this fellow so proud and stiff,
That sits in the seat of the scorner?
Wherever he sniff he seems to get a whiff
Of a Jesuit priest round the corner.

CRANE:

I dip my bill where clear streams roll,
I fish in muddy levels,
And so you see a pious soul
Consorting with the devils.

WORLDLING:

Pious people will always expect
Golden eggs when a grey goose cackles:
That's why on Blocksberg they erect
Their little tin tabernacles.

DANCERS:

New music comes; I hear the drums,
Their deep and distant humming;
But pay no heed; through the hollow reed,
It's a bittern's eternal bumming.

DANCING MASTER:

They all make shift to shake a leg,
And don't care how they blunder,—
Crooked and crank and round as an egg,
Though the world and his wife may wonder.

FIDDLER:

In their clouts and their clogs they fight like dogs,
Of tearing they never tire,

The whole ragged pack to the bagpipe jogs
Like the beasts to Orpheus' lyre.

DOGMATIST:

No critical doubt shall make me shout
Nonsense; I'll keep my head level.
If the devil's nothing, how comes it about
That there is such a thing as a devil?

IDEALIST:

To-night the power of phantasy
Has come to such a pass
That, since there's nothing that's not me,
It follows I'm an ass.

REALIST:

The actual makes me feel queer,
And everything looks foggy:
For the first time in my career
My legs are gettting groggy.

MYSTIC:

I say "The more the merrier";
Give me happy hearts, not sad ones;
If there are devils, I infer
Good spirits from the bad ones.

SKEPTIC:

They're all in the dark and they follow a spark
And think they've a treasure in chase;
To be sure if skeptic can be rhymed with Old Nick
You can't say that I'm out of place.

CONDUCTOR:

Greentree-frog and grasshopper spry,
Accurséd dilettanti;
Neb of gnat and snout of fly
You're musicians, aren't ye?

VERSATILE PEOPLE:

Sans-souci, never in the dumps,
We're called by molly-coddles.
Since we can't walk upon our stumps
We walk upon our noddles.

HANGERS-ON:

We used to cadge for beer and meat,
But now God rest such doles.

We've danced the shoes from off our feet,
So we dance on our bare soles.

WILL-O'-THE WISP:

We are the fire that comes from the mire
That bred our brilliant talents:
But now we are nigher the goal of desire
And glitter among the gallants.

SHOOTING STAR:

I am the snuff of a shooting star
And I shone out of heaven's height:
But low on the grass I have fallen far:
Who'll help me to stand upright?

HEAVYWEIGHTS:

Room! Make room! the trodden grass
Is all around laid flat.
Spirits come and spirits pass,
And they're lusty fellows at that.

PUCK:

Don't rollick about so clumsy and stout
Like baby-elephants hobblin'.
On the first night of May you will have to make way
For Puck, the stalwart goblin.

ARIEL:

If boon Nature gave you wings
Or genius, ere night closes
Follow where my light foot springs
Up the hill of roses.

ORCHESTRA (*pianissimo*):

Look, the light breaks. The low clouds lead
Aloft their shining masses:
Lilt of leaf and wind in reed—
So in dust all passes.

GLOOMY DAY. PLAIN.

FAUST:

In misery! In despair! Long a fugitive and now taken. Locked
up in gaol with agonizing thoughts, poor little soul, so gentle,
so unhappy! This is the end.—And you, you traitor, you
trumpery fiend, you concealed all this. Stop, do you hear me?

165

Stay where you are and roll your devil's eyes in your ugly devil's head. Stand still! Your insufferable presence is provocation enough.—Taken! In helpless, irretrievable misery! The prey of evil spirits, waiting the judgment of unfeeling men! And you were amusing me all the time, weren't you? You and your stale dissipations, silencing my conscience, hiding her sufferings, while she sank deeper and deeper, and there was none to stretch a helping hand.

MEPHIST.:

She's not the first.

FAUST:

Hound! Obscene beast! Transform him, illimitable Spirit. Make the viper the dog he was when he used to scamper in front of me, roll on the ground, trip up the unoffending traveller in the dark and jump on his back. Transform him into the shape he loves, let him crawl on his belly in the dust that I may crush him with my foot! Not the first! Sad, sad, past all conception tragic that more souls than one have fallen into this pit of misery, that the mortal anguish of the first that fell was not enough in the eyes of the Eternal Pardoner to expiate the offence of all! The wretchedness of one eats into the very marrow of my bones, and you gloat and grin over the fate of thousands!

MEPHIST.:

Now we're back again at the breaking point; we're at our wit's end as we have been before. What did you want to join us for if you can't carry the thing through? He'd fly but can't get rid of the vertigo! Did you conjure us up or we you?

MEPHIST.:

Don't gnash your teeth at me, it makes me sick. Great Master Spirit, that deigned'st to appear to me and knowest all my heart, why chain me in irons to a villain whose business is crime and who feeds fat on the wreck of souls?

MEPHIST.:

Have you finished?

FAUST:

Save her, or look to yourself! My consuming curse light on you for a thousand ages!

MEPHIST.:

I cannot loosen the bonds of the Avenger or unlock His bolts. Save her! Who brought her to wreck and ruin? I or you?

(FAUST *looks wildly around.*)

MEPHIST.:

Can't lay your hand on the thunder? No, it wasn't given to the human worm, and a good job, too. Crush your innocent adversary, that's the tyrant's way of letting in a little air when he's in a tight place.

FAUST:

Take me to her! She must be freed!

MEPHIST.:

And what about the risk? The blood you shed is not forgotten; avenging spirits haunt the spot and wait for the assassin.

FAUST:

Do you tell me that—the guilt of a whole world that you murdered on your head, you monster! Take me to her and set her free!

MEPHIST.:

I'll take you, and what I can do you shall hear. Have I all power in Heaven and earth? I'll fuddle the gaolers; do you get hold of the keys and let her out yourself. I'll look out for you. The magic horses are ready and I'll take you along. That's all I can do.

FAUST:

Away! Away!

NIGHT. PLAIN.

FAUST *and* MEPHISTOPHELES *riding headlong on black horses.*

FAUST:

What are they at round the Raven Stone?

MEPHIST.:

Don't know; boiling or baking or marring or making.

FAUST:

Swooping up, swooping down, bending, stooping.

MEPHIST.:

'Tis a Witches' Guild.

FAUST:

Scattering—chattering and muttering charms.

MEPHIST.:

Come on! Come on!

Johann Wolfgang von Goethe

PRISON

FAUST *with a bunch of keys and a lamp in front of
a small iron door.*

FAUST:

I bade good-bye to horror long ago:
But now I feel the sum of human woe.
These damp walls are her home; her sin
A mockery. You are afraid to enter in?
You dare not look upon her? While you stay
And palter with your fears Death stalks this way.
    (He lays hold of the padlock. Singing within.)
  My mother's a harlot,
   My father's a thief;
  He gobbled me up
   When she'd brought me to grief.
  But kind little Sissy
   Picked up my bones
  And put them all under
   The cold damp stones:
 So I hopped like a bird on the greenwood tree:
 Fly away, birdie, and then you'll be free.

FAUST *(unlocking)*:

She doesn't guess her lover's listening,
Hears the straw rustle and the irons ring.
         (He goes in.)

MARGARET *(hiding herself on the bed)*:

They've come! Oh bitter death! They've come.
Oh! Oh!

FAUST *(gently)*:

Hush, dearest, hush! I've come to set you free!

MARGARET *(throwing herself on the ground)*:

If you're a man have pity upon me.

FAUST:

You'll wake the warders if you cry out so.
    (He seizes the irons to unlock them.)

MARGARET *(on her knees)*:

Hangman, who gave you power over me?
It's only twelve o'clock now; won't it be .

Time enough to-morrow? Won't you let me live?
(She stands up.)
Spare me! I am so young, so young to die!
And I was pretty once and that is why
I went wrong and there's so much to forgive.
I had a friend, but now my friend is fled.
My bride wreath's torn and all the blossom shed.
Don't be so violent! Spare me! I
Did you no wrong or saw you till this hour.

FAUST:
I can't stand this!

MARGARET:
I'm wholly in your power,
Do let me give my little one the breast,—
I have been kissing it the whole night long.
And now they say I killed it. I can't rest
And I shall never be glad. They've made a song
About me; sing it up and down the street.
They are so cruel. Some old tale ends so;
But why they sing it of me I do not know.

FAUST *(flinging himself on the floor)*:
It is your lover lying at your feet
To knock away the fetters of your woe.

MARGARET *(kneeling beside him)*:
We'll both kneel down and call on the Saints.
Look there!
Under the stone-stair
Below the threshold hell boils up through the floor!
The Evil One is wroth; I hear him roar.

FAUST *(with a loud voice)*:
Gretchen! Gretchen!

MARGARET:
That's my friend's voice! But where
(She rises and the chains fall off her.)
Is he? I heard him call me, and I'm free;
I can't be kept a prisoner any more.
I'll put my arms about his neck and lie
In his bosom. "Gretchen" I heard him cry.
He stood upon the threshold, at his feet
Hell roared and howled; but through

> The savage laughter of the fiends
> I heard a voice that sounded, oh, so sweet,
> Like love's voice, and I knew
> It was my friend's.

FAUST:

> I'm here.

MARGARET:

> Here? Say it again!
> (*Embracing him*) It is my love. Then where is all my pain?
> My prison and my chain?
> It's you! You've come to save me! I *am* saved.
> There is the street where I saw you first that day,
> And there's the sunny garden that we knew,
> Where I and Martha waited once for you.

FAUST:

> Come, come with me!

MARGARET:

> Not yet! I love to stay where you are.

FAUST:

> Come! There's danger in delay.

MARGARET:

> Not kiss me? Such a little while away
> And you've forgotten how?
> Why do I fear to fold you to me now?
> Your voice, your look once whelmed me with the bliss
> Of heaven on earth, and, when you drew
> Me to you, you half smothered me.
> Give me a kiss.
> You won't? Then I'll kiss you!

> > (*She kisses him.*)

> Oh me! Your lips are cold!
> They're cold and dumb!
> Is love so soon grown old?
> Who wronged me then?

> > (*She turns away from him.*)

FAUST:

> Come! Come!
> Follow me! Sweet, you must be brave!
> I love you now more by a thousandfold;
> But you must follow me; it's all I crave.

MARGARET:

　　Are you he? Are you really he?

FAUST:

　　Yes! Come!

MARGARET:

　　You have undone my chain,
　　And now you'll take me on your knee again.
　　How is it that you're not afraid of me?
　　Do you know who it is you're setting free?

FAUST:

　　Come! Come! Night pales, and heaven's profound
　　Begins to glimmer with the morning gleam.

MARGARET:

　　I killed my mother and I drowned
　　My child. God gave him me and you;
　　Oh, yes, you, too! But is it really you?
　　I can't believe it yet.
　　Give me your hand! It is no dream.
　　Your dear hand!—but it's wet!
　　Wipe it. Oh, God, it's bloody! What have you done?
　　Put up your sword for dear God's sake!

FAUST:

　　My own! Let all that's past alone!
　　If you talk so my heart will break!

MARGARET:

　　No, no; you'll be the one to live
　　When we are dead of sorrow.
　　You'll see about the graves to-morrow;
　　You must give
　　Mother the best:
　　And you must lay
　　My brother near her: put me apart from the rest—
　　But not too far away—
　　And baby here, on my right breast.
　　No one else will lie near me.
　　Ah, it was sweet to wind
　　My arms about you; but now that can't be.
　　Somehow it's on my mind
　　That you push me away,
　　And yet it's you, and you look good and kind.

FAUST:

    Oh, if you think I am, come with me!

MARGARET:

    There?

FAUST:

    Into the free sweet air!

MARGARET:

    Come, where the grave is, where
    Death waits! One little step to dare
    And then to bed and everlasting rest.
    You're going? Heinrich, can't I go with you?

FAUST:

    You can—the door is open—if you will!

MARGARET:

    I daren't; there's no more hope for me; at best
    What use is it to flee?
    They wait for me.
    It's misery to beg your bread
    When a bad conscience follows where you tread;
    In the wide world to have no friend;
    Besides they'll take me in the end.

FAUST:

    I'll stay with you.

MARGARET:

    Be quick! Be quick!
    Save your child! That's the way we took
    Over the bridge beside the brook,
    Along the path where the wood is thick,
    To the left there's a plank and then beyond
    A little pond.
    Quick! Drag it out! It isn't dead—
    It's struggling—it lifts up its head.
    Save it! Save it!

FAUST:

    Remember where you are, my own!
    One step and you'll be free!

MARGARET:

    I wish we'd passed the hill.
    There my mother sits on a stone:
    I feel so chill!
    There my mother sits on a stone;

And shakes her head, but she's not beckoning me;
Her head's too heavy; she's slept so long
That she can't wake. She slept that we
Might toy and kiss.
Oh, those were the hours when love was strong,
Those were the hours of bliss!

FAUST:

It's useless now to weep and pray;
If you won't come I must carry you away.

MARGARET:

Let me alone! I won't be forced!
Don't wrench as if you meant to murder me!
I gave you all for love.

FAUST:

My darling! See!
It's day!

MARGARET:

Day! Yes, it's day; it's the Last Day;
My wedding day that was to be.
Don't say you've been with Gretchen! Oh!
My bride-wreath! Well, it's over now;
Finished and done with. We shall meet
Again, but not to dance. The people crush,
But not a word is spoken.
The square and the street
Can't hold them. Hush!
The death-bell tolls. The wand is broken.
They tie my hands, they drag my feet
To the bloody block. Every neck is bare
To the blade that flashes through the air
To sever mine. The world is silent as the grave.

FAUST:

Would God that I had never seen the light of day!

MEPHIST. (*appearing outside*):

You're a lost man if you delay!
What are you jabbering here for? Come away!
My horses shiver, and the gray
Dawn breaks.

MARGARET:

What's this that rises from the ground? It's he!
It's he! Send him away!

173

What does he in this holy place where we knelt down to pray?
He's coming to take me!

FAUST:

No! You shall live!

MARGARET:

Justice of God, I yield my life to thee!

MEPHIST.:

Come, or I'll leave the pair of you to your fate.

MARGARET:

Thine am I, Father! Save, receive, forgive!
Good angels keep me! Bright
Battalions, round me pitch your tents of light!
Heinrich! I'm full of fear
For you!

MEPHIST.:

She's judged!

VOICE (*above*):

She's saved!

MEPHIST.:

Come here!

(*Vanishes with* FAUST.)

A VOICE (*dying away within*):

Heinrich! Heinrich!

Egmont

Dramatis Personae

   EGMONT
   HIS SECRETARY
   MARGARET OF PARMA, *Regent of the Netherlands*
   MACHIAVEL, *her secretary*
   THE PRINCE OF ORANGE
   THE DUKE OF ALVA
   FERDINAND, *his son*
   SILVA   } *officers of the Duke*
   GOMEZ
   CLARA, *in love with Egmont*
   BRACKENBURG, *her suitor*
   CLARA'S MOTHER
   BUYCK   } *Dutch soldiers*
   RUYSUM
   JETTER   }
   SOEST   } *Citizens*
   VANSEN }
   A MASTER CARPENTER
   A SOAP-BOILER
   Other soldiers, other citizens, courtiers, pages, servants

Egmont

ACT I

SCENE I. *Soldiers and Citizens (with cross-bows).*

(JETTER *steps forward, and bends his cross-bow*).

SOEST:

Come, shoot away, and have done with it! You won't beat me! Three black rings, you never made such a shot in all your life. And so I'm master for this year.

JETTER:

Master and king to boot; who envies you? You'll have to pay double reckoning; 'tis only fair you should pay for your dexterity.

BUYCK:

Jetter, I'll buy your shot, share the prize, and treat the company. I have already been here so long, and am a debtor for so many civilities. If I miss, then it shall be as if you had shot.

SOEST:

I ought to have a voice, for in fact I am the loser. No matter! Come, Buyck, shoot away.

BUYCK (*shoots*):

Now, corporal, look out! — One! Two! Three! Four!

SOEST:

Four rings! So be it!

ALL:

Hurrah! Long live the king. Hurrah! Hurrah!

BUYCK:

Thanks, sirs, master even were too much! Thanks for the honor.

JETTER:

You have no one to thank but yourself.

Translated by Anna Swanwick

177

RUYSUM:

Let me tell you! —

SOEST:

How now, gray-beard?

RUYSUM:

Let me tell you! — He shoots like his master, he shoots like Egmont.

BUYCK:

Compared with him I am only a bungler. He aims with the rifle as no one else does. Not only when he's lucky or in the vein; no! he levels, and the bull's-eye is pierced. I have learned from him. He were, indeed, a block-head, who could serve under him and learn nothing! — But, sirs, let us not forget: A king maintains his followers; and so, wine here, at the king's charge!

JETTER:

We have agreed among ourselves that each —

BUYCK:

I am a foreigner and a king, and care not a jot for your laws and customs.

JETTER:

Why you are worse than the Spaniard, who has not yet ventured to meddle with them.

RUYSUM:

What does he say?

SOEST *(loud to* RUYSUM*)*:

He wants to treat us; he will not hear of our clubbing together, the king paying only a double share.

RUYSUM:

Let him! under protest, however! 'Tis his master's fashion, too, to be munificent, and to let the money flow in good cause. *(Wine is brought.)*

ALL:

Here's to his majesty! Hurrah!

JETTER: *(to* BUYCK*)*:

That means your majesty, of course.

BUYCK:

My hearty thanks, if it be so.

SOEST:

Assuredly! A Netherlander does not find it easy to drink the health of his Spanish majesty from his heart.

RUYSUM:

Who?

SOEST *(aloud)*:

Philip the Second, King of Spain.

RUYSUM:

Our most gracious king and master! Long life to him.

SOEST:

Did you not like his father, Charles the Fifth, better?

RUYSUM:

God bless him! He was a king, indeed! His hand reached over the whole earth, and he was all in all. Yet, when he met you, he'd greet you just as one neighbor greets another, — and if you were frightened, he knew so well how to put you at your ease — ay, you understand me — he walked out, rode out, just as it came into his head, with very few followers. We all wept when he resigned the government here to his son. You understand me — he is another sort of man, he's more majestic.

JETTER:

When he was here, he never appeared in public, except in pomp and royal state. He speaks little, they say.

SOEST:

He is no king for us Netherlanders. Our princes must be joyous and free like ourselves, must live and let live. We will neither be despised nor oppressed, good-natured fools though we be.

JETTER:

The king, methinks, were a gracious sovereign enough, if he had only better counsellors.

SOEST:

No, no! He has no affection for us Netherlanders; he has no heart for the people; he loves us not; how then can we love him? Why is everybody so fond of Count Egmont? Why are we all so devoted to him? Why, because one can read in his face that he loves us; because joyousness, open-heartedness, and good-nature speak in his eyes; because he possesses nothing that he does not share with him who needs it, ay, and with him who needs it not. Long live Count Egmont! Buyck, it is for you to give the first toast; give us your master's health.

BUYCK:

With all my heart; here's to Count Egmont! Hurrah!

RUYSUM:

Conqueror of St. Quentin.

BUYCK:

The hero of Gravelines.

ALL:

Hurrah!

RUYSUM:

St. Quentin was my last battle. I was hardly able to crawl along, and could with difficulty carry my heavy rifle. I managed, notwithstanding, to singe the skin of the French once more, and, as a parting gift, received a grazing shot in my right leg.

BUYCK:

Gravelines! Ha, my friends, we had sharp work of it there! The victory was all our own. Did not those French dogs carry fire and desolation into the very heart of Flanders? We gave it them, however! The old, hard-fisted veterans held out bravely for a while, but we pushed on, fired away, and laid about us till they made wry faces, and their lines gave way. Then Egmont's horse was shot under him; and for a long time we fought pell-mell, man to man, horse to horse, troop to troop, on the broad, flat sea-sand. Suddenly, as if from heaven, down came the cannon-shot from the mouth of the river, bang, bang, right into the midst of the French. These were English who, under Admiral Malin, happened to be sailing past from Dunkirk. They did not help us much, 'tis true; they could only approach with their smallest vessels, and that not near enough; — besides their shot fell sometimes among our troops. It did some good, however! It broke the French lines, and raised our courage. Away they went. Helter-skelter! topsy-turvy! all struck dead, or forced into the water; the fellows were drowned the moment they tasted the water, while we Hollanders dashed in after them. Being amphibious, we were as much in our element as frogs, and hacked away at the enemy, and shot them down as if they had been ducks. The few who struggled through were struck dead in their flight by the peasant women, armed with hoes and pitchforks. His Gallic majesty was compelled at once to hold out his paw and make peace. And that peace you owe to us, to the great Egmont.

ALL:

Hurrah for the great Egmont! Hurrah! Hurrah!

JETTER:

Had they but appointed him Regent instead of Margaret of Parma!

SOEST:

Not so! Truth is truth! I'll not hear Margaret abused. Now it is my turn. Long live our gracious lady!

ALL:

Long life to her!

SOEST:

Truly, there are excellent women in that family. Long live the Regent!

JETTER:

Prudent she is, and moderate in all she does; if she would only not hold so fast and stiffly with the priests. It is partly her fault, too, that we have the fourteen new mitres in the land. Of what use are they, I should like to know? Why, that foreigners may be shoved into the good benefices, where formerly abbots were chosen out of the chapters! And we're to believe it's for the sake of religion. We know better. Three bishops were enough for us; things went on decently and reputably. Now each must busy himself as if he were needed; and this gives rise every moment to dissensions and ill-will. And the more you agitate the matter, so much the worse it grows. (*They drink.*)

SOEST:

But it was the will of the king; she cannot alter it one way or another.

JETTER:

Then we may not even sing the new psalms; but ribald songs, as many as we please. And why? There is heresy in them, they say, and heaven knows what. I have sung some of them, however; they are new, to be sure, but I see no harm in them.

BUYCK:

Ask their leave, forsooth! In our province we sing just what we please. That's because Count Egmont is our stadtholder, who does not trouble himself about such matters. In Ghent, Ypres, and throughout the whole of Flanders, anybody sings them that chooses. (*Aloud to* RUYSUM.) There is nothing more harmless than a church hymn — is there, father?

181

RUYSUM:

What, indeed! It is a godly work, and truly edifying.

JETTER:

They say, however, that they are not of the right sort, not of their sort, and, since it is dangerous, we had better leave them alone. The officers of the Inquisition are always lurking and spying about; many an honest fellow has already fallen into their clutches. They had not gone so far as to meddle with conscience! If they will not allow me to do what I like, they might at least let me think and sing as I please.

SOEST:

The Inquisition won't do here. We are not made like the Spaniards, to let our consciences be tyrannized over. The nobles must look to it, and clip its wings betimes.

JETTER:

It is a great bore. Whenever it comes into their worships' heads to break into my house, and I am sitting there at my work, humming a French psalm, thinking nothing about it, neither good nor bad—singing it just because it is in my throat;—forthwith I am a heretic, and am clapped into prison. Or, if I am passing through the country, and stand near a crowd listening to a new preacher, one of those who have come from Germany; instantly I am called a rebel, and am in danger of losing my head! Have you ever heard one of these preachers?

SOEST:

A worthy set of people! Not long ago I heard one of them preach in a field, before thousands and thousands of people. He gave us a sort of dish very different from that of our humdrum preachers, who, from the pulpit, choke their hearers with scraps of Latin. He spoke from his heart; told us how we had till now been led by the nose, how we had been kept in darkness, and how we might procure more light;—ay, and he proved it all out of the Bible.

JETTER:

There may be something in it. I always said as much, and have often pondered over the matter. It has long been running in my head.

BUYCK:

All the people run after them.

SOEST:

> No wonder, since they hear both what is good and what is new.

JETTER:

> And what is it all about? Surely they might let every one preach after his own fashion.

BUYCK:

> Come, sirs! While you are talking, you forget the wine and the Prince of Orange.

JETTER:

> We must not forget him. He's a very wall of defence. In thinking of him, one fancies that if one could only hide behind him, the devil himself could not get at one. Here's to William of Orange! Hurrah!

ALL:

> Hurrah! Hurrah!

SOEST:

> Now, gray-beard, let's have your toast.

RUYSUM:

> Here's to old soldiers! To all soldiers! War forever!

BUYCK:

> Bravo, old fellow. Here's to all soldiers. War forever!

JETTER:

> War! War! Do ye know what ye are shouting about? That is should slip glibly from your tongue is natural enough; but what wretched work it is for us, I have not words to tell you. To be stunned the whole year round by the beating of the drum; to hear of nothing except how one troop marched here, and another there; how they came over this height, and halted near that mill; how many were left dead on this field, and how many on that; how they press forward, and how one wins, and another loses, without being able to comprehend what they are fighting about; how a town is taken, how the citizens are put to the sword, and how it fares with the poor women and innocent children. This is a grief and a trouble, and then one thinks every moment, "Here they come! It will be our turn next."

SOEST:

> Therefore every citizen must be practised in the use of arms.

JETTER:

> Fine talking, indeed, for him who has a wife and children. And yet I would rather hear of soldiers than see them.

183

BUYCK:

I might take offence at that.

JETTER:

It was not intended for you, countryman. When we got rid of the Spanish garrison we breathed freely again.

SOEST:

Faith! they pressed on you heavily enough.

JETTER:

Mind your own business.

SOEST:

They came to sharp quarters with you.

JETTER:

Hold your tongue.

SOEST:

They drove him out of kitchen, cellar, chamber—and bed.

(They laugh.)

JETTER:

You are a blockhead.

BUYCK:

Peace, sirs! Must the soldier cry peace? Since you will not hear anything about us, let us have a toast of your own—a citizen's toast.

JETTER:

We're all ready for that! Safety and peace!

SOEST:

Order and freedom!

BUYCK:

Bravo! That will content us all.

(They ring their glasses together, and joyously repeat the words, but in such a manner that each utters a different sound, and it becomes a kind of chant. The old man listens, and at length joins in.

ALL:

Safety and peace! Order and freedom.

SCENE II. *Palace of the Regent,* MARGARET OF PARMA.

REGENT *(in a hunting dress)*:

Put off the hunt, I shall not ride to-day. Bid Machiavel attend me.

[*Exeunt all but the* REGENT.

The thought of these terrible events leaves me no repose!

Nothing can amuse, nothing divert my mind. These images, these cares are always before me. The king will now say that these are the natural fruits of my kindness, of my clemency; yet my conscience assures me that I have adopted the wisest, the most prudent course. Ought I sooner to have kindled and spread abroad these flames with the breath of wrath? my hope was to keep them in, to let them smoulder in their own ashes. Yes, my inward conviction, and my knowledge of the circumstances, justify my conduct in my own eyes; but in what light will it appear to my brother? For can it be denied that the insolence of these foreign teachers waxes daily more audacious? They have desecrated our sanctuaries, unsettled the dull minds of the people, and conjured up amongst them a spirit of delusion. Impure spirits have mingled among the insurgents, horrible deeds have been perpetrated, which to think of makes one shudder, and of these a circumstantial account must be transmitted to court instantly. Prompt and minute must be my communication, lest rumor outrun my messenger, and the king suspect that some particulars have been purposely withheld. I can see no means, severe or mild, by which to stem the evil. Oh, what are we great ones on the waves of humanity? We think to control them, and are ourselves driven to and fro, hither and thither.

Enter MACHIAVEL

REGENT:

Are the despatches to the king prepared?

MACHIAVEL:

In an hour they will be ready for your signature.

REGENT:

Have you made the report sufficiently circumstantial?

MACHIAVEL:

Full and circumstantial, as the king loves to have it. I relate how the rage of the iconoclasts first broke out at St. Omer. How a furious multitude, with staves, hatchets, hammers, ladders and cords, accompanied by a few armed men, first assailed the chapels, churches, and convents, drove out the worshipers, forced the barred gates, threw everything into confusion, tore down the altars, destroyed the statues of the saints, defaced the pictures, and dashed to atoms, and trampled under foot whatever that was consecrated and holy came in their way. How the crowd increased as it advanced, and how the inhabitants of Ypres opened their gates at its approach. How, with incredible rapidity, they demolished the cathedral, and burned the library of the bishop. How a vast multitude, possessed by the like frenzy, dispersed themselves through Menin, Comines, Verviers, Lille, nowhere encountered opposition; and how, through almost the whole of Flanders, in a single moment, the monstrous conspiracy declared itself and was accomplished.

REGENT:

Alas! Your recital rends my heart anew; and the fear that the evil will wax greater and greater adds to my grief. Tell me your thoughts, Machiavel!

MACHIAVEL:

Pardon me, your Highness, my thoughts will appear to you but as idle fancies; and though you always seem well satisfied with my services, you have seldom felt inclined to follow my advice. How often have you said in jest: "You see too far, Machiavel! You should be an historian; he who acts must provide for the exigency of the hour." And yet, have I not predicted this terrible history? Have I not foreseen it all?

REGENT:

I, too, foresee many things without being able to avert them.

MACHIAVEL:

In one word, then:—you will not be able to suppress the new faith. Let it be recognized, separate its votaries from the true believers, give them churches of their own, include them within the pale of social order, subject them to the restraints of law,—do this, and you will at once tranquillize the insurgents. All other measures will prove abortive, and you will depopulate the country.

REGENT:

Have you forgotten with what aversion the mere suggestion of toleration was rejected by my brother? Know you not, how in every letter he urgently recommends to me the maintenance of the true faith? That he will not hear of tranquillity and order being restored at the expense of religion? Even in the provinces, does he not maintain spies, unknown to us, in order to ascertain who inclines to the new doctrines? Has he not, to our astonishment, named to us this or that individual residing in our very neighborhood, who, without its being known, was obnoxious to the charge of heresy?

Does he not enjoin harshness and severity? and am I to be lenient? Am I to recommend for his adoption measures of indulgence and toleration? Should I not thus lose all credit with him, and at once forfeit his confidence?

MACHIAVEL:

I know it. The king commands, and puts you in full possession of his intentions. You are to restore tranquillity and peace by measures which cannot fail still more to embitter men's minds, and which must inevitably kindle the flames of war from one extremity of the country to the other. Consider well what you are doing. The principal merchants are infected—nobles, citizens, soldiers. What avails persisting in our opinion when everything is changing around us? Oh, that some good genius would suggest to Philip that it better becomes a monarch to govern burghers of two different creeds, than to excite them to mutual destruction!

REGENT:

Never let me hear such words again. Full well I know that the policy of statesmen rarely maintains truth and fidelity; that it excludes from the heart candor, charity, toleration. In secular affairs, this is, alas! only too true; but shall we trifle with God as we do with each other? Shall we be indifferent to our established faith, for the sake of which so many have sacrificed their lives? Shall we abandon it to these far-fetched, uncertain, and self-contradicting heresies?

MACHIAVEL:

Think not the worse of me for what I have uttered.

REGENT:

I know you and your fidelity. I know, too, that a man may be both honest and sagacious, and yet miss the best and nearest way to the salvation of his soul. There are others, Machiavel, men whom I esteem, yet whom I needs must blame.

MACHIAVEL:

To whom do you refer?

REGENT:

I must confess that Egmont caused me to-day deep and heartfelt annoyance.

MACHIAVEL:

How so?

REGENT:

By his accustomed demeanor, his usual indifference and

levity. I received the fatal tidings as I was leaving church, attended by him and several others. I did not restrain my anguish, I broke forth into lamentations, loud and deep, and turning to him, exclaimed, "See what is going on in your province! Do you suffer it, Count, you in whom the king confided so implicitly?"

MACHIAVEL:

And what was his reply?

REGENT:

As if it were a mere trifle, an affair of no moment, he answered: "Were the Netherlanders but satisfied as to their constitution, the rest would soon follow."

MACHIAVEL:

There was, perhaps, more truth than discretion or piety in his words. How can we hope to acquire and to maintain the confidence of the Netherlander when he sees that we are more interested in appropriating his possessions than in promoting his welfare, temporal or spiritual? Does the number of souls saved by the new bishops exceed that of the fat benefices they have swallowed? And are they not for the most part foreigners? As yet, the office of stadtholder has been held by Netherlanders; but do not the Spaniards betray their great and irresistible desire to possess themselves of these places? Will not people prefer being governed by their own countrymen, and according to their ancient customs, rather than by foreigners, who, from their first entrance into the land, endeavor to enrich themselves at the general expense, who measure everything by a foreign standard, and exercise their authority without cordiality or sympathy?

REGENT:

You take part with our opponents?

MACHIAVEL:

Assuredly not in my heart. Would that with my understanding I could be wholly on our side.

REGENT:

If such is your opinion, it were better I should resign the regency to them; for both Egmont and Orange entertained great hopes of occupying this position. Then they were adversaries; now they are leagued against me, and have become friends—inseparable friends.

MACHIAVEL:

A dangerous pair.

REGENT:

To speak candidly, I fear Orange.—I fear for Egmont.— Orange meditates some dangerous scheme, his thoughts are far-reaching, he is reserved, appears to accede to everything, never contradicts, and while maintaining the show of reverence, with clear foresight accomplishes his own designs.

MACHIAVEL:

Egmont, on the contrary, advances with a bold step, as if the world were all his own.

REGENT:

He bears his head as proudly as if the hand of majesty were not suspended over him.

MACHIAVEL:

The eyes of all the people are fixed upon him, and he is the idol of their hearts.

REGENT:

He has never assumed the least disguise, and carries himself as if no one had a right to call him to account. He still bears the name of Egmont. Count Egmont is the title by which he loves to hear himself addressed, as though he would fain be reminded that his ancestors were masters of Guelderland. Why does he not assume his proper title,—Prince of Gaure? What object has he in view? Would he again revive extinguished claims?

MACHIAVEL:

I hold him to be a faithful servant of the king.

REGENT:

Were he so inclined, what important service he could render to the government! Whereas now, without benefiting himself, he has caused us unspeakable vexation. His banquets and entertainments have done more to unite the nobles and to knit them together than the most dangerous secret associations. With his toasts his guests have drunk in a permanent intoxication, a giddy frenzy, that never subsides. How often have his facetious jests stirred up the minds of the populace? and what an excitement was produced among the mob by the new liveries and the extravagant devices of his followers?

MACHIAVEL:

I am convinced he had no design.

Johann Wolfgang von Goethe

REGENT:

Be that as it may, it is bad enough. As I said before, he injures us without benefiting himself. He treats as a jest matters of serious import; and, not to appear negligent and remiss, we are forced to treat seriously what he intended as a jest. Thus one urges on the other; and what we are endeavoring to avert is actually brought to pass. He is more dangerous than the acknowledged head of a conspiracy; and I am much mistaken if it is not all remembered against him at court. I cannot deny that scarcely a day passes in which he does not wound me—deeply wound me.

MACHIAVEL:

He appears to me to act on all occasions according to the dictates of his conscience.

REGENT:

His conscience has a convenient mirror. His demeanor is often offensive. He carries himself as if he felt he were the master here, and were withheld by courtesy alone from making us feel his supremacy; as if he would not exactly drive us out of the country; there'll be no need for that.

MACHIAVEL:

I entreat you, put not too harsh a construction upon his frank and joyous temper, which treats lightly matters of serious moment. You but injure yourself and him.

REGENT:

I interpret nothing. I speak only of inevitable consequences, and I know him. His patent of nobility and the Golden Fleece upon his breast strengthen his confidence, his audacity. Both can protect him against any sudden outbreak of royal displeasure. Consider the matter closely, and he is alone responsible for the whole mischief that has broken out in Flanders. From the first, he connived at the proceedings of the foreign teachers, avoided stringent measures, and perhaps rejoiced in secret that they gave us so much to do. Let me alone; on this occasion, I will give utterance to that which weighs upon my heart; I will not shoot my arrow in vain. I know where he is vulnerable. For he is vulnerable.

MACHIAVEL:

Have you summoned the council? Will Orange attend?

REGENT:

I have sent for him to Antwerp. I will lay upon their shoulders the burden of responsibility; they shall either strenuously co-operate with me in quelling the evil, or at once declare themselves rebels. Let the letters be completed without delay, and bring them for my signature. Then hasten to despatch the trusty Vasca to Madrid; he is faithful and indefatigable; let him use all diligence, that he may not be anticipated by common report, that my brother may receive the intelligence first through him. I will myself speak with him ere he departs.

MACHIAVEL:

Your orders shall be promptly and punctually obeyed.

SCENE III. *Citizen's House.*

CLARA:

Will you not hold the yarn for me, Brackenburg?

BRACKENBURG:

I entreat you, excuse me, Clara.

CLARA:

What ails you? Why refuse me this trifling service?

BRACKENBURG:

When I hold the yarn, I stand as it were spell-bound before you, and cannot escape your eyes.

CLARA:

Nonsense! Come and hold!

MOTHER *(knitting in her arm-chair)*:

Give us a song! Brackenburg sings so good a second. You used to be merry once, and I had always something to laugh at.

BRACKENBURG:

Once!

CLARA:

Well, let us sing.

BRACKENBURG:

As you please.

CLARA:

Merrily, then, and sing away. 'Tis a soldier's song, my favorite. *(She winds yarn, and sings with* BRACKENBURG.*)*

> The drum is resounding,
> And shrill the fife plays;
> My love, for the battle,
> His brave troop arrays;
> He lifts his lance high,

And the people he sways.
My blood it is boiling!
My heart throbs pit-pat!
Oh, had I a jacket,
With hose and with hat!

How boldly I'd follow,
And march through the gate;
Through all the wide province
I'd follow him straight.
The foe yield, we capture
Or shoot them! Ah, me!
What heart-thrilling rapture
A soldier to be!

(During the song, BRACKENBURG *has frequently looked at* CLARA; *at length his voice falters, his eyes fill with tears, he lets the skein fall, and goes to the window.* CLARA *finishes the song alone, her mother motions to her, half displeased, she rises, advances a few steps towards him, turns back as if irresolute, and again sits down.)*

MOTHER:
What is going on in the street, Brackenburg? I hear soldiers marching.

BRACKENBURG:
It is the Regent's body-guard.

CLARA:
At this hour? What can it mean? *(She rises and joins* BRACK- ENBURG *at the window.)* That is not the daily guard; it is more numerous! almost all the troops! Oh, Brackenburg, go! Learn what it means. It must be something unusual. Go, good Brackenburg, do me this favor.

BRACKENBURG:
I am going! I will return immediately. *(He offers his hand to* CLARA, *and she gives him hers.)*

[*Exit* BRACKENBURG.

MOTHER:
Thou sendest him away so soon!

CLARA:
I am curious; and, besides—do not be angry, mother—his presence pains me. I never know how I ought to behave towards him. I have done him a wrong, and it goes to my very

heart to see how deeply he feels it. Well, it can't be helped now!

MOTHER:

He is such a true-hearted fellow!

CLARA:

I cannot help it, I must treat him kindly. Often, without a thought, I return the gentle, loving pressure of his hand. I reproach myself that I am deceiving him, that I am nourishing in his heart a vain hope. I am in a sad plight! God knows I do not willingly deceive him. I do not wish him to hope, yet I cannot let him despair!

MOTHER:

That is not as it should be.

CLARA:

I liked him once, and in my soul I like him still. I could have married him; yet I believe I was never really in love with him.

MOTHER:

Thou wouldst always have been happy with him.

CLARA:

I should have been provided for, and have led a quiet life.

MOTHER:

And through thy fault it has all been trifled away.

CLARA:

I am in a strange position. When I think how it has come to pass, I know it, indeed, and I know it not. But I have only to look upon Egmont, and I understand it all; ay, and stranger things would seem natural then. Oh, what a man he is! All the provinces worship him. And in his arms should not I be the happiest creature in the world?

MOTHER:

And how will it be in the future?

CLARA:

I only ask does he love me?—does he love me?—as if there were any doubt about it.

MOTHER:

One has nothing but anxiety of heart with one's children. Always care and sorrow, whatever may be the end of it! It cannot come to good! Thou hast made thyself wretched! Thou hast made thy mother wretched, too.

CLARA *(quietly)*:

Yet thou didst allow it in the beginning.

193

MOTHER:

Alas! I was too indulgent; I am always too indulgent.

CLARA:

When Egmont rode by, and I ran to the window, did you chide me then? Did you not come to the window yourself? When he looked up, smiled, nodded, and greeted me, was it displeasing to you? Did you not feel yourself honored in your daughter?

MOTHER:

Go on with your reproaches.

CLARA *(with emotion)*:

Then, when he passed more frequently, and we felt sure that it was on my account that he came this way, did you not remark it yourself with secret joy? Did you call me away when I stood behind the window-pane and awaited him?

MOTHER:

Could I imagine that it would go so far?

CLARA *(with faltering voice, and repressed tears)*:

And then, one evening, when, enveloped in his mantle, he surprised us as we sat at our lamp, who busied herself in receiving him, while I remained, lost in astonishment, as if fastened to my chair?

MOTHER:

Could I imagine that the prudent Clara would so soon be carried away by this unhappy love? I must now endure that, my daughter—

CLARA *(bursting into tears)*:

Mother! How can you? You take pleasure in tormenting me!

MOTHER *(weeping)*:

Ay, weep away! Make me yet more wretched by thy grief. Is it not misery enough that my only daughter is a castaway!

CLARA *(rising, and speaking coldly)*:

A castaway! The beloved of Egmont a castaway!—What princess would not envy the poor Clara a place in his heart? Oh, mother,—my own mother, you were not wont to speak thus! Dear mother, be kind!—Let the people think, let the neighbors whisper what they like—this chamber, this lowly house, is a paradise since Egmont's love has had its abode in it.

MOTHER:

One cannot help liking him, that is true. He is always so kind, frank, and open-hearted.

CLARA:

There is not a drop of false blood in his veins. And then, mother, he is indeed the great Egmont; yet, when he comes to me, how tender he is, how kind! How he tries to conceal from me his rank, his bravery! How anxious he is about me! so entirely the man, the friend, the lover.

MOTHER:

Do you expect him to-day?

CLARA:

Have you not seen how often I go the window? Have you not noticed how I listen to every noise at the door?—Though I know that he will not come before night, yet, from the time when I rise in the morning, I keep expecting him every moment. Were I but a boy, to follow him always, to the court and everywhere! Could I but carry his colors in the field!—

MOTHER:

You were always such a lively, restless creature; even as a little child, now wild, now thoughtful. Will you not dress yourself a little better?

CLARA:

Perhaps, mother, if I have nothing better to do.—Yesterday, some of his people went by singing songs in his honor. At least his name was in the songs! The rest I could not understand. My heart leaped up into my throat,—I would fain have called them back if I had not felt ashamed.

MOTHER:

Take care! Thy impetuous nature will ruin all. Thou wilt betray thyself before the people; as, not long ago, at thy cousin's, when thou foundest out the woodcut with the description, and didst exclaim, with a cry: "Count Egmont!" —I grew as red as fire.

CLARA:

Could I help crying out? It was the battle of Gravelines, and I found in the picture the letter C. and then looked for it in the description below. There it stood, "Count Egmont, with his horse shot under him." I shuddered, and afterwards I could not help laughing at the woodcut figure of Egmont, as tall as the neighboring tower of Gravelines, and the English ships at the side.—When I remember how I used to conceive of a battle, and what an idea I had, as a girl, of Count Egmont; when I listened to descriptions of him, and of all the other earls and princes;—and think how it is with me now!

Enter BRACKENBURG.

CLARA:

Well, what is going on?

BRACKENBURG:

Nothing certain is known. It is rumored that an insurrection has lately broken out in Flanders; the Regent is afraid of its spreading here. The castle is strongly garrisoned, the burghers are crowding to the gates, and the streets are thronged with people. I will hasten at once to my old father. *(As if about to go.)*

CLARA:

Shall we see you to-morrow? I must change my dress a little. I am expecting my cousin, and I look too untidy. Come, mother, help me a moment. Take the book, Brackenburg, and bring me such another story.

MOTHER:

Farewell.

BRACKENBURG *(extending his hand)*:

Your hand!

CLARA *(refusing hers)*:

When you come next.

[*Exeunt* MOTHER *and* DAUGHTER.

BRACKENBURG *(alone)*:

I had resolved to go away again at once; and yet, when she takes me at my word, and lets me leave her, I feel as if I could go mad.—Wretched man! Does the fate of thy fatherland, does the growing disturbance fail to move thee?—Are countryman and Spaniard the same to thee? and carest thou not who rules, and who is in the right?—I was a different sort of fellow as a schoolboy!—Then, when an exercise in oratory was given; "Brutus' Speech for Liberty," for instance, Fritz was ever the first, and the rector would say: "If it were only spoken more deliberately, the words not all huddled together."—Then my blood boiled, and longed for action.—Now I drag along, bound by the eyes of a maiden. I

cannot leave her! yet she, alas, cannot love me!—ah—no—she—
she cannot have entirely rejected me—not entirely—yet half
love is no love!—I will endure it no longer!—Can it be true
what a friend lately whispered in my ear, that she secretly
admits a man into the house by night, when she always sends
me away modestly before evening? No, it cannot be true!
It is a lie! A base, slanderous lie! Clara is as innocent as I am
wretched.—She has rejected me, has thrust me from her
heart—and shall I live on thus? I cannot, I will not endure it.
Already my native land is convulsed by internal strife, and
do I perish abjectly amid the tumult? I will not endure it!
When the trumpet sounds, when a shot falls, it thrills
through my bone and marrow! But, alas, it does not rouse
me! It does not summon me to join the onslaught, to rescue,
to dare.—Wretched, degrading position! Better end it at
once! Not long ago I threw myself into the water; I sank—
but nature in her agony was too strong for me; I felt that I
could swim, and saved myself against my will. Could I but
forget the time when she loved me, seemed to love me!—
Why has this happiness penetrated my very bone and marrow? Why have these hopes, while disclosing to me a distant
paradise, consumed all the enjoyment of life?—And that first,
that only kiss!—Here *(laying his hand upon the table)*, here
we were alone,—she had always been kind and friendly towards me,—then she seemed to soften,—she looked at me,—
my brain reeled,—I felt her lips on mine,—and—and now?—
Die, wretch! Why dost thou hesitate? *(He draws a phial
from his pocket.)* Thou healing poison, it shall not have
been in vain that I stole thee from my brother's medicine
chest? From this anxious fear, this dizziness, this death-
agony, thou shalt deliver me at once.

Johann Wolfgang von Goethe

ACT II

SCENE I. *Square in Brussels.*

CARPENTER *(meeting* JETTER*)*:

Did I not tell you beforehand? Eight days ago at the guild I said there would be serious disturbances?

JETTER:

Is it really true that they have plundered the churches in Flanders?

CARPENTER:

They have utterly destroyed both churches and chapels. They have left nothing standing but the four bare walls. The lowest rabble! And this it is that damages our good cause. We ought rather to have laid our claims before the Regent, formally and decidedly, and then have stood by them. If we speak now, if we assemble now, it will be said that we are joining the insurgents.

JETTER:

Ay, so every one thinks at first. Why should you thrust your nose into the mess? The neck is closely connected with it.

CARPENTER:

I am always uneasy when tumults arise among the mob— among people who have nothing to lose. They use as a pretext that to which we also must appeal, and plunge the country in misery.

Enter SOEST.

SOEST:

Good-day, sirs? What news? Is it true that the image-breakers are coming straight in this direction?

CARPENTER:

Here they shall touch nothing at any rate.

SOEST:

A soldier came into my shop just now to buy tobacco! I questioned him about the matter. The Regent, though so brave and prudent a lady, has for once lost her presence of mind. Things must be bad, indeed, when she thus takes refuge behind her guards. The castle is strongly garrisoned. It is even rumored that she means to flee from the town.

CARPENTER:

Forth she shall not go! Her presence protects us, and we will insure her safety better than her mustachioed gentry. If she only maintains our rights and privileges, we will stand faithfully by her.

Enter a SOAP-BOILER.

SOAP-BOILER:

An ugly business this! a bad business! Troubles are beginning; all things are going wrong! Mind you keep quiet, or they'll take you also for rioters.

SOEST:

Here come the seven wise men of Greece.

SOAP-BOILER:

I know there are many who in secret hold with the Calvinists, abuse the bishops, and care not for the king. But a loyal subject, a sincere Catholic!——*(By degrees others join the speakers and listen.)*

Enter VANSEN.

VANSEN:

God save you, sirs! What news?

CARPENTER:

Have nothing to do with him, he's a dangerous fellow.

JETTER:

Is he not secretary to Dr. Wiets?

CARPENTER:

He has had several masters. First he was a clerk, and as one patron after another turned him off, on account of his roguish tricks, he now dabbles in the business of notary and advocate, and is a brandy-drinker to boot. *(More people gather round and stand in groups.)*

VANSEN:

So here you are putting your heads together. Well, it is worth talking about.

SOEST:

I think so, too.

VANSEN:

Now, if only one of you had heart and another head enough for the work, we might break the Spanish fetters at once.

SOEST:

Sirs! you must not talk thus. We have taken our oath to the king.

VANSEN:

And the king to us. Mark that!

OTHERS:

Hearken to him; he's a clever fellow. He's sharp enough.

VANSEN:

I had an old master once, who possessed a collection of parchments, among which were charters of ancient constitutions, contracts, and privileges. He set great store too, by the rarest books. One of these contained our whole constitution; how, at first we Netherlanders had princes of our own, who governed according to hereditary laws, rights, and usages; how our ancestors paid due honor to their sovereign so long as he governed them equitably; and how they were immediately on their guard the moment he was for overstepping his bounds. The states were down upon him at once; for every province, however small, had its own chamber and representatives.

CARPENTER:

Hold your tongue! we knew that long ago! Every honest citizen learns as much about the constitution as he needs.

JETTER:

Let him speak; one may always learn something.

SOEST:

He is quite right.

SEVERAL CITIZENS:

Go on! Go on! One does not hear this every day.

VANSEN:

You, citizens, forsooth! You live only in the present; and as you tamely follow the trade inherited from your fathers, so you let the government do with you just as it pleases. You make no inquiry into the origin, the history, or the rights of a Regent; and in consequence of this negligence, the Spaniard has drawn the net over your ears.

SOEST:

Who cares for that, if one only has daily bread?

JETTER:

The devil! Why did not some one come forward and tell us this in time?

VANSEN:

I tell it you now. The King of Spain, whose good fortune it is to bear sway over these provinces, has no right to govern them otherwise than the petty princes who formerly possessed them separately. Do you understand that?

JETTER:

Explain it to us.

VANSEN:

Why it is as clear as the sun. Must you not be governed according to your provincial laws? How comes that?

A CITIZEN:

Certainly!

VANSEN:

Has not the burgher of Brussels a different law from the burgher of Antwerp? The burgher of Antwerp from the burgher of Ghent? How comes that?

ANOTHER CITIZEN:

By heaven!

VANSEN:

But if you let matters run on thus they will soon tell you a different story. Fie on you! Philip, through a woman, now ventures to do what neither Charles the Bold, Frederick the Warrior, nor Charles the Fifth could accomplish.

SOEST:

Yes, yes! The old princes tried it also.

VANSEN:

Ay! but our ancestors kept a sharp lookout. If they thought themselves aggrieved by their sovereign, they would perhaps get his son and heir into their hands, detain him as a hostage, and surrender him only on the most favorable conditions. Our fathers were men! They knew their own interests! They knew how to lay hold on what they wanted, and to get it established! They were men of the right sort; and hence it is that our privileges are so clearly defined, our liberties so well secured.

SOEST:

What are you saying about our liberties?

ALL:

Our liberties, our privileges! Tell us about our privileges.

VANSEN:

All the provinces have their peculiar advantages, but we of Brabant are the most splendidly provided for. I have read it all.

SOEST:

Say on.

JETTER:

Let us hear.

A CITIZEN:

Pray do.

VANSEN:

First, it stands written:—The Duke of Brabant shall be to us a good and faithful sovereign.

SOEST:

Good! Stands it so?

JETTER:

Faithful? Is that true?

VANSEN:

As I tell you. He is bound to us as we are to him. Secondly: in the exercise of his authority he shall neither exert arbitrary power nor exhibit caprice himself, nor shall he, either directly or indirectly, sanction them in others.

JETTER:

Bravo! Bravo! Not exert arbitrary power.

SOEST:

Nor exhibit caprice.

ANOTHER:

And not sanction them in others! That is the main point. Not sanction them, either directly or indirectly.

VANSEN:

In express words.

JETTER:

Get us the book.

A CITIZEN:

Yes, we must see it.

OTHERS:

The book! The book!

ANOTHER:

We will to the Regent with the book.

ANOTHER:

Sir doctor, you shall be spokesman.

SOAP-BOILER:

Oh, the dolts!

OTHERS:

Something more out of the book!

SOAP-BOILER:

I'll knock his teeth down his throat if he says another word.

PEOPLE:

We'll see who dares to lay hands upon him. Tell us about our privileges! Have we any more privileges?

VANSEN:

Many, very good and very wholesome ones, too. Thus it stands: The sovereign shall neither benefit the clergy, nor increase their number without the consent of the nobles and of the states. Mark that! Nor shall he alter the constitution of the country.

SOEST:

Stands it so?

VANSEN:

I'll show it you, as it was written down two or three centuries ago.

A CITIZEN:

And we tolerate the new bishop? The nobles must protect us, we will make a row else!

OTHERS:

And we suffer ourselves to be intimidated by the Inquisition?

VANSEN:

It is your own fault.

PEOPLE:

We have Egmont! We have Orange! They will protect our interests.

VANSEN:

Your brothers in Flanders are beginning the good work.

SOAP-BOILER:

Dog! *(Strikes him.)*

OTHERS *oppose the* SOAP-BOILER, *and exclaim,* Are you also a Spaniard?

ANOTHER:

What! This honorable man?

ANOTHER:

This learned man?

(They attack the SOAP-BOILER.*)*

CARPENTER:

For heaven's sake, peace!

(Others mingle in the fray.)

CARPENTER:

Citizens, what means this?

(Boys whistle, throw stones, set on dogs; citizens stand and gape,

people come running up, others walk quietly to and fro, others play all sorts of pranks, shout and huzza.)

OTHERS:

Freedom and privilege! Privilege and freedom!

Enter EGMONT, *with followers.*

EGMONT:

Peace! Peace! good people. What is the matter? Peace, I say! Separate them.

CARPENTER:

My good lord, you come like an angel from heaven. Hush! See you nothing? Count Egmont! Honor to Count Egmont!

EGMONT:

Here, too! What are you about? Burgher against burgher! Does not even the neighborhood of our royal mistress oppose a barrier to this frenzy? Disperse yourselves, and go about your business. 'Tis a bad sign when you thus keep holiday on working days. How did the disturbance begin?

(The tumult gradually subsides, and the people gather around EGMONT.*)*

CARPENTER:

They are fighting about their privileges.

EGMONT:

Which they will forfeit through their own folly—and who are you? You seem honest people.

CARPENTER:

'Tis our wish to be so.

EGMONT:

Your calling?

CARPENTER:

A carpenter, and master of the guild.

EGMONT:

And you?

SOEST:

A shopkeeper.

EGMONT:

And you?

JETTER:

A tailor.

EGMONT:

I remember, you were employed upon the liveries of my people. Your name is Jetter.

JETTER:

To think of your grace remembering it!

EGMONT:

I do not easily forget any one whom I have seen or conversed with. Do what you can, good people, to keep the
peace; you stand in bad enough repute already. Provoke not
the king still farther. The power, after all, is in his hands. An
honest burgher, who maintains himself industriously, has
everywhere as much freedom as he needs.

CARPENTER:

To be sure; that is just our misfortune! With all due defer-
ence, your grace, 'tis the idle portion of the community,
your drunkards and vagabonds, who quarrel for want of
something to do, and clamor about privilege because they
are hungry; they impose upon the curious and the credulous,
and, in order to obtain a pot of beer, excite disturbances
that will bring misery upon thousands. That is just what
they want. We keep our houses and chests too well guarded;
they would fain drive us away from them with firebrands.

EGMONT:

You shall have all needful assistance; measures have been
taken to stem the evil by force. Make a firm stand against the
new doctrines, and do not imagine that privileges are secured
by sedition. Remain at home; suffer no crowds to assemble
in the streets. Sensible people can accomplish much. *(In the
meantime the crowd has for the most part dispersed.)*

CARPENTER:

Thanks, your excellency—thanks for your good opinion! We
will do what in us lies. *(Exit* EGMONT.*)* A gracious lord! A
true Netherlander! Nothing of the Spaniard about him.

JETTER:

If we had only him for a regent. 'Tis a pleasure to follow
him.

SOEST:

The king won't hear of that. He takes care to appoint his
own people to the place.

JETTER:

Did you notice his dress? It was of the newest fashion—after
the Spanish cut.

CARPENTER:

A handsome gentleman.

JETTER:

His head now were a dainty morsel for a headsman.

SOEST:

Are you mad? What are you thinking about?

JETTER:

It is stupid enough that such an idea should come into one's head! But so it is. Whenever I see a fine, long neck, I cannot help thinking how well it would suit the block. These cursed executions! One cannot get them out of one's head. When the lads are swimming, and I chance to see a naked back, I think forthwith of the dozens I have seen beaten with rods. If I meet a portly gentleman, I fancy I already see him being roasted at the stake. At night, in my dreams, I am tortured in every limb; one cannot have a single hour's enjoyment; all merriment and fun have long been forgotten. These terrible images seem burnt in upon my brain.

SCENE II. EGMONT's *residence.*

SECRETARY *(at a desk with papers. He rises impatiently)*

He is not yet here! And I have been waiting already full two hours, pen in hand, the paper before me; and just to-day I am anxious to be off early. The floor burns under my feet. I can with difficulty restrain my impatience. "Be punctual to the hour." Such was his parting injunction; now he comes not. There is so much business to get through, I shall not have finished before midnight. He overlooks one's faults, it is true; methinks it would be better, though, were he more strict, so he dismissed one at the appointed time. One could then arrange one's plans. It is now full two hours since he came away from the Regent; who knows whom he may have chanced to meet by the way?

Enter EGMONT.

EGMONT:

Well, how do matters look?

SECRETARY:

I am ready, and three couriers are waiting.

EGMONT:

I have detained you too long; you look somewhat out of humor.

SECRETARY:

In obedience to your command I have been in attendance for some time. Here are the papers.

EGMONT:

Donna Elvira will be angry with me when she learns that I have detained you.

SECRETARY:

You are pleased to jest.

EGMONT:

No, no. Be not ashamed. I admire your taste. She is pretty, and I have no objection that you should have a friend at the castle. What say the letters?

SECRETARY:

Much, my lord, but withal little that is satisfactory.

EGMONT:

'Tis well that we have pleasures at home; we have the less occasion to seek them from abroad. Is there much that requires attention?

SECRETARY:

Enough, my lord; three couriers are in attendance.

EGMONT:

Proceed! The most important.

SECRETARY:

All are important.

EGMONT:

One after the other; only be prompt.

SECRETARY:

Captain Breda sends an account of the occurrences that have further taken place in Ghent and the surrounding districts. The tumult is for the most part allayed.

EGMONT:

He doubtless reports individual acts of folly and temerity?

SECRETARY:

He does, my lord.

EGMONT:

Spare me the recital.

SECRETARY:

Six of the mob who tore down the image of the Virgin at Verviers have been arrested. He inquires whether they are to be hanged like the others.

EGMONT:

I am weary of hanging; let them be flogged and discharged.

207

SECRETARY:

There are two women; are they to be flogged also?

EGMONT:

He may admonish them and let them go.

SECRETARY:

Brink, of Breda's company, wants to marry; the captain hopes you will not allow it. There are so many women among the troops, he writes, that when on the march they resemble a gang of gypsies rather than regular soldiers.

EGMONT:

We must overlook it in his case. He is a fine young fellow, and moreover entreated me so earnestly before I came away. This must be the last time, however; though it grieves me to refuse the poor fellows their best pastime; they have enough without that to torment them.

SECRETARY:

Two of your people, Seter and Hart, have ill-treated a damsel, the daughter of an inn-keeper. They got her alone, and she could not escape from them.

EGMONT:

If she be an honest maiden, and they used violence, let them be flogged three days in succession; and if they have any property, let him retain as much as will portion the girl.

SECRETARY:

One of the foreign preachers has been discovered passing secretly through Comines. He swore that he was on the point of leaving for France. According to orders, he ought to be beheaded.

EGMONT:

Let him be conducted quietly to the frontier, and there admonished that the next time he will not escape so easily.

SECRETARY:

A letter from your steward. He writes that money comes in slowly; he can with difficulty send you the required sum within the week; the late disturbances have thrown everything into the greatest confusion.

EGMONT:

Money must be had! It is for him to look to the means.

SECRETARY:

He says he will do his utmost, and at length proposes to sue and imprison Raymond, who has been so long in your debt.

EGMONT:

But he has promised to pay!

SECRETARY:

The last time he fixed a fortnight himself.

EGMONT:

Well, grant him another fortnight; after that he may proceed against him.

SECRETARY:

You do well. His non-payment of the money proceeds not from inability, but from want of inclination. He will trifle no longer when he sees that you are in earnest. The steward further proposes to withhold, for half a month, the pensions which you allow to the old soldiers, widows, and others. In the meantime some expedient may be devised; they must make their arrangements accordingly.

EGMONT:

But what arrangements can be made here? These poor people want the money more than I. He must not think of it.

SECRETARY:

How then, my lord, is he to raise the required sum?

EGMONT:

It is his business to think of that. He was told so in a former letter.

SECRETARY:

And therefore he makes these proposals.

EGMONT:

They will never do;—he must think of something else. Let him suggest expedients that are admissible, and, above all, let him procure the money.

SECRETARY:

I have again before me the letter from Count Oliva. Pardon my recalling it to your remembrance. Above all others, the aged count deserves a detailed reply. You proposed writing to him with your own hand. Doubtless, he loves you as a father.

EGMONT:

I cannot command the time;—and of all detestable things, writing is to me the most detestable. You imitate my hand so admirably, do you write in my name. I am expecting Orange. I cannot do it;—I wish, however, that something soothing should be written to allay his fears.

SECRETARY:

Just give me a notion of what you wish to communicate; I will at once draw up the answer, and lay it before you. It shall be so written that it might pass for your hand in a court of justice.

EGMONT:

Give me the letter. *(After glancing over it.)* Good, honest, old man! Wert thou so cautious in thy own youth? Didst thou never mount a breach? Didst thou remain in the rear of battle at the suggestion of prudence?—What affectionate solicitude! He has, indeed, my safety and happiness at heart, but considers not that he who lives but to save his life is already dead.—Charge him not to be anxious on my account; I act as circumstances require, and shall be upon my guard. Let him use his influence at court in my favor, and be assured of my warmest thanks.

SECRETARY:

Is that all? He expects still more.

EGMONT:

What can I say? If you choose to write more fully, do so. The matter turns upon a single point; he would have me live as I cannot live. That I am joyous, live fast, take matters easily, is my good fortune; nor would I exchange it for the safety of a sepulchre. My blood rebels against the Spanish mode of life, nor have I the least inclination to regulate my movements by the new and cautious measures of the court. Do I live only to think of life? Am I to forego the enjoyment of the present moment in order to secure the next? And must that in its turn be consumed in anxieties and idle fears?

SECRETARY:

I entreat you, my lord, be not so harsh towards the venerable man. You are wont to be friendly towards every one. Say a kindly word to allay the anxiety of your noble friend. See how considerate he is, with what delicacy he warns you.

EGMONT:

Yet he harps continually on the same string. He knows of old how I detest these admonitions. They serve only to perplex and are of no avail. What if I were a somnambulist, and trod the giddy summit of a lofty house,—were it the part of friendship to call me by my name, to warn me of my danger, to waken, to kill me? Let each choose his own path, and provide for his own safety.

SECRETARY:

It may become you to be without a fear, but those who know and love you—

EGMONT *(looking over the letter)*:

Then he recalls the old story of our sayings and doings one evening in the wantonness of conviviality and wine; and what conclusions and inferences were thence drawn and circulated throughout the whole kingdom! Well, we had a cap and bells embroidered on the sleeves of our servants' liveries, and afterwards exchanged this senseless device for a bundle of arrows;—a still more dangerous symbol for those who are bent upon discovering a meaning where nothing is meant. These and similar follies were conceived and brought forth in a moment of merriment. It was at our suggestion that a noble troop, with beggars' wallets and a self-chosen nick-name, with mock humility recalled the king's duty to his remembrance. It was at our suggestion, too—well, what does it signify? Is a carnival jest to be construed into high treason? Are we to be grudged the scanty, variegated rags, wherewith a youthful spirit and heated imagination would adorn the poor nakedness of life? Take life too seriously, and what is it worth? If the morning wake us to no new joys, if in the evening we have no pleasures to hope for, is it worth the trouble of dressing and undressing? Does the sun shine on me to-day that I may reflect on what happened yesterday? That I may endeavor to foresee and control what can neither be foreseen nor controlled,—the destiny of the morrow? Spare me these reflections, we will leave them to scholars and courtiers. Let them ponder and contrive, creep hither and thither, and surreptitiously achieve their ends.— If you can make use of these suggestions, without swelling your letter into a volume, it is well. Everything appears of exaggerated importance to the good old man. 'Tis thus the friend, who has long held our hand, grasps it more warmly ere he quits his hold.

SECRETARY:

Pardon me, the pedestrian grows dizzy when he beholds the charioteer drive past with whirling speed.

Johann Wolfgang von Goethe

EGMONT:

Child! Child! Forbear! As if goaded by invisible spirits, the sun-steeds of time bear onward the light car of our destiny; and nothing remains for us, but with calm self-possession, firmly to grasp the reins, and now right, now left, to steer the wheels here from the precipice and there from the rock. Whither he is hasting, who knows? He hardly remembers whence he came?

SECRETARY:

My lord! my lord!

EGMONT:

I stand high, but I can and must rise yet higher. Courage, strength, and hope possess my soul. Not yet have I attained the height of my ambition; that once achieved, I want to stand firmly and without fear. Should I fall, should a thunder-clap, a storm-blast, ay, a false step of my own, precipitate me into the abyss, so be it! I shall lie there with thousands of others. I have never disdained, even for a trifling stake, to throw the bloody die with my gallant comrades; and shall I hesitate now, when all that is most precious in life is set upon the cast?

SECRETARY:

Oh, my lord! you know not what you say! May Heaven protect you!

EGMONT:

Collect your papers. Orange is coming. Despatch what is most urgent, that the couriers may set forth before the gates are closed. The rest may wait. Leave the Count's letter till to-morrow. Fail not to visit Elvira, and greet her from me. Inform yourself concerning the Regent's health. She cannot be well, though she would fain conceal it.

[*Exit* SECRETARY.

Enter ORANGE.

EGMONT:

Welcome, Orange; you appear somewhat disturbed.

ORANGE:

What say you to our conference with the Regent?

EGMONT:

I found nothing extraordinary in her manner of receiving us. I have often seen her thus before. She appeared to me to be somewhat indisposed.

ORANGE:

Marked you not that she was more reserved than usual? She began by cautiously approving our conduct during the late insurrection; glanced at the false light in which, nevertheless, it might be viewed; and finally turned the discourse to her favorite topic—that her gracious demeanor, her friendship for us Netherlanders, had never been sufficiently recognized, never appreciated as it deserved; that nothing came to a prosperous issue; that for her part she was beginning to grow weary of it; that the king must at last resolve upon other measures. Did you hear that?

EGMONT:

Not all; I was thinking at the time of something else. She is a woman, good Orange, and all women expect that every one shall submit passively to their gentle yoke; that every Hercules shall lay aside his lion's skin, assume the distaff, and swell their train; and, because they are themselves peaceably inclined, imagine, forsooth, that the ferment which seizes a nation, the storm which powerful rivals excite against one another, may be allayed by one soothing word, and the most discordant elements be brought to unite in tranquil harmony at their feet. 'Tis thus with her; and since she cannot accomplish her object, why she has no resource left but to lose her temper, to menace us with direful prospects for the future, and to threaten to take her departure.

ORANGE:

Think you not that this time she will fulfil her threat?

EGMONT:

Never! How often have I seen her actually prepared for the journey? Whither should she go? Being here a stadtholder, a queen, think you that she could endure to spend her days in insignificance at her brother's court, or to repair to Italy, and there drag on her existence among her old family connections?

ORANGE:

She is held incapable of this determination, because you have already seen her hesitate and draw back; nevertheless, it is in her to take this step; new circumstances may impel her to the long-delayed resolve. What if she were to depart, and the king to send another?

EGMONT:

Why, he would come, and he also would have business

enough upon his hands. He would arrive with vast projects and schemes to reduce all things to order, to subjugate, and combine; and to-day he would be occupied with this trifle, to-morrow with that, and the day following have to deal with some unexpected hindrance. He would spend one month in forming plans, another in mortification at their failure, and half a year would be consumed in cares for a single province. With him also time would pass, his head grow dizzy, and things hold on their ordinary course, till, instead of sailing into the open sea, according to the plan which he had previously marked out, he might thank God if, amid the tempest, he were able to keep his vessel off the rocks.

ORANGE:

What if the king were advised to try an experiment?

EGMONT:

Which should be—?

ORANGE:

To try how the body would get on without the head.

EGMONT:

What?

ORANGE:

Egmont, our interests have for years weighed upon my heart; I ever stand as over a chess-board, and regard no move of my adversary as insignificant; and as men of science carefully investigate the secrets of nature, so I hold it to be the duty, ay, the very vocation of a prince, to acquaint himself with the dispositions and intentions of all parties. I have reason to fear an outbreak. The king has long acted according to certain principles; he finds that they do not lead to a prosperous issue; what more probable than that he should seek it some other way?

EGMONT:

I do not believe it! When a man grows old, has attempted much, and finds that the world cannot be made to move according to his will, he must needs grow weary of it at last.

ORANGE:

One thing he has not yet attempted.

EGMONT:

What?

ORANGE:

To spare the people, and to put an end to the princes.

EGMONT:

How many have long been haunted by this dread? There is no cause for such anxiety.

ORANGE:

Once I felt anxious; gradually I became suspicious; suspicion has at length grown into certainty.

EGMONT:

Has the king more faithful servants than ourselves?

ORANGE:

We serve him after our own fashion; and, between ourselves, it must be confessed that we understand pretty well how to make the interests of the king square with our own.

EGMONT:

And who does not? He has our duty and submission in so far as they are his due.

ORANGE:

But what if he should arrogate still more, and regard as disloyalty what we esteem the maintenance of our just rights?

EGMONT:

We shall know in that case how to defend ourselves. Let him assemble the Knights of the Golden Fleece; we will submit ourselves to their decision.

ORANGE:

What if the sentence were to precede the trial? Punishment the sentence?

EGMONT:

It were an injustice of which Philip is incapable; a folly which I cannot impute either to him or to his counsellors.

ORANGE:

And what if they were both unjust and foolish?

EGMONT:

No, Orange, it is impossible. Who would venture to lay hands on us? The attempt to capture us were a vain and fruitless enterprise. No, they dare not raise the standard of tyranny so high. The breeze that should waft these tidings over the land would kindle a mighty conflagration. And what object would they have in view? The king alone has no power either to judge or to condemn us; and would they attempt our lives by assassination? They cannot intend it. A terrible league would unite the entire people. Direful hate and eternal separation from the crown of Spain would, on the instant, be forcibly declared.

ORANGE:

The flames would then rage over our grave, and the blood of our enemies flow, a vain oblation. Let us consider, Egmont.

EGMONT:

But how could they effect this purpose?

ORANGE:

Alva is on the way.

EGMONT:

I do not believe it.

ORANGE:

I know it.

EGMONT:

The Regent appeared to know nothing of it.

ORANGE:

And, therefore, the stronger is my conviction. The Regent will give place to him. I know his bloodthirsty disposition, and he brings an army with him.

EGMONT:

To harass the provinces anew? The people will be exasperated to the last degree.

ORANGE:

Their leaders will be secured.

EGMONT:

No! No!

ORANGE:

Let us retire, each to his province. There we can strengthen ourselves; the duke will not begin with open violence.

EGMONT:

Must we not greet him when he comes?

ORANGE:

We will delay.

EGMONT:

What if, on his arrival, he should summon us in the king's name?

ORANGE:

We will answer evasively.

EGMONT:

And if he is urgent?

ORANGE:

We will excuse ourselves.

EGMONT:

If he insist?

ORANGE:

We shall be the less disposed to come.

EGMONT:

Then war is declared; and we are rebels. Do not suffer prudence to mislead you, Orange. I know it is not fear that makes you yield. Consider this step.

ORANGE:

I have considered it.

EGMONT:

Consider for what you are answerable if you are wrong. For the most fatal war that ever yet desolated a country. Your refusal is the signal that at once summons the provinces to arms, that justifies every cruelty for which Spain has hitherto so anxiously sought a pretext. With a single nod you will excite to the direst confusion what, with patient effort, we have so long kept in abeyance. Think of the towns, the nobles, the people; think of commerce, agriculture, trade! Realize the murder, the desolation! Calmly the soldier beholds his comrade fall beside him in the battlefield. But towards you, carried down by the stream, will float the corpses of citizens, of children, of maidens, till aghast with horror, you shall no longer know whose cause you are defending, since you will see those for whose liberty you drew the sword perish around you. And what will be your emotions when conscience whispers, "It was for my own safety that I drew it?"

ORANGE:

We are not ordinary men, Egmont. If it becomes us to sacrifice ourselves for thousands, it becomes us no less to spare ourselves for thousands.

EGMONT:

He who spares himself becomes an object of suspicion even to himself.

ORANGE:

He who is sure of his own motives can with confidence advance or retreat.

EGMONT:

Your own act will render certain the evil that you dread.

ORANGE:

Wisdom and courage alike prompt us to meet an inevitable evil.

EGMONT:

When the danger is imminent the faintest hope should be taken into account.

ORANGE:

We have not the smallest footing left; we are on the very brink of the precipice.

EGMONT:

Is the king's favor on ground so narrow?

ORANGE:

Not narrow, perhaps, but slippery.

EGMONT:

By heavens! he is belied. I cannot endure that he should be so meanly thought of! He is Charles' son, and incapable of meanness.

ORANGE:

Kings of course do nothing mean.

EGMONT:

He should be better known.

ORANGE:

Our knowledge counsels us not to wait the result of a dangerous experiment.

EGMONT:

No experiment is dangerous the result of which we have the courage to meet.

ORANGE:

You are irritated, Egmont.

EGMONT:

I must see with my own eyes.

ORANGE:

Oh, that for once you saw with mine! My friend, because your eyes are open you imagine that you see. I go! Await Alva's arrival, and God be with you! My refusal to do so may perhaps save you. The dragon may deem the prey not worth seizing if he cannot swallow us both. Perhaps he may delay in order more surely to execute his purpose; in the meantime you may see matters in their true light. But, then, be prompt! Lose not a moment! Save,—oh, save yourself! Farewell!—Let nothing escape your vigilance:—how many troops he brings with him; how he garrisons the town; what force the Regent retains; how your friends are prepared. Send me tidings—Egmont—

EGMONT:

What would you?

ORANGE *(grasping his hand)*:

Be persuaded! Go with me!

EGMONT:

What? Tears, Orange?

ORANGE:

To weep for a lost friend is not unmanly.

EGMONT:

You deem me lost?

ORANGE:

You are lost! Consider! Only a brief respite is left you. Farewell.   [*Exit.*

EGMONT:

Strange that the thoughts of other men should exert such an influence over us. These fears would never have entered my mind; and this man infects me with his solicitude. Away! 'Tis a foreign drop in my blood! Kind nature cast it forth! And to erase the furrowed lines from my brow there yet remains, indeed, a friendly means.

ACT III

Scene I. *Palace of the Regent.*

REGENT:

I might have expected it. Ha! when we live immersed in anxiety and toil we imagine that we achieve the utmost that is possible; while he, who, from a distance, looks on and commands, believes that he requires only the possible. Oh, ye kings! I had not thought it could have galled me thus. It is so sweet to reign!—and to abdicate? I know not how my father could do so; but I will also.

MACHIAVEL *appears in the background.*

REGENT:

Approach, Machiavel. I am pondering over my brother's letter.

MACHIAVEL:

May I know what it contains?

REGENT:

As much tender consideration for me as anxiety for his states. He extols the firmness, the industry, the fidelity, with which I have hitherto watched over the interests of his majesty in these provinces. He condoles with me that the unbridled people occasion me so much trouble. He is so thoroughly convinced of the depth of my views, so extraordinarily satisfied with the prudence of my conduct, that I must almost say the letter is too politely written for a king —certainly for a brother.

MACHIAVEL:

It is not the first time that he has testified to you his just satisfaction.

REGENT:

But the first time that it is a mere rhetorical figure.

MACHIAVEL:

I do not understand you.

REGENT:

You soon will. For after this preamble he is of opinion that without soldiers, without a small army, indeed, I shall always cut a sorry figure here! We did wrong, he says, to withdraw our troops from the provinces at the remonstrance of the inhabitants; a garrison, he thinks, which shall press upon the neck of the burgher, will prevent him, by its weight, from making any lofty spring.

MACHIAVEL:

It would irritate the public mind to the last degree.

REGENT:

The king thinks, however, do you hear?—he thinks that a clever general, one who never listens to reason, will be able to deal promptly with all parties;—people and nobles, citizens and peasants; he therefore sends, with a powerful army, the Duke of Alva.

MACHIAVEL:

Alva?

REGENT:

You are surprised.

MACHIAVEL:

You say he sends, he asks, doubtless, whether he should send.

REGENT:

The king asks not, he sends.

MACHIAVEL:

You will then have an experienced warrior in your service.

REGENT:

In my service? Speak your mind, Machiavel.

MACHIAVEL:

I would not anticipate you.

REGENT:

And I would I could dissimulate. It wounds me—wounds me to the quick. I had rather my brother would speak his mind than attach his signature to formal epistles drawn up by a secretary of state.

Machiavel:

Can they not comprehend?

REGENT:

I know them both within and without. They would fain make a clean sweep; and since they cannot set about it themselves, they give their confidence to any one who comes with a besom in his hand. Oh, it seems to me as if I saw the king and his council worked upon this tapestry.

MACHIAVEL:

So distinctly!

REGENT:

No feature is wanting. There are good men among them.

The honest Roderigo, so experienced and so moderate, who does not aim too high, yet lets nothing sink too low; the upright Alonzo, the diligent Freneda, the steadfast Las Vargas, and others who join them when the good party are in power. But there sits the hollow-eyed Toledan, with brazen front and deep fire-glance, muttering between his teeth about womanish softness, ill-timed concession, and that women can ride trained steeds well enough, but are themselves bad masters of the horse, and the like pleasantries, which in former times I have been compelled to hear from political gentlemen.

MACHIAVEL:

You have chosen good colors for your picture.

REGENT:

Confess, Machiavel, among the tints from which I might select, there is no hue so livid, so jaundicelike as Alva's complexion, and the color he is wont to paint with. He regards every one as a blasphemer or traitor; for under this head they can all be racked, impaled, quartered, and burnt at pleasure. The good I have accomplished here appears as nothing seen from a distance, just because it is good. Then he dwells on every outbreak that is past, recalls every disturbance that is quieted, and brings before the king such a picture of mutiny, sedition, and audacity, that we appear to him to be actually devouring one another, when with us the transient explosion of a rude people has been long forgotten. Thus he conceives a cordial hatred for the poor people; he views them with horror, as beasts and monsters; looks around for fire and sword, and imagines that by such means human beings are subdued.

MACHIAVEL:

You appear to me too vehement; you take the matter too seriously. Do you not remain Regent?

REGENT:

I am aware of that. He will bring his instructions. I am old enough in state affairs to understand how people can be supplanted without being actually deprived of office. First, he will produce a commission couched in terms somewhat obscure and equivocal; he will stretch his authority, for the power is in his hands; if I complain, he will hint at secret instructions; if I desire to see them, he will answer evasively;

if I insist, he will produce a paper of totally different import; and if this fail to satisfy me, he will go on precisely as if I had never interfered. Meanwhile he will have accomplished what I dread, and will have frustrated my most cherished schemes.

MACHIAVEL:

I wish I could contradict you.

REGENT:

His harshness and cruelty will again arouse the turbulent spirit, which, with unspeakable patience, I have succeeded in quelling; I shall see my work destroyed before my eyes, and have besides to bear the blame of his wrong-doing.

MACHIAVEL:

Await it, your highness.

REGENT:

I have sufficient self-command to remain quiet. Let him come; I will make way for him with the best grace ere he pushes me aside.

MACHIAVEL:

So important a step thus suddenly?

REGENT:

'Tis harder than you imagine. He who is accustomed to rule, to hold daily in his hand the destiny of thousands, descends from the throne as into the grave. Better thus, however, than linger a spectre among the living, and with hollow aspect endeavor to maintain a place which another has inherited, and already possesses and enjoys.

SCENE II. CLARA's *dwelling.*

MOTHER:

Such a love as Brackenburg's I have never seen! I thought it was to be found only in romance books.

CLARA (*walking up and down the room, humming a song*):

           With love's thrilling rapture
           What joy can compare!

MOTHER:

He suspects thy intercourse with Egmont; and yet, if thou wouldst but treat him somewhat kindly, I do believe he would marry thee still, if thou wouldst have him.

CLARA *(sings)*:

> Blissful
> And tearful,
> With thought-teeming brain;
> Hoping
> And fearing
> In wavering pain;
> Now shouting in triumph,
> Now sunk in despair;—
> With love's thrilling rapture
> What joy can compare!

MOTHER:
Have done with such baby nonsense!

CLARA:
Nay, do not abuse it; 'tis a song of marvellous virtue. Many a time have I lulled a grown child to sleep with it.

MOTHER:
Ay! Thou canst think of nothing but thy love. If only it did not put everything else out of thy head. Thou shouldst have more regard for Brackenburg, I tell thee. He may make thee happy yet some day.

CLARA:
He?

MOTHER:
Oh, yes! A time will come! You children live only in the present, and give no ear to our experience. Youth and happy love, all has an end; and there comes a time when one thanks God if one has any corner to creep into.

CLARA *(shudders, and after a pause starts up)*:
Mother, let that time come—like death. To think of it beforehand is horrible! And if it come! If we must—then—we will bear ourselves as we may. Live without thee, Egmont! *(Weeping.)* No! It is impossible.

Enter EGMONT *(enveloped in a horseman's cloak, his hat drawn over his face).*

EGMONT:
Clara!

CLARA *(utters a cry and starts back)*:
Egmont! *(She hastens towards him.)* Egmont! *(She embraces and leans upon him.)* O thou good, kind, sweet Egmont! Art thou come? Art thou here, indeed!

EGMONT:

Good evening, mother.

MOTHER:

God save you, noble sir! My daughter has well-nigh pined to death because you have stayed away so long; she talks and sings about you the livelong day.

EGMONT:

You will give me some supper?

MOTHER:

You do us too much honor. If we only had anything——

CLARA:

Certainly! Be quiet, mother! I have provided everything; there is something prepared. Do not betray me, mother.

MOTHER:

There's little enough.

CLARA:

Never mind! And then I think when he is with me I am never hungry; so he cannot, I should think, have any great appetite when I am with him.

EGMONT:

Do you think so? *(Clara stamps her foot and turns pettishly away.)* What ails you?

CLARA:

How cold you are today! You have not yet offered me a kiss. Why do you keep your arms enveloped in your mantle, like a new-born babe? It becomes neither a soldier nor a lover to keep his arms muffled up.

EGMONT:

Sometimes, dearest, sometimes. When the soldier stands in ambush and would delude the foe, he collects his thoughts, gathers his mantle around him, and matures his plan; and a lover——

MOTHER:

Will you not take a seat and make yourself comfortable? I must to the kitchen. Clara thinks of nothing when you are here. You must put up with what we have.

EGMONT:

Your good-will is the best seasoning.

[*Exit* MOTHER.

CLARA:

And what then is my love?

225

EGMONT:

Just what thou wilt.

CLARA:

Liken it to anything, if you have a heart.

EGMONT:

But first. *(He flings aside his mantle, and appears arrayed in a magnificent dress.)*

CLARA:

Oh, heavens!

EGMONT:

Now my arms are free! *(Embraces her.)*

CLARA:

Don't! You will spoil your dress. *(She steps back.)* How magnificent! I dare not touch you.

EGMONT:

Art thou satisfied! I promised to come once arrayed in Spanish fashion.

CLARA:

I had ceased to remind you of it; I thought you did not like it—ah, and the Golden Fleece!

EGMONT:

Thou seest it now.

CLARA:

And did the emperor really hang it round thy neck!

EGMONT:

He did, my child! And this chain and Order invest the wearer with the noblest privileges. On earth I acknowledge no judge over my actions, except the grand master of the Order, with the assembled chapter of knights.

CLARA:

Oh, thou mightest let the whole world sit in judgment over thee. The velvet is too splendid! and the braiding! and the embroidery! One knows not where to begin.

EGMONT:

There, look thy fill.

CLARA:

And the Golden Fleece! You told me its history, and said it is the symbol of everything great and precious, of everything that can be merited and won by diligence and toil. It is very precious—I may liken it to thy love;—even so I wear it next my heart;—and then—

EGMONT:

What wilt thou say?

CLARA:

And then again it is not like.

EGMONT:

How so?

CLARA:

I have not won it by diligence and toil, I have not deserved it.

EGMONT:

It is otherwise in love. Thou dost deserve it because thou hast not sought it—and, for the most part, those only obtain who seek it not.

CLARA:

Is it from thine own experience that thou hast learned this? Didst thou make that proud remark in reference to thyself? Thou, whom all the people love?

EGMONT:

Would that I had done something for them! That I could do anything for them! It is their own good pleasure to love.

CLARA:

Thou hast doubtless been with the Regent today?

EGMONT:

I have.

CLARA:

Art thou upon good terms with her?

EGMONT:

So it would appear. We are kind and serviceable to each other.

CLARA:

And in thy heart?

EGMONT:

I like her. True, we have each our own views; but that is nothing to the purpose. She is an excellent woman, knows with whom she has to deal, and would be penetrating enough were she not quite so suspicious. I give her plenty of employment, because she is always suspecting some secret motive in my conduct when, in fact, I have none.

CLARA:

Really none?

EGMONT:

Well, with one little exception, perhaps. All wine deposits lees in the cask in the course of time. Orange furnishes her still better entertainment, and is a perpetual riddle. He has got the credit of harboring some secret design; and she studies his brow to discover his thoughts, and his steps, to learn in what direction they are bent.

CLARA:

Does she dissemble?

EGMONT:

She is Regent—and do you ask?

CLARA:

Pardon me; I meant to say, is she false?

EGMONT:

Neither more nor less than every one who has his own objects to attain.

CLARA:

I should never feel at home in the world. But she has a masculine spirit, and is another sort of woman than we housewives and seamstresses. She is great, steadfast, resolute.

EGMONT:

Yes, when matters are not too much involved. For once, however, she is a little disconcerted.

CLARA:

How is that?

EGMONT:

She has a moustache, too, on her upper lip, and occasionally an attack of the gout. A regular Amazon.

CLARA:

A majestic woman! I should dread to appear before her.

EGMONT:

Yet thou art not wont to be timid! It would not be fear, only maidenly bashfulness.

(CLARA *casts down her eyes, takes his hand, and leans upon him.*)

EGMONT:

I understand thee, dearest! Thou mayest raise thine eyes.

(He kisses her eyes.)

CLARA:

Let me be silent! Let me embrace thee! Let me look into thine eyes, and find there everything—hope and comfort, joy and sorrow! *(She embraces and gazes on him.)* Tell me!

Oh, tell me! It seems so strange—art thou, indeed, Egmont! Count Egmont! The great Egmont, who makes so much noise in the world, who figures in the newspapers, who is the support and stay of the provinces?

EGMONT:

No, Clara, I am not he.

CLARA:

How?

EGMONT:

Seest thou, Clara! Let me sit down! *(He seats himself, she kneels on a footstool before him, rests her arms on his knees, and looks up in his face.)* That Egmont is a morose, cold, unbending Egmont, obliged to be upon his guard, to assume now this appearance and now that; harassed, misapprehended and perplexed, when the crowd esteem him light-hearted and gay; beloved by a people who do not know their own mind; honored and extolled by the intractable multitude; surrounded by friends in whom he dares not confide; observed by men who are on the watch to supplant him; toiling and striving, often without an object, generally without a reward. O let me conceal how it fares with him, let me not speak of his feelings! But this Egmont, Clara, is calm, unreserved, happy, beloved and known by the best of hearts, which is also thoroughly known to him, and which he presses to his own with unbounded confidence and love. *(He embraces her.)* This is thy Egmont.

CLARA:

So let me die! The world has no joy after this!

ACT IV

SCENE I. *A Street.*

JETTER:
Hist! neighbor,—a word!

CARPENTER:
Go your way and be quiet

JETTER:
Only one word. Is there nothing new?

CARPENTER:
Nothing, except that we are anew forbidden to speak.

JETTER:
How?

CARPENTER:
Step here, close to this house. Take heed! Immediately on his arrival, the Duke of Alva published a decree, by which two or three, found conversing together in the streets, are, without trial, declared guilty of high treason.

JETTER:
Alas!

CARPENTER:
To speak of state affairs is prohibited on pain of perpetual imprisonment.

JETTER:
Alas for our liberty!

CARPENTER:
And no one, on pain of death, shall censure the measures of government.

JETTER:
Alas for our heads!

CARPENTER:
And fathers, mothers, children, kindred, friends, and servants are invited, by the promise of large rewards, to disclose what passes in the privacy of our homes, before an expressly appointed tribunal.

JETTER:
Let us go home.

CARPENTER:
And the obedient are promised that they shall suffer no injury either in person or estate.

JETTER:

How gracious!—I felt ill at ease the moment the duke entered the town. Since then it has seemed to me as though the heavens were covered with black crape, which hangs so low that one must stoop down to avoid knocking one's head against it.

CARPENTER:

And how do you like his soldiers? They are a different sort of crabs from those we have been used to.

JETTER:

Faugh! It gives one the cramp at one's heart to see such a troop march down the street. As straight as tapers, with fixed look, only one step, however many there may be; and when they stand sentinel, and you pass one of them, it seems as though he would look you through and through; and he looks so stiff and morose that you fancy you see a task-master at every corner. They offend my sight. Our militia were merry fellows; they took liberties, stood their legs astride, their hats over their ears, they lived and let live! These fellows are like machines with a devil inside them.

CARPENTER:

Were sure an one to cry "Halt!" and to level his musket, think you one would stand?

JETTER:

I should fall dead upon the spot.

CARPENTER:

Let us go home!

JETTER:

No good can come of it. Farewell.

Enter SOEST.

SOEST:

Friends! Neighbors!

CARPENTER:

Hush! Let us go.

SOEST:

Have you heard?

JETTER:

Only too much!

SOEST:

The Regent is gone.

231

JETTER:

Then Heaven help us.

CARPENTER:

She was some stay to us.

SOEST:

Her departure was sudden and secret. She could not agree with the duke; she has sent word to the nobles that she intends to return. No one believes it, however.

CARPENTER:

God pardon the nobles for letting this new yoke be laid upon our necks. They might have prevented it. Our privileges are gone.

JETTER:

For Heaven's sake not a word about privileges. I already scent an execution; the sun will not come forth; the fogs are rank.

SOEST:

Orange, too, is gone.

CARPENTER:

Then we are quite deserted.

SOEST:

Count Egmont is still here.

JETTER:

God be thanked! Strengthen him, all ye saints, to do his utmost; he is the only man who can help us.

Enter VANSEN.

VANSEN:

Have I at length found a few, brave citizens who have not crept out of sight?

JETTER:

Do us the favor to pass on.

VANSEN:

You are not civil.

JETTER:

This is no time for compliments. Does your back itch again? Are your wounds already healed?

VANSEN:

Ask a soldier about his wounds! Had I cared for blows, nothing good would have come of me.

JETTER:

Matters may grow more serious.

VANSEN:

You feel from the gathering storm a pitiful weakness in your limbs it seems.

CARPENTER:

Your limbs will soon be in motion elsewhere if you do not keep quiet.

VANSEN:

Poor mice! The master of the house procures a new cat, and ye are straight in despair! The difference is very trifling; we shall get on as we did before, only be quiet.

CARPENTER:

You are an insolent knave.

VANSEN:

Gossip! Let the duke alone. The old cat looks as though he had swallowed devils instead of mice, and could not now digest them. Let him alone, I say; he must eat, drink, and sleep like other men. I am not afraid if we only watch our opportunity. At first he makes quick work of it; by-and-by, however, he too will find that it is pleasanter to live in the larder, among flitches of bacon, and to rest by night, than to entrap a few solitary mice in the granary. Go to! I know the stadtholders.

CARPENTER:

What such a fellow can say with impunity! Had I said such a thing I should not hold myself safe a moment.

VANSEN:

Do not make yourselves uneasy! God in heaven does not trouble himself about you poor worms, much less the Regent.

JETTER:

Slanderer!

VANSEN:

I know some for whom it would be better if, instead of their own high spirits, they had a little tailor's blood in their veins.

CARPENTER:

What means you by that?

VANSEN:

Hum! I mean the count.

JETTER:

Egmont! What has he to fear?

Johann Wolfgang von Goethe

VANSEN:

> I'm a poor devil, and could live a whole year round on what he loses in a single night; yet he would do well to give me his revenue for a twelvemonth, to have my head upon his shoulders for one quarter of an hour.

JETTER:

> You think yourself very clever; yet there is more sense in the hairs of Egmont's head than in your brains.

VANSEN:

> Perhaps so! Not more shrewdness, however. These gentry are the most apt to deceive themselves. He should be more chary of his confidence.

JETTER:

> How his tongue wags! Such a gentleman!

VANSEN:

> Just because he is not a tailor.

JETTER:

> You audacious scoundrel!

VANSEN:

> I only wish he had your courage in his limbs for an hour to make him uneasy, and plague and torment him till he were compelled to leave the town.

JETTER:

> What nonsense you talk; why he's as safe as a star in heaven.

VANSEN:

> Have you ever seen one snuff itself out? Off it went!

CARPENTER:

> Who would dare to meddle with him?

VANSEN:

> Will you interfere to prevent it? Will you stir up an insurrection if he is arrested?

JETTER:

> Ah!

VANSEN:

> Will you risk your ribs for his sake?

SOEST:

> Eh!

VANSEN (*mimicking them*):

> Eh! Oh! Ah! Run through the alphabet in your wonderment. So it is, and so it will remain. Heaven help him!

JETTER:

Confound your impudence. Can such a noble, upright man have anything to fear?

VANSEN:

In this world the rogue has everywhere the advantage. At the bar, he makes a fool of the judge; on the bench, he takes pleasure in convicting the accused. I have had to copy out a protocol, where the commissary was handsomely rewarded by the court, both with praise and money, because, through his cross-examination, an honest devil, against whom they had a grudge, was made out to be a rogue.

CARPENTER:

Why, that again is a downright lie. What can they want to get out of a man if he is innocent?

VANSEN:

Oh, you blockhead! When nothing can be worked out of a man by cross-examination they work it into him. Honesty is rash and withal somewhat presumptuous; at first they question quietly enough, and the prisoner, proud of his innocence, as they call it, comes out with much that a sensible man would keep back; then, from these answers the inquisitor proceeds to put new questions, and is on the watch for the slightest contradictions; there he fastens his line; and, let the poor devil lose his self-possession, say too much here or too little there, or, Heaven knows from what whim or other, let him withhold some trifling circumstance, or at any moment give way to fear—then we're on the right track, and I assure you no beggar-woman seeks for rags among the rubbish with more care than such a fabricator of rogues, from trifling, crooked, disjointed, misplaced, misprinted, and concealed facts and information, acknowledged or denied, endeavors at length to patch up a scare-crow, by means of which he may at least hang his victim in effigy: and the poor devil may thank Heaven if he is in a condition to see himself hanged.

JETTER:

He has a ready tongue of his own.

CARPENTER:

This may serve well enough with flies. Wasps laugh at your cunning web.

235

VANSEN:

According to the kind of spider. The tall duke, now, has just the look of your garden-spider; not the large-bellied kind—they are less dangerous; but your long-footed, meagre-bodied gentleman, that does not fatten on his diet, and whose threads are slender, indeed, but not the less tenacious.

JETTER:

Egmont is knight of the Golden Fleece; who dares lay hands on him? He can be tried only by his peers, by the assembled knights of his Order. Your own foul tongue and evil conscience betray you into this nonsense.

VANSEN:

Think you that I wish him ill? I like it well enough. He is an excellent gentleman. He once let off with a sound drubbing some good friends of mine who would else have been hanged. Now take yourselves off! begone, I advise you! Yonder I see the patrol again commencing their round. They do not look as if they would be willing to fraternize with us over a glass. We must wait, and bide our time. I have a couple of nieces and a tapster; if after enjoying themselves in their company, they are not tamed, they are regular wolves.

SCENE II. *The Palace of Eulenberg, Residence of the* DUKE OF ALVA.

SILVA *(meeting* GOMEZ*)*:

Have you executed the duke's commands?

GOMEZ:

Punctually. All the day-patrols have received orders to assemble at the appointed time, at the various points that I have indicated. Meanwhile, they march as usual through the town to maintain order. Each is ignorant respecting the movements of the rest, and imagines the command to have reference to him alone; thus in a moment the cordon can be formed, and all the avenues to the palace occupied. Know you the reason of this command?

SILVA:

I am accustomed blindly to obey; and to whom can one more easily render obedience than to the duke, since the event always proves the wisdom of his commands?

GOMEZ:

Well! Well! I am not surprised that you are become as reserved and monosyllabic as the duke, since you are obliged to be always about his person; to me, however who am accustomed to the lighter service of Italy, it seems strange enough. In loyalty and obedience, I am the same old sailor as ever; but I am wont to indulge in gossip and discussion; here you are all silent, and seem as though you knew not how to enjoy yourselves. The duke, methinks, is like a brazen tower without gates, the garrison of which must be furnished with wings. Not long ago I heard him say at the table of a gay, jovial fellow that he was like a bad spirit-shop, with a brandy sign displayed, to allure idlers, vagabonds, and thieves.

SILVA:

And has he not brought us hither in silence?

GOMEZ:

Nothing can be said against that. Of a truth, we, who witnessed the address with which he led the troops hither out of Italy, have seen something. How he advanced warily through friends and foes; through the French, both royalists and heretics; through the Swiss and their confederates; maintained the strictest discipline, and accomplished with ease, and without the slightest hindrance, a march that was esteemed so perilous!—We have seen and learned something.

SILVA:

Here, too! Is not everything as still and quiet as though there had been no disturbance?

GOMEZ:

Why, as for that, it was tolerably quiet when we arrived.

SILVA:

The provinces have become much more tranquil; if there is any movement now it is only among those who wish to escape; and to them, methinks, the duke will speedily close every outlet.

GOMEZ:

This service cannot fail to win for him the favor of the king.

SILVA:

And nothing is more expedient for us than to retain his. Should the king come hither, the duke doubtless and all whom he recommends will not go without their reward.

GOMEZ:

Do you really believe then that the king will come?

SILVA:

So many preparations are made that the report appears highly probable.

GOMEZ:

I am not convinced, however.

SILVA:

Keep your thoughts to yourself then. For if it should not be the king's intention to come it is at least certain that he wishes the rumor to be believed.

Enter FERDINAND.

FERDINAND:

Is my father not yet abroad?

SILVA:

We are waiting to receive his commands.

FERDINAND:

The princes will soon be here.

GOMEZ:

Are they expected today?

FERDINAND:

Orange and Egmont.

GOMEZ *(aside to* SILVA):

A light breaks in upon me.

SILVA:

Well, then, say nothing about it.

Enter the DUKE OF ALVA *(as he advances the rest draw back).*

ALVA:

Gomez.

GOMEZ *(steps forward)*:

My lord.

ALVA:

You have distributed the guards and given them your instructions?

GOMEZ:

Most accurately. The day-patrols——

ALVA:

Enough. Attend to the gallery. Silva will announce to you the moment when you are to draw them together, and to occupy the avenues leading to the palace. The rest you know.

GOMEZ:

I do, my lord.   [*Exit.*

ALVA:

Silva.

SILVA:

Here, my lord.

ALVA:

I shall require you to manifest today all the qualities I have hitherto prized in you: courage, resolve, unswerving execution.

SILVA:

I thank you for the opportunity of showing that your old servant is unchanged.

ALVA:

The moment the princes enter my cabinet hasten to arrest Egmont's private secretary. You have made all needful preparations for securing the others who are specified?

SILVA:

Rely upon us. Their doom, like a well-calculated eclipse, will overtake them with terrible certainty.

ALVA:

Have you had them all narrowly watched?

SILVA:

All. Egmont especially. He is the only one whose demeanor since your arrival remains unchanged. The livelong day he is now on one horse and now on another; he invites guests as usual, is merry and entertaining at table, plays at dice, shoots, and at night steals to his mistress. The others, on the contrary, have made a manifest pause in their mode of life; they remain at home, and, from the outward aspect of their houses, you would imagine that there was a sick man within.

ALVA:

To work then ere they recover in spite of us.

SILVA:

I shall bring them without fail. In obedience to your commands we load them with officious honors; they are

239

alarmed; cautiously, yet anxiously they tender their thanks, feel that flight would be the most prudent course, yet none venture to adopt it; they hesitate, are unable to work together, while the bond which unites them prevents their acting boldly as individuals. They are anxious to withdraw themselves from suspicion, and thus only render themselves more obnoxious to it. I already contemplate with joy the successful realization of your scheme.

ALVA:

I rejoice only over what is accomplished, and not easily over that; for there ever remains ground for serious and anxious thought. Fortune is capricious; the common, the worthless, she oft-times ennobles, while she dishonors with a contemptible issue the most maturely-considered schemes. Await the arrival of the princes, then order Gomez to occupy the streets, and hasten yourself to arrest Egmont's secretary, and the others who are specified. This done, return, and announce to my son that he may bring me the tidings of the council.

SILVA:

I trust this evening I shall dare to appear in your presence. (ALVA *approaches his son, who has hitherto been standing in the gallery.*) I dare not whisper it even to myself my mind misgives me. The event will, I fear, be different from what he anticipates. I see before me spirits who, still and thoughtful, weigh in ebon scales the doom of princes and of many thousands. Slowly the beam moves up and down; deeply the judges appear to ponder; at length one scale sinks, the other rises, breathed on by the caprice of destiny, and all is decided.   [*Exit.*

ALVA (*advancing with his son*):
How did you find the town?

FERDINAND:

All is quiet again. I rode, as for pastime, from street to street. Your well-distributed patrols hold Fear so tightly yoked that she does not venture even to whisper. The town resembles a plain when the lightning's glare announces the impending storm: no bird, no beast is to be seen, that is not stealing to a place of shelter.

ALVA:

Has nothing further occurred?

240

FERDINAND:

Egmont, with a few companions, rode into the market-place; we exchanged greetings; he was mounted on an un-broken charger, which excited my admiration. "Let us hasten to break in our steeds," he exclaimed; "we shall need them ere long!" He said that he should see me again today; he is coming here at your desire to deliberate with you.

ALVA:

He will see you again.

FERDINAND:

Among all the knights whom I know here he pleases me the best. I think we shall be friends.

ALVA:

You are always rash and inconsiderate. I recognize in you your mother's levity, which threw her unconditionally into my arms. Appearances have already allured you precipitate-ly into many dangerous connections.

FERDINAND:

You will find me ever submissive.

ALVA:

I pardon this inconsiderate kindness, this heedless gaiety, in consideration of your youthful blood. Only forget not on what mission I am sent, and what part in it I would as-sign to you.

FERDINAND:

Admonish me, and spare me not, when you deem it needful.

ALVA *(after a pause)*:

My son!

FERDINAND:

Father!

ALVA:

The princes will be here anon; Orange and Egmont. It is not mistrust that has withheld me till now from disclosing to you what is about to take place. They will not depart hence.

FERDINAND:

What do you purpose?

ALVA:

It has been resolved to arrest them. You are astonished! Learn what you have to do; the reasons you shall know when all is accomplished. Time fails now to unfold them.

With you alone I wish to deliberate on the weightiest, the most secret matters; a powerful bond holds us linked together; you are dear and precious to me; on you I would bestow everything. Not the habit of obedience alone would I impress upon you; I desire also to implant within your mind the power to realize, to command, to execute; to you I would bequeath a vast inheritance, to the king a most useful servant; I would endow you with the noblest of my possessions, that you may not be ashamed to appear among your brethren.

FERDINAND:

How deeply I am indebted to you for this love, which you manifest for me alone, while a whole kingdom stands in fear of you!

ALVA:

Now hear what is to be done. As soon as the princes have entered every avenue to the palace will be guarded. This duty is confided to Gomez. Silva will hasten to arrest Egmont's secretary, together with those whom we hold most in suspicion. You, meanwhile, will take the command of the guards stationed at the gates and in the courts. Above all, take care to occupy the adjoining apartment with the trustiest soldiers. Wait in the gallery till Silva returns, then bring me any unimportant paper, as a signal that his commission is executed. Remain in the antechamber till Orange retires; follow him; I will detain Egmont here as though I had some further communication to make to him. At the end of the gallery demand Orange's sword, summon the guards, secure promptly the most dangerous man; I meanwhile will seize Egmont here.

FERDINAND:

I obey, my father—for the first time with a heavy and an anxious heart.

ALVA:

I pardon you; this is the first great day of your life.

Enter SILVA.

SILVA:

A courier from Antwerp. Here is Orange's letter. He is not coming.

ALVA:

Says the messenger so?

SILVA:

No, my own heart tells me.

ALVA:

In thee speaks my evil genius. *(After reading the letter he makes a sign to the two, and they retire to the gallery.* ALVA *remains alone in front of the stage.)* He comes not! Till the last moment he delays declaring himself. He dares not to come! So, then, the cautious man, contrary to all expectation, is for once cautious enough to lay aside his wonted caution. The hour moves on. Let the hand travel but a short space over the dial, and a great work is done or lost—irrevocably lost; for the opportunity can never be retrieved, nor can our intention remain concealed. Long had I maturely weighed everything, foreseen even this contingency, and firmly resolved in my own mind what in that case was to be done; and now, when I am called upon to act, I can with difficulty guard my mind from being again distracted by conflicting doubts. Is it expedient to seize the others if he escape me? Shall I delay, and suffer Egmont to elude my grasp, together with his friends, and so many others who now, and perhaps for today only, are in my hands? Thus destiny controls even thee—the uncontrollable! How long matured! How well prepared! How great, how admirable the plan! How nearly had hope attained the goal! And now, at the decisive moment, thou art placed between two evils; as into a lottery thou dost grasp into the dark future; what thou hast drawn remains still unrolled, to thee unknown whether it is a prize or a blank! *(He becomes attentive, like one who hears a noise, and steps to the window.)* 'Tis he! Egmont! Did thy steed bear thee hither so lightly, and started not at the scent of blood, at the spirit with the naked sword who received thee at the gate? Dismount! Lo, now thou hast one foot in the grave! And now both! Aye, caress him, and for the last time stroke his neck for the gallant service he has rendered thee. And for me no choice is left. The delusion in which Egmont ventures here today cannot a second time deliver him into my hands! Hark! *(*FERDINAND *and* SILVA *enter hastily.)* Obey my orders. I swerve not from my purpose. I shall detain Egmont here as best I may till you bring me tidings from Silva. Then remain at hand. Thee, too, fate has robbed of the

proud honor of arresting with thine own hand the king's
greatest enemy.

(To SILVA*):*
Be prompt!

(To FERDINAND*):*
Advance to meet him.

*(*ALVA *remains some moments alone, pacing the chamber in
silence.)*

Enter EGMONT.

EGMONT:
I come to learn the king's commands; to hear what service
he demands from our loyalty, which remains eternally devoted to him.

ALVA:
He desires above all to hear your counsel.

EGMONT:
Upon what subject? Does Orange come also? I thought I
should find him here.

ALVA:
I regret that he fails us at this important crisis. The king desires your counsel, your opinion as to the best means of tran-
quillizing these states. He trusts, indeed, that you will zealously co-operate with him in quelling these disturbances,
and in securing to these provinces the benefit of complete
and permanent order.

EGMONT:
You, my lord, should know better than I that tranquillity is
already sufficiently restored, and was still more so till the
appearance of fresh troops again agitated the public mind,
and filled it anew with anxiety and alarm.

ALVA:
You seem to intimate that it would have been more advisable
if the king had not placed me in a position to interrogate you.

EGMONT:
Pardon me! It is not for me to determine whether the king
acted advisedly in sending the army hither, whether the
might of his royal presence alone would not have operated
more powerfully. The army is here, the king is not. But we
should be most ungrateful were we to forget what we owe
to the Regent. Let it be acknowledged! By her prudence and
valor, by her judicious use of authority and force, of persua-

sion and finesse, she pacified the insurgents, and, to the astonishment of the world, succeeded, in the course of a few months, in bringing a rebellious people back to their duty.

ALVA:

I deny it not. The insurrection is quelled; and the people appear to be already forced back within the bounds of obedience. But does it not depend upon their caprice alone to overstep these bounds? Who shall prevent them from again breaking loose? Where is the power capable of restraining them? Who will be answerable to us for their future loyalty and submission? Their own good-will is the sole pledge we have.

EGMONT:

And is not the good-will of a people the surest, the noblest pledge? By heaven! when can a monarch hold himself more secure, ay, against both foreign and domestic foes, than when all can stand for one, and one for all?

ALVA:

You would not have us believe, however, that such is the case here at present?

EGMONT:

Let the king proclaim a general pardon; he will thus tranquillize the public mind; and it will be seen how speedily loyalty and affection will return when confidence is restored.

ALVA:

How! And suffer those who have insulted the majesty of the king, who have violated the sanctuaries of our religion, to go abroad unchallenged! living witnesses that enormous crimes may be perpetrated with impunity!

EGMONT:

And ought not a crime of frenzy, of intoxication, to be excused rather than cruelly chastised? Especially when there is the sure hope, nay, more, where there is positive certainty, that the evil will never again recur? Would not sovereigns thus be more secure? Are not those monarchs most extolled by the world and by posterity who can pardon, pity, despise an offence against their dignity? Are they not on that account likened to God himself, who is far too exalted to be assailed by every idle blasphemy?

ALVA:

And, therefore, should the king contend for the honor of

God and of religion, we for the authority of the king. What the supreme power disdains to avert, it is our duty to avenge. Were I to counsel, no guilty person should live to rejoice in his impunity.

EGMONT:

Think you that you will be able to reach them all? Do we not daily hear that fear is driving them to and fro, and forcing them out of the land? The more wealthy will escape to other countries with their property, their children, and their friends; while the poor will carry their industrious hands to our neighbors.

ALVA:

They will, if they cannot be prevented. It is on this account that the king desires counsel and aid from every prince, zealous co-operation from every stadtholder; not merely a description of the present posture of affairs, or conjectures as to what might take place were events suffered to hold on their course without interruption. To contemplate a mighty evil, to flatter oneself with hope, to trust to time, to strike a blow, like the clown in a play, so as to make a noise and appear to do something, when in fact one would fain do nothing; is not such conduct calculated to awaken a suspicion that those who act thus contemplate with satisfaction a rebellion, which they would not indeed excite, but which they are by no means unwilling to encourage?

EGMONT *(about to break forth, restrains himself, and after a brief pause, speaks with composure)*:

Not every design is obvious, and many a man's design is misconstrued. It is widely rumored, however, that the object which the king has in view is not so much to govern the provinces according to uniform and clearly-defined laws, to maintain the majesty of religion, and to give his people universal peace, as unconditionally to subjugate them, to rob them of their ancient rights, to appropriate their possessions, to curtail the fair privileges of the nobles, for whose sake alone they are ready to serve him with life and limb. Religion, it is said, is merely a splendid device, behind which every dangerous design may be contrived with the greater ease; the prostrate crowds adore the sacred symbols pictured there, while behind lurks the fowler ready to ensnare them.

ALVA:

This I must hear from you?

EGMONT:

I speak not my own sentiments! I but repeat what is loudly rumored, and uttered now here and now there by great and by humble, by wise men and fools. The Netherlanders fear a double yoke, and who will be surety to them for their liberty?

ALVA:

Liberty! A fair word when rightly understood. What liberty would they have? What is the freedom of the most free? To do right! And in that the monarch will not hinder them. No! No! They imagine themselves enslaved when they have not the power to injure themselves and others. Would it not be better to abdicate at once rather than rule such a people? When the country is threatened by foreign invaders, the burghers, occupied only with their immediate interests, bestow no thought upon the advancing foe, and when the king requires their aid, they quarrel among themselves, and thus, as it were, conspire with the enemy. Far better is it to circumscribe their power, to control and guide them for their good, as children are controlled and guided. Trust me, a people grows neither old nor wise, a people remains always in its infancy.

EGMONT:

How rarely does a king attain wisdom! And is it not fit that the many should confide their interests to the many rather than to the one? And not even to the one, but to the few servants of the one, men who have grown old under the eyes of their master. To grow wise, it seems, is the exclusive privilege of these favored individuals.

ALVA:

Perhaps for the very reason that they are not left to themselves.

EGMONT:

And therefore they would fain leave no one else to his own guidance. Let them do what they like, however; I have replied to your questions, and I repeat, the measures you propose will never succeed! They cannot succeed! I know my countrymen. They are men worthy to tread God's earth; each complete in himself, a little king, steadfast, active, capable, loyal, attached to ancient customs. It may be difficult to win their confidence, but it is easy to retain it. Firm and unbending! They may be crushed but not subdued.

ALVA *(who during this speech has looked round several times):*
Would you venture to repeat what you have uttered in the king's presence?

EGMONT:

It were the worse, if in his presence I were restrained by fear! The better for him and for his people if he inspired me with confidence, if he encouraged me to give yet freer utterance to my thoughts.

ALVA:

What is profitable I can listen to as well as he.

EGMONT:

I would say to him—'Tis easy for the shepherd to drive before him a flock of sheep; the ox draws the plough without opposition; but if you would ride the noble steed, you must study his thoughts, you must require nothing unreasonable, nor unreasonably, from him. The burgher desires to retain his ancient constitution; to be governed by his own countrymen; and why? Because he knows in that case how he shall be ruled, because he can rely upon their disinterestedness, upon their sympathy with his fate.

ALVA:

And ought not the Regent to be empowered to alter these ancient usages? Should not this constitute his fairest privilege? What is permanent in this world? And shall the constitution of a state alone remain unchanged? Must not every relation alter in the course of time, and, on that very account, an ancient constitution become the source of a thousand evils, because not adapted to the present condition of the people? These ancient rights afford, doubtless, convenient loopholes, through which the crafty and the powerful may creep, and wherein they may lie concealed to the injury of the people and of the entire community; and it is on this account, I fear, that they are held in such high esteem.

EGMONT:

And these arbitrary changes, these unlimited encroachments of the supreme power, are they not indications that one will permit himself to do what is forbidden to thousands? The monarch would alone be free, that he may have it in his power to gratify his every wish, to realize his every thought. And though we should confide in him as a good and virtuous sovereign, will he be answerable to us for his successors? That none who come after him shall rule without consideration, without forbearance! And who would deliver us from absolute caprice, should he send hither his servants, his minions, who, without knowledge of the country and its requirements, should govern according to their own good pleasure, meet with no opposition, and know themselves exempt from all responsibility?

ALVA *(who has meanwhile again looked round)*:

There is nothing more natural than that a king should choose to retain the power in his own hands, and that he should select as the instruments of his authority those who best understand him, who desire to understand him, and who will unconditionally execute his will.

EGMONT:

And just as natural is it that the burgher should prefer being governed by one born and reared in the same land, whose notions of right and wrong are in harmony with his own, and whom he can regard as his brother.

ALVA:

And yet the noble, methinks, has shared rather unequally with these brethren of his.

EGMONT:

That took place centuries ago, and is now submitted to without envy. But should new men, whose presence is not needed in the country, be sent to enrich themselves a second time at the cost of the nation; should the people see themselves exposed to their bold, unscrupulous rapacity, it would excite a ferment that would not soon be quelled.

ALVA:

You utter words to which I ought not to listen;—I, too, am a foreigner.

EGMONT:

That they are spoken in your presence is a sufficient proof that they have no reference to you.

ALVA:

Be that as it may, I would rather not hear them from you. The king sent me here in the hope that I should obtain the support of the nobles. The king wills, and will have his will

249

obeyed. After profound deliberation, the king at length discerns what course will best promote the welfare of the people; matters cannot be permitted to go on as heretofore; it is the king's intention to limit their power for their own good; if necessary, to force upon them their salvation: to sacrifice the more dangerous burghers in order that the rest may find repose, and enjoy in peace the blessing of a wise government. This is his resolve; this I am commissioned to announce to the nobles; and in his name I require from them advice, not as to the course to be pursued—on that he is resolved—but as to the best means of carrying his purpose into effect.

EGMONT:

Your words, alas, justify the fears of the people, the universal fear! The king then has resolved as no sovereign ought to resolve. In order to govern his subjects more easily, he would crush, subvert, nay, ruthlessly destroy, their strength, their spirit and their self-respect! He would violate the inmost core of their individuality, doubtless with the view of promoting their happiness. He would annihilate them, that they may assume a new, a different form. Oh! if his purpose be good, he is fatally misguided! It is not the king whom we resist;—we but place ourselves in the way of the monarch, who, unhappily, is about to take the first rash step in a wrong direction.

ALVA:

Such being your sentiments, it were a vain attempt for us to endeavor to agree. You must, indeed, think poorly of the king, and contemptibly of his counsellors, if you imagine that everything has not already been thought of and maturely weighed. I have no commission a second time to balance conflicting arguments. From these people I demand submission;—and from you, their leaders and princes, I demand counsel and support as pledges of this unconditional duty.

EGMONT:

Demand our heads, and your object is attained; to a noble soul it must be indifferent whether he stoop his neck to such a yoke or lay it upon the block. I have spoken much to little purpose. I have agitated the air, but accomplished nothing.

Enter FERDINAND.

FERDINAND:

Pardon my intrusion. Here is a letter, the bearer of which urgently demands an answer.

ALVA:

Allow me to peruse its contents. *(Steps aside)*.

FERDINAND *(to* EGMONT*)*:

'Tis a noble steed that your people have brought to carry you away.

EGMONT:

I have seen worse. I have had him some time; I think of parting with him. If he pleases you we shall probably soon agree as to the price.

FERDINAND:

We will think about it.

*(*ALVA *motions to his son, who retires to the background.)*

EGMONT:

Farewell! Allow me to retire; for, by heaven, I know not what more I can say.

ALVA:

Fortunately for you, chance prevents you from making a fuller disclosure of your sentiments. You incautiously lay bare the recesses of your heart, and your own lips furnish evidence against you more fatal than could be produced by your bitterest adversary.

EGMONT:

This reproach disturbs me not. I know my own heart; I know with what honest zeal I am devoted to the king; I know that my allegiance is more true than that of many who, in his service, seek only to serve themselves. I regret that our discussion should terminate so unsatisfactorily, and trust that, in spite of our opposing views, the service of the king, our master, and the welfare of our country, may speedily unite us; another conference, the presence of the princes who to-day are absent, may, perchance, in a more propitious moment, accomplish what at present appears impossible. In this hope I take my leave.

ALVA *(who at the same time makes a sign to* FERDINAND*)*:

Hold, Egmont!—Your sword!—*(The centre door opens and discloses the gallery, which is occupied with guards, who remain motionless.)*

Johann Wolfgang von Goethe

EGMONT *(after a pause of astonishment)*:

This was the intention? For this thou hast summoned me? *(Grasping his sword as if to defend himself.)* Am I then weaponless?

ALVA:

The king commands. Thou art my prisoner. *(At the same time guards enter from both sides.)*

EGMONT *(after a pause)*:

The king?—Orange! Orange! *(After a pause, resigning his sword.)* Take it! It has been employed far oftener in defending the cause of my king than in protecting this breast. *(He retires by the centre door, followed by the guard and* ALVA'S *son.* ALVA *remains standing while the curtain falls.)*

ACT V

SCENE I. *A Street. Twilight.*

BRACKENBURG:
> Dearest, for heaven's sake, what wouldst thou do?

CLARA:
> Come with me, Brackenburg! Thou canst not know the people, we are certain to rescue him; for what can equal their love for him? Each feels, I could swear it, the burning desire to deliver him, to avert danger from a life so precious, and to restore freedom to the most free. Come! A voice only is wanting to call them together. In their souls the memory is still fresh of all they owe him, and well they know that his mighty arm alone shields them from destruction. For his sake, for their own sake, they must peril everything. And what do we peril? At most our lives, which, if he perish, are not worth preserving.

BRACKENBURG:
> Unhappy girl! Thou seest not the power that holds us fettered as with bands of iron.

CLARA:
> To me it does not appear invincible. Let us not lose time in idle words. Here comes some of our old, honest, valiant burghers! Hark ye, friends! Neighbors! Hark— Say, how fares it with Egmont?

CARPENTER:
> What does the girl want? Tell her to hold her peace.

CLARA:
> Step nearer, that we may speak low, till we are united and more strong. Not a moment is to be lost! Audacious tyranny, that dared to fetter him, already lifts the dagger against his life. Oh, my friends! With the advancing twilight my anxiety grows more intense. I dread this night. Come! Let us disperse; let us hasten from quarter to quarter, and call out the burghers. Let every one grasp his ancient weapons. In the market-place we meet again, and every one will be carried onward by our gathering stream. The enemy will see themselves surrounded, overwhelmed, and be compelled to yield. How can a handful of slaves resist us? And he will return among us, he will see himself rescued, and can for

once thank us, us, who are already so deeply in his debt. He
will behold, perchance, ay, doubtless, he will again behold
the morn's red dawn in the free heavens.

CARPENTER:

What ails thee, maiden?

CLARA:

Can ye misunderstand me? I speak of the Count! I speak of
Egmont.

JETTER:

Speak not the name! 'tis deadly.

ALVA:

Not speak his name? How? Not Egmont's name? It is not on
every tongue? Where stands it not inscribed? Often have I
read it emblazoned with all its letters among these stars. Not
utter it? What mean ye? Friends! good, kind neighbors, ye
are dreaming; collect yourselves. Gaze not upon me with
those fixed and anxious looks! Cast not such timid glances
on every side! I but give utterance to the wish of all. It not
my voice the voice of your own hearts? Who, in this fearful
night, ere he seeks his restless couch, but on bended knee
will, in earnest prayer, seek to wrest his life as a cherished
boon from heaven? Ask each other! Let each ask his own
heart! And who but exclaims with me,—"Egmont's liberty,
or death!"

JETTER:

God help us! This is a sad business.

CLARA:

Stay! Stay! Shrink not away at the sound of his name, to
meet whom ye were wont to press forward so joyously!—
When rumor announced his approach, when the cry arose,
"Egmont comes! He comes from Ghent!"—then happy, indeed, were those citizens who dwelt in the streets through
which he was to pass. And when the neighing of his steed
was heard, did not every one throw aside his work, while a
ray of hope and joy, like a sunbeam from his countenance,
stole over the toil-worn faces that peered from every window. Then, as ye stood in the doorways, ye would lift up
your children in your arms, and, pointing to him, exclaim:
"See, that is Egmont, he who towers above the rest? 'Tis
from him that ye must look for better times than those your
poor fathers have known." Let not your children inquire at

some future day, "Where is he? Where are the better times
ye promised us?"—Thus we waste the time in idle words!
do nothing,—betray him.

SOEST:

Shame on thee, Brackenburg! Let her not run on thus! Prevent the mischief!

BRACKENBURG:

Dear Clara! Let us go! What will your mother say? Perchance—

CLARA:

Thinkest thou I am a child, or frantic? What avails perchance?—With no vain hope canst thou hide from me this
dreadful certainty . . . Ye shall hear me and ye will: for I
see it, ye are overwhelmed, ye cannot hearken to the voice
of your own hearts. Through the present peril cast but one
glance into the past,—the recent past. Send your thoughts
forward into the future. Could ye live, would ye live, were
he to perish? With him expires the last breath of freedom.
What was he not to you? For whose sake did he expose himself to the direst perils? His blood flowed, his wounds were
healed for you alone. The mighty spirit that upheld you all
a dungeon now confines, while the horrors of secret murder
are hovering around. Perhaps he thinks of you—perhaps he
hopes in you,—he who has been accustomed only to grant
favors to others and to fulfill their prayers.

CARPENTER:

Come, gossip.

CLARA:

I have neither the arms nor the vigor of a man; but I have
that which ye all lack—courage and contempt of danger. Oh,
that my breath could kindle your souls! That, pressing you
to this bosom, I could arouse and animate you! Come! I will
march in your midst!—As a waving banner, though weaponless, leads on a gallant army of warriors, so shall my spirit
hover, like a flame, over your ranks, while love and courage
shall unite the dispersed and wavering multitude into a terrible host.

JETTER:

Take her away; I pity her, poor thing!

[*Exeunt* BURGHERS.

BRACKENBURG:

Clara! Seest thou not where we are?

CLARA:

Where! Under the dome of heaven, which has so often seemed to arch itself more gloriously as the noble Egmont passed beneath it. From these windows I have seen them look forth, four or five heads one above the other; at these doors the cowards have stood, bowing and scraping, if he but chanced to look down upon them! Oh, how dear they were to me when they honored him. Had he been a tyrant they might have turned with indifference from his fall! But they loved him! Oh, ye hands so prompt to wave caps in his honor, can ye not grasp a sword? Brackenburg, and we?—do we chide them? These arms that have so often embraced him, what do they for him now? Stratagem has accomplished so much in the world. Thou knowest the ancient castle, every passage, every secret way. Nothing is impossible,—suggest some plan—

BRACKENBURG:

That we might go home!

CLARA:

Well.

BRACKENBURG:

There, at the corner, I see Alva's guard; let the voice of reason penetrate to thy heart! Dost thou deem me a coward? Dost thou doubt that for thy sake I would peril my life? Here we are both mad, I as well as thou. Dost thou not perceive that thy scheme is impracticable? Oh, be calm! Thou art beside thyself.

CLARA:

Beside myself! Horrible. You, Brackenburg, are beside yourself. When you hailed the hero with loud acclaim, called him your friend, your hope, your refuge, shouted vivats as he passed;—then I stood in my corner, half-opened the window, concealed myself while I listened, and my heart beat higher than yours who greeted him so loudly. Now it again beats higher! In the hour of peril you conceal yourselves, deny him, and feel not, that if he perish, you are lost.

BRACKENBURG:

Come home.

CLARA:

Home?

BRACKENBURG:

Recollect thyself! Look around thee! These are the streets in which thou wert wont to appear only on the Sabbath-day, when didst walk modestly to church; where, over-decorous perhaps, thou wert displeased if I but joined thee with a kindly greeting. And now thou dost stand, speak, and act before the eyes of the whole world. Recollect thyself, love! How can this avail us?

CLARA:

Home! Yes, I remember. Come, Brackenburg, let us go home! Knowest thou where my home lies?

[*Exeunt.*

SCENE II. *A Prison. Lighted by a lamp, a couch in the back-ground.*

EGMONT *(alone)*:

Old friend! Ever faithful sleep, dost thou, too, forsake me like my other friends? How thou wert wont of yore to descend unsought upon my free brow, cooling my temples as with a myrtle wreath of love! Amidst the din of battle, on the waves of life, I rested in thine arms, breathing lightly as a growing boy. When tempests whistled through the leaves and boughs, when the summits of the lofty trees swung creaking in the blast, the inmost core of my heart remained unmoved. What agitates thee now? What shakes thy firm and steadfast mind? I feel it; 'tis the sound of the murderous axe gnawing at thy root. Yet I stand erect, but an inward shudder runs through my frame. Yes, it prevails, this treacherous power; it undermines the firm, the lofty stem, and ere the bark withers thy verdant crown falls crashing to the earth.

Yet wherefore now, thou who hast so often chased the weightiest cares like bubbles from thy brow, wherefore canst thou not dissipate this dire foreboding which incessantly haunts thee in a thousand different shapes? Since when hast thou trembled at the approach of death, amid whose varying forms thou wert wont calmly to dwell, as with the other shapes of this familiar earth? But 'tis not he, the sudden foe, to encounter whom the sound bosom emulously pants; —'tis the dungeon, emblem of the grave, revolting alike to the hero and the coward. How intolerable I used to feel it, in the stately hall, girt round by gloomy walls, when, seated on my cushioned chair in the solemn assembly of the princes, questions which scarcely required deliberation were overlaid with endless discussions, while the rafters of the ceiling seemed to stifle and oppress me. Then I would hurry forth as soon as possible, fling myself upon my horse with deep-drawn breath, and away to the wide champaign, man's natural element, where, exhaling from the earth, nature's richest treasures are poured forth around us, while, from the wide heavens, the stars shed down their blessings through the still air; where, like earth-born giants, we spring aloft, invigorated by our mother's touch; where our entire humanity and our human desires throb in every vein; where the desire to press forward, to vanquish, to snatch, to use his clenched fist, to possess, to conquer glows through the soul of the young hunter; where the warrior, with rapid stride, assumes his inborn right to dominion over the world, and, with terrible liberty, sweeps like a desolating hail-storm over field and grove, knowing no boundaries traced by the hand of man.

Thou art but a shadow, a dream of the happiness I so long possessed; where has treacherous fate conducted thee? Did she deny thee to meet the rapid stroke of never-shunned death in the open face of day only to prepare for thee a fore-taste of the grave, in the midst of this loathsome corruption? How revoltingly its rank odor exhales from these damp stones! Life stagnates, and my foot shrinks from the couch as from the grave.

O care, care! Thou who dost begin prematurely the work of murder, forbear;—since when has Egmont been alone, so utterly alone in the world? 'Tis doubt renders thee insensible, not happiness. The justice of the king, in which through life thou hast confided, the friendship of the regent, which, thou may'st confess it, was akin to love,—have these suddenly vanished, like a meteor of the night, and left thee alone upon thy gloomy path? Will not Orange, at the head of thy friends, contrive some daring scheme? Will not the people assemble, and with gathering might attempt the rescue of their faithful friend?

Ye walls, which thus gird me round, separate me not from the well-intentioned zeal of so many kindly souls. And may the courage with which my glance was wont to inspire them now return again from their hearts to mine. Yes! they assemble in thousands! they come! they stand beside me! their pious wish rises urgently to heaven, and implores a miracle; and if no angel stoops for my deliverance, I see them grasp eagerly their lance and sword. The gates are forced, the bolts are riven, the walls fall beneath their conquering hands, and Egmont advances, joyously, to hail the freedom of the rising morn. How many well-known faces receive me with loud acclaim! O Clara! wert thou a man I should see thee here the very first, and thank thee for that which it is galling to owe even to a king—liberty.

SCENE III. *Clara's House.*

CLARA *(enters from her chamber with a lamp and a glass of water; she places the glass upon the table and steps to the window)*: Brackenburg, is it you? What noise was that? No one yet? No one! I will set the lamp in the window, that he may see that I am still awake, that I still watch for him. He promised me tidings. Tidings? horrible certainty!—Egmont condemned!—what tribunal has the right to summon him?— And they dare to condemn him!—Does the king condemn him, or the duke? And the regent withdraws herself! Orange hesitates, and all his friends?—Is this the world, of whose fickleness and treachery I have heard so much, and as yet experienced nothing? Is this the world?—Who could be so base as to bear malice against one so dear? Could villainy itself be audacious enough to overwhelm with sudden destruction the object of a nation's homage? Yet so it is—it is —O Egmont, I held thee safe before God and man, safe as in my arms! What was I to thee? Thou hast called me thine, my whole being was devoted to thee. What am I now? In vain I stretch out my hand to the toils that environ thee. Thou helpless and I free!—Here is the key that unlocks my chamber door. My going out and my coming in depend upon my own caprice; yet, alas, to aid thee I am powerless! —Oh, bind me that I may not despair; hurl me into the deepest dungeon, that I may dash my head against the damp walls, groan for freedom, and dream how I would rescue him if fetters did not hold me bound.—Now I am free, and in freedom lies the anguish of impotence.—Conscious of my own existence, yet unable to stir a limb in his behalf, alas! even this insignificant portion of thy being, thy Clara, is, like thee, a captive, and, separated from thee, consumes her expiring energies in the agonies of death.—I hear a stealthy step,—a cough—Brackenburg,—'tis he!—Kind, unhappy man, thy destiny remains ever the same; thy love opens to thee the door at night, alas! to what a doleful meeting. *(Enter* BRACKEN-BURG.*)* Thou comest so pale, so terrified! Brackenburg! What is it?

BRACKENBURG:

I have sought thee through perils and circuitous paths. The principal streets are occupied with troops;—through lanes and by-ways have I stolen to thee!

CLARA:

Tell me, how is it?

BRACKENBURG *(seating himself)*:

O Clara, let me weep. I loved him not. He was the rich man who lured to better pasture the poor man's solitary lamb. I have never cursed him, God has created me with a true and tender heart. My life was consumed in anguish, and each day I hoped would end my misery.

CLARA:

Let that be forgotten, Brackenburg! Forget thyself. Speak to me of him! Is it true? Is he condemned?

BRACKENBURG:

He is! I know it.

CLARA:

And still lives?

BRACKENBURG:

Yes, he still lives.

CLARA:

How canst thou be sure of that? Tyranny murders the hero in the night! His blood flows concealed from every eye. The people, stunned and bewildered, lie buried in sleep, dream of deliverance, dream of the fulfilment of their impotent wishes, while, indignant at our supineness, his spirit abandons the world. He is no more! Deceive me not; deceive not thyself!

BRACKENBURG:

No,—he lives! and the Spaniards, alas, are preparing for the people, on whom they are about to trample, a terrible spectacle, in order to crush forever, by a violent blow, each heart that yet pants for freedom.

CLARA:

Proceed! Calmly pronounce my death-warrant also! Near and more near I approach that blessed land, and already from those realms of peace I feel the breath of consolation. Say on.

BRACKENBURG:

From casual words, dropped here and there by the guards, I learned that secretly in the market-place they were preparing some terrible spectacle. Through by-ways and familiar lanes I stole to my cousin's house, and from a back window looked out upon the market-place. Torches waved to and fro, in the hands of a wide circle of Spanish soldiers. I sharpened my unaccustomed sight, and out of the darkness there arose before me a scaffold, black, spacious and lofty! The sight filled me with horror. Several persons were employed in covering with black cloth such portions of the woodwork as yet remained white and visible. The steps were covered last, also with black;—I saw it all. They seemed preparing for the celebration of some horrible sacrifice. A white crucifix, that shone like silver through the night, was raised on one side. As I gazed, the terrible conviction strengthened in my mind. Scattered torches still gleamed here and there; gradually they flickered and went out. Suddenly the hideous birth of night returned into its mother's womb.

CLARA:

Hush, Brackenburg! Be still! Let this veil rest upon my soul. The spectres are vanished; and thou, gentle night, lend thy mantle to the inwardly fermenting earth, she will no longer endure the loathsome burden, shuddering, she rends open her yawning chasms, and with a crash swallows the murderous scaffold. And that God, whom in their rage they have insulted, sends down His angel from on high; at the hallowed touch of the messenger bolts and bars fly back; he pours around our friend a mild radiance, and leads him gently through the night to liberty. My path leads also through the darkness to meet him.

BRACKENBURG (*detaining her*):

My child, whither wouldst thou go? What wouldst thou do?

CLARA:

Softly, my friend, lest some one should awake! Lest we should awake ourselves! Knowest thou this phial, Brackenburg? I took it from thee once in jest, when thou, as was thy

wont, didst threaten, in thy impatience, to end thy days.
And now my friend—

BRACKENBURG:

In the name of all the saints!

CLARA:

Thou canst not hinder me. Death is my portion! Grudge me
not the quiet and easy death which thou hadst prepared for
thyself. Give me thine hand! At the moment when I unclose
that dismal portal through which there is no return, I may
tell thee, with this pressure of the hand, how sincerely I have
loved, how deeply I have pitied thee. My brother died
young; I chose thee to fill his place; thy heart rebelled, thou
didst torment thyself and me, demanding, with ever-increas-
ing fervor, that which fate had not destined for thee. Forgive
me and farewell! Let me call thee brother. 'Tis a name that
embraces many names. Receive, with a true heart, the last
fair token of the departing spirit—take this kiss. Death unites
all, Brackenburg—us too it will unite!

BRACKENBURG:

Let me then die with thee! Share it! oh, share it! There is
enough to extinguish two lives!

CLARA:

Hold! Thou must live, thou canst live. Support my mother,
who, without thee, would be a prey to want. Be to her what
I can no longer be, live together, and weep for me. Weep
for our country, and for him who could alone have upheld
it. The present generation must still endure this bitter woe;
vengeance itself could not obliterate it. Poor souls, live on,
through this gap in time, which is time no longer. To-day
the world suddenly stands still, its course is arrested, and
my pulse will beat but for a few minutes longer. Farewell.

BRACKENBURG:

Oh, live with us, as we live only for thy sake! In taking thine
own life thou wilt take ours also; still live and suffer. We
will stand by thee; nothing shall sever us from thy side, and
love, with ever-watchful solicitude, shall prepare for thee
the sweetest consolation in its loving arms. Be ours! Ours! I
dare not say, mine.

CLARA:

Hush, Brackenburg! Thou feelest not what chord thou
touchest. Where hope appears to thee I see only despair.

BRACKENBURG:

Share hope with the living! Pause on the brink of the precipice, cast one glance into the gulf below, and then look back on us.

CLARA:

I have conquered; call me not back to the struggle.

BRACKENBURG:

Thou art stunned; enveloped in night, thou seekest the abyss. Every light is not yet extinguished, yet many days!—

CLARA:

Alas! Alas! Cruelly thou dost rend the veil from before mine eyes. Yes, the day will dawn! Despite its misty shroud it needs must dawn. Timidly the burgher gazes from his window, night leaves behind an ebon speck; he looks, and the scaffold looms fearfully in the morning light. With reawakened anguish the desecrated image of the Saviour lifts to the Father its imploring eyes. The sun veils his beams, he will not mark the hero's death-hour. Slowly the fingers go their round—one hour strikes after another—hold! Now is the time. The thought of the morning scares me into the grave. *(She goes to the window as if to look out, and drinks secretly.)*

BRACKENBURG:

Clara! Clara!

CLARA *(goes to the table and drinks water)*:

Here is the remainder. I invite thee not to follow me. Do as thou wilt: farewell. Extinguish this lamp silently and without delay; I am going to rest. Steal quietly away, close the door after thee. Be still! Wake not my mother! Go, save thyself, if thou wouldst not be taken for my murderer.

[*Exit.*

BRACKENBURG:

She leaves me for the last time as she has ever done. What human soul could conceive how cruelly she lacerates the heart that loves her. She leaves me to myself, leaves me to choose between life and death, and both are alike hateful to me. To die alone! Weep, ye tender souls! Fate has no sadder doom than mine. She shares with me the death-potion, yet sends me from her side! She draws me after her, yet thrusts me back into life! Oh, Egmont, how enviable a lot falls to thee! She goes before thee! The crown of victory from her hand is thine, she brings all heaven to meet thee!—And shall I follow? Again to stand aloof? To carry the inextinguishable jealousy even to yon distant realms? Earth is no longer a tarrying place for me, and hell and heaven both offer equal torture. Now welcome to the wretched the dread hand of annihilation! [*Exit.*

(*The scene remains some time unchanged. Music sounds, indicating* CLARA's *death; the lamp, which* BRACKENBURG *had forgotten to extinguish, flares up once or twice, and then suddenly expires. The scene changes to*

SCENE IV. *A Prison.*

EGMONT *is discovered sleeping on a couch. A rustling of keys is heard; the door opens; servants enter with torches;* FERDINAND *and* SILVA *follow, accompanied by soldiers;* EGMONT *starts from his sleep.*

EGMONT:

Who are ye that thus rudely banish slumber from my eyes? What mean these vague and insolent glances? Why this fearful procession? With what dream of horror come ye to delude my half awakened soul?

SILVA:

The duke sends us to announce your sentence.

EGMONT:

Do you also bring the headsman who is to execute it?

SILVA:

Listen, and you will know the doom that awaits you.

EGMONT:

It is in keeping with the rest of your infamous proceedings. Hatched in night and in night achieved, so would this audacious act of injustice shroud itself from observation!—Step boldly forth, thou who dost bear the sword concealed beneath thy mantle; here is my head, the freest ever severed by tyranny from the trunk.

SILVA:

You err! The righteous judges who have condemned you will not conceal their sentence from the light of day.

EGMONT:

Then does their audacity exceed all imagination and belief.

SILVA (*takes the sentence from an attendant, unfolds it, and reads*):

264

"In the king's name, and invested by his majesty with authority to judge all his subjects of whatever rank, not excepting the knights of the Golden Fleece, we declare—"

EGMONT:

Can the king transfer that authority?

SILVA:

"We declare, after a strict and legal investigation, thee, Henry, Count Egmont, Prince of Gaure, guilty of high treason, and pronounce thy sentence:—That at early dawn thou be led from this prison to the market-place, and that there, in sight of the people, and as a warning to all traitors, thou with the sword be brought from life to death. Given at Brussels." *(Date and year so indistinctly read as to be imperfectly heard by the audience.)* "Ferdinand, Duke of Alva, President of the Tribunal of Twelve." Thou knowest now thy doom. Brief time remains for the impending stroke, to arrange thy affairs, and to take leave of thy friends. [*Exit* SILVA *with followers.* FERDINAND *remains with two torch-bearers. The stage is dimly lighted.*

EGMONT *(stands for a time as if buried in thought, and allows* SILVA *to retire without looking round. He imagines himself alone, and, on raising his eyes, beholds* ALVA'S *son)*:

Thou tarriest here? Wouldst thou by thy presence augment my amazement, my horror? Wouldst thou carry to thy father the welcome tidings that in unmanly fashion I despair. Go. Tell him that he deceives neither the world nor me. At first it will be whispered cautiously behind his back, then spoken more and more loudly, and when at some future day the ambitious man descends from his proud eminence, a thousand voices will proclaim—that 'twas not the welfare of the state, not the honor of the king, not the tranquillity of the provinces, that brought him hither. For his own selfish ends he, the warrior, has counselled war, that in war the value of his services might be enhanced. He has excited this monstrous insurrection that his presence might be deemed necessary in order to quell it. And I fall a victim to his mean hatred, his contemptible envy. Yes, I know it, dying and mortally wounded I may utter it; long has the proud man envied me, long has he meditated and planned my ruin.

Even then, when still young, we played at dice together, and the heaps of gold, one after the other, passed rapidly from his side to mine; he would look on with affected composure, while inwardly consumed with rage, more at my success than at his own loss. Well do I remember the fiery glance, the treacherous pallor that overspread his features, when, at a public festival, we shot for a wager before assembled thousands. He challenged me, and both nations stood by; Spaniards and Netherlanders wagered on either side; I was the victor; his ball missed, mine hit the mark, and the air was rent by acclamations from my friends. His shot now hits me. Tell him that I know this, that I know him, that the world despises every trophy that a paltry spirit erects for itself by base and surreptitious arts. And thou! If it be possible for a son to swerve from the manners of his father, practise shame betimes, while thou art compelled to feel shame for him whom thou wouldst fain revere with thy whole heart.

FERDINAND:

I listen without interrupting thee! Thy reproaches fall like blows upon a helmet. I feel the shock, but I am armed. They strike, they wound me not; I am sensible only to the anguish that lacerates my heart. Alas! Alas! Have I lived to witness such a scene? Am I sent hither to behold a spectacle like this?

EGMONT:

Dost thou break out into lamentations? What moves, what agitates thee thus? Is it a late remorse at having lent thyself to this infamous conspiracy? Thou art so young, thy exterior is so prepossessing. Thy demeanor towards me was so friendly, so unreserved! So long as I beheld thee, I was reconciled with thy father; and crafty, ay, more crafty than he, thou hast lured me into the toils. Thou art the wretch! The monster! Whoso confides in him does so at his own peril; but who could apprehend danger in trusting thee? Go! Go! rob me not of the few moments that are left to me! Go, that I may collect my thoughts, forget the world, and first of all thee!

FERDINAND:

What can I say? I stand and gaze on thee, yet see thee not; I am scarcely conscious of my own existence. Shall I seek to excuse myself? Shall I assure thee that it was not till the last moment that I was made aware of my father's inten-

tions? That I acted as a constrained, a passive instrument of
his will? What signifies now the opinion thou mayest entertain of me? Thou art lost; and I, miserable wretch, stand
here only to assure thee of it, only to lament thy doom.

EGMONT:

What strange voice, what unexpected consolation comes
thus to cheer my passage to the grave? Thou, the son of
my first, of almost my only enemy, thou dost pity me, thou
art not associated with my murderers? Speak! In what light
must I regard thee?

FERDINAND:

Cruel father! Yes, I recognize thy nature in this command.
Thou didst know my heart, my disposition, which thou hast
so often censured as the inheritance of a tender-hearted
mother. To mould me into thine own likeness thou hast sent
me hither. Thou dost compel me to behold this man on
the verge of the yawning grave, in the grasp of an arbitrary
doom, that I may experience the profoundest anguish;
that thus, rendered callous to every fate, I may henceforth
meet every event with a heart unmoved.

EGMONT:

I am amazed! Be calm! Act, speak like a man.

FERDINAND:

Oh, that I were a woman! That they might say—what
moves, what agitates thee? Tell me of a greater, a more
monstrous crime, make me the spectator of a more direful
deed; I will thank thee, I will say: this was nothing.

EGMONT:

Thou dost forget thyself. Consider where thou art!

FERDINAND:

Let this passion rage, let me give vent to my anguish! I will
not seem composed when my whole inner being is convulsed. Thee must I behold here? Thee? It is horrible!
Thou understandest me not! How shouldst thou understand me? Egmont! Egmont!

EGMONT:

Explain this mystery.

FERDINAND:

It is no mystery.

(Falling on his neck.)

EGMONT:

Why art thou moved so deeply by the fate of a stranger?

FERDINAND:

Not a stranger! Thou art no stranger to me. Thy name it was that, even from my boyhood, shone before me like a star in heaven! How often have I made inquiries con--cerning thee, and listened to the story of thy deeds. The youth is the hope of the boy, the man of the youth. Thus didst thou walk before me, ever before me; I saw thee without envy, and followed after, step by step; at length I hoped to see thee—I saw thee, and my heart flew to thy embrace. I had destined thee for myself, and when I be-held thee, I made choice of thee anew. I hoped now to know thee, to live with thee, to be thy friend,—thy—'tis over now and I see thee here!

EGMONT:

My friend, if it can be any comfort to thee, be assured that the very moment we met my heart was drawn to-wards thee. Now listen! Let us exchange a few quiet words. Tell me: is it the stern, the settled purpose of thy father to take my life?

FERDINAND:

It is.

EGMONT:

This sentence is not a mere empty scare-crow, designed to terrify me, to punish me through fear and intimidation, to humiliate me, that he may then raise me again by the royal favor?

FERDINAND:

Alas, no! At first I flattered myself with this delusive hope; and even then my heart was filled with grief and anguish to behold thee thus. Thy doom is real! is certain! No, I cannot command myself. Who will counsel, who will aid me, to meet the inevitable?

EGMONT:

Hearken then to me! If thy heart is impelled so power-fully in my favor, if thou dost abhor the tyranny that holds me fettered, then deliver me! The moments are precious. Thou art the son of the all-powerful, and thou hast power thyself. Let us fly! I know the roads; the means of effecting our escape cannot be unknown to thee. These walls, a few short miles, alone separate me from my friends. Loose these fetters, conduct me to them; be ours. The king, on some future day, will doubtless thank my deliverer. Now he is taken by surprise, or perchance he is ignorant of the whole proceeding. Thy father ventures on this daring step, and majesty, though horror-struck at the deed, must needs sanction the irrevocable. Thou dost deliberate? Oh, contrive for me the way to freedom! Speak; nourish hope in a living soul.

FERDINAND:

Cease! Oh, cease! Every word deepens my despair. There is here no outlet, no counsel, no escape.—'Tis this thought that tortures me, that seizes my heart, and rends it as with talons. I have myself spread the net. I know its firm, inextricable knots; I know that every avenue is barred alike to courage and to stratagem. I feel that I, too, like thyself, like all the rest, am fettered. Think'st thou that I should give way to lamentation if any means of safety remained untried? I have thrown myself at his feet, remonstrated, implored. He has sent me hither, in order to blast in this fatal moment every remnant of joy and happiness that yet survived within my heart.

EGMONT:

And is there no deliverance?

FERDINAND:

None!

EGMONT *(stamping his foot)*:

No deliverance!—Sweet life! Sweet pleasant habitude of existence and of activity! from thee must I part! Not in the tumult of battle, amid the din of arms, the excitement of the fray, dost thou send me a hasty farewell; thine is no hurried leave; thou dost not abridge the moment of separation. Once more let me clasp thy hand, gaze once more into thine eyes, feel with keen emotion, thy beauty and thy worth, then resolutely tear myself away, and say;—depart!

FERDINAND:

Must I stand by and look passively on; unable to save thee or to give thee aid! What voice avails for lamentation! What heart but must break under the pressure of such anguish!

EGMONT:

Be calm!

FERDINAND:

Thou canst be calm, thou canst renounce, led on by necessity, thou canst advance to the direful struggle with the courage of a hero. What can I do? What ought I to do? Thou dost conquer thyself and us; thou art the victor; I survive both myself and thee. I have lost my light at the banquet, my honor on the field. The future lies before me dark, desolate, perplexed.

EGMONT:

Young friend, whom by a strange fatality, at the same moment I both win and lose, who dost feel for me, who dost suffer for me the agonies of death,—look on me;—thou wilt not lose me. If my life was a mirror in which thou didst love to contemplate thyself so be also my death. Men are not together only when in each other's presence;—the distant, the departed, also live for us. I shall live for thee, and for myself I have lived long enough. I have enjoyed each day; each day I have performed, with prompt activity, the duties enjoined by my conscience. Now my life ends, as it might have ended, long, long ago, on the sands of Gravelines. I shall cease to live; but I have lived. My friend, follow in my steps, lead a cheerful and a joyous life, and dread not the approach of death.

FERDINAND:

Thou shouldst have saved thyself for us, thou couldst have saved thyself. Thou art the cause of thine own destruction. Often have I listened when able men discoursed concerning thee; foes and friends, they would dispute long as to thy worth; but on one point they were agreed, none ventured to deny, every one confessed, that thou wert treading a dangerous path. How often have I longed to warn thee; Hadst thou then no friends?

EGMONT:

I was warned.

FERDINAND:

And when I found all these allegations, point for point, in the indictment, together with thy answers, containing much that might serve to palliate thy conduct, but no evidence weighty enough fully to exculpate thee——

EGMONT:

No more of this. Man imagines that he directs his life, that he governs his actions, when in fact his existence is irresistibly controlled by his destiny. Let us not dwell upon this subject; these reflections I can dismiss with ease—not so my apprehensions for these provinces; yet they too will be cared for. Could my blood flow for many, bring peace to my people, how freely should it flow! Alas! This may not be. Yet it ill becomes a man idly to speculate when the power to act is no longer his. If thou canst restrain or guide the fatal power of thy father, do so. Alas, who can?—Farewell!

FERDINAND:

I cannot leave thee.

EGMONT:

Let me urgently recommend my followers to thy care! I have worthy men in my service; let them not be dispersed, let them not become destitute! How fares it with Richard, my secretary?

FERDINAND:

He is gone before thee. They have beheaded him as thy accomplice in high treason.

EGMONT:

Poor soul!—Yet one word, and then farewell, I can no more. However powerfully the spirit may be stirred, nature at length irresistibly asserts her rights; and like a child, who, enveloped in a serpent's folds, enjoys refreshing slumber, so the weary one lays himself down to rest before the gates of death, and sleeps soundly, as though a toilsome journey yet lay before him.—One word more,—I know a maiden; thou wilt not despise her because she was mine. Since I can recommend her to thy care, I shall die in peace. Thy soul is noble! in such a man a woman is sure to find a protector. Lives my old Adolphus? Is he free?

FERDINAND:

The active old man, who always attended thee on horseback?

EGMONT:

The same.

FERDINAND:

He lives, he is free.

EGMONT:

He knows her dwelling; let him guide thy steps thither, and reward him to his dying day for having shown thee the way to this jewel.—Farewell!

FERDINAND:

I cannot leave thee.

EGMONT *(urging him towards the door):*
Farewell!

FERDINAND:

Oh, let me linger yet a moment!

EGMONT:

No leave-taking, my friend.

(He accompanies FERDINAND *to the door, and then tears himself away;* FERDINAND, *overwhelmed with grief, hastily retires.)*

EGMONT:

Hostile man! Thou didst not think thou would render me this service through thy son. He has been the means of relieving my mind from the pressure of care and sorrow, from fear and every anxious feeling. Gently, yet urgently, nature claims her final tribute. 'Tis past!—'Tis resolved! And the reflections which, in the suspense of last night, kept me wakeful on my couch, now lull my senses to repose with invincible certainty. *(He seats himself upon the couch; music.)* Sweet sleep! Like the purest happiness, thou comest most willingly, uninvited, unsought. Thou dost loosen the knots of earnest thoughts, dost mingle all images of joy and of sorrow; unimpeded the circle of inner harmony flows on, and, wrapped in fond delusion, we sink away and cease to be.

(He sleeps; music accompanies his slumber. Behind his couch the wall appears to open and discovers a brilliant apparition. Freedom in a celestial garb, surrounded by a glory, reposes on a cloud. Her features are those of CLARA, *and she inclines towards the sleeping hero. Her countenance betokens compassion, she seems to lament his fate. Quickly she recovers herself, and with an encouraging gesture exhibits the symbols of freedom, the bundle of arrows, and the staff and cap. She encourages him to be of good cheer, and while she signifies to him that his death will secure the freedom of the provinces, she hails him as a conqueror, and extends*

to him a laurel crown. As the wreath approaches his head,
EGMONT *moves like one asleep, and reclines with his face
towards her. She holds the wreath suspended over his head;
—martial music is heard in the distance; at the first sound the
vision disappears. The music grows louder and louder.*
EGMONT *awakes. The prison is dimly illuminated by the
dawn.—His first impulse is to lift his hand to his head; he
stands up, and gazes round, his hand still upraised.)*

The crown is vanished! Beautiful vision, the light of day
has frighted thee! Yes, they revealed themselves to my
sight uniting in one radiant form the two sweetest joys of
my heart. Divine Liberty borrowed the mien of my beloved one; the lovely maiden arrayed herself in the celestial garb of my friend. In a solemn moment they appeared
united, with aspect more earnest than tender. With blood-
stained feet the vision approached; the waving folds of her
robe also were tinged with blood. It was my blood, and
the blood of many brave hearts. No! It shall not be shed in
vain! Forward! Brave people! The goddess of liberty leads
you on! And as the sea breaks through and destroys the
barriers that would oppose its fury, so do ye overwhelm
the bulwark of tyranny, and with her impetuous flood
sweep it away from the land which it usurps.
(Drums.)
Hark! Hark! How often has this sound summoned my
joyous steps to the field of battle and of victory! How
bravely did I tread, with my gallant comrades, the dangerous path of fame! And now from this dungeon I shall go
forth to meet a glorious death; I die for freedom, for the
cause of which I have lived and fought, and for which I
now offer myself up a sorrowing sacrifice.
(The background is occupied by Spanish soldiers with halberts.)
Yes, lead them on! Close your ranks; ye terrify me not.
I am accustomed to stand amid the serried ranks of war,
and environed by the threatening forms of death; to feel,
with double zest, the energy of life.
(Drums.)
The foe closes round on every side! Swords are flashing;
courage, friends! Behind are your parents, your wives, your
children!

(Pointing to the guard.)
> And these are impelled by the word of their leader, not by their own free will. Protect your homes! And to save those who are most dear to you, be ready to follow my example, and to fall with joy.

(Drums. As he advances through the guards towards the door in the background the curtain falls. The music joins in, and the scene closes with a symphony of victory.)

Iphigenia in Tauris

Dramatis Personae

IPHIGENIA
THOAS, *King of Tauris*
ARKAS, *an official of King Thoas*
ORESTER, *brother of Iphigenia*
PYLADES, *companion of Orestes*

Iphigenia in Tauris

ACT I

SCENE I.—*A Grove before the Temple of Diana.*

IPHIGENIA *(Alone)*:

BENEATH your leafy gloom, ye waving boughs
Of this old, shady, consecrated grove,
As in the goddess' silent sanctuary,
With the same shuddering feeling forth I step,
As when I trod it first; nor ever here
Doth my unquiet spirit feel at home.
Long as a higher will, to which I bow,
Hath kept me here concealed, still, as at first,
I feel myself a stranger. For the sea
Doth sever me, alas! from those I love:
And day by day upon the shore I stand,
The land of Hellas seeking with my soul;
But, to my sighs, the hollow-sounding waves
Bring, save their own hoarse murmurs, no reply.
Alas for him! who, friendless and alone,
Remote from parents and from brethren dwells:
From him grief snatches every coming joy
Ere it doth reach his lip. His yearning thoughts
Throng back forever to his father's halls,
Where first to him the radiant sun unclosed
The gates of heaven; where closer, day by day,
Brothers and sisters, leagued in pastime sweet,
Around each other twined love's tender bonds.
I will not reckon with the gods; yet truly
Deserving of lament is woman's lot.

Translated by Anna Swanwick

Man rules alike at home and in the field,
Nor is in foreign climes without resource:
Him conquest crowneth, him possession gladdens,
And him an honorable death awaits.
How circumscribed is woman's destiny!
Obedience to a harsh, imperious lord,
Her duty and her comfort: sad her fate,
Whom hostile fortune drives to lands remote!
Thus Thoas holds me here, a noble man,
Bound with a heavy though a sacred chain.
Oh, how it shames me, goddess, to confess
That with repugnance I perform these rites
For thee, divine protectress! unto whom
I would in freedom dedicate my life.
In thee, Diana, I have always hoped;
And still I hope in thee, who didst infold
Within the holy shelter of thine arm
The outcast daughter of the mighty king.
Daughter of Jove! hast thou from ruined Troy
Led back in triumph to his native land
The mighty man, whom thou didst sore afflict,
His daughter's life in sacrifice demanding,—
Hast thou for him, the god-like Agamemnon,
Who to thine altar led his darling child,
Preserved his wife, Electra, and his son,
His dearest treasures?—then at length restore
Thy suppliant also to her friends and home,
And save her, as thou once from death didst save,
So now, from living here, a second death.

SCENE II.

ARKAS:

The king hath sent me hither, bade me greet
With hail, and fair salute, Diana's priestess.
For new and wondrous conquest, this the day,
When to her goddess Tauris renders thanks.
I hasten on before the king and host,
Himself to herald, and its near approach.

IPHIGENIA:

We are prepared to give them worthy greeting:
Our goddess doth behold with gracious eye

The welcome sacrifice from Thoas' hand.

ARKAS:

Would that I also found the priestess' eye,
Much honored, much revered one, found thine eye,
O consecrated maid, more calm, more bright,
To all a happy omen! Still doth grief,
With gloom mysterious, shroud thy inner mind:
Vainly, through many a tedious year, we wait
For one confiding utterance from thy breast.
Long as I've known thee in this holy place,
That look of thine hath ever made me shudder;
And, as with iron hands, thy soul remains
Locked in the deep recesses of thy breast.

IPHIGENIA:

As doth become the exile and the orphan.

ARKAS:

Dost thou, then, here seem exiled and an orphan?

IPHIGENIA:

Can foreign scenes our fatherland replace?

ARKAS:

Thy fatherland is foreign now to thee.

IPHIGENIA:

Hence is it that my bleeding heart ne'er heals.
In early youth, when first my soul, in love,
Held father, mother, brethren fondly twined,
A group of tender germs, in union sweet,
We sprang in beauty from the parent stem,
And heavenward grew: alas! a foreign curse
Then seized and severed me from those I loved,
And wrenched with iron grasp the beauteous bands.
It vanished then, the fairest charm of youth,
The simple gladness of life's early dawn;
Though saved, I was a shadow of myself,
And life's fresh joyance blooms in me no more.

ARKAS:

If thou wilt ever call thyself unblest,
I must accuse thee of ingratitude.

IPHIGENIA:

Thanks have you ever.

ARKAS:

                  Not the honest thanks
Which prompt the heart to offices of love;

The joyous glance, revealing to the host
A grateful spirit, with its lot content.
When thee a deep mysterious destiny
Brought to this sacred fane, long years ago,
To greet thee, as a treasure sent from heaven,
With reverence and affection, Thoas came.
Benign and friendly was this shore to thee,
To every stranger else with horror fraught;
For, till thy coming, none e'er trod our realm
But fell, according to an ancient rite,
A bloody victim at Diana's shrine.

IPHIGENIA:

Freely to breathe alone is not to live.
Say, is it life within this holy fane,
Like a poor ghost around its sepulchre
To linger out my days? Or call you that
A life of conscious happiness and joy,
When every hour, dreamed listlessly away,
Still leadeth onward to those gloomy days
Which the sad troop of the departed spend
In self-forgetfulness on Lethe's shore?
A useless life is but an early death:
This woman's destiny hath still been mine.

ARKAS:

I can forgive, though I must needs deplore,
The noble pride which underrates itself:
It robs thee of the happiness of life.
But hast thou, since thy coming here, done naught?
Who hath the monarch's gloomy temper cheered?
Who hath with gentle eloquence annulled,
From year to year, the usage of our sires,
By which, a victim at Diana's shrine,
Each stranger perished, thus from certain death
Sending so oft the rescued captive home?
Hath not Diana, harboring no revenge
For this suspension of her bloody rites,
In richest measure heard thy gentle prayer?
On joyous pinions o'er the advancing host,
Doth not triumphant conquest proudly soar?
And feels not every one a happier lot,
Since Thoas, who so long hath guided us

With wisdom and with valor, swayed by thee,
The joy of mild benignity approves,
Which leads him to relax the rigid claims
Of mute submission? Call thyself useless! Thou,
When, from thy being, o'er a thousand hearts,
A healing balsam flows? when to a race,
To whom a god consigned thee, thou dost prove
A fountain of perpetual happiness,
And from this dire, inhospitable coast,
Dost to the stranger grant a safe return?

IPHIGENIA:

The little done doth vanish to the mind
Which forward sees how much remains to do.

ARKAS:

Him dost thou praise, who underrates his deeds?

IPHIGENIA:

Who weigheth his own deeds is justly blamed.

ARKAS:

He too, real worth too proudly who condemns,
As who, too vainly, spurious worth o'errateth.
Trust me, and heed the counsel of a man
With honest zeal devoted to thy service:
When Thoas comes today to speak with thee,
Lend to his purposed words a gracious ear.

IPHIGENIA:

Thy well-intentioned counsel troubles me:
His offer I have ever sought to shun.

ARKAS:

Thy duty and thy interest calmly weigh.
Sithence King Thoas lost his son and heir,
Among his followers he trusts but few,
And trusts those few no more as formerly.
With jealous eye he views each noble's son
As the successor of his realm: he dreads
A solitary, helpless age—perchance
Sudden rebellion and untimely death.
A Scythian studies not the rules of speech,
And least of all the king. He who is used
To act and to command, knows not the art,
From far, with subtle tact, to guide discourse
Through many windings to its destined goal.

Thwart not his purpose by a cold refusal,
By an intended misconception. Meet,
With gracious mien, half-way the royal wish.

IPHIGENIA:

Shall I, then, speed the doom that threatens me?

ARKAS:

His gracious offer canst thou call a threat?

IPHIGENIA:

'Tis the most terrible of all to me.

ARKAS:

For his affection grant him confidence.

IPHIGENIA:

If he will first redeem my soul from fear.

ARKAS:

Why dost thou hide from him thy origin?

IPHIGENIA:

A priestess secrecy doth well become.

ARKAS:

Naught to a monarch should a secret be;
And, though he doth not seek to fathom thine,
His noble nature feels, ay, deeply feels,
That thou with care dost hide thyself from him.

IPHIGENIA:

Ill-will and anger harbors he against me?

ARKAS:

Almost it seems so. True, he speaks not of thee;
But casual words have taught me that the wish
Thee to possess hath firmly seized his soul:
Oh, leave him not a prey unto himself,
Lest his displeasure, ripening in his breast,
Should work thee woe, so with repentance thou
Too late my faithful counsel shalt recall!

IPHIGENIA:

How! doth the monarch purpose what no man
Of noble mind, who loves his honest name,
Whose bosom reverence for the gods restrains,
Would ever think of? Will he force employ
To drag me from the altar to his bed?
Then will I call the gods, and chiefly thee,
Diana, goddess resolute, to aid me:
Thyself a virgin, wilt a virgin shield,
And to thy priestess gladly render aid.

ARKAS:

Be tranquil! Passion, and youth's fiery blood,
Impel not Thoas rashly to commit
A deed so lawless. In his present mood,
I fear from him another harsh resolve,
Which (for his soul is steadfast and unmoved)
He then will execute without delay.
Therefore I pray thee, canst thou grant no more,
At least be grateful—give thy confidence.

IPHIGENIA:

Oh, tell me what is further known to thee.

ARKAS:

Learn it from him. I see the king approach:
Him thou dost honor, thine own heart enjoins
To meet him kindly and with confidence.
A man of noble mind may oft be led
By woman's gentle word.

IPHIGENIA *(alone)*:

How to observe
His faithful counsel see I not in sooth.
But willingly the duty I perform
Of giving thanks for benefits received,
And much I wish that to the king my lips
With truth could utter what would please his ear.

SCENE III.

IPHIGENIA:

Her royal gifts the goddess shower on thee,
Imparting conquest, wealth, and high renown,
Dominion, and the welfare of thy house;
With the fulfilment of each pious wish,
That thou, whose sway for multitudes provides,
Thyself mayest be supreme in happiness!

THOAS:

Contented were I with my people's praise;
My conquests others more than I enjoy.
Oh! be he king or subject, he's most blest,
Whose happiness is centred in his home.
My deep affliction thou didst share with me
What time, in war's encounter, the fell sword
Tore from my side my last, my dearest son:

So long as fierce revenge possessed my heart,
I did not feel my dwelling's dreary void;
But now, returning home, my rage appeased,
Their kingdom wasted, and my son avenged,
I find there nothing left to comfort me.
The glad obedience I was wont to see
Kindling in every eye, is smothered now
In discontent and gloom: each, pondering, weighs
The changes which a future day may bring,
And serves the childless king because he must.
To-day I come within this sacred fane,   •
Which I have often entered to implore
And thank the gods for conquest. In my breast
I bear an old and fondly cherished wish,
To which methinks thou canst not be a stranger:
I hope, a blessing to myself and realm,
To lead thee to my dwelling as my bride.

IPHIGENIA:
Too great thine offer, king, to one unknown:
Abashed the fugitive before thee stands,
Who on this shore sought only what thou gavest,—
Safety and peace.

THOAS:
                    Thus still to shroud thyself
From me, as from the lowest, in the veil
Of mystery which wrapped thy coming here,
Would in no country be deemed just or right.
Strangers this shore appalled: 'twas so ordained,
Alike by law and stern necessity.
From thee alone,—a kindly welcomed guest,
Who hast enjoyed each hallowed privilege,
And spent thy days in freedom unrestrained,—
From thee I hoped that confidence to gain
Which every faithful host may justly claim.

IPHIGENIA:
If I concealed, O king! my name, my race,
It was embarrassment, and not mistrust.
For didst thou know who stands before thee now,
And what accursed head thine arm protects,
Strange horror would possess thy mighty heart;
And, far from wishing me to share thy throne,

Thou, ere the time appointed, from thy realm
Wouldst banish me; wouldst thrust me forth, perchance.
Before a glad re-union with my friends
And period to my wanderings is ordained,
To meet that sorrow, which, in every clime,
With cold, inhospitable, fearful hand,
Awaits the outcast, exiled from his home.

THOAS:

Whate'er respecting thee the gods decree,
Whate'er their doom for thee and for thy house,
Since thou hast dwelt amongst us, and enjoyed
The privilege the pious stranger claims,
To me hath failed no blessing sent from heaven;
And to persuade me, that protecting thee
I shield a guilty head, were hard indeed.

IPHIGENIA:

Thy bounty, not the guest, draws blessings down

THOAS:

The kindness shown the wicked is not blest.
End, then, thy silence, priestess: not unjust
Is he who doth demand it. In my hands
The goddess placed thee; thou hast been to me
As sacred as to her, and her behest
Shall for the future also be my law:
If thou canst hope in safety to return
Back to thy kindred, I renounce my claims;
But is thy homeward path forever closed,
Or doth thy race in hopeless exile rove,
Or lie extinguished by some mighty woe,
Then may I claim thee by more laws than one.
Speak openly: thou knowest I keep my word.

IPHIGENIA:

Its ancient bands reluctantly my tongue
Doth loose, a long-hid secret to divulge;
For, once imparted, it resumes no more
The safe asylum of the inmost heart,
But thenceforth, as the powers above decree,
Doth work its ministry of weal or woe.
Attend! I issue from the Titan's race.

THOAS:

A word momentous calmly hast thou spoken.
Him namest thou ancestor whom all the world

285

Knows as a sometime favorite of the gods?
Is it that Tantalus, whom Jove himself
Drew to his council and his social board?
On whose experienced words, with wisdom fraught,
As on the language of an oracle,
E'en gods delighted hung?

IPHIGENIA:

'Tis even he:
But the immortal gods with mortal men
Should not, on equal terms, hold intercourse;
For all too feeble is the human race,
Not to grow dizzy on unwonted heights.
Ignoble was he not, and no betrayer;
To be the Thunderer's slave, he was too great;
To be his friend and comrade,—but a man.
His crime was human, and their doom severe;
For poets sing, that treachery and pride
Did from Jove's table hurl him headlong down
To grovel in the depths of Tartarus.
Alas! and his whole race must bear their hate.

THOAS:
Bear they their own guilt, or their ancestor's?

IPHIGENIA:
The Titan's mighty breast and nervous frame
Was his descendants' certain heritage;
But round their brow Jove forged a band of brass.
Wisdom and patience, prudence and restraint,
He from their gloomy, fearful eye concealed;
In them each passion grew to savage rage,
And headlong rushed with violence unchecked.
Already Pelops, Tantalus' loved son,
Mighty of will, obtained his beauteous bride,
Hippodamia, child of Oenomaus,
Through treachery and murder: she, ere long,
To glad her consort's heart, bare him two sons,
Thyest and Atreus. They with envy marked
The ever-growing love their father bare
To his first-born, sprung from another union.
Hate leagued the pair; and secretly they wrought.
In fratricide, the first dread crime. The sire
Hippodamia held as murderess:

With savage rage he claimed from her his son,
And she in terror did destroy herself—

THOAS:

Thou'rt silent? Pause not in thy narrative;
Repent not of thy confidence—say on!

IPHIGENIA:

How blest is he who his progenitors
With pride remembers, to the listener tells
The story of their greatness, of their deeds,
And, silently rejoicing, sees himself
The latest link of this illustrious chain!
For seldom does the self-same stock produce
The monster and the demigod: a line
Or good or evil ushers in, at last,
The glory or the terror of the world.—
After the death of Pelops, his two sons
Ruled o'er the city with divided sway.
But such an union could not long endure.
His brother's honor first Thyestes wounds.
In vengeance Atreus drove him from the realm.
Thyestes, planning horrors, long before
Had stealthily procured his brother's son,
Whom he in secret nurtured as his own.
Revenge and fury in his breast he poured,
Then to the royal city sent him forth,
That in his uncle he might slay his sire.
The meditated murder was disclosed,
And by the king most cruelly avenged,
Who slaughtered, as he thought, his brother's son.
Too late he learned whose dying tortures met
His drunken gaze; and, seeking to assuage
The insatiate vengeance that possessed his soul,
He planned a deed unheard of. He assumed
A friendly tone; seemed reconciled, appeased;
And lured his brother, with his children twain,
Back to his kingdom; these he seized and slew,
Then placed the loathsome and abhorrent food
At his first meal before the unconscious sire.
And when Thyestes had his hunger stilled
With his own flesh, a sadness seized his soul:
He for his children asked,—their steps, their voice,

Fancied he heard already at the door;
And Atreus, grinning with malicious joy,
Threw in the members of the slaughtered boys.—
Shuddering, O king, thou dost avert thy face!
So did the sun his radiant visage hide,
And swerve his chariot from the eternal path.
These, monarch, are thy priestess' ancestors;
And many a dreadful fate of mortal doom,
And many a deed of the bewildered brain,
Dark night doth cover with her sable wing,
Or shroud in gloomy twilight.

THOAS:

                    Hidden there
Let them abide. A truce to horror now,
And tell me by what miracle thou sprangest
From race so savage.

IPHIGENIA:

                Atreus' eldest son
Was Agamemnon,—he, O king, my sire!
But I may say with truth, that, from a child,
In him the model of a perfect man
I witnessed ever. Clytemnestra bore
To him, myself, the firstling of their love,
Electra then. Peaceful the monarch ruled,
And to the house of Tantalus was given
A long-withheld repose. A son alone
Was wanting to complete my parents' bliss:
Scarce was this wish fulfilled, and young Orestes,
The household's darling, with his sisters grew,
When new misfortunes vexed our ancient house.
To you hath come the rumor of the war,
Which, to avenge the fairest woman's wrongs,
The force united of the Grecian kings
Round Ilion's walls encamped. Whether the town
Was humbled, and achieved their great revenge,
I have not heard. My father led the host.
In Aulis vainly for a favoring gale
They waited; for, enraged against their chief,
Diana stayed their progress, and required,
Through Chaleas' voice, the monarch's eldest daughter.
They lured me with my mother to the camp:

They dragged me to the altar, and this head
There to the goddess doomed.—She was appeased;
She did not wish my blood, and shrouded me
In a protecting cloud: within this temple
I first awakened from the dream of death;
Yes, I myself am she, Iphigenia,
Grandchild of Atreus, Agamemnon's child,
Diana's priestess, I who speak with thee.

THOAS:

I yield no higher honor or regard
To the king's daughter than the maid unknown:
Once more my first proposal I repeat;
Come, follow me, and share what I possess.

IPHIGENIA:

How dare I venture such a step, O king?
Hath not the goddess who protected me
Alone a right to my devoted head?
'Twas she who chose for me this sanctuary,
Where she perchance reserves me for my sire,
By my apparent death enough chastised,
To be the joy and solace of his age.
Perchance my glad return is near; and how,
If I, unmindful of her purposes,
Had here attached myself against her will?
I asked a signal, did she wish my stay.

THOAS:

The signal is, that still thou tarriest here.
Seek not evasively such vain pretexts.
Not many words are needed to refuse,
The *no* alone is heard by the refused.

IPHIGENIA:

Mine are not words meant only to deceive:
I have to thee my inmost heart revealed.
And doth no inward voice suggest to thee,
How I with yearning soul must pine to see
My father, mother, and my long-lost home?
Oh, let thy vessels bear me thither, king!
That in the ancient halls, where sorrow still
In accents low doth fondly breathe my name,
Joy, as in welcome of a new-born child,

289

May round the columns twine the fairest wreath.
New life thou wouldst to me and mine impart.

THOAS:

Then, go! Obey the promptings of thy heart,
And to the voice of reason and good counsel
Close thou thine ear. Be quite the woman, give
To every wish the rein, that, bridleless,
May seize on thee, and whirl thee here and there.
When burns the fire of passion in her breast,
No sacred tie withholds her from the wretch
Who would allure her to forsake for him
A husband's or a father's guardian arms;
Extinct within her heart its fiery glow,
The golden tongue of eloquence in vain
With words of truth and power assails her ear.

IPHIGENIA:

Remember now, O king, thy noble words!
My trust and candor wilt thou thus repay?
Thou seemest, methinks, prepared to hear the truth.

THOAS:

For this unlooked-for answer not prepared.
Yet 'twas to be expected: knew I not
That with a woman I had now to deal?

IPHIGENIA:

Upbraid not thus, O king, our feeble sex!
Though not in dignity to match with yours,
The weapons woman wields are not ignoble.
And trust me, Thoas, in thy happiness
I have a deeper insight than thyself.
Thou thinkest, ignorant alike of both,
A closer union would augment our bliss;
Inspired with confidence and honest zeal
Thou strongly urgest me to yield consent:
And here I thank the gods, who give me strength
To shun a doom unratified by them.

THOAS:

'Tis not a god, 'tis thine own heart, that speaks.

IPHIGENIA:

'Tis through the heart alone they speak to us.

THOAS:

To hear them have I not an equal right?

IPHIGENIA:
> The raging tempest drowns the still small voice.

THOAS:
> This voice no doubt the priestess hears alone.

IPHIGENIA:
> Before all others should the prince attend it.

THOAS:
> Thy sacred office, and ancestral right
> To Jove's own table, place thee with the gods
> In closer union than an earth-born savage.

IPHIGENIA:
> Thus must I now the confidence atone
> Thyself didst wring from me!

THOAS:
>   I am a man.
> And better 'tis we end this conference.
> Hear, then, my last resolve. Be priestess still
> Of the great goddess who selected thee;
> And may she pardon me, that I from her,
> Unjustly, and with secret self-reproach,
> Her ancient sacrifice so long withheld!
> From olden time no stranger neared our shore
> But fell a victim at her sacred shrine.
> But thou, with kind affection (which at times
> Seemed like a gentle daughter's tender love,
> At times assumed to my enraptured heart
> The modest inclination of a bride),
> Didst so inthrall me, as with magic bonds,
> That I forgot my duty. Thou didst rock
> My senses in a dream: I did not hear
> My people's murmurs; now they cry aloud,
> Ascribing my poor son's untimely death
> To this my guilt. No longer for thy sake
> Will I oppose the wishes of the crowd,
> Who urgently demand the sacrifice.

IPHIGENIA:
> For mine own sake I ne'er desired it from thee.
> Who to the gods ascribe a thirst for blood
> Do misconceive their nature, and impute
> To them their own inhuman dark desires.

291

Did not Diana snatch me from the priest,
Holding my service dearer than my death?

THOAS:

'Tis not for us, on reason's shifting grounds,
Lightly to guide and construe rites divine.
Perform thy duty: I'll accomplish mine.
Two strangers, whom in caverns of the shore
We found concealed, and whose arrival here
Bodes to my realm no good, are in my power.
With them thy goddess may once more resume
Her ancient, pious, long-suspended rites!
I send them here,—thy duty not unknown.   [Exit.

IPHIGENIA (alone):

Gracious protectress! thou hast clouds
To shelter innocence distressed,
And from the arms of iron fate,
Gently to waft her o'er the sea,
O'er the wide earth's remotest realms,
Where'er it seemeth good to thee.
Wise art thou,—thine all-seeing eye
The future and the past surveys:
Thy glance doth o'er thy children rest,
E'en as thy light, the life of night,
Keeps o'er the earth its silent watch.
O Goddess! keep my hands from blood!
Blessing it never brings, and peace;
And still in evil hours the form
Of the chance-murdered man appears
To fill the unwilling murderer's soul
With horrible and gloomy fears.
For fondly the Immortals view
Man's widely scattered, simple race;
And the poor mortal's transient life
Gladly prolong, that he may lift
Awhile to their eternal heavens
His sympathetic joyous gaze.

ACT II

SCENE I.

ORESTES:
> It is the path of death that now we tread:
> At every step my soul grows more serene.
> When I implored Apollo to remove
> The grisly band of Furies from my side,
> He seemed, with hope-inspiring god-like words,
> To promise aid and safety in the fane
> Of his loved sister, who o'er Tauris rules.
> Thus the prophetic word fulfils itself,
> That with my life shall terminate my woe.
> How easy 'tis for me, whose heart is crushed,
> Whose sense is deadened by a hand divine,
> Thus to renounce the beauteous light of day!
> And must the son of Atreus not intwine
> The wreath of conquest round his dying brow?
> Must I, as my forefathers, as my sire,
> Bleed like a victim,—an ignoble death?
> So be it! Better at the altar here,
> Than in a nook obscure, where kindred hands
> Have spread assassination's wily net.
> Yield me this brief repose, infernal Powers!
> Ye, who, like loosened hounds, still scent the blood
> Which, trickling from my feet, betrays my path.
> Leave me! ere long I come to you below.
> Nor you, nor I, should view the light of day.
> The soft green carpet of the beauteous earth
> Is no arena for unhallowed fiends.
> Below I seek you, where an equal fate
> Binds all in murky, never-ending night.
> Thee only, thee, my Pylades, my friend,
> The guiltless partner of my crime and curse,
> Thee am I loath, before thy time, to take
> To yonder cheerless shore! Thy life or death
> Alone awakens in me hope or fear.

PYLADES:
> Like thee, Orestes, I am not prepared
> Downwards to wander to yon realm of shade.

293

I purpose still, through the entangled paths,
Which seem as they would lead to blackest night,
Again to wind our upward way to life.
Of death I think not: I observe and mark
Whether the gods may not perchance present
Means and fit moment for a joyful flight.
Dreaded or not, the stroke of death must come,
And though the priestess stood with hand upraised,
Prepared to cut our consecrated locks,
Our safety still should be my only thought:
Uplift thy soul above this weak despair;
Desponding doubts but hasten on our peril.
Apollo pledged to us his sacred word,
That in his sister's holy fane for thee
Were comfort, aid, and glad return prepared.
The words of Heaven are not equivocal,
As in despair the poor oppressed one thinks.

ORESTES:

The mystic web of life my mother cast
Around my infant head, and so I grew
An image of my sire; and my mute look
Was aye a bitter and a keen reproof
To her and base Aegisthus. Oh, how oft,
When silently within our gloomy hall
Electra sat, and mused beside the fire,
Have I with anguished spirit climbed her knee,
And watched her bitter tears with sad amaze!
Then would she tell me of our noble sire:
How much I longed to see him—be with him!
Myself at Troy one moment fondly wished,
My sire's return the next. The day arrived—

PYLADES:

Oh, of that awful hour let fiends of hell
Hold nightly converse! Of a time more fair
May the remembrance animate our hearts
To fresh heroic deeds. The gods require
On this wide earth the service of the good,
To work their pleasure. Still they count on thee;
For in thy father's train they sent thee not,
When he to Orcus went unwilling down.

ORESTES:

> Would I had seized the border of his robe,
> And followed him!

PYLADES:

> They kindly cared for me
> Who held thee here: for, hadst thou ceased to live,
> I know not what had then become of me;
> Since I with thee, and for thy sake alone,
> Have from my childhood lived, and wish to live.

ORESTES:

> Remind me not of those delightsome days
> When me thy home a safe asylum gave:
> With fond solicitude thy noble sire
> The half-nipped tender floweret gently reared;
> While thou, a friend and playmate always gay,
> Like to a light and brilliant butterfly
> Around a dusky flower, didst day by day
> Around me with new life thy gambols urge,
> And breathe thy joyous spirit in my soul,
> Until, my cares forgetting, I with thee
> Was lured to snatch the eager joys of youth.

PYLADES:

> My very life began when thee I loved.

ORESTES:

> Say, then thy woes began, and thou speakest truly.
> This is the sharpest sorrow of my lot,
> That, like a plague-infected wretch, I bear
> Death and destruction hid within my breast;
> That, where I tread, e'en on the healthiest spot,
> Ere long the blooming faces round betray
> The anguished features of a lingering death.

PYLADES:

> Were thy breath venom, I had been the first
> To die that death, Orestes. Am I not,
> As ever, full of courage and of joy?
> And love and courage are the spirit's wings
> Wafting to noble actions.

ORESTES:

> Noble actions?
> Time was, when fancy painted such before us!
> When oft, the game pursuing, on we roamed

O'er hill and valley; hoping, that ere long,
Like our great ancestors in heart and hand,
With club and weapon armed, we so might track
The robber to his den, or monster huge.
And then at twilight, by the boundless sea,
Peaceful we sat, reclined against each other;
The waves came dancing to our very feet,
And all before us lay the wide, wide world;
Then on a sudden one would seize his sword,
And future deeds shone round us like the stars,
Which gemmed in countless throngs the vault of night.

PYLADES:

Endless, my friend, the projects which the soul
Burns to accomplish. We would every deed
At once perform as grandly as it shows
After long ages, when from land to land
The poet's swelling song hath rolled it on.
It sounds so lovely what our fathers did,
When, in the silent evening-shade reclined,
We drink it in with music's melting tones;
And what we do is, as their deeds to them,
Toilsome and incomplete!
Thus we pursue what always flies before:
We disregard the path in which we tread,
Scarce see around the footsteps of our sires,
Or heed the trace of their career on earth.
We ever hasten on to chase their shades,
Which, god-like, at a distance far remote,
On golden clouds, the mountain summits crown.
The man I prize not who esteems himself
Just as the people's breath may chance to raise him.
But thou, Orestes, to the gods give thanks,
That they through thee have early done so much.

ORESTES:

When they ordain a man to noble deeds,
To shield from dire calamity his friends,
Extend his empire, or protect its bounds,
Or put to flight its ancient enemies,
Let him be grateful! For to him a god
Imparts the first, the sweetest, joy of life.
Me have they doomed to be a slaughterer,

To be an honored mother's murderer,
And, shamefully a deed of shame avenging,
Me through their own decree they have o'erwhelmed.
Trust me, the race of Tantalus is doomed;
And I, his last descendant, may not perish,
Or crowned with honor or unstained by crime.

PYLADES:

The gods avenge not on the son the deeds
Done by the father. Each, or good or bad,
Of his own actions reaps the due reward.
The parents' blessing, not their curse, descends.

ORESTES:

Methinks their blessing did not lead us here.

PYLADES:

It was at least the mighty gods' decree.

ORESTES:

Then is it their decree which doth destroy us.

PYLADES:

Perform what they command, and wait the event.
Do thou Apollo's sister bear from hence,
That they at Delphi may united dwell,
There by a noble-thoughted race revered:
Thee, for this deed, the lofty pair will view
With gracious eye, and from the hateful grasp
Of the infernal Powers will rescue thee.
E'en now none dares intrude within this grove.

ORESTES:

So shall I die at least a peaceful death.

PYLADES:

Far other are my thoughts, and not unskilled
Have I the future and the past combined
In quiet meditation. Long, perchance,
Hath ripened in the counsel of the gods
The great event. Diana yearns to leave
The savage coast of these barbarians,
Foul with their sacrifice of human blood.
We were selected for the high emprise:
To us it is assigned, and strangely thus
We are conducted to the threshold here.

ORESTES:

My friend, with wondrous skill thou linkest thy wish

With the predestined purpose of the gods.

PYLADES:

Of what avail is prudence, if it fail
Heedful to mark the purposes of Heaven?
A noble man, who much hath sinned, some god
Doth summon to a dangerous enterprise,
Which to achieve appears impossible.
The hero conquers, and atoning serves
Mortals and gods, who thenceforth honor him.

ORESTES:

Am I foredoomed to action and to life,
Would that a god from my distempered brain
Might chase this dizzy fever, which impels
My restless steps along a slippery path,
Stained with a mother's blood, to direful death,
And, pitying, dry the fountain, whence the blood,
Forever spouting from a mother's wounds,
Eternally defiles me!

PYLADES:

                Wait in peace!
Thou dost increase the evil and dost take
The office of the Furies on thyself.
Let me contrive—be still! And when at length
The time for action claims our powers combined,
Then will I summon thee, and on we'll stride,
With cautious boldness to achieve the event.

ORESTES:

I hear Ulysses speak.

PYLADES:

                Nay, mock me not.
Each must select the hero after whom
To climb the steep and difficult ascent
Of high Olympus. And to me it seems
That him nor stratagem nor art defiles
Who consecrates himself to noble deeds.

ORESTES:

I most esteem the brave and upright man.

PYLADES:

And therefore have I not desired thy counsel.
One step's already taken. From our guards
E'en now I this intelligence have gained,—

A strange and godlike woman holds in check
The execution of that bloody law:
Incense and prayer, and an unsullied heart,—
These are the gifts she offers to the gods.
Rumor extols her highly: it is thought
That from the race of Amazon she springs,
And hither fled some great calamity.

ORESTES:

Her gentle sway, it seems lost all its power
When hither came the culprit whom the curse,
Like murky night, envelops and pursues.
Our doom to seal, the pious thirst for blood
The ancient cruel rite again unchains:
The monarch's savage will decrees our death;
A woman cannot save when he condemns.

PYLADES:

That 'tis a woman, is a ground for hope!
A man, the very best, with cruelty
At length may so familiarize his mind,
His character through custom so transform,
That he shall come to make himself a law
Of what at first his very soul abhorred.
But woman doth retain the stamp of mind
She first assumed. On her we may depend
In good or evil with more certainty.
She comes: leave us alone. I dare not tell
At once our names nor unreserved confide
Our fortunes to her. Now, retire a while;
And ere she speaks with thee we'll meet again.

SCENE II.

IPHIGENIA:

Whence art thou? Stranger, speak! To me thy bearing
Stamps thee of Grecian, not of Scythian, race.
(She unbinds his chains.)
The freedom that I give is dangerous:
The gods avert the doom that threatens you!

PYLADES:

Delicious music! dearly welcome tones
Of our own language in a foreign land!

299

With joy my captive eye once more beholds
The azure mountains of my native coast.
Oh, let this joy that I too am a Greek
Convince thee, priestess! How I need thine aid
A moment I forget, my spirit rapt
In contemplation of so fair a vision.
If fate's dread mandate doth not seal thy lips,
From which of our illustrious races say,
Dost thou thy god-like origin derive?

IPHIGENIA:

The priestess whom the goddess hath herself
Selected and ordained doth speak with thee.
Let that suffice; but tell me, who art thou,
And what unblessed o'erruling destiny
Hath hither led thee with thy friend?

PYLADES:

The woe,
Whose hateful presence ever dogs our steps,
I can with ease relate. Oh, would that thou
Couldst with like ease, divine one, shed on us
One ray of cheering hope! We are from Crete,
Adrastus' sons, and I, the youngest born,
Named Cephalus; my eldest brother, he,
Laodamas. Between us stood a youth
Savage and wild, who severed e'en in sport
The joy and concord of our early youth.
Long as our father led his powers at Troy,
Passive our mother's mandate we obeyed;
But when, enriched with booty, he returned,
And shortly after died, a contest fierce,
Both for the kingdom and their father's wealth,
His children parted. I the eldest joined;
He slew our brother; and the Furies hence
For kindred murder dog his restless steps.
But to this savage shore the Delphian god
Hath sent us, cheered by hope. He bade us wait
Within his sister's consecrated fane
The blessed hand of aid. Captives we are;
And, hither brought, before thee now we stand
Ordained for sacrifice. My tale is told.

IPHIGENIA:

    Fell Troy! Dear man, assure me of its fall.

PYLADES:

    Prostrate it lies. Oh, unto us insure
    Deliverance! The promised aid of heaven
    More swiftly bring. Take pity on my brother.
    Oh, say to him a kind, a gracious word:
    But spare him when thou speakest,—earnestly
    This I implore: for all too easily,
    Through joy and sorrow and through memory,
    Torn and distracted is his inmost being.
    A feverish madness oft doth seize on him,
    Yielding his spirit, beautiful and free,
    A prey to furies.

IPHIGENIA:

                    Great as is thy woe,
    Forget it, I conjure thee, for a while,
    Till I am satisfied.

PYLADES:

                    The stately town,
    Which ten long years withstood the Grecian host,
    Now lies in ruins, ne'er to rise again;
    Yet many a hero's grave will oft recall
    Our sad remembrance to that barbarous shore.
    There lies Achilles and his noble friend.

IPHIGENIA:

    So are ye god-like forms reduced to dust!

PYLADES:

    Nor Palamede, nor Ajax, e'er again
    The daylight of their native land beheld.

IPHIGENIA:

    He speaks not of my father, doth not name
    Him with the fallen. He may yet survive!
    I may behold him! still hope on, fond heart!

PYLADES:

    Yet happy are the thousands who received
    Their bitter death-blow from a hostile hand!
    For terror wild, and end most tragical,
    Some hostile, angry deity prepared,
    Instead of triumph, for the home-returning
    Do human voices never reach this shore?

Far as their sound extends, they bear the fame
Of deeds unparalleled. And is the woe
Which fills Mycene's halls with ceaseless sighs
To thee a secret still?—And knowest thou not
That Clytemnestra, with Aegisthus' aid,
Her royal consort artfully ensnared,
And murdered on the day of his return?—
The monarch's house thou honorest! I perceive
Thy breast with tidings vainly doth contend
Fraught with such monstrous and unlooked-for woe.
Art thou the daughter of a friend? art born
Within the circuit of Mycene's walls?
Conceal it not, nor call me to account
That here the horrid crime I first announce.

IPHIGENIA:

Proceed, and tell me how the deed was done.

PYLADES:

The day of his return, as from the bath
Arose the monarch, tranquil and refreshed,
His robe demanding from his consort's hand,
A tangled garment, complicate with folds,
She o'er his shoulders flung and noble head:
And when, as from a net, he vainly strove
To extricate himself, the traitor, base
Aegisthus, smote him; and, enveloped thus,
Great Agamemnon sought the shades below.

IPHIGENIA:

And what reward received the base accomplice?

PYLADES:

A queen and kingdom he possessed already.

IPHIGENIA:

Base passion prompted, then, the deed of shame?

PYLADES:

And feelings, cherished long, of deep revenge.

IPHIGENIA:

How had the monarch injured Clytemnestra?

PYLADES:

By such a dreadful deed, that, if on earth
Aught could exculpate murder, it were this.
To Aulis he allured her, when the fleet
With unpropitious winds the goddess stayed;

And there, a victim at Diana's shrine,
The monarch, for the welfare of the Greeks,
Her eldest daughter doomed, Iphigenia.
And this, so rumor saith, within her heart
Planted such deep abhorrence, that forthwith
She to Aegisthus hath resigned herself,
And round her husband flung the web of death

IPHIGENIA *(veiling herself)*:
It is enough! Thou wilt again behold me.

PYLADES *(alone)*:
The fortune of this royal house, it seems,
Doth move her deeply. Whosoe'er she be,
She must herself have known the monarch well;—
For our good fortune, from a noble house,
She hath been sold to bondage. Peace, my heart!
And let us steer our course with prudent zeal
Toward the star of hope which gleams upon us.

ACT III

Scene I.

IPHIGENIA:

Unhappy man, I only loose thy bonds
In token of a still severer doom.
The freedom which the sanctuary imparts,
Like the last life-gleam o'er the dying face,
But heralds death. I cannot, dare not, say
Your doom is hopeless; for, with murderous hand,
Could I inflict the fatal blow myself?
And, while I here am priestess of Diana,
None, be he who he may, dare touch your heads.
But the incensed king, should I refuse
Compliance with the rites himself enjoined,
Will choose another virgin from my train
As my successor. Then, alas! with naught,
Save ardent wishes, can I succor you,
Much-honored countrymen! The humblest slave,
Who had but neared our sacred household hearth,
Is dearly welcome in a foreign land:
How with proportioned joy and blessing, then,
Shall I receive the man who doth recall
The image of the heroes, whom I learned
To honor from my parents, and who cheers
My inmost heart with flattering gleams of hope!

ORESTES:

Does prudent forethought prompt thee to conceal
Thy name and race? or may I hope to know
Who, like a heavenly vision, meets me thus?

IPHIGENIA:

Yes, thou shalt know me. Now conclude the tale
Of which thy brother only told me half:
Relate their end, who, coming home from Troy,
On their own threshold met a doom severe
And most unlooked for. Young I was in sooth
When first conducted to this foreign shore,
Yet well I recollect the timid glance
Of wonder and amazement which I cast
On those heroic forms. When they went forth,

It seemed as though Olympus had sent down
The glorious figures of a by-gone world,
To frighten Ilion; and above them all,
Great Agamemnon towered pre-eminent!
Oh, tell me! Fell the hero in his home,
Through Clytemnestra's and Aegisthus' wiles?

ORESTES:
   .   He fell!

IPHIGENIA:
          Unblest Mycene! Thus the sons
Of Tantalus, with barbarous hands, have sown
Curse upon curse; and, as the shaken weed
Scatters around a thousand poison-seeds,
So they assassins ceaseless generate,
Their children's children ruthless to destroy.—
Now tell the remnant of thy brother's tale,
Which horror darkly hid from me before.
How did the last descendant of the race,—
The gentle child, to whom the gods assigned
The office of avenger,—how did he
Escape that day of blood? Did equal fate
Around Orestes throw Avernus' net?
Say, was he saved? and is he still alive?
And lives Electra too?

ORESTES:
          They both survive.

IPHIGENIA:
Golden Apollo, lend thy choicest beams!
Lay them an offering at the throne of Jove!
For I am poor and dumb!

ORESTES:
               If social bonds,
Or ties more close, connect thee with this house,
As this thy rapturous joy betrayeth to me,
Oh, then, rein in thy heart and hold it fast!
For insupportable the sudden plunge
From happiness to sorrow's gloomy depth.
Thou knowest only Agamemnon's death.

IPHIGENIA:
And is not this intelligence enough?

Johann Wolfgang von Goethe

ORESTES:
> Half of the horror only hast thou heard.

IPHIGENIA:
> What should I fear? Oreste, Electra, live.

ORESTES:
> And fearest thou for Clytemnestra naught?

IPHIGENIA:
> Her, neither hope nor fear hath power to save.

ORESTES:
> She to the land of hope hath bid farewell.

IPHIGENIA:
> Did her repentant hand shed her own blood?

ORESTES:
> Not so; yet her own blood inflicted death.

IPHIGENIA:
> More plainly speak, nor leave me in suspense.
> Uncertainty around my anxious head
> Her dusky, thousand-folded pinion waves.

ORESTES:
> Have, then, the powers above selected me
> To be the herald of a dreadful deed,
> Which in the drear and soundless realms of night
> I fain would hide forever? 'Gainst my will
> Thy gentle voice constrains me: it demands,
> And shall receive, a tale of direst woe.
> Electra, on the day when fell her sire,
> Her brother from impending doom concealed:
> Him Strophius, his father's relative,
> Received with kindest care, and reared him up,
> With his own son, named Pylades, who soon
> Around the stranger twined love's fairest bonds.
> And as they grew, within their inmost souls,
> There sprang the burning longing to revenge
> The monarch's death. Unlooked for, and disguised,
> They reach Mycene, feigning to have brought
> The mournful tidings of Orestes' death,
> Together with his ashes. Them the queen
> Gladly receives. Within the house they enter:
> Orestes to Electra shows himself;
> She fans the fires of vengeance into flame,
> Which, in the sacred presence of a mother,

Had burned more dimly. Silently she leads
Her brother to the spot where fell their sire;
Where lurid blood-marks, on the oft-washed floor,
With pallid streaks anticipate revenge.
With fiery eloquence she pictured forth
Each circumstance of that atrocious deed,—
Her own oppressed and miserable life,
The prosperous traitor's insolent demeanor,
The perils threatening Agamemnon's race
From her who had become their stepmother.—
Then in his hand the ancient dagger thrust,
Which often in the house of Tantalus
With savage fury raged,—and by her son
Was Clytemnestra slain.

IPHIGENIA:

Immortal powers!
Whose pure and blest existence glides away
'Mid ever-shifting clouds, me have ye kept
So many years secluded from the world,
Retained me near yourselves, consigned to me
The child-like task to feed the sacred fire,
And taught my spirit, like the hallowed flame,
With never-clouded brightness to aspire
To your pure mansions,—but at length to feel
With keener woe the horror of my house?
Oh, tell me of the poor unfortunate!
Speak of Orestes!

ORESTES:

Oh, could I speak to tell thee of his death!
Forth from the slain one's spouting blood arose
His mother's ghost;
And to the ancient daughters of the night
Cries, "Let him not escape,—the matricide!
Pursue the victim, dedicate to you!"
They hear, and glare around with hollow eyes,
Like greedy eagles. In their murky dens
They stir themselves; and from the corners creep
Their comrades, dire Remorse and pallid Fear;
Before them fumes a mist of Acheron;
Perplexingly around the murderer's brow
The eternal contemplation of the past

307

Rolls in its cloudy circles. Once again
The grisly band, commissioned to destroy,
Pollute earth's beautiful and heaven-sown fields,
From which an ancient curse had banished them.
Their rapid feet the fugitive pursue:
They only pause to start a wilder fear.

IPHIGENIA:

Unhappy one: thy lot resembles his;
Thou feelest what he, poor fugitive, must suffer.

ORESTES:

What sayest thou? Why presume my fate like his?

IPHIGENIA:

A brother's murder weighs upon thy soul:
Thy younger brother told the mournful tale.

ORESTES:

I cannot suffer that thy noble soul
Should by a word of falsehood be deceived.
In cunning rich and practised in deceit,
A web ensnaring let the stranger weave
To snare the stranger's feet: between us twain
Be truth!
I am Orestes! and this guilty head
Is stooping to the tomb, and covets death:
It will be welcome now in any shape.
Whoe'er thou art, for thee and for my friend
I wish deliverance;—I desire it not.
Thou seemest to linger here against thy will:
Contrive some means of flight, and leave me here;
My lifeless corpse hurled headlong from the rock,
My blood shall mingle with the dashing waves,
And bring a curse upon this barbarous shore!
Return together home to lovely Greece,
With joy a new existence to commence.

(ORESTES *retires.*)

IPHIGENIA:

At length Fulfilment, fairest child of Jove,
Thou dost descend upon me from on high!
How vast thine image! scarce my straining eye
Can reach thy hands, which, filled with golden fruit
And wreaths of blessing, from Olympus' height
Shower treasures down. As by his bounteous gifts

We recognize the monarch (for what seems
To thousands opulence, is naught to him);
So you, ye heavenly Powers, are also known
By bounty long withheld, and wisely planned.
Ye only know what things are good for us:
Ye view the future's wide-extended realm,
While from our eye a dim or starry veil
Thy project shrouds. Calmly ye hear our prayers,
When we like children sue for greater speed.
Not immature ye pluck heaven's golden fruit,
And woe to him who with impatient hand,
His date of joy forestalling, gathers death.
Let not this long-awaited happiness,
Which yet my heart hath scarcely realized,
Like to the shadow of departed friends,
Glide vainly by with triple sorrow fraught!

ORESTES *(returning):*

Dost thou for Pylades and for thyself
Implore the gods, blend not my name with yours:
Thou wilt not save the wretch whom thou wouldst join,
But will participate his curse and woe.

IPHIGENIA:

My destiny is firmly bound to thine.

ORESTES:

No, say not so: alone and unattended
Let me descend to Hades. Though thou shouldst
In thine own veil enwrap the guilty one,
Thou couldst not shroud him from his wakeful foes;
And e'en thy sacred presence, heavenly maid,
But driveth them aside and scares them not.
With brazen, impious feet they dare not tread
Within the precincts of this sacred grove;
Yet in the distance, ever and anon,
I hear their horrid laughter, like the howl
Of famished wolves, beneath the tree wherein
The traveller hides. Without, encamped they lie;
And should I quit this consecrated grove,
Shaking their serpent locks, they would arise,
And, raising clouds of dust on every side,
Ceaseless pursue their miserable prey.

IPHIGENIA:

    Orestes, canst thou hear a friendly word?

ORESTES:

    Reserve it for one favored by the gods.

IPHIGENIA:

    To thee they give anew the light of hope.

ORESTES:

    Through clouds and smoke I see the feeble gleam
    Of the death-stream which lights me down to hell.

IPHIGENIA:

    Hast thou one sister only, thy Electra?

ORESTES:

    I knew but one; yet her kind destiny,
    Which seemed to us so terrible, betimes
    Removed an elder sister from the woe
    Which o'er the house of Pelops aye impends.
    Oh, cease thy questions, nor thus league thyself
    With the Erinnys! still they blow away,
    With fiendish joy, the ashes from my soul,
    Lest the last embers of the fiery brand,
    The fatal heritage of Pelops' house,
    Should there be quenched. Must, then, the fire for aye,
    Deliberately kindled and supplied
    With hellish sulphur, sear my tortured soul?

IPHIGENIA:

    I scatter fragrant incense in the flame.
    Oh, let the pure, the gentle, breath of love,
    Low murmuring, cool thy bosom's fiery glow!
    Orestes, fondly loved,—canst thou not hear me?
    Hath the terrific Furies' grisly band
    Dried up the blood of life within thy veins?
    Creeps there, as from the Gorgon's direful head,
    A petrifying charm through all thy limbs?
    With hollow accents from a mother's blood,
    If voices call thee to the shades below,
    May not a sister's word, with blessing rife,
    Call from Olympus' height help-rendering gods?

ORESTES:

    She calls! she calls!— Dost thou desire my doom?
    Is there a Fury shrouded in thy form?

Who art thou, that thy voice thus horribly
Can harrow up my bosom's inmost depths?

IPHIGENIA:

Thine inmost heart reveals it. I am she,—
Iphigenia,—look on me, Orestes!

ORESTES:

Thou!

IPHIGENIA:

      My own brother.

ORESTES:

                Hence, away, begone!
I counsel thee, touch not these fatal locks!
As from Creusa's bridal robe, from me
An inextinguishable fire is kindled.
Leave me! Like Hercules, a death of shame,
Unworthy wretch, locked in myself, I'll die!

IPHIGENIA:

Thou shalt not perish! Would that I might hear
One quiet word from thee! dispel my doubts,
Make sure the bliss I have implored so long.
A wheel of joy and sorrow in my heart
Ceaseless revolves. I from a man unknown
With horror turn, but with resistless might
My inmost heart impels me to my brother.

ORESTES:

Is this Lyaeus' temple? Doth the glow
Of holy rage unbridled thus possess
The sacred priestess?

IPHIGENIA:

           Hear me! Oh, look up!
See how my heart, which hath been closed so long,
Doth open to the bliss of seeing thee,
The dearest treasure that the world contains,—
Of falling on thy neck, and folding thee
Within my longing arms, which have till now
Met the embraces of the empty wind.
Do not repulse me,—the eternal spring,
Whose crystal waters from Parnassus flow,
Bounds not more gayly on from rock to rock,
Down to the golden vale, than from my heart
The waters of affection freely gush,

311

And round me form a circling sea of bliss.
Orestes! O my brother!

ORESTES:

       Lovely nymph!
Nor thy caresses, nor thyself, I trust:
Diana claims attendants more severe,
And doth avenge her desecrated fane.
Remove thy circling arm! Wilt thou indeed
Safety and love upon a youth bestow,
And fondly tender him earth's fairest joy?
Unto my friend, more worthy than myself,
Impart thy favors; 'mong yon rocks he roves:
Go, seek him, guide him hence, and heed not me.

IPHIGENIA:

Brother, command thyself, and better know
Thy sister, newly found! Misconstrue not
Her pure and heavenly rapture, blaming it
As lustful heat unbridled. O ye gods,
Remove delusion from his rigid gaze,
Lest that this moment, fraught with bliss supreme,
Should make us trebly wretched! She is here,
Thine own, thy long-lost sister! From the altar
The goddess rescued me, and placed me here,
Secure within her consecrated fane—
A captive thou, prepared for sacrifice,
And findest here a sister in the priestess.

ORESTES:

Unblesséd one! So may the radiant sun
The final horror of our house behold!
Is not Electra here? That she with us
May also perish, nor her life prolong
For heavier destiny and direr woe.
'Tis well—I follow, priestess! Fratricide
Is an old custom of our ancient house;
And you, ye gods, I thank, that ye resolve
Childless to root me hence. Thee let me counsel
To view too fondly neither sun nor stars.
Come, follow to the gloomy realms below!
As dragons, gendered in the sulphur pool,
Swallow each other with voracious rage,
So our accursed race destroys itself.

Childless and guiltless come below with me!
There's pity in thy look! oh, gaze not so!—
'Twas with such looks that Clytemnestra sought
An entrance to her son Orestes' heart,
And yet his upraised arm her bosom pierced.
His mother fell!— Appear, indignant shade!
Within the circle step, ye fiends of hell,
Be present at the welcome spectacle,
The last, most horrible, that ye prepare!
Nor hate, nor vengeance whets the poniard now:
A loving sister is constrained to deal
The fatal blow. Weep not! Thou hast no guilt.
From earliest infancy I naught have loved,
As thee I could have loved, my sister. Come,
The weapon raise, spare not, this bosom rend,
And make an outlet for its boiling streams!

(He sinks exhausted.)

IPHIGENIA:

Alone I cannot bear this bliss and woe.
Where art thou, Pylades? Thine aid I need.

*(*IPHIGENIA *retires.)*

Scene II.

ORESTES *(recovering from his swoon and standing up)*:

Give yet another! reach from Lethe's stream
The last reviving draught of cool refreshment!
Soon shall its waters in my bosom still
Life's fitful fever; and my spirit then
Adown oblivion's stream shall glide to you,
Ye spirits shrouded in eternal mist.
With tranquil pleasure in your deep repose,
A weary son of earth may lave his soul!—
What whispering sounds pervade the dreary grove?
What hollow murmurs haunt its twilight gloom?—
They gather round to view the stranger guest!
Who are yon troop in high communion met,
Like an assembled family of princes?
They mingle peacefully, of every age,
Of either sex: godlike, of kindred mould,
Appear the gliding figures. Yes, 'tis they,
The fathers of my race! With Atreus,

313

In friendly converse glides Thyestes' shade;
And children playfully around them sport.
Is there no enmity among you now?
And is revenge extinguished with the sun?
So am I also welcome, and may hope
To mingle in your solemn company.
Welcome, my sires! Orestes bids you hail!
The seed that ye have sowed, that hath he reaped.
Laden with curses he descends to you.
But burdens here are lighter far to bear.
Receive him, oh, receive him in your circle!
Thee, Atreus, I revere, and thee, Thyestes:
Here all are free from enmity and hate.—
Show me my father, whom I only once
In life beheld.— Art thou my father, thou,
My mother leading thus familiarly?
Dares Clytemnestra reach her hand to thee?
Then may Orestes also draw near her,
And say, Behold thy son!—my ancestors,
Behold your son, and bid him welcome here.
Among the sons of ancient Tantalus,
A kind salute on earth was murder's watchword;
And all their joys commence beyond the grave.
Ye welcome me! Ye bid me join your circle!
Oh, lead me to my honored ancestor!
Where is our aged sire? Let me behold
The dear, the venerable head of him
Who with the immortal gods in council sat.
Ye seem to shudder, and to turn away!
What may this mean? Suffers the god-like man?
Alas! the mighty gods, with ruthless hate,
To his heroic breast, with brazen chains,
Have cruel pangs indissolubly bound.

SCENE III.

ORESTES:

How! Are ye come already here below?
Welcome, my sister! Still Electra fails:
Oh that some kindly god, with gentle arrow,
Her too, full speedily, would downward send!
Thee, hapless friend, I must compassionate!

Come with me! Come! To Pluto's gloomy throne,
There to salute our hosts like stranger guests.

IPHIGENIA:

Celestial pair, who from the realms above
By night and day shed down the beauteous light
To cheer mankind, but who may not illume
Departed spirits, save a mortal pair,
A brother's and a sister's anguish pity!
For thou, Diana, lovest thy gentle brother
Beyond what earth and heaven can offer thee;
And dost, with quiet yearning, ever turn
Thy virgin face to his eternal light.
Let not my only brother, found so late,
Rave in the darkness of insanity!
And is thy will, when thou didst here conceal me,
At length fulfilled,—wouldst thou to me through him,
To him through me, thy gracious aid extend,—
Oh, free him from the fetters of this curse,
Lest vainly pass the precious hours of safety.

PYLADES:

Dost thou not know us, and this sacred grove,
And this blest light, which shines not on the dead?
Dost thou not feel thy sister and thy friend,
Who hold the living in their firm embrace?
Us firmly grasp: we are not empty shades.
Mark well my words! Collect thy scattered thoughts!
Attend! Each moment is of priceless worth;
And our return hangs on a slender thread,
Which, as it seems, some gracious fate doth spin.

ORESTES *(to* IPHIGENIA*)*:

My sister, let me for the first time taste,
With open heart, pure joy within thine arms!
Ye gods, who charge the heavy clouds with dread,
And, sternly gracious, send the long-sought rain
With thunder and the rush of mighty winds,
A horrid deluge on the trembling earth,
Yet dissipate at length man's dread suspense,
Exchanging timid wonder's anxious gaze
For grateful looks and joyous songs of praise,
When, in each sparkling drop which gems the leaves,
Apollo, thousand-fold, reflects his beam,

315

And Iris colors with a magic hand
The dusty texture of the parting clouds,
Oh, let me also in my sister's arms,
And on the bosom of my friend, enjoy
With grateful thanks the bliss ye now bestow!
My heart assures me that your curses cease.
The dread Eumenides at length retire:
The brazen gates of Tartarus I hear
Behind them closing with a thunderous clang.
A quickening odor from the earth ascends,
Inviting me to chase, upon its plains,
The joys of life and deeds of high emprise.

PYLADES:

Lose not the moments which are limited!
The favoring gale, which swells our parting sail,
Must to Olympus waft our perfect joy.
Quick counsel and resolve the time demands.

ACT IV

SCENE I.

.IPHIGENIA:

When the Powers on high decree
For a feeble child of earth
Dire perplexity and woe,
And his spirit doom to pass
With tumult wild from joy to grief,
And back again from grief to joy,
In fearful alternation,
They in mercy then provide,
In the precincts of his home,
Or upon the distant shore,
That to him may never fail
Ready help in hours of need,
A tranquil, faithful friend.
Oh, bless, ye heavenly powers, our Pylades,
And whatsoever he may undertake!
He is in fight the vigorous arm of youth,
And his the thoughtful eye of age in counsel:
For tranquil is his soul; he guardeth there
Of calm a sacred and exhaustless dower,
And from its depths, in rich supply, outpours
Comfort and counsel for the sore distressed.
He tore me from my brother, upon whom,
With fond amaze, I gazed and gazed again:
I could not realize my happiness,
Nor loose him from my arms, and heeded not
The danger's near approach that threatens us.
To execute their project of escape,
They hasten to the sea, where, in a bay,
Their comrades in the vessel lie concealed,
Waiting a signal. Me they have supplied
With artful answers, should the monarch send
To urge the sacrifice. Alas! I see
I must consent to follow like a child:
I have not learned deception, nor the art
To gain with crafty wiles my purposes.
Detested falsehood! it doth not relieve
The breast like words of truth: it comforts not,

317

But is a torment in the forger's heart,
And, like an arrow which a god directs,
Flies back and wounds the archer. Through my heart
One fear doth chase another: perhaps with rage,
Again on the unconsecrated shore,
The Furies' grisly band my brother seize.
Perchance they are surprised. Methinks I hear
The tread of arméd men. A messenger
Is coming from the king, with hasty steps.
How throbs my heart, how troubled is my soul,
Now that I gaze upon the face of one
Whom with a word untrue I must encounter!

SCENE II.

ARKAS:
Priestess, with speed conclude the sacrifice!
Impatiently the king and people wait.

IPHIGENIA:
I had performed my duty and thy will,
Had not an unforeseen impediment
The execution of my purpose thwarted.

ARKAS:
What is it that obstructs the king's commands?

IPHIGENIA:
Chance, which from mortals will not brook control.

ARKAS:
Possess me with the reason, that with speed
I may inform the king, who hath decreed
The death of both.

IPHIGENIA:
The gods have not decreed it.
The elder of these men doth bear the guilt
Of kindred murder: on his steps attend
The dread Erinnys. In the inner fane
They seized upon their prey, polluting thus
The holy sanctuary. I hasten now,
Together with my virgin-train, to bathe
The goddess' image in the sea, and there
With solemn rites its purity restore.
Let none presume our silent march to follow!

ARKAS:
> This hinderance to the monarch I'll announce:
> Commence not thou the rite till he permit.

IPHIGENIA:
> The priestess interferes alone in this.

ARKAS:
> An incident so strange the king should know.

IPHIGENIA:
> Here nor his counsel nor command avails.

ARKAS:
> Oft are the great consulted out of form.

IPHIGENIA:
> Do not insist on what I must refuse.

ARKAS:
> A needful and a just demand refuse not.

IPHIGENIA:
> I yield, if thou delay not.

ARKAS:
>   I with speed
> Will bear these tidings to the camp, and soon
> Acquaint thee, priestess, with the king's reply.
> There is a message I would gladly bear him,—
> 'Twould quickly banish all perplexity:
> Thou didst not heed thy faithful friend's advice.

IPHIGENIA:
> I willingly have done whate'er I could.

ARKAS:
> E'en now 'tis not too late to change thy purpose.

IPHIGENIA:
> To do so is, alas! beyond our power.

ARKAS:
> What thou wouldst shun, thou deemest impossible.

IPHIGENIA:
> Thy wish doth make thee deem it possible.

ARKAS:
> Wilt thou so calmly venture every thing?

IPHIGENIA:
> My fate I have committed to the gods.

ARKAS:
> The gods are wont to save by human means.

319

Johann Wolfgang von Goethe

IPHIGENIA:

By their appointment every thing is done.

ARKAS:

Believe me, all doth now depend on thee.
The irritated temper of the king
Alone condemns these men to bitter death.
The soldiers from the cruel sacrifice
And bloody service long have been disused;
Nay, many, whom their adverse fortunes cast
In foreign regions, there themselves have felt
How god-like to the exiled wanderer
The friendly countenance of man appears.
Do not deprive us of thy gentle aid!
With ease thou canst thy sacred task fulfill;
For nowhere doth benignity, which comes
In human form from heaven, so quickly gain
An empire o'er the heart, as where a race,
Gloomy and savage, full of life and power,
Without external guidance, and oppressed
With vague forebodings, bear life's heavy load.

IPHIGENIA:

Shake not my spirit, which thou canst not bend
According to thy will.

ARKAS:

                While there is time,
Nor labor nor persuasion shall be spared.

IPHIGENIA:

Thy labor but occasions pain to me;
Both are in vain: therefore, I pray, depart.

ARKAS:

I summon pain to aid me: 'tis a friend
Who counsels wisely.

IPHIGENIA:

              Though it shakes my soul,
It doth not banish thence my strong repugnance.

ARKAS:

Can, then, a gentle soul repugnance feel
For benefits bestowed by one so noble?

IPHIGENIA:

Yes, when the donor, for those benefits,
Instead of gratitude, demands myself.

ARKAS:

Who no affection feels doth never want
Excuses. To the king I will relate
What hath befallen. Oh that in thy soul
Thou wouldst revolve his noble conduct to thee
Since thy arrival to the present day!

SCENE III.

IPHIGENIA *(alone)*:

These words at an unseasonable hour
Produce a strong revulsion in my breast:
I am alarmed!—For as the rushing tide
In rapid currents eddies o'er the rocks
Which lie among the sand upon the shore,
E'en so a stream of joy o'erwhelmed my soul.
I grasped what had appeared impossible.
It was as though another gentle cloud
Around me lay, to raise me from the earth,
And rock my spirit in the same sweet sleep
Which the kind goddess shed around my brow,
What time her circling arm from danger snatched me.
My brother forcibly engrossed my heart;
I listened only to his friend's advice;
My soul rushed eagerly to rescue them;
And as the mariner with joy surveys
The lessening breakers of a desert isle,
So Tauris lay behind me. But the voice
Of faithful Arkas wakes me from my dream,
Reminding me that those whom I forsake
Are also men. Deceit doth now become
Doubly detested. O my soul, be still!
Beginnest thou now to tremble and to doubt?
Thy lonely shelter on the firm-set earth
Must thou abandon, and, embarked once more,
At random drift upon tumultuous waves,
A stranger to thyself and to the world?

SCENE IV.

PYLADES:

Where is she? that my words with speed may tell
The joyful tidings of our near escape!

321

Johann Wolfgang von Goethe

IPHIGENIA:

>Oppressed with gloomy care, I much require
>The certain comfort thou dost promise me.

PYLADES:

>Thy brother is restored! The rocky paths
>Of this unconsecrated shore we trod
>In friendly converse; while behind us lay,
>Unmarked by us, the consecrated grove;
>And ever with increasing glory shone
>The fire of youth around his noble brow.
>Courage and hope his glowing eye inspired;
>And his exultant heart resigned itself
>To the delight, the joy, of rescuing
>Thee, his deliverer, also me, his friend.

IPHIGENIA:

>The gods shower blessings on thee, Pylades!
>And from those lips which breathe such welcome news,
>Be the sad note of anguish never heard!

PYLADES:

>I bring yet more; for fortune, like a prince,
>Comes not alone, but well accompanied.
>Our friends and comrades we have also found.
>Within a bay they had concealed the ship,
>And mournful sat expectant. They beheld
>Thy brother, and a joyous shout upraised,
>Imploring him to haste the parting hour.
>Each hand impatient longed to grasp the oar;
>While from the shore a gently murmuring breeze,
>Perceived by all, unfurled its wing auspicious.
>Let us then hasten: guide me to the fane,
>That I may tread the sanctuary, and win
>With sacred awe the goal of our desires.
>I can unaided on my shoulder bear
>The goddess' image: how I long to feel
>The precious burden!

(While speaking the last words, he approaches the Temple, without perceiving that he is not followed by IPHIGENIA: *at length he turns round.)*

>   Why thus lingering stand?
>Why art thou silent? wherefore thus confused?
>Doth some new obstacle oppose our bliss?

Inform me, hast thou to the king announced
The prudent message we agreed upon?

IPHIGENIA:

I have, dear Pylades; yet wilt thou chide.
Thy very aspect is a mute reproach.
The royal messenger arrived; and I,
According to thy counsel, framed my speech.
He seemed surprised, and urgently besought,
That to the monarch I should first announce
The rite unusual, and attend his will.
I now await the messenger's return.

PYLADES:

Danger again doth hover o'er our heads!
Alas! Why hast thou failed to shroud thyself
Within the veil of sacerdotal rites?

IPHIGENIA:

I never have employed them as a veil.

PYLADES:

Pure soul! thy scruples will destroy alike
Thyself and us. Why did I not foresee
Such an emergency, and tutor thee
This counsel also wisely to elude?

IPHIGENIA:

Chide only me, for mine alone the blame.
Yet other answer could I not return
To him, who strongly and with reason urged
What my own heart acknowledged to be right.

PYLADES:

The danger thickens; but let us be firm,
Nor with incautious haste betray ourselves,
Calmly await the messenger's return,
And then stand fast, whatever his reply;
For the appointment of such sacred rites
Doth to the priestess, not the king, belong.
Should he demand the stranger to behold,
Who is by madness heavily oppressed,
Evasively pretend, that in the fane,
Well guarded, thou retainest him and me.
Thus you secure us time to fly with speed,
Bearing the sacred treasure from this race,
Unworthy its possession. Phoebus sends

323

Auspicious omens, and fulfils his word,
Ere we the first conditions have performed.
Free is Orestes, from the curse absolved!
Oh, with the freed one, to the rocky isle
Where dwells the god, waft us, propitious gales!
Thence to Mycene, that she may revive;
That from the ashes of the extinguished hearth,
The household gods may joyously arise,
And beauteous fire illumine their abode!
Thy hand from golden censers first shall strew
The fragrant incense. O'er that threshold thou
Shalt life and blessing once again dispense,
The curse atone, and all thy kindred grace
With the fresh bloom of renovated life.

IPHIGENIA:

As doth the flower revolve to meet the sun,
Once more my spirit to sweet comfort turns,
Struck by thy words' invigorating ray.
How dear the counsel of a present friend,
Lacking whose god-like power, the lonely one
In silence droops! for, locked within his breast,
Slowly are ripened purpose and resolve,
Which friendship's genial warmth had soon matured.

PYLADES:

Farewell! I haste to re-assure our friends,
Who anxiously await us: then with speed
I will return, and, hid within the brake,
Attend thy signal.— Wherefore, all at once,
Doth anxious thought o'ercloud thy brow serene?

IPHIGENIA:

Forgive me! As light clouds athwart the sun,
So cares and fears float darkling o'er my soul.

PYLADES:

Oh, banish fear! With danger it hath formed
A close alliance,—they are constant friends.

IPHIGENIA:

It is an honest scruple, which forbids
That I should cunningly deceive the king,
And plunder him who was my second father.

PYLADES:

Him thou dost fly, who would have slain thy brother.

IPHIGENIA:

 To me, at least, he hath been ever kind.

PYLADES:

 What fate commands is not ingratitude.

IPHIGENIA:

 Alas! it still remains ingratitude:

 Necessity alone can justify it.

PYLADES:

 Thee, before gods and men, it justifies.

IPHIGENIA:

 But my own heart is still unsatisfied.

PYLADES:

 Scruples too rigid are a cloak for pride.

IPHIGENIA:

 I cannot argue, I can only feel.

PYLADES:

 Conscious of right, thou shouldst respect thyself.

IPHIGENIA:

 Then only doth the heart know perfect ease,

 When not a stain pollutes it.

PYLADES:

        In this fane

 Pure hast thou kept thy heart. Life teaches us

 To be less strict with others and ourselves:

 Thou'lt learn the lesson too. So wonderful

 Is human nature, and its varied ties

 Are so involved and complicate, that none

 May hope to keep his inmost spirit pure,

 And walk without perplexity through life.

 Nor are we called upon to judge ourselves:

 With circumspection to pursue his path,

 Is the immediate duty of a man;

 For seldom can he rightly estimate,

 Or his past conduct or his present deeds.

IPHIGENIA:

 Almost thou dost persuade me to consent.

PYLADES:

 Needs there persuasion when no choice is granted?

 To save thyself, thy brother, and a friend,

 One path presents itself; and canst thou ask

 If we shall follow it?

IPHIGENIA:

　　　　　　　　Still let me pause,
For such injustice thou couldst not thyself
Calmly return for benefits received.

PYLADES:

If we should perish, bitter self-reproach,
Forerunner of despair, will be thy portion.
It seems thou art not used to suffer much,
When, to escape so great calamity,
Thou canst refuse to utter one false word.

IPHIGENIA:

Oh, that I bore within a manly heart!
Which, when it hath conceived a bold resolve,
'Gainst every other voice doth close itself.

PYLADES:

In vain thou dost refuse: with iron hand
Necessity commands; her stern decree
Is law supreme, to which the gods themselves
Must yield submission. In dread silence rules
The uncounselled sister of eternal fate.
What she appoints thee to endure,—endure;
What to perform,—perform. The rest thou knowest.
Ere long I will return, and then receive
The seal of safety from thy sacred hand.

SCENE V.

IPHIGENIA *(alone)*:

I must obey him, for I see my friends
Beset with peril. Yet my own sad fate
Doth with increasing anguish move my heart.
May I no longer feed the silent hope
Which in my solitude I fondly cherished?
Shall the dire curse eternally endure?
And shall our fated race ne'er rise again
With blessings crowned?— All mortal things decay!
The noblest powers, the purest joys of life,
At length subside,—then, wherefore not the curse?
And have I vainly hoped, that guarded here,
Secluded from the fortunes of my race,
I, with pure heart and hands, some future day,

Might cleanse the deep defilement of our house?
Scarce was my brother in my circling arms,
From raging madness suddenly restored,
Scarce had the ship, long prayed for, neared the strand,
Once more to waft me to my native shores,
When unrelenting fate, with iron hand,
A double crime enjoins; commanding me
To steal the image, sacred and revered,
Confided to my care, and him deceive
To whom I owe my life and destiny.
Let not abhorrence spring within my heart!
Nor the old Titan's hate toward you, ye gods,
Infix its vulture talons in my breast!
Save me, and save your image in my soul!

An ancient song comes back upon mine ear,—
I had forgotten it, and willingly,—
The Parcae's song, which horribly they sang,
What time hurled headlong from his golden seat,
Fell Tantalus. They with their noble friend
Keen anguish suffered: savage was their breast,
And horrible their song. In days gone by,
When we were children, oft our ancient nurse
Would sing it to us; and I marked it well.

> Oh, fear the immortals,
> Ye children of men!
> Eternal dominion
> They hold in their hands,
> And o'er their wide empire
> Wield absolute sway.

> Whom they have exalted
> Let him fear them most!
> Around golden tables,
> On cliffs and clouds resting,
> The seats are prepared.

> If contest ariseth,
> The guests are hurled headlong,
> Disgraced and dishonored,

To gloomy abysses,
And, fettered in darkness,
Await, with vain longing,
A juster decree.

But in feasts everlasting,
Around the gold tables,
Still dwell the immortals.
From mountain to mountain
They stride; while, ascending
From fathomless chasms,
The breath of the Titans,
Half-stifled with anguish,
Like volumes of incense
Fumes up to the skies.

From races ill-fated,
Their aspect joy-bringing,
Oft turn the celestials,
And shun in the children
To gaze on the features,
Once loved and still speaking,
Of their mighty sire.

So chanted the Parcae:
The banished one hearkens
The song; the hoar captive,
Immured in his dungeon,
His children's doom ponders,
And boweth his head.

ACT V

SCENE I.

ARKAS:

I own I am perplexed, and scarcely know
'Gainst whom to point the shaft of my suspicion,—
Whether the priestess aids the captives' flight,
Or they themselves clandestinely contrive it.
'Tis rumored that the ship which brought them here
Is lurking somewhere in à bay concealed.
This stranger's madness, these new lustral rites,
The specious pretext for delay, excite
Mistrust, and call for vigilance.

THOAS:

Summon the priestess to attend me here;
Then go with speed, and strictly search the shore.
From yonder headland to Diana's grove;
Forbear to violate its sacred depths;
A watchful ambush set; attack and seize,
According to your wont, whome'er ye find.

(ARKAS *retires.*)

SCENE II.

THOAS (*alone*):

Fierce anger rages in my riven breast,
First against her, whom I esteemed so pure;
Then 'gainst myself, whose foolish lenity
Hath fashioned her for treason. Man is soon
Inured to slavery, and quickly learns
Submission, when of freedom quite deprived.
If she had fallen in the savage hands
Of my rude sires, and had their holy rage
Forborne to slay her, grateful for her life,
She would have recognized her destiny,
Have shed before the shrine the stranger's blood,
And duty named what was necessity.
Now my forbearance in her breast allures
Audacious wishes. Vainly I had hoped
To bind her to me: rather she contrives

> To shape an independent destiny.
> She won my heart through flattery, and, now
> That I oppose her, seeks to gain her ends
> By fraud and cunning, and my kindness deems
> A worthless and prescriptive property.

SCENE III.

IPHIGENIA:
> Me hast thou summoned? wherefore art thou here?

THOAS:
> Wherefore delay the sacrifice? inform me.

IPHIGENIA:
> I have acquainted Arkas with the reasons.

THOAS:
> From thee I wish to hear them more at large.

IPHIGENIA:
> The goddess for reflection grants thee time.

THOAS:
> To thee this time seems also opportune.

IPHIGENIA:
> If to this cruel deed thy heart is steeled,
> Thou shouldst not come! A king who meditates
> A deed inhuman, may find slaves enow,
> Willing for hire to bear one-half the curse,
> And leave the monarch's presence undefiled.
> Enrapt in gloomy clouds he forges death:
> Flaming destruction then his ministers
> Hurl down upon his wretched victim's head;
> While he abideth high above the storm,
> Calm and untroubled, an impassive god.

THOAS:
> A wild song, priestess, issued from thy lips.

IPHIGENIA:
> No priestess, king, but Agamemnon's daughter!
> While yet unknown, thou didst respect my words:
> A princess now,—and thinkest thou to command me?
> From youth I have been tutored to obey,
> My parents first and then the deity;
> And, thus obeying, ever hath my soul
> Known sweetest freedom. But nor then nor now

330

Have I been taught compliance with the voice
And savage mandates of a man.

THOAS:

Not I:
An ancient law doth thy obedience claim.

IPHIGENIA:

Our passions eagerly catch hold of laws
Which they can wield as weapons. But to me
Another law, one far more ancient, speaks,
And doth command me to withstand thee, king!
That law declaring sacred every stranger.

THOAS:

These men, methinks, lie very near thy heart,
When sympathy with them can lead thee thus
To violate discretion's primal law,
That those in power should never be provoked.

IPHIGENIA:

Speaking or silent, thou canst always know
What is, and ever must be, in my heart.
Doth not remembrance of a common doom
To soft compassion melt the hardest heart?
How much more mine? in them I see myself.
I trembling kneeled before the altar once,
And solemnly the shade of early death
Environed me. Aloft the knife was raised
To pierce my bosom, throbbing with warm life;
A dizzy horror overwhelmed my soul;
My eyes grew dim;—I found myself in safety.
Are we not bound to render the distressed
The gracious kindness from the gods received?
Thou knowest we are, and yet wilt thou compel me?

THOAS:

Obey thine office, priestess, not the king.

IPHIGENIA:

Cease! nor thus seek to cloak the savage force
Which triumphs o'er a woman's feebleness.
Though woman, I am born as free as man.
Did Agamemnon's son before thee stand,
And thou requiredst what became him not,
His arm and trusty weapon would defend
His bosom's freedom. I have only words;

But it becomes a noble-minded man
To treat with due respect the words of woman.

THOAS:

I more respect them than a brother's sword.

IPHIGENIA:

Uncertain ever is the chance of arms;
No prudent warrior doth despise his foe;
Nor yet defenceless 'gainst severity
Hath nature left the weak,—she gives him craft
And wily cunning: artful he delays,
Evades, eludes, and finally escapes.
Such arms are justified by violence.

THOAS:

But circumspection countervails deceit.

IPHIGENIA:

Which a pure spirit doth abhor to use.

THOAS:

Do not incautiously condemn thyself.

IPHIGENIA:

Oh, couldst thou see the struggle of my soul,
Courageously to ward the first attack
Of an unhappy doom, which threatens me!
Do I, then, stand before thee weaponless?
Prayer, lovely prayer, fair branch in woman's hand,
More potent far than instruments of war,
Thou dost thrust back. What now remains for me
Wherewith my inborn freedom to defend?
Must I implore a miracle from heaven?
Is there no power within my spirit's depths?

THOAS:

Extravagant thy interest in the fate
Of these two strangers. Tell me who they are
For whom thy heart is thus so deeply moved.

IPHIGENIA:

They are—they seem at least—I think them Greeks.

THOAS:

Thy countrymen: no doubt they have renewed
The pleasing picture of return.

IPHIGENIA *(after a pause)*:

                            Doth man
Lay undisputed claim to noble deeds?

Doth he alone to his heroic breast
Clasp the impossible? What call we great?
What deeds, though oft narrated, still uplift
With shuddering horror the narrator's soul,
But those which, with improbable success,
The valiant have attempted? Shall the man
Who all alone steals on his foes by night.
And, raging like an unexpected fire,
Destroys the slumbering host, and, pressed at length
By roused opponents on his foeman's steeds,
Retreats with booty, be alone extolled?
Or he who, scorning safety, boldly roams
Through woods and dreary wilds, to scour the land
Of thieves and robbers? Is naught left for us?
Must gentle woman quite forego her nature,
Force against force employ,—like Amazons,—
Usurp the sword from man, and bloodily
Revenge oppression? In my heart I feel
The stirrings of a noble enterprise;
But if I fail—severe reproach, alas!
And bitter misery will be my doom.
Thus on my knees I supplicate the gods!
Oh, are ye truthful, as men say ye are,
Now prove it by your countenance and aid!
Honor the truth in me! Attend, O king!
A secret plot deceitfully is laid:
Touching the captives thou dost ask in vain;
They have departed hence, and seek their friends,
Who, with the ship, await them on the shore.
The eldest,—whom dire madness lately seized,
And hath abandoned now,—he is Orestes,
My brother, and the other Pylades,
His early friend and faithful confidant.
From Delphi, Phoebus sent them to this shore
With a divine command to steal away
The image of Diana, and to him
Bear back the sister thither; and for this
He promised to the blood-stained matricide,
The Fury-haunted son, deliverance.
I have surrendered now into thy hands

The remnants of the house of Tantalus.
Destroy us—if thou canst.

THOAS:

               And dost thou think
That the uncultured Scythian will attend
The voice of truth and of humanity
Which Atreus, the Greek, heard not?

IPHIGENIA:

             'Tis heard
By every one, born 'neath whatever clime,
Within whose bosom flows the stream of life,
Pure and unhindered.— What thy thought? O king!
What silent purpose broods in thy deep soul?
Is it destruction? Let me perish first!
For now, deliverance hopeless, I perceive
The dreadful peril into which I have
With rash precipitancy plunged my friends.
Alas! I soon shall see them bound before me!
How to my brother shall I say farewell?—
I, the unhappy author of his death.
Ne'er can I gaze again in his dear eyes!

THOAS:

The traitors have contrived a cunning web,
And cast it round thee, who, secluded long,
Givest willing credence to thine own desires.

IPHIGENIA:

No, no! I'd pledge my life these men are true.
And shouldst thou find them otherwise, O king,
Then let them perish both, and cast me forth,
That on some rock-girt island's dreary shore
I may atone my folly! Are they true,
And is this man indeed my dear Orestes,
My brother, long implored, release us both,
And o'er us stretch the kind protecting arm,
Which long hath sheltered me. My noble sire
Fell through his consort's guilt,—she by her son:
On him alone the hope of Atreus' race
Doth now repose. Oh, with pure heart, pure hand,
Let me depart to purify our house!
Yes, thou wilt keep thy promise: thou didst swear,
That, were a safe return provided me,

I should be free to go. The hour is come.
A king doth never grant like common men,
Merely to gain a respite from petition;
Nor promise what he hopes will ne'er be claimed.
Then first he feels his dignity supreme
When he can make the long-expecting happy.

THOAS:
As fire opposes water, and doth seek
With hissing rage to overcome its foe,
So doth my anger strive against thy words.

IPHIGENIA:
Let mercy, like the consecrated flame
Of silent sacrifice, encircled round
With songs of gratitude and joy and praise,
Above the tumult gently rise to heaven.

THOAS:
How often hath this voice assuaged my soul?

IPHIGENIA:
Extend thy hand to me in sign of peace.

THOAS:
Large thy demand within so short a time.

IPHIGENIA:
Beneficence doth no reflection need.

THOAS:
'Tis needed oft, for evil springs from good.

IPHIGENIA:
'Tis doubt which good doth oft to evil turn.
Consider not: act as thy feelings prompt thee.

Scene IV.

ORESTES *(armed, addressing his followers)*:
Redouble your exertions! hold them back!
Few moments will suffice: maintain your ground,
And keep a passage open to the ship
For me and for my sister.
                    (To IPHIGENIA, *without perceiving* THOAS.*)*
                    Come with speed!
We are betrayed,—brief time remains for flight.
                    (He perceives the king.)

335

THOAS *(laying his hand on his sword)*:
> None in my presence with impunity
> His naked weapon wears.

IPHIGENIA:
>   Do not profane
> Diana's sanctuary with rage and blood.
> Command your people to forbear a while,
> And listen to the priestess, to the sister.

ORESTES:
> Say, who is he that threatens us?

IPHIGENIA:
>   In him
> Revere the king, who was my second father.
> Forgive me, brother, that my child-like heart
> Hath placed our fate thus wholly in his hands.
> I have betrayed your meditated flight,
> And thus from treachery redeemed my soul.

ORESTES:
> Will he permit our peaceable return?

IPHIGENIA:
> Thy gleaming sword forbids me to reply.

ORESTES *(sheathing his sword)*:
> Then, speak! thou seest I listen to thy words.

Scene V.

Enter PYLADES, *soon after him* ARKAS, *both with drawn swords.*

PYLADES:
> Do not delay! our friends are putting forth
> Their final strength, and, yielding step by step,
> Are slowly driven backward to the sea.—
> A conference of princes find I here?
> Is this the sacred person of the king?

ARKAS:
> Calmly, as doth become thee, thou dost stand,
> O king, surrounded by thine enemies!
> Soon their temerity shall be chastised:
> Their yielding followers fly,—their ship is ours:
> Speak but the word, and it is wrapt in flames.

THOAS:
> Go and command my people to forbear!

Let none annoy the foe while we confer.

(ARKAS *retires.*)

ORESTES:

I willingly consent. Go, Pylades!
Collect the remnant of our friends, and wait
The appointed issue of our enterprise.

(PYLADES *retires.*)

SCENE VI.

IPHIGENIA:

Relieve my cares ere ye begin to speak.
I fear contention, if thou wilt not hear
The voice of equity, O king,—if thou
Wilt not, my brother, curb thy headstrong youth!

THOAS:

I, as becomes the elder, check my rage.
Now answer me: how dost thou prove thyself
The priestess' brother, Agamemnon's son?

ORESTES:

Behold the sword with which the hero slew
The valiant Trojans. From his murderer
I took the weapon, and implored the gods
To grant me Agamemnon's mighty arm,
Success, and valor, with a death more noble.
Select one of the leaders of thy host,
And place the best as my opponent here.
Where'er on earth the sons of heroes dwell,
This boon is to the stranger ne'er refused.

THOAS:

This privilege hath ancient custom here
To strangers ne'er accorded.

ORESTES:

Then from us

Commence the novel custom! A whole race
In imitation soon will consecrate
Its monarch's noble action into law.
Nor let me only for our liberty,—
Let me, a stranger, for all strangers, fight.
If I should fall, my doom be also theirs;
But, if kind fortune crown me with success,

337

Let none e'er tread this shore, and fail to meet
The beaming eye of sympathy and love,
Or unconsoled depart!

THOAS:

               Thou dost not seem
Unworthy of thy boasted ancestry.
Great is the number of the valiant men
Who wait upon me; but I will myself,
Although advanced in years, oppose the foe,
And am prepared to try the chance of arms.

IPHIGENIA:

No, no! such bloody proofs are not required.
Unhand thy weapon, king! my lot consider;
Rash combat oft immortalizes man;
If he should fall, he is renowned in song:
But after-ages reckon not the tears
Which ceaseless the forsaken woman sheds;
And poets tell not of the thousand nights
Consumed in weeping, and the dreary days,
Wherein her anguished soul, a prey to grief,
Doth vainly yearn to call her loved one back.
Fear warned me to beware lest robbers' wiles
Might lure me from this sanctuary, and then
Betray me into bondage. Anxiously
I questioned them, each circumstance explored,
Demanded proofs, now is my heart assured.
See here, the mark on his right hand impressed
As of three stars, which on his natal day
Were by the priest declared to indicate
Some dreadful deed therewith to be performed.
And then this scar, which doth his eyebrow cleave,
Redoubles my conviction. When a child,
Electra, rash and inconsiderate,—
Such was her nature,—loosed him from her arms:
He fell against a tripos. Oh, 'tis he!—
Shall I adduce the likeness to his sire,
Or the deep rapture of my inmost heart,
In further token of assurance, king?

THOAS:

E'en though thy words had banished every doubt,
And I had curbed the anger in my breast,

Still must our arms decide. I see no peace.
Their purpose, as thou didst thyself confess,
Was to deprive me of Diana's image.
And think ye I will look contented on?
The Greeks are wont to cast a longing eye
Upon the treasures of barbarians,—
A golden fleece, good steeds, or daughters fair;—
But force and guile not always have availed
To lead them, with their booty, safely home.

ORESTES:

The image shall not be a cause of strife!
We now perceive the error which the god,
Our journey here commanding, like a veil,
Threw o'er our minds. His counsel I implored,
To free me from the Furies' grisly band.
He answered, "Back to Greece the sister bring,
Who in the sanctuary on Tauris' shore
Unwillingly abides; so ends the curse!"
To Phoebus' sister we applied the words,
And he referred to thee. The bonds severe,
Which held thee from us, holy one, are rent;
And thou art ours once more. At thy blest touch,
I felt myself restored. Within thine arms,
Madness once more around me coiled its folds,
Crushing the marrow in my frame, and then
Forever, like a serpent, fled to hell.
Through thee the daylight gladdens me anew:
The counsel of the goddess now shines forth
In all its beauty and beneficence.
Like to a sacred image, unto which
An oracle immutably hath bound
A city's welfare, thee she bore away,
Protectress of our house, and guarded here
Within this holy stillness, to become
A blessing to thy brother and thy race.
Now when each passage to escape seems closed,
And safety hopeless, thou dost give us all.
O king, incline thine heart to thoughts of peace!
Let her fulfill her mission, and complete
The consecration of our father's house;
Me to their purified abode restore,

339

And place upon my brow the ancient crown!
Requite the blessing which her presence brought thee,
And let me now my nearer right enjoy!
Cunning and force, the proudest boast of man,
Fade in the lustre of her perfect truth;
Nor unrequited will a noble mind
Leave confidence, so child-like and so pure.

IPHIGENIA:

Think on thy promise: let thy heart be moved
By what a true and honest tongue hath spoken!
Look on us, king! an opportunity
For such a noble deed not oft occurs.
Refuse thou canst not,—give thy quick consent.

THOAS:

Then, go!

IPHIGENIA:

Not so, my king! I cannot part
Without thy blessing, or in anger from thee:
Banish us not! the sacred right of guests
Still let us claim: so not eternally
Shall we be severed. Honored and beloved
As mine own father was, art thou by me;
And this impression in my soul abides,
Let but the least among thy people bring
Back to mine ear the tones I heard from thee,
Or should I on the humblest see thy garb,
I will with joy receive him as a god,
Prepare his couch myself, beside our hearth
Invite him to a seat, and only ask
Touching thy fate and thee. Oh, may the gods
To thee the merited reward impart
Of all thy kindness and benignity!
Farewell! Oh, turn thou not away, but give
One kindly word of parting in return!
So shall the wind more gently swell our sails,
And from our eyes with softened anguish flow
The tears of separation. Fare thee well!
And graciously extend to me thy hand,
In pledge of ancient friendship.

THOAS (*extending his hand*):

Fare thee well!

BALLADS

Ballads

THE ERL-KING*

O who rides by night thro' the woodland so wild?
It is the fond father embracing his child;
And close the boy nestles within his loved arm,
To hold himself fast, and to keep himself warm.

"O father, see yonder! see yonder!" he says;
"My boy, upon what dost thou fearfully gaze?"
"O, 'tis the Erl-King with his crown and his shroud."
"No, my son, it is but a dark wreath of the cloud."

The Erl-King Speaks
"O come and go with me, thou loveliest child;
By many a gay sport shall thy time be beguiled;
My mother keeps for thee full many a fair toy,
And many a fine flower shall she pluck for my boy."

"O father, my father, and did you not hear
The Erl-King whisper so low in my ear?"
"Be still, my heart's darling—my child, be at ease;
It was but the wild blast as it sung thro' the trees."

Erl-King
"O wilt thou go with me, thou loveliest boy?
My daughter shall tend thee with care and with joy;
She shall bear thee so lightly thro' wet and thro' wild,
And press thee, and kiss thee, and sing to my child."

Translated by Sir Walter Scott

343

"O father, my father, and saw you not plain
The Erl-King's pale daughter glide past thro' the rain?"
"O yes, my loved treasure, I knew it full soon;
It was the grey willow that danced to the moon."

ERL-KING

"C come and go with me, no longer delay,
Or else, silly child, I will drag thee away."
"O father! O father! now, now, keep your hold,
The Erl-King has seized me—his grasp is so cold!"

Sore trembled the father; he spurr'd thro' the wild,
Clasping close to his bosom his shuddering child;
He reaches his dwelling in doubt and in dread,
But, clasp'd to his bosom, the infant was dead.

THE DANCE OF DEATH*

THE WARDER looked down at the dead of night
On the graves where the dead were sleeping,
And, clearly as day, was the pale moonlight
O'er the quiet churchyard creeping.
One after another the gravestones began
To heave and to open, and woman and man
Rose up in their ghastly apparel!

Ho, ho for the dance!—and the phantoms outsprung
In skeleton roundel advancing,
The rich and the poor, and the old and the young,
But the winding-sheets hindered their dancing.
No shame had these revellers wasted and grim,
So they shook off the cerements from body and limb,
And scattered them over the hillocks.

They crooked their thigh bones, and they shook
their long shanks,
And wild was their reeling and limber;

---

*Translated by Theodore Martin

344

And each bone as it crosses, it clinks and it clanks,
Like the clapping of timber on timber.
The warder he laughed, tho' his laugh was not loud;
And the Fiend whispered to him—"Go, steal me the shroud
Of one of these skeleton dancers."

He has done it! and backward with terrified glance,
To the sheltering door ran the warder;
As calm as before the moon looked on the dance,
Which they footed in hideous order.
But one and another retiring at last,
Slipped on their white garments and onward they passed,
And a hush settled over the greensward.

Still, one of them stumbles and tumbles along,
And taps at each tomb that it seizes;
But 'tis none of its mates who has done it this wrong,
For it scents its grave-clothes in the breezes.
It shakes the tower gate, but that drives it away,
For 'twas nailed o'er with crosses—a goodly array—
And well was it so for the warder!

It must have its shroud—it must have it betimes—
The quaint Gothic carving it catches;
And upwards from story to story it climbs,
And scrambles with leaps and with snatches.
Now woe to the warder, poor sinner, betides!
Like a spindle-legged spider the skeleton strides
From buttress to buttress, still upward!

The warder he shook, and the warder grew pale,
And gladly the shroud would have yielded!
The ghost had its clutch on the last iron rail,
Which the top of the watch-tower shielded.
When the moon was obscured by the rush of a cloud,
ONE! thundered the bell, and unswarthed by a shroud,
Down went the gaunt skeleton crashing!

Johann Wolfgang von Goethe

THE GOD AND THE BAJADERE*

MAHADEVAH, Lord of earth,
　　For the sixth time was born again,
So as to be one of our birth
　　To share our joy and pain.

He was content to come down here,
Himself arranging it to happen,
For, to punish or to spare,
He must be a man with men.
And when through the whole of the town ne had wandered,
Observed well the rich, and on the poor pondered,
He left it at night to continue again.

As he was going out at the place
Where the final houses are,
He saw there, with her painted face
A lost lovely child appear.
"Greeting, maiden," "Thank you, sir,
Wait, I'm going by the same way—"
"And who are you?" "A Bajadere,
And this house is for love's play."
She hurries to strike on the cymbals the dances,
She knows how to turn in the maze which entrances
She bends and extends to him the nosegay.

Smiling, she makes him cross the threshold
In the house out of the night.
"Dear stranger, you will soon behold
My room shine in the bright lamplight.
If you're tired, then I will rest you,
And I'll bathe your weary feet.
What you want I'll do my best through
Jest and rest and joy to meet."
She busily soothes the wounds he affects, and
Smiling the god with pleasure detects a
Heart through her life of corruption beat.

---

*Translated by Stephen Spender

He makes her act out a slave's part,
But ever she grows more his creature.
What at first with her was art
Later becomes second nature.
Thus where first the blossom stood
There stands soon the fruit below;
Where there's the obedient mood
The loving is not slow to follow.
But ever more sharply and harder to try her
The seer invokes powers lower and higher
Feigning lust and disgust and bitterest sorrow.

And he kissed her painted face
And she felt love's anguish climb,
Until, a prisoner in one place,
The maiden wept for the first time.
Down she sinks and clasps his knees
Not for pleasure nor for gain.
Ah, the fainting limbs now cease
To move, she cannot work again.
And so for the favouring feast of the bed
A pleasuring veil in the dark is outspread
By the hours of the night, greatest beauty they spin.

Sleeping late, after much pleasure,
Waking early, from short rest,
She finds against her heart, her treasure
Dead, the much beloved guest.
She shrieks, then throws herself upon him
But he will not reawaken,
And the god, cold in each limb,
To a grave of flames is taken.
She hears then the priests and the death requiem,
Raving she runs through the crowd and divides them.
"Who are you? Why press to the grave to look in?"

Then she kneels beside the grave.
Her cry of grief rings to the skies.
"My husband I once more must have
Though I follow where he lies.

Shall these limbs of a god fall
Into ashes in my sight?
Mine, mine he was, mine before all.
Ah one, for only one, sweet night."
The priests are incanting: "We bear out the old
Who a long time were weary, and recently cold.
We bear out the young, before they had thought it.

"The lesson of your priest now hear.
This man was no husband to you.
Continue then as bajadere
That is all you need must do.
Only shadows follow bodies
To the still and silent land.
Such the fame and duty is
Of the wife to follow husband.
Then shrill out ye trumpets in holy complaint
Receive O ye gods the youth without taint
Receive him through flames into your hand."

Thus the choir remorselessly
Adds to her anguish here beneath.
Until with arms outstretching, she
Springs into the flaming death.
And the youthful god then raises
His living body from the flame,
In his arms at last encloses
The loved one worthy of his name.
The godly rejoice in those who repent
And deathlessly these lost children ascend
With arms of fire to a heaven of fame.

THE SORCERER'S APPRENTICE*

HUZZAH, huzzah! His back is fairly
Turned about, the wizard old;
And I'll now his spirits rarely
To my will and pleasure mould!

*Translated by Theodore Martin

His spells and orgies—ha'nt I
Marked them all aright?
And I'll do wonders, sha'nt I?
And deeds of mickle might.
 Hear ye! hear ye!
 Hence! your spritely
 Office rightly,
 Featly showing!
 Toil, until with water clear, ye
 Fill the bath to overflowing!

Ho, thou battered broomstick! Take ye
This old seedy coat and wear it—
Ha, thou household drudge! I'll make ye
Do my bidding; ay, and fear it.
Don of legs a pair, now;
A head, too, for the nonce!
To the river there, now
Bear the pail at once!
 Hear ye! hear ye!
 Hence! your spritely
 Office rightly,
 Featly showing!
 Toil, until with water clear, ye
 Fill the bath to overflowing.

See, 'tis off—'tis at the river
In the stream the bucket flashes;
Now 'tis back—and down, or ever
You can wink, the burden dashes.
Again, again, and quicker!
The floor is in a swim,
And every stoup and bicker
Is running o'er the brim.
 Stop, now stop!
 You have granted
 All I wanted.
 Stop! Od rot it!
 Running still? I'm like to drop!
 What's the word? I've clean forgot it!

Oh, the word, so strong and baleful,
To make it what it was before!
There it skips with pail on pailful—
Would thou wert a broom once more!
Still now streams he scatters,
Round and ever round me—
Oh, a hundred waters,
Rushing in, confound me!
 No—no longer,
 Can I brook it!
 I'll rebuke it!
 Vile abortion!
 Woe is me, my fears grow stronger,
 What grimacing, what contortion!

Wilt thou, offspring of the devil,
Drench the house in hellish funning?
Even now, above the level
Of the door, the water's running.
Stop, wretch! won't you hear me?
You for this shall pay.
Only you come near me!
Stop, broom, stop, I say!
 Stop, I tell you,
 I'll not bear it,
 No, I swear it!
 Let me catch you,
 And upon the spot I'll fell you
 With my hatchet, and despatch you.

Back it comes—will nought prevent it?
If I only tackle to thee,
Soon, O Kobold! thou'lt repent it,
When the steel goes crashing thro' thee.
Bravely struck, and surely!
There it goes in twain;
Now I move securely,
And I breathe again!

Woe and wonder!
As it parted,
Straight up started,
'Quipped aright,
Goblins twain that rush asunder.
Help, O help, ye powers of might!

Deep and deeper grows the water
On the stairs and in the hall,
Rushing in with roar and clatter—
Lord and master, hear me call!
Ah, here comes the master—
Sore, sir, is my strait;
I raised this spirit faster
Far than I can lay't.
 "Broom, avaunt thee!
 To thy nook there!
Lie, thou spook, there!
 Only answer,
When for mine own ends I want thee,
I, the master necromancer!"

BEFORE THE JUDGE*

FROM WHOM I have got it, I never shall tell you
The child that's inside me.
"Shame! Shame!" you spit, "there goes that whore."
It is an honest woman you see.

With whom I trusted myself, I never shall say.
My love's kind and true-bred.
He wears a gold chain round his neck
A straw hat on his head.

If hate and scorn must be endured
I'll bear that scorn alone.
I know him well, he knows me well,
And this to God is known.

*Translated by Stephen Spender

Johann Wolfgang von Goethe

THE FISHER*

The water plash'd, the water play'd,
  A fisher sat thereby,
And mark'd as to and fro it sway'd,
  His float with quiet eye;
And as he sits and watches there,
  He sees the flood unclose,
And from the parting waves a fair
  Mermaiden slowly rose.

She sang to him with witching wile,
  "My brood why wilt thou snare,
With human craft and human guile,
  To die in scorching air?
Ah! didst thou know how happy we,
  Who dwell in waters clear,
Thou wouldst come down at once to me,
  And rest for ever here.

"The sun and ladye-moon they lave
  Their tresses in the main,
And, breathing freshness from the wave,
  Come doubly bright again.
The deep-blue sky so moist and clear,
  Hath it for thee no lure?
Does thine own face not woo thee down

  Unto our waters pure?"
The water plash'd, the water play'd—
  It lapp'd his naked feet;
He thrill'd as though he felt the touch
  Of maiden kisses sweet.
She spoke to him, she sang to him—
  Resistless was her strain—
Half-drawn, he sank beneath the wave,
  And ne'er was seen again.

*Translated by Theodore Martin

352

THE BRIDE OF CORINTH*

YOUTH to Corinth, whilst the city slumbered,
   Came from Athens: though a stranger there,
Soon among its townsmen to be numbered,
   For a bride awaits him, young and fair.
      From their childhood's years
      They were plighted feres,
So contracted by their parents' care.

But may not his welcome there be hindered?
   Dearly must he buy it, would he speed.
He is still a heathen with his kindred,
   She and hers washed in the Christian creed.
      When new faiths are born,
      Love and troth are torn
Rudely from the heart, howe'er it bleed.

All the house is hushed;—to rest retreated
   Father, daughters—not the mother quite;
She the guest with cordial welcome greeted,
   Led him to a room with tapers bright;
      Wine and food she brought,
      Ere of them he thought,
Then departed with a fair good-night.

But he felt no hunger, and unheeded
   Left the wine, and eager for the rest
Which his limbs, forspent with travel, needed,
   On the couch he laid him, still undressed.
      There he sleeps—when lo!
      Onwards gliding slow,
At the door appears a wondrous guest.

By the waning lamp's uncertain gleaming
   There he sees a youthful maiden stand,
Robed in white, of still and gentle seeming,
   On her brow a black and golden band.
      When she meets his eyes,
      With a quick surprise
Starting, she uplifts a pallid hand.

*Translated by W. E. Aytoun and Theodore Martin

"Is a stranger here, and nothing told me?
　Am I then forgotten even in name?
Ah! 'tis thus within my cell they hold me,
　And I now am covered o'er with shame!
　　Pillow still thy head
　　There upon thy bed,
I will leave thee quickly as I came."

"Maiden—darling! Stay, O stay!" and, leaping
　From the couch before her stands the boy:
"Ceres—Bacchus, here their gifts are heaping,
　And thou bringest Amor's gentle joy!
　　Why with terror pale?
　　Sweet one, let us hail
These bright gods their festive gifts employ."

"Oh, no—no! Young stranger, come not nigh me;
　Joy is not for me, nor festive cheer.
Ah! such bliss may ne'er be tasted by me,
　Since my mother, in fantastic fear,
　　By long sickness bowed,
　　To heaven's service vowed
Me, and all the hopes that warmed me here.

"They have left our hearth, and left it lonely,—
　The old gods, that bright and jocund train.
One, unseen, in heaven, is worshipped only,
　And upon the cross a Saviour slain;
　　Sacrifice is here,
　　Not of lamb nor steer,
But of human woe and human pain."

And he asks, and all her words doth ponder,—
　"Can it be that in this silent spot,
I behold thee, thou surpassing wonder!
　My sweet bride, so strangely to me brought?
　　Be mine only now—
　　See, our parents' vow
Heaven's good blessing hath for us besought."

354

"No! thou gentle heart," she cried in anguish;
  " 'Tis not mine, but 'tis my sister's place;
When in lonely cell I weep and languish,
  Think, oh, think of me in her embrace!
     I think but of thee—
     Pining drearily,
Soon beneath the earth to hide my face!"

"Nay! I swear by yonder flame which burneth,
  Fanned by Hymen, lost thou shalt not be;
Droop not thus, for my sweet bride returneth
  To my father's mansion back with me!!
     Dearest, tarry here!
     Taste the bridal cheer,
For our spousal spread so wondrously!"

Then with word and sigh their troth they plighted,
  Golden was the chain she bade him wear,
But the cup he offered her she slighted,
  Silver, wrought with cunning past compare.
     "That is not for me;
     All I ask of thee
Is one little ringlet of thy hair!"

Dully boomed the midnight hour unhallowed,
  And then first her eyes began to shine;
Eagerly with pallid lips she swallowed
  Hasty draughts of purple-tinctured wine;
     But the wheaten bread
     As in shuddering dread,
Put she always by with loathing sign.

And she gave the youth the cup: he drained it,
  With impetuous haste he drained it dry;
Love was in his fevered heart, and pained it,
  Till it ached for joy she must deny.
     But the maiden's fears
     Stayed him, till in tears
On the bed he sank, with sobbing cry.

And she leans above him—"Dear one, still thee!
　Ah, how sad am I to see thee so!
But alas! these limbs of mine would chill thee:
　Love! they mantle not with passion's glow;
　　　Thou wouldst be afraid,
　　　Didst thou find the maid
Thou hast chosen, cold as ice or snow."

Round her waist his eager arms he bended,
　With the strength that youth and love inspire;
"Wert thou even from the grave ascended,
　I could warm thee well with my desire!"
　　　Panting kiss on kiss!
　　　Overflow of bliss!
"Burn'st thou not, and feelest me on fire?"

Closer yet they cling, and intermingling,
　Tears and broken sobs proclaim the rest;
His hot breath through all her frame is tingling,
　There they lie, caressing and caressed.
　　　His impassioned mood
　　　Warms her torpid blood.
Yet there beats no heart within her breast!

Meanwhile goes the mother, softly creeping
　　Through the hous, on needful cares intent,
Hears a murmur, and, while all are sleeping,
　Wonders at the sounds, and what they meant.
　　　Who was whispering so?—
　　　Voices soft and low,
In mysterious converse strangely blent.

Straightway by the door herself she stations,
　There to be assured what was amiss;
And she hears love's fiery protestations,
　Words of ardor and endearing bliss:
　　　"Hark, the cock! 'Tis light!
　　　But to-morrow night
Thou wilt come again?" and kiss on kiss.

Quick the latch she raises, and, with features
    Anger-flushed, into the chamber hies.
"Are there in my house such shameless creatures,
    Minions to the stranger's will?" she cries.
        By the dying light,
        Who is't meets her sight?
God! 'tis her own daughter she espies!

And the youth in terror sought to cover,
    With her own light veil, the maiden's head,
Clasped her close; but, gliding from her lover,
    Back the vestment from her brow she spread,
        And her form upright,
        As with ghostly might,
Long and slowly rises from the bed.

"Mother! mother! wherefore thus deprive me
    Of such joy as I this night have known?
Wherefore from these warm embraces drive me?
    Was I wakened up to meet thy frown?
        Did it not suffice
        That in virgin guise,
To an early grave you forced me down?

"Fearful is the weird that forced me hither,
    From the dark-heaped chamber where I lay;
Powerless are your drowsy anthems, neither
    Can your priests prevail, howe'er they pray.
        Salt nor lymph can cool,
        Where the pulse is full,
Love must still burn on, though wrapped in clay.

"To this youth my early troth was plighted,
    Whilst yet Venus ruled within the land;
Mother! and that vow ye falsely slighted,
    At your new and gloomy faith's command.
        But no god will hear,
        If a mother swear
Pure from love to keep her daughter's hand.

"Nightly from my narrow chamber driven,
  Come I to fulfil my destined part,
Him to seek to whom my troth was given,
  And to draw the life-blood from his heart.
      He hath served my will;
      More I yet must kill,
  For another prey I now depart.

"Fair young man! thy thread of life is broken,
  Human skill can bring no aid to thee.
There thou hast my chain—a ghastly token—
  And this lock of thine I take with me.
      Soon must thou decay,
      Soon thou wilt be gray,
  Dark although to-night thy tresses be!

"Mother! hear, oh, hear my last entreaty!
  Let the funeral-pile arise once more;
Open up my wretched tomb for pity:
  And in flames our souls to peace restore.
      When the ashes glow,
      When the fire-sparks flow,
  To the ancient gods aloft we soar."

FICTION

FICTION.

The Sorrows of Young Werther

WHATEVER I have been able to discover of the story of poor Werther I have industriously collected, and put it now before you, and I know that you will thank me for it. You will not be able to withhold your admiration and love for his mind and character or your tears for his fate.

And you, good soul, who are labouring under the same distress as he, draw consolation from his sufferings and, if you should be prevented by fate or your own fault from finding one more intimate, let this little book be your friend.

4 May, 1771.

How GLAD I am to have got away! My dear friend, what a thing is the heart of man! To leave you whom I love so much, from whom I was inseparable—and yet be cheerful! I know you will forgive me. Were not all my other friendships veritably chosen by Fate to oppress a heart like mine? Poor Leonore! And yet the blame was not mine! Could I help it if her poor heart conceived a passion for me while the capricious charms of her sister afforded me agreeable entertainment! And yet—am I altogether blameless! Did I not feed her emotions? Did I not myself find pleasure in the sincere manifestations of Nature which so often made us laugh, however little conducive they were to laughter! Did I not—Oh! what is man, that he may bewail his lot?—I will, dear friend, I promise you, I will mend my ways; I will no longer chew the cud of misfortune that Fate ekes out to us, as I have always done. I will enjoy the present, and the

Translated by William Rose

past shall be done with. You are surely right, my best of friends. The sufferings of men would be less if they did not so busily engage their imagination—God knows why they are so constituted—in recalling the memory of bygone ills, rather than bear an indifferent present.

Will you be so good as to tell my mother that I shall look after her business as well as I can and that I shall write to her about it in a day or two? I called on my aunt and did not by any means find the ill-tempered woman that they make her out to be at home. She is lively, impetuous and very warm-hearted. I explained to her my mother's grievances about the legacy that had been held back. She told me the reasons that had impelled her to do it and the terms under which she would be ready to hand everything over—more, in fact, than we asked.—In short, I don't want to write about it now, but tell my mother everything will be all right. And in dealing with this little matter I have again found that misunderstandings and indolence are perhaps the cause of more disturbance in the world than cunning or malice. At any rate the last two are certainly more rare.

For the rest, I am quite happy here. Solitude is delicious balm to my heart in this heavenly spot, and this youthful season pours the fulness of its warmth into my oft-shivering heart. Every tree, every hedge is a nosegay, and one would like to turn into a cockchafer to float in a sea of fragrance and find in it all the nourishment one needs.

The town itself is not very agreeable, but it lies amidst the most inexpressible natural beauty, which led the late Count von M. to lay out a garden on one of the intersecting hills which form the most charming valleys in the loveliest diversity of Nature. The garden is simple, and one feels as soon as one enters that it was planned not by a scientific gardener but by an impressionable soul that wanted here to take its pleasure. I have shed many a tear for the departed owner in the crumbling arbour which was his favourite sojourn, and is also mine. Soon I shall be the master of the garden. The gardener has become devoted to me during the few days I have been here, and he will not do at all badly by it.

10 May.

MY WHOLE SOUL is imbued with a wondrous serenity, like the pleasant Spring mornings which I enjoy with all my heart. I am completely alone and find life so enjoyable in this spot which was created for souls like mine. I am so happy, so absorbed in the sensation of a tranquil existence, that my art is suffering. I could not draw a line at this moment, and yet I have never been more of a painter than I am now. When the mist is rising from the lovely valley and the sun is high above the impenetrable shade of my wood, so that only now and then a ray steals into the inner sanctuary, and I lie in the tall grass by the falling brook, and discover a thousand different grasses on the surface of the earth; when I feel nearer to my heart the teeming little world among the blades, the innumerable, unfathomable creatures in the shape of worms and insects, and when I feel the presence of the Almighty Spirit Who created us all in His image, the breath of the All-loving One who sustains us as we float in illimitable bliss—Oh! friend, when the world then grows dim before my eyes and earth and sky are absorbed into my soul like the form of a beloved, I am often consumed with longing and think, ah! would that I could express it, would that I could breathe on to paper that which lives so warm and full within me, so that it might become the mirror of my soul as my soul is the mirror of the eternal God! My friend—but it is beyond my power, and I succumb to the splendour of what lies before me.

12 May.

I KNOW not whether deluding spirits are hovering round this spot, or whether it is the divine and ardent fancy of my heart which turns everything around me into a Paradise. Right in front of the gate is a spring, a spring by which I am enchanted like Melusine and her sisters. On descending a small hill you come to an arch, with about twenty steps going down to where the clearest of water gushes from the marble rock. The little wall above which encloses it, the tall trees all round, the coolness of the place—there is something so attractive, so awesome about it all. Hardly a day passes without my sitting there for an hour. Then the girls come from the town to fetch water, the most innocent and necessary of services which once even the daughters of kings performed. As I sit there I am reminded vividly of the days of the patriarchs, all striking up acquaintance or plighting their troth at the well, and kindly spirits hovering round the springs and fountains. Oh! he can never have refreshed himself at the coolness of a spring, after a hard walk on a summer's day, who is unable to sympathise with my emotion.

13 May.

You ask whether you are to send my books along? I entreat you, for the Lord's sake, do not bother me with books. I no longer want to be guided, enlivened or excited. This heart is in sufficient of a ferment without their help. I need lullabies and I have found them in abundance in my Homer. How often do I lull my stormy spirit, for never have you seen anything so restless, so changeable as this heart. Dear friend! do I need to tell *you* who have so often borne the burden of my transition from grief to excessive joy, from gentle melancholy to devastating passion? I treat my heart like a sick child and gratify its every whim. Don't repeat this, there are people who would take it amiss.

15 May.

The poor folk here know me already and have an affection for me, especially the children. I have noticed something which saddens me. When I first mixed with them and asked in a friendly manner about one thing or another, some of them thought I wanted to scoff, and they put me off very rudely. I did not take offence, but I felt very keenly, what I have often noticed, that people in a better position always keep coldly aloof from the common folk as though they feared to lose something by proximity, and there are even heedless, mischievous wags who appear to act condescendingly in order to make poor people all the more sensitive to their arrogance. I know quite well that we are not all equal, and that we never can be so. But I maintain that anyone who thinks it necessary to hold himself aloof from the so-called rabble, in order to keep its respect, is quite as blameworthy as a coward who hides from the enemy because he is afraid of defeat.

A little while ago I came to the spring and found a young maidservant who had put her pitcher on the lowest step and was looking round for one of her friends to help her lift it on to her head. I went down and looked at her. "Shall I help you, young woman?" I asked. She blushed to the roots of her hair. "Oh no sir!" she said. "Come, don't stand on ceremony."—She adjusted her head piece and I helped her. She thanked me and went up the steps.

17 May.

I HAVE made all sorts of acquaintances but have not yet got into any circle. I do not know what there is about me that attracts people, so many like me and become attached to me, and it always grieves me when our paths are the same for only such a very short distance. When you ask what the people here are like, I must reply, like everywhere else. The human race does not vary much. Most people pass the greater part of their lives in work, in order to live, and the modicum of free time they have to themselves makes them so uneasy that they seek every means they can to kill it. Alas, the destiny of man!

But they are a very worthy type of folk! When I on occasion forget myself, and am able to enjoy with them the pleasures that still remain to man, to exchange jests in all candour and sincerity at a well-set board, to arrange a walk or a dance at the proper time and so on, it has a good effect on me, so long as I do not remember all the other forces lying dormant in me, all untried and becoming atrophied, which I must carefully conceal. Oh! all this clutches at my heart—and yet! It is the fate of a man like me to be misunderstood.

Alas! that the friend of my youth is gone, alas! that I ever knew her! I would say to myself "You are a fool! You are seeking what does not exist down here." But she was mine, I felt the heart, the great soul in whose presence I seemed to myself to be more than I really was, since I was everything that I could be. God! was there a single force in my soul that remained untried, was I not able to develop in her presence all the wondrous perception with which my heart embraces Nature, was not our intercourse an endless weaving of the most delicate feeling, the keenest wit, whose variations were all stamped, even to the extent of extravagance, with the impress of genius? And now— Alas! she descended before me to the grave, for she had the advantage in years. Never shall I forget her, never shall I cease to recall her steadfast mind and divine fortitude.

A few days ago I met a young man named V., a straightforward youth with very pleasing features. He has just come down from the University, does not exactly consider himself a sage but yet thinks he knows more than other people. He was very diligent, as I can tell from various signs, in short, he is pretty well informed. As he had heard that I draw a great deal and know Greek (two unusual phenomena in these parts) he came to me and dug out his store of learning, from Batteux to Wood, from de Piles to Winckelmann, assuring me that he had read right through the first part of Sulzer's *Theory* and possessed a manuscript of Heyne's about the study of antiquity. I did not pursue the subject.

I have made the acquaintance of another very worthy fellow, the prince's bailiff. A straightforward, simple man. They say it does one's heart good to see him among his children, of whom he has nine. In particular they talk a great deal about his eldest daughter. He has invited me to come and see him, and I am going to call on him very soon. He lives in one of the prince's hunting lodges, an hour and a half from here, to which he received permission to move after the death of his wife, since he found staying here in the town, in the bailiff's lodge, too painful.

In addition I have come across a few eccentric oddities whom I find quite insufferable, most insupportable of all being their attestations of friendship.

Farewell! you will like this letter, it is all about things that have happened.

22 May.

THAT THE LIFE of man is only a dream has already occurred to many, and I also am always haunted by this feeling. When I see the restrictions by which the active, speculative powers of man are hemmed in, when I see how all activity is directed toward the satisfaction of needs which themselves have no other purpose than to prolong our wretched existence, and that the only way to meet certain speculations is by a dreamy resignation, in which we paint the walls of our prison with coloured figures and bright prospects—all this, Wilhelm, makes me dumb. I turn in upon myself and find a world! But again more with presentiment and obscure craving than plastic power and vital force. Everything swims before my senses and I continue on my way through the world with a dreamy smile.

All learned teachers and instructors are agreed that children do not know the reason for their desires. But nobody likes to believe that grown-ups are also walking unsteadily upon this earth, that, like children, they do not know whence they come nor whither they are going, that their actions are equally devoid of true purpose, that they are ruled in the same way by the promise of biscuits, cake or the birch, and yet it seems to me the thing is evident.

I willingly admit, for I know what your reply will be, that the happiest mortals are those who, like children, live for the day, drag about their dolls, don and doff their clothes, creep respectfully round the cupboard where mother keeps the tarts and, when they at last snatch what they are after, stuff their cheeks and cry for more.—Such beings are happy. And they also are well-off who give high-sounding names to their miserable pursuits, or even their passions, and attribute to them a colossal influence on the welfare and prosperity of the human race. He is lucky who can do so! But whoever in his humbleness recognizes what all this leads to, who sees how neatly every contented citizen trims his little garden into an Eden, and how even unhappy mortals pant along patiently under their heavy load and everybody alike is eager to see the light of the sun for another minute—such a man is tranquil and likewise creates his world out of his own soul, happy because he is a human being. And then, circumscribed as he is, he yet always preserves in his heart the sweet feeling of freedom and the thought that he can leave this prison when he will.

26 May.

YOU KNOW of old the way I settle down, build myself a cabin in some intimate spot and take up my modest quarters there. I have again found a corner that attracts me.

About an hour's journey from the town lies a hamlet called Wahlheim.* It is very interestingly situated on a hill and, when you walk out of the village by the footpath above, you see the whole valley spread out at your feet. A kindly landlady, obliging and cheerful in her old age, dispenses wine, beer and coffee and, what is most delightful of all, there are two limes whose spreading branches cast their shade over the little open space

---

* The reader need not exert himself to find out which are the places referred to here, as it has been necessary to change the names mentioned in the original letters.

in front of the church, which is closed in on all sides by the cottages of the peasants, their barns and farmyards. I have rarely found a spot more intimate or cosy, and I have my little table and chair brought out from the inn, drink my coffee and read my Homer. The first time I came by accident upon the limes one fine afternoon, the place was a solitude. Everybody was in the fields. Only one little boy about four years of age was sitting on the ground, holding a child of about six months between his feet, clasping him with both arms to his breast so that he formed a kind of armchair for him and, in spite of the vivacity which sparkled in his black eyes, he was quite still. The sight pleased me and, sitting down on a plough opposite them, I amused myself by drawing their brotherly attitude, including the neighbouring hedge, the doorway of a threshing-floor and some broken cartwheels, just as they all stood, so that in an hour I had made a well-grouped and very interesting sketch without adding anything at all that was not in my model. This strengthened my resolution to keep to Nature in the future. Nature alone is infinitely rich, and Nature alone forms the great artist. Much can be adduced in favour of rules that can be applied with more or less equal justice in praise of middle-class society. The man who models himself on them will never produce anything inferior or in bad taste, just as one who allows his life to be fashioned by precepts and the laws of propriety will never become a disagreeable neighbour or a remarkable villain; on the other hand, whatever people may say, rules destroy the true feeling for Nature and its true expression. You will say, "That is too severe! they only act as a check, prune the rank tendrils, and so on." My good friend, shall I submit a parable to you? It is like love. A youth cleaves wholly to a maid, passes all his hours in her company, expends all his forces, all his fortune, to express to her at every moment that he is completely devoted to her. And then there comes a Philistine, a man engaged in a public office, who says to him, "Young Man, to love is human, only you must love in a human way! Divide up your hours, giving some to work, and your hours of recreation you may dedicate to your maid; calculate your fortune, and from whatever you have beyond your needs you may offer her a gift, say on her birth or name day, only not too often, and so on." If he obeys, he will become an efficient young man and I would advise any prince to give him a post in the government service; but there will be an end to his love and, if he is an artist, to his art. Oh my friends! Why does the stream of genius break forth so rarely, so rarely roar down in a raging torrent, mountain high, to convulse your wondering souls? My friends, there are tranquil fellows dwelling on both banks whose arbours, tulip-beds and cabbage-plots would be devastated, and so they are able to ward off the threatening danger by timely damming and draining.

27 May.

I SEE that I have lapsed into parable and ecstatic declamation, and have quite forgotten to tell you the sequel to my adventure with the children. I had been sitting on my plough for about two hours entirely absorbed in perceptions of the picturesque which my letter of yesterday will have transmitted to you in a very fragmentary manner. Towards evening a young woman comes up to the children, who during all this time had not moved, with a little basket on her arm, and calls out when she is still some distance away, "Philip, you are a very good boy." She greeted me, I thanked her, stood up, went up to her and enquired whether she was the mother of the children. She said she was and, giving the older one half a roll, she picked up the baby and kissed it with every sign of maternal affection. "I gave my Philip the baby to hold," she said, "and went into the town with my eldest boy to buy white bread and sugar and an earthenware saucepan for porridge." I saw all this in the basket from which the lid had fallen off. "I want to cook Hans (that was the name of the baby) some broth before he goes to bed; my scamp of an eldest broke my saucepan yesterday as he was quarrelling with Philip over what was left of the porridge." I enquired about the eldest boy, and she had hardly told me that he was chasing a couple of geese on the common when he came running up with a hazel switch for Philip. In further conversation with the mother I learned that she was the daughter of the schoolmaster, and that her husband was on his way to Switzerland to fetch a legacy that had been left him by a cousin. "They tried to cheat him out of it," she said, "and did not answer his letters, so he has gone there himself. I hope nothing has happened to him, as I have not heard from him since." I found it difficult to tear myself away. I gave each of the children a *Kreuzer*, including one for the baby which I gave to the mother to buy him a roll for his broth when she went into the town, and so I left them.

I tell you, my dear fellow, when my mind is all a riot, it is soothed by the sight of such a mortal pursuing in tranquil contentment the narrow round of her existence, making both ends meet from day to day, and with no other thought, when she sees the leaves falling, but that winter is near.

I have often gone out since, and the children have become quite used to me. When I drink my coffee they have their share of the sugar, and they share my bread and butter and sour milk in the evening. On Sundays they never fail to receive their *Kreuzer*, and if I am not there after the hour of prayer the landlady has orders to pay it to them.

I have won their confidence and they tell me all sorts of things. I find it particularly delightful to watch them vent their passions and express their desires so naively when a number of children from the village are collected together.

I had a lot of trouble to relieve the mother of her apprehension lest they might "incommode the gentleman."

16 June.

WHY DON'T I write to you? You ask me that though you are also numbered among the scholars! You should be able to divine that I am well, and indeed—in short, I have met someone in whom my heart is interested. I have—I do not know.

To tell you in proper order how it happened that I made the acquaintance of one of the most charming of beings will be no easy matter; I am content and happy, so am not likely to be a satisfactory narrator.

An angel! By Heaven, everybody says that of his mistress! Doesn't he? And yet I am incapable of telling you how perfect she is, or why she is perfect, enough, she has taken complete possession of my mind.

So much naïvete combined with such intelligence, such kindness and such resolve, such tranquillity of soul in such an active life.

This is all hopeless twaddle that I am saying about her, mere abstractions which fail to express a single feature of her real self. Another time—No, not another time, I will tell you now, immediately. If I don't do it now, I never shall. For, between ourselves, since I began this letter I have been three times on the verge of laying down my pen, saddling my horse and riding off though I vowed early this morning that I would not—and yet every minute I go to the window to see how high the sun stands . . . .

I could not help it, I had to go out to her. I am back once more, Wilhelm, and will eat my supper and finish this letter. How it enraptures my soul to see her among the dear happy children, her eight brothers and sisters.

If I continue like this, you will be no wiser at the end than you were at the beginning, so listen, I will force myself to give you details.

I wrote to you recently that I had made the acquaintance of the bailiff S., and that he had invited me to come and visit him soon at his hermitage, or rather his little kingdom. I neglected to do so and would perhaps never have gone, if there had not been revealed to me by accident the treasure concealed in that tranquil spot.

The young people here had arranged a ball in the country, and I gladly agreed to go. I offered my escort to a nice, good-looking, but not otherwise interesting girl in this town, and it was settled that I was to hire a coach to drive out to the scene of the festivities with my partner and her cousin, and that we were to pick up Charlotte S. on the way. "You will make the acquaintance of a beautiful girl," my partner said, as we drove through a broad avenue in the wood towards the hunting lodge. "Take care," her cousin added, "that you don't fall in love." "What do you mean?" I asked. "She is already betrothed," the former replied, "to a very worthy man who has gone to put his affairs in order after his father's death and to apply for an important post." The information did not interest me particularly.

The sun was still a quarter of an hour from the hill top when we reached the lodge gate; it was very sultry and the ladies expressed their anxiety lest we should be overtaken by a storm which we could see gathering in heavy, whitish-gray little clouds round the horizon. I relieved their fears by pretending to a knowledge of the weather, though I began myself to have a foreboding that our festivities would be interrupted.

I had alighted, and a maid who came to the gate begged us to wait a moment, Mamselle Lottchen would be with us straightway. I went across the courtyard to the well-built house and, when I had ascended the steps in front and entered at the door, I caught sight of the most charming scene that I have ever witnessed. In

371

the entrance hall there swarmed six children, from two to eleven years of age, round a handsome girl of middle height, who wore a simple white frock with pink bows on the breast and arms. She was holding a loaf of black bread and cutting a slice for each of the children round her in proportion to its age and appetite, offering it with such an amiable air and each one crying "Thank you!" so artlessly, after he had stretched his little hands up as high as he could before his slice was cut, and then springing away contentedly with his supper or, if he was of a quieter nature, walking tranquilly towards the gate to see the strangers and the coach in which their Lotte was to drive away.—"I beg your pardon," she said, "for giving you the trouble of coming in and making the ladies wait. While I was dressing and making all sorts of arrangements for the house in my absence, I forgot to give my children their supper, and they won't have their bread cut by anyone but me." I paid her some harmless compliment while my whole soul was absorbed in the contemplation of her figure, her voice, her bearing, and I had just time to recover from my surprise when she ran into the room to fetch her gloves and fan. The children kept at a little distance, casting sidelong glances at me, and I went up to the youngest who was a most pleasant looking child. He had just drawn back when Lotte appeared in the doorway and said, "Louis, shake hands with your cousin." The boy did so with a very frank air, and I could not refrain from kissing him heartily in spite of his dirty little nose. "Cousin?" I said, as I offered her my hand. "Do you consider that I deserve the happiness of being related to you?" "Oh!" she said, with a roguish smile, "our circle of cousins is very extensive, and I should be very sorry if you were the least worthy among them." As we went she ordered Sophie, the next oldest sister to herself, a girl of about eleven, to keep an eye on the little ones, and greet their father when he came back from his ride. The little ones she admonished to obey their sister Sophie as they would herself, and some of them expressly promised to do so. A pert little blonde, however, of about six years, said, "But it isn't you, after all, Lottchen! we like you better." The two eldest boys had climbed up behind the coach, and at my request she allowed them to travel with us until we reached the edge of the wood, so long as they promised not to tease each other and to hold on firmly.

Hardly had we fitted ourselves in and the ladies greeted one another, each in turn expressing her views about the others' costumes, particularly bonnets, and duly passing in review the company that they expected to meet, when Lotte stopped the coach for her brothers to descend; they asked to kiss her hand once more, and the older one did so with all the delicacy that could be expected of a boy of fifteen, the other with impetuousness and levity. She bade them give her love once more to the little ones, and the coach rolled on.

The cousin enquired whether she had finished the book she had recently sent her. "No," said Lotte. "I do not like it; you can have it back. The one you sent me before was no better."* When I asked what the books were, I was amazed at her reply.* There was so much character in all she said, and with every word I discovered fresh charms, saw new flashes of intelligence lighting up her features, which appeared gradually to brighten with pleasure because she felt that I understood her.

"When I was younger," she said, "I liked nothing so much as novels. Heaven knows I felt happy when I could sit in some corner on Sundays and share with my whole heart the fortune or distress of some Miss Jenny. Nor do I deny that this kind of romance still has some charm for me. But since I now so seldom have time for a book, it must be suited to my taste. And the author I most prefer is the one in whom I find my own world again, who describes happenings such as I see around me and yet whose story I find as interesting, as sympathetic as my own domestic existence, which is, to be sure, not a Paradise, but nevertheless on the whole a source of inexpressible bliss."

I did my best to conceal my emotions at these words. I was not, it is true, very successful, for when I heard her speak incidentally, but with such truth, about the Vicar of Wakefield and about—,† I lost my control and told her everything that forced itself to my lips, and only noticed after some time, when Lotte directed her remarks to the others, that these had been sitting there the whole time with wide-open eyes, as though they

---

* It has been thought necessary to suppress this passage in the Manuscript so as not to afford anyone grounds for complaint. Although, as a matter of fact, no author can be much concerned at the judgment of a single girl and an unbalanced young man.

† The names of some of our native authors have been omitted here also. Whoever shares Lotte's appreciation will certainly feel in his own heart who they are, if he should read these lines. And there is no necessity for anybody else to know.

were not there at all. The cousin looked at me more than once with a mocking air, which however was of little consequence to me.

The conversation turned upon the pleasure of dancing. "If this passion is a fault," said Lotte, "I willingly confess I know nothing that excels dancing. And when I have something on my mind and drum out a quadrille on my squeaky old harpsichord, then everything is all right again."

How I gazed into her black eyes as she spoke, how her vivacious lips and her fresh, lively mien drew my whole soul on, how totally absorbed I became in the glorious feeling of listening to her, so that I often did not even hear the words by which she expressed herself!—Of this you can have some idea, since you know me. In short, I descended from the coach as though in a dream when we came to a halt in front of the summer house, and I was still so immersed in dreams amid the darkling world around me that I hardly noticed the music which was wafted down to us from the brightly lit hall.

Two gentlemen named Audran and a certain N.N.—who can remember everybody's name!—who were the partners of Lotte and the cousin, met us at the coach door, took charge of their ladies, and I escorted mine upstairs.

We glided round one another in minuets, I engaged one lady after another, and it was just the least attractive ones who could not manage to change hands and end the figure. Lotte and her partner began an English quadrille, and you can imagine how happy I was when the turn came for her to begin the figure with us. You should see her dance! She is so absorbed in it, heart and soul, her whole body *one* harmony, as care-free, as unaffected, as though nothing else mattered, as though she thought or felt nothing else, and it is certain that at such moments everything else has ceased to exist for her.

I asked her for the second quadrille, but she promised me the third, and with the most charming ingenuousness in the world she assured me that she was very fond of dancing in the German way. "It is the fashion here," she continued, "that each couple who are together remain together in the German dance, but my partner is an indifferent waltzer and he will be grateful if I relieve him of the labour. Your lady can't waltz either and doesn't like it, and I saw during the quadrille that you waltz well; if you care to be my partner for the German dance, go and ask leave of my partner while I go and ask your lady." I agreed, and it was soon arranged that her partner should sit out the waltz with mine.

We then began, and took delight in interlacing our arms in diverse ways. What charm, what fleetness of movement! And when we came to the waltz, and the dancers revolved round each other like planets, there was at first a certain amount of confusion since very few are expert at it. We were prudent and let them wear themselves out, and when the clumsiest couples had left the floor we joined in and held out valiantly to the end together with another pair, Audran and his partner. Never have I danced so easily. I was no longer a mortal. To have the most charming creature in the world in my arms and to fly around with her like lightning, so that everything round about ceased to exist and—Wilhelm, to be candid, I *did* vow that the girl I loved, on whom I had claims, should never waltz with another, even if it meant the end of me. You understand!

We took a turn or two round the room after the dance in order to recover our breath. Then she sat down, and the lemons I had stolen when the punch was being brewed, which were now the only ones left and which I brought her cut into slices with sugar, had an excellent refreshing effect, except that with every slice the lady sitting next to her took out of the cup a stab went through my heart, though for the sake of decency I had to offer it to her also.

In the third quadrille we were the second couple. As we danced through the ranks and I, God knows with what rapture, kept my eyes, as she hung upon my arm, fixed upon hers, in which shone the sincerest expression of frank and pure enjoyment, we reached a lady who had attracted my attention on account of her sympathetic mien, though her face was no longer exactly young. She looked at Lotte with a smile, lifted a minatory finger, and mentioned the name Albert twice with considerable emphasis as she whirled past.

"Who is Albert," I asked Lotte, "if it is not presumption on my part?" She was about to reply when we had to separate to make the figure of eight, and it seemed to me that I saw a certain pensiveness shade her brow as we crossed in front of each other. "Why should I keep it from you?" she said, as she gave me her hand for the promenade. "Albert is a worthy man to whom I am as good as betrothed." This was not news to me, for the girls had told me in the carriage, and yet it *was* entirely new to me, since I had not thought of it in connection with her who had come to mean so much to me in such a short time. Enough—I became confused, forgot the steps, and danced in between the wrong couple so that everything became mixed up and Lotte's whole presence of mind and pulling and tugging were necessary to restore order.

The dance had not yet come to an end when the flashes of lightning, which we had for some time seen gleaming on the horizon and which I had pretended were sheet lightning, began to grow more pronounced and the thunder drowned the music. Three ladies ran out of the ranks, followed by their partners, confusion became general, and the music ceased. It is natural, when our pleasure is interrupted by an accident or something terrifying, that the impression made upon us should be stronger than usual, partly because of the contrast which is felt so vividly, partly and even more because our senses are susceptible and receive an impression all the more quickly. To these causes must be attributed the wondrous grimaces which I saw appear on the faces of several ladies. The wisest of them sat down in a corner with her back to the window and held her hands over her ears, another knelt down and buried her face in the lap of the first one, a third pushed her way in between them both and clasped her little sisters to her with a thousand tears. Some wanted to drive home, others, who were even less aware what they were doing, had not sufficient presence of mind to avoid the impertinences of some of the young gentlemen who had had a little to drink, and who appeared to be busily engaged in capturing from the lips of the beauties in distress the timorous prayers which were meant for Heaven. Some of the gentlemen had gone downstairs to smoke a quiet pipe, and the rest of the company did not refuse when the hostess hit upon the clever idea of showing us into a room which had curtains and shutters. Hardly had we entered when Lotte began to arrange chairs in a circle, to seat the guests and suggest a game.

I saw more than one gentleman purse his lips and stretch his limbs in expectation of a luscious forfeit. "We are going to play at Counting," she said, "so pay attention. I am going round in a circle from right to left, and each of you must also count round the number that comes to him, but it must go like wildfire, and whoever hesitates or makes a mistake receives a box on the ears, and so on to a thousand."—It was a merry sight. She went round the circle with her arm stretched out. "One," cried the first, his neighbour "two," "three" the next and so on. Then she began to go more quickly, more and more quickly. One man missed his number, *smack!* a box on the ears; the next man laughed so much that he also missed, *smack!* And more and more quickly. I received two slaps on the face myself, and with secret pleasure I thought I felt that they were harder than those she gave the others. A general uproar and outburst of laughter brought the game to an end before the thousand was counted. Those who were most intimate with each other drew aside, the storm was over, and I followed Lotte into the ballroom. On the way she said, "During the ear-boxing they forgot the weather and everything!" I did not know what to reply. "I was one of the most timorous," she said, "and by pretending to be brave in order to give the others courage I became courageous myself." We stepped to the window, the thunder could be heard away to the side, and the glorious rain was pattering down on to the earth, while the most refreshing fragrance rose up to us in a full, warm vapour. She stood leaning on her elbow, her gaze searching the landscape; she looked up to the heavens and then at me, I saw her eyes fill with tears, she put her hand on mine and murmured —*Klopstock!* I became submerged in the flood of emotions which this name let loose upon me. I could not bear it, I bent over her hand and kissed it amidst the most ecstatic tears. And looked up again into her eyes—Noble Poet! would that thou hadst seen thy apotheosis in that gaze, and would that I might never hear again thy so oft desecrated name!

19 June.

I NO LONGER know where I broke off my story. All I know is that it was two o'clock in the morning when I went to bed, and that if, instead of writing, I had been able to babble to you, I should probably have kept you up till daybreak.

I have not yet told you what happened on our way home from the ball and I haven't time to tell you to-day either.

There was a lovely sunrise. The dripping wood and the freshened fields round about. Our companions in the coach were nodding off. She asked if I did not want to join them, as far as she was concerned I need not be embarrassed. "As long as I see your eyes open," I said, looking at her firmly, "there is no danger of that." And we both held out until we reached the gates of her home, when the maid opened gently and assured her, in answer to her enquiries, that her father and the little ones were all right and were still asleep. Then I took leave with the protestation that I would see her that same day, and I kept my promise; and since that time sun, moon and stars can journey calmly on their round, I know not whether it is night or day and the whole world about me has ceased to have any existence.

21 June.

MY DAYS are as happy as those God allots to His saints; and whatever the future may have in store for me, I shall not be able to say that I have not experienced the joys, the purest joys of life. You know my Wahlheim. I am quite settled there. It is only half an hour away from Lotte, and there I feel I am myself and possess all the happiness that is granted to mankind.

Had I but thought, when I selected Wahlheim as the goal of my walks, that it lies so near to Heaven! How often in the course of my long wanderings did I see the hunting lodge, which now encompasses all my desires, either from the hill or in the plain across the river.

Dear Wilhelm, I have pondered over so many things, man's craving to extend, to make new discoveries, to rove about; and then again his inward urge to submit willingly to his limitations, to travel along the path of custom and have no thought for the right hand or the left.

It is wonderful how I came here and gazed down from the hilltop into the lovely valley, how I was enchanted by everything round about. There the little wood! Oh could you but mingle in its shade! There the summit of the mount! Oh could you but survey from there the broad landscape! The chain of hills and intimate valleys! Oh could I but lose myself in them! I hurried thither and returned, and had not found that which I sought. Oh! distant vistas are like the distant future! A vast darkling whole lies before our soul, our emotions merge into it, like our gaze, and we yearn to surrender our entire being, to be filled with all the rapture of a single great glorious feeling.—And oh! when we rush up to it, when the distant *there* becomes *here*, everything is as it was before, and we stand hemmed in by our

378

poverty, while our soul pants for the draught that is beyond its reach.

And so even the most restless wanderer longs at last for his native land, and finds in his poor cabin, at the breast of his wife, amidst his children and the occupations necessary for their sustenance, all the rapture which he sought in vain in the wide and dreary world.

When I set out at daybreak to walk to my Wahlheim and pick peas for myself in the garden of the inn, and sit down and shell them while I read my Homer; when I then go into the little kitchen to find a pot, cut off a piece of butter, put my peas on the fire, cover the pot and sit down to keep turning them—then I feel so vividly how the glorious haughty suitors of Penelope slaughtered oxen and swine, cut them up and roasted them. Nothing so fills me with a sincere, calm emotion as the features of patriarchal life which I, thanks be to God, am able without affectation to weave into my mode of living.

How happy I am that my heart can feel the simple, innocent joy of the man who brings to his table a cabbage that he has grown himself, and enjoys at the same moment not only the cabbage but also all the fine days, the beautiful morning when he planted it, the pleasant evenings when he watered it and when he rejoiced in its increasing size.

29 June.

THE PHYSICIAN came here from the town the day before yesterday to visit the bailiff and found me on the floor among Lotte's children, some crawling over me and the others teasing me while I was tickling them, and we all made a great uproar. The doctor, who is a very dogmatic puppet and arranges the folds of his cuffs while he is discoursing and pulls out his frill as far as his navel, thought this beneath the dignity of an intelligent person, as I could see by the way he turned up his nose. I did not let myself be put out, however, but let him pursue his wise disquisition, and continued to rebuild a house of cards that the children had knocked down. He afterwards went about the town complaining that the bailiff's children were sufficiently badly brought up without that fellow Werther spoiling them completely.

Yes, Wilhelm, children are nearer to my heart than anything else on earth. When I watch them and see in the little creatures the germs of all the virtues and all the powers that they will one day find so indispensable, when I see in their obstinacy all the future constancy and firmness of character, in their wantonness all the future good humour and facility in gliding over the hazards of life, all so unspoilt, so undiminished—I always, always repeat the golden words of the Teacher of men, "Unless ye become even as one of these!" And yet we treat them, who are such as we, whom we should look upon as our models, after the manner of inferior beings. They are said to be lacking in will!— Have we then none? And in what lies our superiority? In our age and maturer wisdom? God in Heaven, Thou seest old children and young children, and that is all, and Thy Son has long since proclaimed in which Thou findest greater joy. But they do not believe in Him and do not hear Him—that is also out of fashion!—and they model their children upon themselves, and—Adieu, Wilhelm, I have no wish to continue this idle talk.

1 July.

WHAT LOTTE must be to a sick man I feel in my own poor heart, which is worse off than many a one which is languishing on a bed of sickness. She is to pass some days in the town at the bedside of an honest woman who, so the doctors say, is nearing her end, and who wishes to have Lotte near her in her last moments. I went with her last week to visit the pastor of St., a hamlet an hour's journey away in the mountains. We arrived about four. Lotte had brought her second sister with her. When we entered the courtyard of the parsonage, which is shaded by two tall walnut trees, we found the good old man sitting on a bench before the house door, and when he saw Lotte it was as though he were imbued with new life. He forgot his knotted stick and made an effort to rise and come towards her. She ran towards him and made him sit down, while she took a seat at his side, gave him her father's best greetings, and embraced his youngest child, an unclean, ugly lad but the darling of his father's old age. You ought to have seen her occupying the old man's attention, raising her voice to reach his half-deaf ears, telling him about robust young people who had unexpectedly died, how excellent Karlsbad was and praising his resolve to go there next summer, and how she thought that he looked much better and more cheerful than the last time she had seen him. I had meantime paid my respects to the pastor's wife. The old man became quite cheerful, and since I could not help praising the handsome walnut trees that shaded us so pleasantly, he began, though with a little difficulty, to tell us their history. "The old one," he said, "we don't know who planted that, some say one pastor, some say another. But the young one over there is the same age as my wife, fifty years next October. Her father planted it the morning of the day she was born. He was my predecessor in the living, and I cannot tell you how much he loved that tree; it is in truth no less dear to me. My wife was seated beneath it on a log with her knitting when I first entered this courtyard as a poor student seven and twenty years ago." Lotte inquired after his daughter, and he told her that she had gone out to the workmen in the meadow with Mr. Schmidt; then, continuing his narrative, he explained how his predecessor had grown fond of him, and the daughter as well, and how he had first become his curate and then his successor. He had hardly finished his story when his daughter came through the garden with the said Mr. Schmidt. She welcomed Lotte with considerable warmth, and I must admit that I found her by no means unattractive. A lively brunette with a good figure, who would have been quite entertaining company during a short stay in the country. Her suitor, for as such Mr. Schmidt soon presented himself, was a cultivated but reserved individual, who did not show any desire to join in our conversation, although Lotte kept turning to him, and what most depressed me was that I thought I could gather from his expression that it was caprice and ill-humour rather than limited intelligence which prevented him from being more communicative. In the sequel this unfortunately grew only too evident, for when Friederike, as we walked along, kept to the side of Lotte or occasionally came over to me, the gentleman's face, which was in any case of a brownish hue, darkened so visibly that it was time for Lotte to tug me by the sleeve and advise me to refrain from making myself agreeable to Friederike. Now nothing aggravates me more than when people torment each other, especially when young couples, who might be most receptive to all the joys that come in the prime of life, spoil the few days that might be so pleasant with crotchets, and only realise when it is too late that they have wasted what cannot be recovered. It vexed me mightily, and when we returned to the parsonage towards evening and were supping at a table in the courtyard on bread dipped in milk, I could not help taking up the subject when the conversation turned on the joys and sorrows of this world, and attacking most heartily the vice of ill-humour. "We mortals frequently complain," I began, "that the days of our happiness are too few and those of our sorrow too many, and I think we are generally wrong. If our hearts were always open to enjoy the good which God gives us each day, then we should also have sufficient strength to bear misfortune when it comes." "But we have not control over our natures," replied the pastor's wife. "How much depends on our bodies! When we feel unwell, everything seems wrong." I admitted that. "Then let us regard it as a disease and enquire whether there is no remedy for it." "That is worth considering," said Lotte. "I believe at least that much depends on ourselves. I know it from my own nature. When anything worries me and is inclined to make me depressed, I jump up and sing a couple of quadrille airs up and down the garden, and it goes immediately." "That is just what I wanted to say," I rejoined. "Ill-humour is like laziness, for it is a kind of laziness; our natures are strongly inclined that way, and yet, when we only have the strength to assume control of ourselves, our tasks are done with no difficulty and we find a real pleasure in activity." Friederike was very attentive, and her young suitor objected that man is not his own master, having control least of all over his emotions. "We are referring here to a disagreeable emotion," I replied. "Everyone is anxious to get rid of it, and nobody knows the extent of his strength until he has tried. A sick man will certainly consult all the physicians and will not reject the greatest trials, the bitterest medicines, in order to win back the health he desires." I noticed that the worthy old man was straining his hearing to take part in the conversation, and I raised my voice as I directed my remarks to him. "People preach against so many vices," I said, "but I have never heard anyone denouncing ill-humour from the pulpit."* "The pastors in the towns ought to do that," he answered, "the peasants are never ill-tempered. Though it would not hurt occasionally and would at least be a lesson to our wives—to say nothing of the bailiff." Everybody burst out laughing, and he joined in heartily until he fell into a fit of coughing, which

---

* We now possess an excellent sermon by Lavater on this text, among those on the Book of Jonah.

interrupted the conversation for a time, before the young man
again took up the thread. "You called ill-humour a vice. I think
that is an exaggeration." "Not at all," I declared, "if that which
harms oneself and one's dear ones deserves the name. Is it not
enough that we cannot make each other happy; must we in
addition deprive each other of the pleasure that each heart is
able at times to afford itself? And I should like to know the name
of the man who is in an ill-humour and yet has the virtue to
conceal it, to bear it alone without destroying the happiness of
those around him. Is it not rather an inward displeasure at our
own unworthiness, a dissatisfaction with ourselves which is
always combined with an envy that a foolish conceit has incited?
We see happy people whose happiness has not been caused by
us, and we cannot bear it." Lotte smiled at me when she saw
the vehemence with which I spoke, and a tear in the eye of
Friederike spurred me on to continue. "Woe be to those," I said,
"who abuse their power over the heart of another to deprive it
of the simplest joys that spring up in it. All the gifts, all the
good-will in the world, cannot replace a moment of pure pleasure
which the envious constraint of a tyrant has embittered."

My whole heart was full at this moment, the memory of so
much that had happened in the past rushed into my soul, and my
eyes filled with tears.

"If people would only think to themselves every day," I cried,
"that you can do nothing for your friends save leave them their
pleasure and augment their happiness by enjoying it with them.
Have you the power, when their inmost soul is tortured by an
agony of passion, torn with grief, to offer them a drop of comfort? And when the last fatal sickness overtakes the being whom
you helped to wear away in the days of her youth, and she lies
there in pitiable exhaustion, her eyes raised unseeingly to Heaven,
the death-sweat coming and going on her brow, and you stand
at the bedside like one of the damned, with the feeling in your
inmost soul that with all your power you can do nothing, you
are inwardly convulsed with the agonising thought that you
would give your all to be able to instill into the dying being a
particle of vigour, a spark of courage."

The memory of such a scene, at which I had been present,
took possession of me with undiminished force as I uttered these
words. I put my handkerchief to my eyes and left the company.
Only the voice of Lotte, who called to me that it was time to go,

brought me to myself. And how she scolded me on the way home for taking too warm an interest in everything, declaring that it would be my ruin, that I should spare myself!—Oh angel! For thy sake I must live!

6 July.

She is still looking after her dying friend and is always the same, always the devoted, lovely creature who soothes pain and spreads happiness wherever she goes. She went for a walk yesterday evening with Marianne and little Amalie. I knew of this and went to meet them. After an hour and a half we had come back to the town and the spring which is so precious to me, and which became a thousand times more precious when Lotte sat down on the wall beside it. I gazed around, and alas! the time when my heart was so solitary again came vividly into my mind. "Beloved spring," I said, "I have not rested since then in thy cool shade, and often have I hastened past thee without a glance." I looked down and saw that Amalie was ascending the steps with a glass of water. I looked at Lotte and felt all that she means to me. Amalie meanwhile approached with the glass and Marianne wanted to take it from her, but "No!" cried the child with the sweetest expression, "no, you shall drink first, Lotte!" I was so enraptured with the sincerity, the goodness with which she said this, that I found no other way to express my emotion but to take the child up in my arms and kiss her so violently that she straightway began to scream and weep. "That was wrong of you," said Lotte. I was disconcerted. "Come, Amy," she continued, taking the child by the hand and leading her down the steps, "quick, wash your face in the running water and it won't hurt you." As I stood there and watched the child busily rubbing her cheeks with her wet hands; when I saw the faith she had that the miraculous spring would wash away all defilement and prevent the disgrace of growing an ugly beard; how she even continued to wash away after Lotte had said, "It's enough!", as though too much was better than too little—I tell you, Wilhelm, I have never felt more reverent at a baptism. And when Lotte came up, I would have liked to cast myself at her feet as before a prophet who has washed away in consecrated water the sins of a nation.

384

That evening I could not help, in the happiness of my heart, relating the incident to a man from whom I expected human understanding, since he is a man of common sense. But what did I find! He said it was very wrong of Lotte, that children should not be told such stories, since they gave rise to all sorts of misconceptions and superstitions, against which children should be guarded at an early age. It occurred to me, however, that he had had a child of his own baptised a week previously, so I said nothing and silently kept to my conviction that we ought to treat children as God treats us.—He makes us happiest when He lets us wander on under the intoxication of agreeable illusions.

8 July.

WHAT CHILDREN we are! How we crave a glance! What children we are! We had gone to Wahlheim. The ladies were driving out, and during our walks I thought I could see in Lotte's black eyes—I am foolish, forgive me, but you should see these eyes. In short, for I can hardly keep my eyes open, the ladies were getting into the coach round which young W., Selstadt, Audran and I were standing. They were talking through the window to the fellows who were, to be sure, pretty thoughtless and frivolous. I sought Lotte's eyes! Alas! they were glancing from one to the other! But on me! me! me! who stood there absorbed in her alone, they did not fall! My heart bade her a thousand adieux! And she did not see me! The coach drove past and a tear stood in my eye. I gazed after her! And I saw Lotte's coiffure leaning out of the window as she turned to look back. Oh! at me?—It is in this uncertainty that I hover! It is this which is my consolation. Perhaps it was I at whom she turned to look. Perhaps —good night! Oh! how childish I am!

10 July.

YOU SHOULD SEE what a foolish figure I make when she is spoken of in company. And when I am asked how I like her—like! I hate the word. What sort of a fellow must he be who likes Lotte and whose whole mind, whose whole heart is not entirely absorbed by her. Like! The other day someone asked me how I liked Ossian!

11 July.

Mrs. M. is very ill. I pray for her, for I suffer with Lotte. I see her rarely at a friend's, and to-day she told me of a marvellous happening. Old M. is a miserly curmudgeon who has curbed and harassed his wife pretty well during her life, though she has always been able to manage tolerably. A few days ago, when the doctor said there was no hope for her, she sent for her husband while Lotte was in the room and spoke to him thus: "I must confess something that might cause you confusion and vexation after my death. Hitherto I have kept house in as orderly and economical a manner as possible, but you will forgive me for having deceived you these thirty years. When we first married, you allowed me a trifling sum for food and other domestic expenses. When our household became larger and our business grew, I could not move you to increase my weekly allowance to meet the altered circumstances. In short, you know that when our expenses were greatest I had to manage with seven florins a week. I accepted this amount without protest and abstracted the remainder from the receipts every week, since no one had any suspicion that your wife would steal from the till. I have never been extravagant and would have gone tranquilly to my eternal rest without confessing this, if it were not that the one who follows me in keeping house for you will not know how to make both ends meet, and yet you might still insist that your first wife had been able to manage."

I talked with Lotte concerning the incredible delusion of the human mind, which can prevent a man from suspecting that there is something wrong when seven florins suffice to cover an obvious outlay of possibly twice as much. I have, however, myself known people who would not have been surprised at the presence in their house of the widow's inexhaustible cruse.

13 July.

No, I am not deceiving myself! I can read in her black eyes a real interest in me and my destiny. Yes, I feel (and in this matter I can trust my heart) that she—Oh! may I, can I express the Paradise that lies in these words?—that she loves me.

Loves me! How the thought exalts me in my own eyes! How I—I may tell you, perhaps, for you can sympathise with such an emotion—how I worship myself since she loves me.

386

And be it presumption or perception of the true state of affairs —I do not know the man whose rivalry I would have to fear in Lotte's heart. And yet—when she speaks of her betrothed with such warmth, with such affection, I feel like one who has been deprived of all his honours and dignities and has had to yield up his sword.

16 July.

OH! HOW the blood rushes through my veins when my finger accidentally touches hers, when our feet meet under the table. I draw back as from a flame, and a secret force thrusts me forward again. All my senses swim. And oh! her innocence, her pure soul, does not feel the torment which these little intimacies occasion me. When she lays her hand on mine as we converse, and moves nearer to me as she grows more interested, so that her divine breath is wafted to my lips—I feel that I am about to sink to the ground as though struck by lightning. And, Wilhelm, if I should ever dare to—but no, my heart is not so depraved! Weak! weak enough! Is that not depravity?

She is sacred to me. All lust ceases in her presence. I am never aware what I feel when I am with her; it is as though my soul were revolving in all my nerves. There is a melody which she plays on the harpsichord with the touch of an angel, so simple and spiritual. It is her favourite song, and I am cured of all my harassing bewilderment and melancholy so soon as she strikes the first note.

I do not find it difficult to believe the stories of the magic power of music in ancient times. How this simple song fascinates me! And how well she knows when to play it, often at a time when I feel like putting a bullet in my brain! All the confusion and gloom in my soul are dispersed, and I breathe more freely again.

18 July.

WHAT MEANING has the world for our souls without love, Wilhelm? It is a magic lantern without its lamp. Hardly have you inserted the lamp when the most colourful pictures appear on the white screen. And even if that were all there is, nothing but passing phantoms, yet it makes us happy when we stand in front like simple children and are enraptured by the wonderful pictures. I was unable to visit Lotte to-day, being detained by an unavoidable engagement. What could I do? I sent my lad out, just to have somebody about me who had been in her presence to-day. How impatiently I awaited his return, how glad I was to see him again! I would have liked to take him in my arms and embrace him, had I not been ashamed to do so.

It is said of the Bologna stone that when it is placed in the sun it attracts the rays, and is luminous for a time by night. So it was with the lad. The feeling that her eyes had rested on his face, his cheeks, his coat buttons, the collar of his surtout, made them all so sacred and precious to me that I would not at that moment have exchanged the lad for a thousand *Talers*. I felt so happy in his presence.—May God preserve you from laughing at this. Can these be phantoms, Wilhelm, that make us so happy?

19 July.

"I AM GOING to see her!" I cry aloud every morning, when I am aroused and gaze happily at the glorious sun. "I am going to see her!" And I have no further wish for the rest of the day. Everything, everything is absorbed in this prospect.

20 July.

I CANNOT yet accept your suggestion that I should accompany the ambassador to * * *. I am not fond of discipline, and we all know that he is, in any case, a disagreeable fellow. You write that my mother would like to see me occupied? It makes me laugh. Am I not now occupied? And is it not, at bottom, a matter of indifference whether I count peas or lentils? Everything in this world ends in nothingness, after all, and a fellow who wears himself out for somebody else's sake, without its being his own ambition, in order to achieve wealth or dignity or anything else, is simply a fool.

24 July.

SINCE YOU are so anxious that I should not neglect my drawing, I would rather say nothing about it than confess that hitherto I have done little.

I was never happier, never has my sympathy with Nature down to the stones and blades of grass been fuller and more ardent, and yet—I know not how to express myself, but my powers of perception are so weak, everything swims and trembles before my soul so that I cannot seize the outline; but I think, if I had clay or wax, I could probably fashion it out. If this lasts much longer I shall procure some clay and mould it, even if all I can make is cakes.

I have begun Lotte's portrait three times, and each time I have made a mess of it, which vexes me all the more since I got it quite successfully some time ago. Then I cut out her silhouette, and that will have to suffice.

26 July.

I HAVE often made up my mind not to see her so frequently. If I could only keep to my resolution! Every day I succumb to temptation and promise myself sacredly that I will stay away next day, and when the morning comes I again discover some irresistible reason and find myself there before I am aware of it. Either she has said the evening before, "You will come to-morrow, won't you?" (who could remain away under such circumstances?)—or the day is so very lovely, I walk to Wahl-heim, and when I am there it is only half an hour to her. I am too near to her presence—in a trice I am there. My grandmother used to tell me a story of a magnetic mountain. The ships which approached too closely to it were suddenly deprived of all their ironwork, the nails shot towards the mountain, and the poor wretches sank amidst the collapsing planks.

30 July.

ALBERT has arrived, and I shall go. Even if he were the best, the most noble of men, to whom I were prepared in every respect to give way, it would be intolerable to see him before my eyes in possession of so many perfections. Possession!—Enough, Wilhelm, her betrothed has arrived. A worthy, agreeable fellow, whom one cannot help liking. Luckily, I was not present when she welcomed him. It would have torn my heartstrings. He is so honourable and has never even kissed Lotte when I was there. May God reward him for it! I must love him for the respect

389

with which he treats the girl. He is well-intentioned towards me, but I suspect that is due to Lotte more than to his own disposition, for in this matter women are delicate, and rightly so. If they can keep two admirers on good terms with each other, the advantage is always theirs, though it is seldom practicable.

Meanwhile I cannot deny Albert my esteem. His outward calm is in very vivid contrast to the restlessness of my character, which I am unable to conceal. He is a man of feeling and knows what he possesses in Lotte. He appears rarely to be in an ill-humour and, as you know, that is the sin I hate more than any other.

He considers me a man of intellect, and my attachment to Lotte, with the ardent pleasure I take in all her actions, increases his triumph, and he loves me all the more. Whether he does not sometimes plague her privately with petty jealousy is a matter about which I will offer no opinion. At any rate, I should not in his place be altogether free from the demon.

Be that as it may, my pleasure in Lotte's company is gone. Am I to call it foolishness or infatuation? What do names matter? The thing itself is evident. I knew everything that I know now before Albert came. I knew that I could have no claim on her, nor did I make any, that is to say, as far as it is possible to be without desire in the case of so many charms. And the ridiculous fellow opens his eyes wide now that the other man has arrived and takes the girl away.

I grit my teeth and mock at my wretchedness, and mock doubly and trebly at those who might say I should be resigned, since it cannot be helped.—Rid me of these fellows!—I wander about in the woods, and when I come to Lotte's and Albert is sitting with her in the summer house in the garden, and I can get no further, I behave in an extravagant manner, practise all sorts of crazy buffoonery. "For Heaven's sake," Lotte said to me to-day, "I beg of you! no more scenes like that of yesterday evening! You are dreadful when you act so wildly." Between ourselves, I wait till he is occupied elsewhere; *presto!* I am there in a trice, and I am always happy when I find her alone.

8 August.

PLEASE, Wilhelm, I did not mean you when I wrote, "Rid me of the fellows who say I ought to be resigned." I really did not think that you could be of that opinion. And at bottom you are right. Only one thing, my dear friend! In this world it is rarely possible to settle matters with an "either, or," since there are as many gradations of emotion and conduct as there are stages between a hooked nose and one that turns up.

So you will not take it amiss if I grant you your whole argument and nevertheless try to steal my way between your "either, or."

Either I have hopes of Lotte, you say, or I have not. Good! In the former case I must seek to realise them, seek to achieve the fulfilment of my desires; in the latter case I must pull myself together and try to rid myself of a wretched emotion which is bound to consume all my energies. That is well said, my friend, and—soon said.

Can you demand of the unhappy man whose life is gradually and irremediably ebbing under the influence of an insidious malady, can you demand of him that he should put an end to his torture with a dagger? Does not the disease which is consuming his energies at the same time rob him of the courage to procure his own deliverance?

You can of course answer me with a similar allegory—who would not rather submit to the amputation of an arm than risk his life by doubts and hesitations? I do not know. And we will not attack each other with allegories. Enough . . . Yes, Wilhelm, I often have such moments of bounding, vehement courage, and then, if I only knew whither, I would probably go.

10 August.

I COULD lead the happiest and best of lives were I not a fool. Such a combination of favourable circumstances is rarely found for the delight of a man's heart as that in which I am now placed. Alas! how true it is that our heart is alone responsible for its own happiness. To be a member of this charming family, loved by the old man like a son, by the little ones like a father, and by Lotte . . . and now this worthy Albert, who never disturbs my happiness by any display of ill-humour, who regards me with sincere friendship, who, next to Lotte, loves me more than anything in the world. Wilhelm, it is a joy to hear us on our walks, when we talk about Lotte. There has never been anything more ridic-

Johann Wolfgang von Goethe

ulous than this relationship, and yet it often brings the tears to my eyes.

When he tells me about her righteous mother, how she entrusted her house and children to Lotte on her deathbed and confided Lotte to his care, how since then Lotte has been imbued with a new spirit, how in her concern for the household she has really become a mother, how not a moment of her time but has been occupied or absorbed in some task of affection, and yet she has not lost her cheerful lightheartedness. I walk along beside him and pluck flowers by the wayside, bind them very carefully into a nosegay and—cast them into the brook that flows past to watch them gently float along. I do not know whether I have written to you that Albert is to remain here and receive a post at a handsome salary from the Court, where he is in very good favour. I have rarely seen his equal for regularity and diligence at his occupation.

12 August.

ALBERT is certainly the most excellent of men. There was an extraordinary scene between us yesterday. I went to his house to take leave of him, for I had conceived a desire to ride into the hills, whence I am now writing to you, and as I was walking up and down the room I caught sight of a pair of pistols. "Lend me your pistols," I said, "for my journey." "Certainly," he replied, "if you will take the trouble to load them; I only keep them here *pro forma.*" I took one of them down, and he continued, "Since my prudence played me such a scurvy trick, I don't like having anything more to do with the things." I was curious to hear the story. "When I was staying with a friend in the country for about three months," he told me, "I had a brace of unloaded pocket-pistols with me and slept unperturbed. One rainy afternoon, as I was sitting idly thinking, it occurred to me for some reason or other that we might be attacked, that we might have need of the pistols and—you know the sort of thing I mean. I gave them to the servant to clean and load. He dallies with the maidservants, tries to frighten them, and, the Lord knows how, the pistol goes off with the ramrod still in it, and shoots the latter through the ball of the thumb of the right hand of one of the girls, smashing it. I had to bear the lamentation and pay the surgeon into the bargain, and since that time I leave

392

my pistols unloaded. My dear fellow, what's the use of precautions? One cannot guard against every peril. To be sure. . . ." Now, you know, I am very fond of the man until he says "to be sure . . ."; for is it not a matter of course that every general proposition is subject to exceptions? But he is so anxious to justify his opinion, that when he thinks he has said anything rash, made a general statement, or uttered a half-truth, he never ceases to qualify, modify, add to, or subtract from what he has said, until finally there is nothing left of his original assertion. On this occasion he dilated at great length on the subject, till I at last ceased to listen to him, subsided into a state of melancholy, and pressed the mouth of the pistol with a flourish to my forehead above the right eye. "Come!" said Albert, snatching at the pistol. "What is the meaning of this?" "It is not loaded," I said. "And even so, what is the meaning of it?" he asked impatiently. "I cannot imagine how a man can be so foolish as to shoot himself. The very thought is repellent."

"Why do you people," I cried, "when you speak of anything, declare immediately 'this is foolish, this is wise, this is good, this is bad!' What is the meaning of it all? Have you discovered the inward circumstances of an action? Can you determine exactly why it happened, why it was bound to happen? Had you done that, you would be less hasty in your judgments."

"You will admit," said Albert, "that certain actions are vicious from whatever motive they may occur."

I shrugged my shoulders and granted him that. "But, my dear fellow," I continued, "even in that case there are exceptions. It is true that thieving is a vice, but does a man who sets out to steal in order to preserve himself and his family from a miserable death by starvation, deserve punishment or sympathy? Who will be the first to cast a stone at the man who sacrifices an unfaithful wife and her worthless seducer to his righteous wrath? Against the girl who in a moment of rapture loses herself amid the impetuous joys of love? Even our laws, those cold-blooded pedants, are not insensible, and refrain from punishment."

"That is a very different matter," Albert replied, "because a man who is swept away by passion is deprived of all power of reflection and is in the same category as a drunkard or a madman."—"Oh you men of reason!" I cried with a smile. "Passion! Drunkenness! Madness! You stand there so calmly, you moral creatures, so unsympathetic, scolding the drunkard, abhorring the lack of reason, passing by like the priest and thanking your God like the Pharisee that he has not made you like one of these. I have been drunk more than once, my passions were never far from madness, and for neither do I feel remorse, for I have learned in my own measure to understand that all men above the ordinary who have done anything great or seemingly impossible have invariably been decried as drunkards or madmen.

But even in our daily life it is intolerable to hear it said of a man who has done anything at all generous, noble or unexpected, 'The fellow is crazy,' or 'The fellow is drunk.' Shame upon you sober beings! Shame upon you sages!"

"This is another of your crotchets," said Albert. "You exaggerate everything, and here at least you are certainly wrong in comparing suicide, which we are now discussing, with exalted actions, since it is not possible to regard it as anything but a weakness, for it is surely easier to die than to bear a life of agony without flinching."

I was about to break off, for no argument in the world so disconcerts me as when a fellow comes out with some insignificant platitude when I am speaking with my whole heart. But I contained myself, for it had often occurred to me and I had often been vexed at it, and rejoined with some heat, "You call that weakness? I beg of you not to be deceived by appearances. When a nation is groaning under the intolerable yoke of a tyrant, can you term it weak if it finally rises up and bursts its fetters? When a man, under the influence of horror at seeing his house break out in flames, is able to put forth all his strength and bear with ease burdens which in a calmer mood he can scarcely move —when a man, in a rage at some injury, attacks half a dozen foes single-handed and conquers them—are these to be called weak? And, my friend, if exertion is strength, why should over-tension be the reverse?"

Albert looked at me and said, "Do not take it amiss, but the instances you quote appear to me to be quite inapplicable." "It may be so," I replied, "I have often been informed that my method of argument verges on the absurd. Let us see then whether we can in any other way depict the state of mind of a man who has resolved to cast off the burden of life, which is generally so agreeable, for only in so far as we experience his emotions can we have the right to discuss the matter."

"Human nature," I continued, "has its limits; it can bear joy,

394

sorrow and pain to a certain degree, but it succumbs when this is exceeded.

The question, therefore, is not whether a man is strong or weak, but whether he can endure the measure of his suffering, moral or physical, and I find it just as extraordinary to say that a man is a coward who takes his own life, as it would be improper to call a man a coward who dies of a virulent fever."

"Paradoxical, very paradoxical," cried Albert. "Not so much as you imagine," I replied. "You will admit we call it a mortal disease when nature is so seriously affected that its forces are partly consumed, partly so put out of action that it cannot be set right, that the ordinary course of life can not by any happy transformation be restored.

Well, let us apply this to the mind. Let us see how man is circumscribed, how he is affected by impressions, obsessed by ideas, until finally a growing passion robs him of the power of calm reflection and brings him to grief.

It is in vain that a cool, reasoning individual perceives the unhappy man's condition and talks to him in a persuasive manner, just as a healthy man is unable to inspire an invalid with even a modicum of his own vigour."

This was speaking in terms too general for Albert. I reminded him of a girl who had been found dead in the water some time previously, and recapitulated her story. "A respectable young creature, who had grown up within the restricted sphere of her domestic occupations, with no other prospect of amusement than being able to walk out on a Sunday in the best clothes which she had gradually accumulated, her companions being girls in a similar situation to herself, with an occasional dance on the chief holidays, or the opportunity of whiling away an hour or two by a lively chat with a neighbour about the cause of a quarrel or some scandalous rumour; whose ardent nature eventually felt more inward cravings, which were intensified by the flatteries of men. All her former pleasures gradually grew insipid, till she finally met a man to whom she was irresistibly attracted by some hitherto unknown emotion, on whom she cast all her hopes, forgetting the world about her, hearing nothing, seeing nothing, sensing nothing but him alone, longing for nothing but him alone. Unspoilt by the empty pleasures of an inconstant vanity, her desire marches straight to its fulfilment; she wants to be his, to find in an indissoluble union all the happiness which she has missed, to experience all the combined joys for which she has longed. Reiterated promises, which seal the certainty of all her hopes, bold caresses, which intensify her cravings, encompass her whole being; she hovers in a semi-conscious state of bliss, with the premonitory feeling of supreme rapture, worked up to the highest pitch, until at last she stretches forth her arms to embrace her desires—and is abandoned by her lover. Stupefied, out of her mind, she stands on the verge of an abyss, everything is dark around her, with no hope for the future, no solace, since he has left her with whom alone her existence was bound up. She is blind to the world which lies before her, to those who could replace what she has lost, she feels herself alone, abandoned by all the world. And unseeingly, oppressed by the dreadful agony in her soul, she hurls herself down to still her torment in an encircling death.—That, Albert, is the story of so many mortals, and tell me, is it not analogous to the condition of an invalid? Nature can find no way out of the entangled labyrinth of confused and contradictory instincts, and the mortal must die.

Woe to him who would say, 'Foolish woman! Had she but waited till time had exerted its healing effect, her despair would have abated and another would have come to give her solace.' That is as though one would say, 'The fool! to die of a fever! Had he but waited till his strength was restored, his humours were adjusted, the tumult of his blood had subsided, all would have been well and he would still be alive today!'"

Albert, who was still unwilling to accept my analogy, continued to put forward objections, among others, that I had only adduced the case of a simple girl; and he wanted to know what excuse could be found for a reasoning being who was not so circumscribed and understood better the connections of things.

"My friend," I cried, "a man is a man, and the little reasoning power he may possess is of small advantage, or of none at all, when passion rages and he is oppressed by the limits of humanity. Much rather—but another time," I said, and seized my hat. Oh! my heart was so full. And we parted, without having understood each other. How difficult it is for one to understand the other in this world!

15 August.

IT IS, AFTER ALL, certain that nothing in the world renders a man indispensable save love. I feel that Lotte would not willingly lose me, and the children have no other notion but that I shall return every morning. I went out to-day to tune Lotte's harpsichord, but I was unable to set to work at it, for the children besought me to tell them a fairy tale, and then Lotte herself asked me to comply with their wish. I cut the bread for their supper, which they now accept almost as eagerly from me as from Lotte, and told them their favourite tale of the princess who was served by hands. It teaches me a great deal, I assure you, and I am amazed at the impression it makes on them. Since I often have to invent an episode, which on the next occasion I forget, they tell me at once that it was different at the previous telling, so that I now practise reciting it mechanically in a sort of chant. This has taught me that an author must necessarily spoil his book when he alters the story for a second edition, however much it may be improved from the artistic point of view. The first impression finds us receptive, and man is so constituted that he can be convinced of the most extravagant incidents; these, however, are immediately embedded in his mind, and woe to him who attempts to erase and obliterate them.

18 August.

WAS IT ORDAINED by Fate that that which renders a man happy becomes later the source of his misery?

My heart's full and ardent sympathy with Nature, which flooded me with such bliss and made the world round about into a Paradise, has now become an unbearable torment, a torturing spirit which pursues me everywhere. When I used to stand upon the rock and survey the fertile valley across the river as far as the distant hills, when I saw everything about me surge forth and germinate, the mountains clad thickly from foot to summit with tall trees, all the vales in their manifold windings shaded by the most delightful forests, with the river gently flowing among the whispering reeds, mirroring the clouds which were wafted along by the gentle evening breeze; when I heard the birds awakening the forest and the myriad swarms of midges danced merrily in the red rays of the setting sun, whose last quivering glance roused the humming chafer from his grassy bed, while the whirring life about me drew my attention to the ground, where the moss, which wrests its nourishment from the hard rock, and the broom, which grows down the arid sandhill, revealed to me the inward, fervent, sacred life of Nature—how I took all this into my ardent heart, lost myself in its unending abundance, while the glorious forms of the unending world stirred within my animated soul. Vast mountains surrounded me, precipices lay at my feet, torrents poured down, rivers streamed below me, and forest and hills resounded. I saw all the unfathomable forces at their interweaving work of creation in the depths of the earth. Above the earth and below the sky there swarm the innumerable species of creatures. Everything, everything populated with a thousand kinds of shapes, and mankind secures itself in little houses and settles down and rules in its own way over the wide world. Poor fool! you who deem everything of little significance because you are yourself so small. From the inaccessible mountain, across the wilderness which no foot has ever trod, to the end of the unknown ocean there breathes the spirit of the Eternal Creator Who rejoices at every speck of dust that receives it and lives. How often have I longed to be borne on the wings of the crane which flew above my head to the shores of the immeasurable ocean, to quaff the swelling rapture of life from the foaming goblet of the infinite, and to feel for but a moment the curbed forces of my soul extended by one drop of the bliss of that Being Who brings forth all things in and through Himself.

Brother, it is only the memory of those hours that gives me ease. Even the exertion of recalling and again clothing in words those inexpressible emotions, exalts my soul above itself, only to let me feel in double measure the anguish of my condition.

It is as though a curtain has been drawn from before my soul, and the scene of eternal life is being transformed before my eyes into the abyss of the ever open grave. Can you say *This is*, when everything is transitory, everything rolls past with the speed of lightning, only rarely endures till its life force is spent, but is carried away by the current, submerged and smashed against the rocks? Not a moment but consumes you and yours, not a moment when you do not yourself destroy something, and inevitably so. The most innocent stroll costs a myriad tiny creatures their lives, one step annihilates the laborious construction of a nation of ants and crushes a world in little to ignominious ruin. It is not the great occasional catastrophes of the world, the floods that sweep away your villages, the earthquakes that devour your cities, by which I am moved. It is the consuming force latent in universal Nature, that has formed nothing that has not destroyed its neighbour and itself, which saps my soul. And so I reel along in anguish, surrounded by earth and sky and all the weaving forces of Nature. I see nothing but a monster, eternally devouring, eternally chewing the cud.

21 August.

IN VAIN I stretch out my arms towards her in the morning when I wake from troubled dreams. In vain I seek her at night in my bed when an innocent dream has made me happy with the illusion that I am sitting beside her in the meadow, holding her hand and covering it with a thousand kisses. Oh! when I put out my hand to touch her, still drunk with sleep, and rouse myself by doing so, a stream of tears wells up from my oppressed heart, and I weep for the hopelessness of the gloomy future.

22 August.

MY CONDITION is wretched, Wilhelm! All my energies are reduced to a restless inactivity. I cannot be idle, and yet I am unable to take up any task. I have no power of imagination, no interest in Nature, and my books all repel me. When we lose ourselves, we have lost everything. I vow I could sometimes wish to be a labourer, so as to have every morning, when I awake, some prospect for the ensuing day, some urge, some hope. I often envy Albert, whom I see buried to the ears in his documents, and pretend to myself that I should like to be in his place. More than once it has suddenly occurred to me to write to you and the minister in order to apply for the post at the legation which you assure me I should not fail to obtain. I believe so too. The minister has long been fond of me, and used frequently to urge me to take up some profession. For an hour or so I occupy myself with the notion, but later, when I think about it again, I remember the fable of the horse that was tired of its freedom, allowed itself to be saddled and bridled, and was ridden to death. I do not know what to do, and is not perhaps my longing for a change in my situation a deep-seated, uneasy impatience which will pursue me wherever I may go?

399

Johann Wolfgang von Goethe

TRULY, if my malady could be cured, these people would do it. It is my birthday to-day, and very early this morning I received a packet from Albert. As soon as I opened it I caught sight of one of the pink bows that Lotte was wearing on her bosom when I first met her, and which I had since then more than once asked her for. There were also two little books in duodecimo in the packet, the Wetstein edition of Homer, which I had so often wanted to possess so as not to have to drag about the edition of Ernesti on my walks. You see! that is how they anticipate my desires, how they think of all the small friendly services which are a thousand times more appreciated than the brilliant presents that humiliate us and are due to the vanity of the giver. I kiss the bow a thousand times, and with every breath I drink in the memory of the rapture which more than filled those few happy days that can return no more. The blossoms of life are only a mirage. It is so, Wilhelm, and I do not complain. How many fade and do not leave a trace behind; how few bear fruit, and how little of the fruit reaches maturity! And yet sufficient remain, but—Oh my brother! can we neglect, despise the ripened fruit, let it wither and rot without having been enjoyed?

Farewell! The summer is glorious and I often sit in the fruit trees in Lotte's orchard, picking pears from the highest branches with a long rod. She stands below and receives them when I reach them down.

FOOLISH wretch that I am! Do I not deceive myself? What is the purpose of all this endless raging passion? I offer no prayers now save to her; no form appears before my mind save hers; and everything in the world about me I see only in relation to her. And this affords me so many happy hours—till I must again tear myself away from her. Oh! Wilhelm, whither does my heart so often urge me! When I have sat with her thus for two hours or three, feasting my eyes on her form, her bearing, listening to the divine words that come from her lips, and then gradually all my senses become taut, my eyes grow dim, I hardly hear what is said, and I feel as though some assassin were gripping me by the throat, while my heart beats wildly in the endeavour to free my oppressed senses but only increases their confusion—

Wilhelm, I am scarcely aware at such times whether I am in this world! And often, if melancholy does not gain the ascendancy and Lotte offer me the wretched solace of pouring forth my anguish in tears upon her hand, I am compelled to rush away, out into the fields where I rove about, or to find pleasure in climbing a steep hill, thrusting my way through a trackless wood, being wounded by hedges and torn by thorns. Then I feel somewhat relieved. Somewhat! And when I sometimes sink down on the way, overcome with weariness and thirst, in the dead of night when the full moon is floating above my head, or sit on a crooked tree in the lonely forest to rest the aching soles of my feet, and fall asleep in the lulling stillness of the half light . . . . Oh! Wilhelm, a solitary cell, a hair-shirt and a belt of thorns were the relief for which my soul is languishing. Adieu! I see no end to all this misery but the grave.

3 September.

I MUST away. I thank you, Wilhelm, that you have confirmed my wavering resolve. For a fortnight I have been trying to make up my mind to leave her. I must. She is again in the town on a visit to a friend. And Albert—and—I must away.

10 September.

WHAT A NIGHT that was! Now, Wilhelm, I can surmount anything. I shall not see her again. Oh! that I cannot fly to your breast, tell you amid a thousand tears and transports all the emotions which are assailing my heart. Here I sit and gasp for air, try to calm myself, and await the morning. The horses are to be ready at dawn.

She sleeps peacefully and does not think that she will never see me again. I have torn myself away, was strong enough, during a conversation lasting two hours, not to reveal my purpose. And God! what a conversation!

Albert had promised me that he would be in the garden with Lotte immediately after supper. I stood on the terrace beneath the tall chestnuts and gazed at the sun, which I saw for the last time sinking over the lovely valley and the gentle stream. How often I had stood with her at this spot watching the same glorious scene, and now . . . . I walked to and fro along the avenue

401

which was so dear to me; I had so often been bound here by some mysterious, sympathetic attraction before ever I knew Lotte—and how we rejoiced when we discovered, at the beginning of our friendship, our mutual inclination for the place, which is really one of the most romantic productions of art that I have ever seen.

First, you have the broad prospect between the chestnut trees— Oh! I remember I have, I think, already written you a lot about how one is finally closed in by a high rampart of beeches and the avenue grows darker and darker on account of a plantation that adjoins it, until one at last emerges into a confined clearing over which there hovers the awe of solitude. I can still feel the queer emotion by which I was stirred when I first entered it one high noon; I had a faint presentiment of all the pain and bliss of which it was to be the scene.

I had been revelling for about half an hour in the sweet languishing thoughts of parting and seeing her again, when I heard them coming up the terrace, ran towards them, seized her hand with an inward shudder and kissed it. We had just reached the top when the moon rose behind the tree-clad hill; we spoke of a diversity of things and approached imperceptibly the gloomy recess. Lotte entered and sat down, Albert at her side, and I also seated myself, but my restlessness soon made me start up again; I stood in front of her, walked to and fro, sat down again and was most distressed. She drew our attention to the beautiful effect of the moonlight which illuminated the whole terrace at the end of the rampart of beeches, a glorious sight which was rendered all the more striking by the deep twilight which closed us in all round. We were silent, and after a time she said, "I never go for a walk in the moonlight without being accompanied by the thought of my dead ones, without being oppressed by the feeling of death, of what is to come. We shall exist, Werther," she continued with the most exalted emotion in her voice, "but shall we meet again? and recognise one another? What do you surmise, what do you say?"

"Lotte," I replied, giving her my hand, my eyes filling with tears, "we shall meet again! Here and beyond!"—I could say no more. . . . Wilhelm, why did she have to ask me that, at the moment when I bore the anguish of this parting in my heart?

"And do our dear departed ones know anything about us?" she continued. "Do they feel, when it fares well with us, that we remember them with warm affection? Oh! my mother's form is always hovering about me, in the quiet evenings when I am sitting among her children, my children, and they are gathered round me as they were once gathered round her. When I gaze yearningly up to Heaven with tears in my eyes and wish that she might for a moment be able to look down and see how I am keeping the promise I gave on her deathbed to be a mother to her children. A hundred times I cry out, 'Forgive me, dearest one, if I am not to them what you were. Oh! I do whate'er I can, they are clad, fed, and oh! what is more than all, cared for and loved. Could you but see the harmony in which we live, dear saint! You would glorify with the most fervent gratitude the God Whom you entreated with your last bitter tears to protect your children!"

That is what she said. Oh! Wilhelm! who can repeat her words, how can the dead cold letter depict the divine efflorescence of her spirit? Albert broke in gently, "It affects you too deeply, dear Lotte; I know your soul clings strongly to these notions, but I beg of you . . ." "Oh! Albert!" she said, "I know you do not forget the evenings when we sat together at the small round table, when father was away on a journey and we had sent the little ones to bed. You often had a good book with you, but you seldom succeeded in reading anything. Was not intercourse with this splendid soul more than all else? The beautiful, gentle, cheerful, ever busy woman! God knows with what tears I often cast myself before Him as I lay in bed, and entreated Him to make me as she was."

"Lotte!" I cried, throwing myself at her feet and seizing her hands, which I moistened with a thousand tears. "Lotte! the blessing of God and the spirit of your mother rest upon you." "If you had known her," she said, pressing my hand, "she was worthy to be known by you." I thought I should swoon. Never had anything so exalted, so proud been said in my praise. She continued, "And this woman was taken away in the prime of her life, when her youngest son was not yet six months old. Her illness did not last long, she was tranquil, resigned, regretting only her children, especially the babe. As the end drew near she said to me, 'Let them come up to me,' and I brought them in, the little ones who did not understand, and the older ones who were beside themselves; they stood round the bed and she raised her hands and prayed over them, and kissed them one after the other and sent them away, and said to me, 'Be a mother to them!' I gave her my hand as I made the vow. 'It is no little thing which you are promising, my daughter,' she said, 'the heart of a mother and the eye of a mother. I have often seen by your grateful tears that you know what that means. Let your brothers and sisters find them in you, and show to your father the faithfulness and obedience of a wife. You will afford him consolation.' She asked after him, but he had gone out to conceal from us the unbearable grief he felt. His heart was lacerated.

You were in the room, Albert! She heard someone walking, inquired who it was, and asked you to approach. And as she gazed at you and at me, with a tranquil look, confident that we should be happy, happy together. . . ." Albert fell on her neck and kissed her, and cried, "We are! we shall be!" The usually serene Albert had entirely lost his self-possession, and I myself was on the verge of losing consciousness.

"Werther," she began, "this is the woman that we have lost! God! when I think, as I so often do, how we thus let the dearest thing in our life be taken away, and no one feels it so keenly as the children; who long continued to complain that the black men had carried away their mama."

She rose, but I was agitated and shaken and remained seated, holding her hand. "We must go," she said, "it is growing late." She wished to withdraw her hand, but I held it more firmly. "We shall meet again," I cried. "We shall come together, under whatever form we shall recognise one another. I go, I go willingly, and yet, if I had to say 'for ever,' I could not bear it. Farewell, Lotte! Farewell, Albert! We shall meet again." "To-morrow, I think," she replied jestingly. I was affected by this "to-morrow." Oh! she did not know as she withdrew her hand from mine . . . They went out along the avenue, I stood, looked after them in the moonlight, then threw myself on the earth and wept my fill, sprang up, ran out on to the terrace and could still perceive below, in the shadow of the tall limes, her white frock gleaming on the way to the garden door, I stretched out my arms, and it disappeared.

20 October.

WE ARRIVED at this place yesterday. The ambassador is unwell, & will therefore keep to the house for some days. If only he were not so ungracious, all would be well. I perceive, I perceive that Fate has hard trials in store for me. But I must be of good courage! A light heart can bear everything. A light heart! I cannot help laughing as the word falls from my pen. A little more lightness of heart would make me the happiest being under the sun. What! where other men, with their modicum of energy and talent, are strutting around me in complacent self-assurance, do I despair of my energy, of my talents? God in Heaven, Who didst endow me with all this, why didst Thou not withhold the half and give me instead self-confidence and contentment!

Patience! Patience! Things will mend. For I tell you my friend, you are right. Since I have been compelled to move about among the people like this every day, and see what they do and how they go about things, I am on much better terms with myself. To be sure, since we are, after all, so constituted that we compare everything with ourselves and ourselves with everything, happiness or misery lies in the things with which we establish the analogy, and so nothing is more dangerous than solitude. Our power of imagination, forced by its nature to assert itself, nourished by the fantastic visions of poetry, raises for itself a series of beings of which we are the lowest, and where everything that is external to ourselves appears more splendid, everyone else more perfect. And the process is quite natural. We feel so often that there is something lacking in us, and it is just what we lack that often appears to us to be possessed by someone else, to whom we then impute, in addition, everything that we have ourselves and a certain ideal ease to boot. And so the happy being is perfect, the creature of our own imagination.

When, on the other hand, weak as we are, we only continue laboriously with our work, we very often find that with all our dawdling and tacking we get further than others with their sails and oars—and—it does impart a feeling of self-confidence when one keeps up with or even outstrips others.

10 November.

I AM BEGINNING to settle down tolerably well here so far. The best of it is that there is enough to do, and then the various kinds of people, the diversity of new faces, present a motley scene to my soul. I have made the acquaintance of Count C., a man whom I learn to esteem more every day. A broad and lofty mind, making allowances for much and therefore by no means unsympathetic. One's connection with him is illumined by such feeling for friendship and affection. He took an interest in me when I had some business to arrange with him, and he perceived at the opening of our conversation that we understood one another, that he could talk to me as he could not talk to everybody. And I cannot sufficiently praise his frank bearing towards me. There is no real ardent pleasure to equal that of being given access to a great soul.

24 December.

THE AMBASSADOR causes me much chagrin, as I anticipated. He is the most meticulous fool that can be imagined. He proceeds step by step and is as fussy as an old woman. A man who is never satisfied with himself and whom therefore nobody can please. I like to work quickly, and as a thing turns out so I leave it, but he is capable of giving me back a memorandum and saying, "It is good, but look through it again, there is always a better word, a more precise particle." It is enough to drive me crazy. No "and" or other conjunction may be omitted, and he is a mortal enemy of all the inversions which occasionally escape me. If one's periods are not ground out in accordance with the time-honoured rhythm, he is unable to understand them. It it a penance to have to deal with such a man.

The confidence of Count von C. is the only thing which compensates me. He confessed to me quite openly the other day how dissatisfied he is with the dull-witted scrupulousness of my ambassador. Such people make things more difficult for themselves and for others. "But," he said, "we must be resigned, like a traveller who has a mountain to cross. Of course, if the mountain weren't there, the way would be easier and shorter, but it *is* there and it has to be got over."

My chief probably feels, also, the preference the Count gives me over him, and that vexes him, so that he seizes every opportunity to speak ill of the Count to me. I oppose him, of course, and thereby only render matters worse. Yesterday he even made me fly into a passion, for he included me in his remarks—that the Count was quite good for affairs of the world, being a very quick worker and having a facile pen, but he was lacking in solid erudition, like all literary folk. I would have liked to thrash him for this, for there is no other way of reasoning with such fellows, but since this was not possible, I disputed with some heat and told him that the Count was a man who inspires esteem not only on account of his character but also of his knowledge. "I have never known anyone," I said, "who has so succeeded in enlarging his mind, to embrace matters innumerable, without surrendering his activity in ordinary life." This was all Greek to his brain, and I took my leave to avoid having to choke down more choler at further nonsensical talk.

You are all responsible for this, who talked me into assuming the yoke and prated so much of 'activity.' Activity! If the man who plants potatoes and rides to town to sell his corn, is not doing more than I, then I will wear myself out for another ten years in the galley to which I am now fettered.

And the gilded misery, the boredom among the loathsome people who are assembled here! Their love of rank, the way they keep watch and guard to steal the smallest march upon each other, their most wretched and pitiable passions which they make no attempt to conceal. There is a woman, for instance, who tells everybody about her noble birth and her country, so that every stranger must think, "What a fool she is with her conceited notions of her trivial patent of nobility and the fame of her country." That isn't the worst of it, however, for this very woman is the daughter of a district clerk in these parts. I cannot understand the human race that has so little sense as to make such a downright fool of itself.

To be sure, I perceive more clearly every day how foolish it is to judge others by oneself . . . And since I have so much to occupy me in myself, and my heart and mind are so tempestuous—oh! I would gladly let the others go their way, if they could only let me go my way too.

What irritates me most of all is the odious social conditions. To be sure, I am as well aware as anybody of the necessity for class distinctions and of the advantages that I myself receive from them; but they ought not to stand in my way just when I could enjoy a little pleasure, a gleam of happiness on this earth. During one of my walks recently I made the acquaintance of a Fräulein von B., a charming creature, who has preserved considerable naturalness in spite of the stiff conventional life here. We found one another's conversation agreeable and, when we parted, I asked permission to call upon her. This she granted with such frankness, that I could hardly await the appropriate hour to go to her. She does not come from this part, and is staying with an aunt, an old maid whose physiognomy was displeasing to me. I paid the latter much attention, applied my conversation mostly to her, and in less than half an hour I had pretty well conjectured what the young lady herself afterwards admitted to me—that the aunt, lacking everything, with neither a respectable fortune nor qualities of mind, has no support in her old age other than her ancestral tree, no protection other than the rank behind which she barricades herself, and no pleasure except to look down from her height and ignore the middle classes. She is said to have been beautiful in her youth and to have trifled away her life, first tormenting many a poor young man with her capriciousness, and in later years bowing to the domination of an elderly officer, who, in return for this and a passable income, passed the brass age with her and then died. And now she has reached the iron age, she is alone, and would not receive any consideration, if her niece were not so charming.

8 January, 1772.

WHAT CREATURES they are whose whole soul is bound up with ceremonial, whose thoughts and aims are for years directed towards the means of worming their way on to a chair which is one move higher up the table! And it is not as though the fellows had no other opportunities. No! there is work in aburdance, for the very reason that the petty vexations hinder the progress of the important matters. Last week there was a quarrel during a sledge drive and all the fun was spoilt.

Fools, not to see that the place does not really matter at all, and that he who occupies the first very rarely plays the chief part! How many kings are ruled by their ministers, and how many ministers by their secretaries! And who is then the first? The one, it seems to me, who can take in the others at a glance, and has sufficient power or cunning to harness their energies and passions to the execution of his plans.

20 January.

I MUST WRITE to you, dear Lotte, here in the taproom of a poor rustic inn where I have taken refuge from a heavy storm. Since I have been moving about in that wretched hole of a town, among strangers, complete strangers to my heart, there has not been a moment, not a single one, when my heart bade me write to you. And now in this hut, in this solitude, where I am so hemmed in, and snow and hail are beating furiously against the window panes, here my first thought was of you. As I entered, your form appeared before my mind. Oh, Lotte! with such sacred fervour! God! the first happy moment recaptured!

If you could see me now, in this deluge of distraction! How dried up my senses are becoming, not one moment when I can allow my heart full play, not one single hour of tearful bliss! Nothing! Nothing! It is as though I am standing in front of a raree-show, watching the mannikins and the little horses moving about, and I often ask myself whether it is not an optical illusion. I join in the general movement, or rather I am moved like a marionette, and often seize the wooden hand of my neighbour and start back with a shudder.

I have only discovered a single feminine being here. A Fräulein von B. She resembles you, Lotte, if it is possible for anyone to resemble you. "Ah!" you will say, "the fellow is paying compliments!" There is some truth in that. For some time I have been very well-mannered, since, after all, I cannot help myself. I have a ready wit, and the ladies say nobody utters such delicate compliments as I do (and lies, you will add, for otherwise they cannot be successful, do you follow me?). I was speaking about Fräulein B. She has much soul which shines from her blue eyes, and is oppressed by her rank which does not satisfy any of her heart's desires. She longs to escape from the turmoil, and we pass many an hour in fanciful conversation about rural scenes of unalloyed happiness—and about you. How often does she have to pay you homage! There is no 'must,' she does it with all her heart, likes so much to hear about you, loves you.

Oh! would that I were sitting at your feet in the dear familiar room, and our little ones were tumbling about around me, and when they grew too noisy for you I would collect them round me and quieten them with a weird fairy tale. The sun is setting gloriously over a gleaming, snow-white earth, and the storm has passed on. And I—must again shut myself up in my cage. Adieu! Is Albert with you? And how—? God forgive me the question!

17 February.

I FEAR that my ambassador and I will not stay together much longer. The fellow is perfectly unbearable. His way of working and doing business is so ridiculous, that I cannot refrain from contradicting him and frequently doing a thing in my own way and to my own mind, which, of course, then never suits him. He recently complained of me at Court on this account, and the minister reproved me, mildly to be sure, but nevertheless it was a reproof, and I was about to send in my resignation when I received a private letter* from him, a letter before which I sank on my knees and worshipped the lofty, wise and noble mind that knows so well how to correct my too great sensitiveness, respecting, indeed, my exaggerated notions of activity, of influence over others, of getting the mastery in affairs, as a praiseworthy, youthful spirit, trying not to eradicate them, but only to temper them and guide them to where they can have full scope and achieve their most useful purpose. I am now fortified for a week, and in harmony with myself. Tranquillity of soul is a glorious thing, and joy in oneself. Dear friend, if only the thing were not just as fragile as it is beautiful and precious.

20 February.

GOD BLESS you, my dear ones, and grant you all the happy days that He takes from me.

I thank you, Albert, for deceiving me; I was awaiting news when your wedding day was to be, and had intended on that day solemnly to take down Lotte's silhouette from the wall and bury it under other papers. Now you are married, and her portrait is still here! Well, it shall stay! Why not? I know that I am also with you, that I am in Lotte's heart, without prejudice to you. I have, yes, I have the second place in it, and will and must retain it. Oh! I would go mad, if she were able to forget. . . . Albert, hell lies in the thought. Albert, farewell! Farewell, angel from heaven, farewell, Lotte!

15 March.

I HAVE BEEN subjected to a mortification that will drive me away from here, and makes me gnash my teeth. The Devil! It cannot be made good, and the whole fault is yours, all of you who

---

* This letter, together with another which is referred to later on, has been withdrawn from this collection out of respect for this excellent man, as it was not thought that such boldness could be excused by the gratitude, however warm, of the public.

spurred me on, and drove me and worried me to accept a post that was not to my mind. Well, here I am! You have got your way! And in order that you may not tell me again that my exaggerated notions spoil everything—here, my dear Sir, is a story, clear and simple, as a chronicler would record it.

Count von C. is fond of me, pays me special attention, that is well known and I have already told you so a hundred times. I was dining with him yesterday, on the particular day when the aristocratic company of ladies and gentlemen assembles at his house in the evening. I had forgotten this, and it never occurred to me that we of inferior rank are not acceptable on such occasions. Good. I dine with the Count, and after table we walk up and down the great hall, I converse with him and with Colonel B. who puts in an appearance, and thus the hour for the party approaches. God knows, I suspect nothing. Then there enters the more-than-gracious Madame von S. with her consort and her nobly hatched little goose of a flat-chested, tight-laced daughter. They widen their eyes and nostrils in the traditional, highly-aristocratic manner *en passant*, and, as I loathe the herd with all my heart, I was about to take my leave, waiting only until the Count should be free from the exchange of dreadful twaddle, when suddenly my Fräulein von B. entered. Since it always raises my spirits a little when I see her, I remained, took my place behind her chair, and only noticed after some time that she was talking to me with less frankness than usual, indeed with some embarrassment. I was struck by this. If she is like all these people, I thought to myself, may the Devil take her! I was irritated and wanted to depart, and yet remained, for I was intrigued and wished for more light on the matter. Meanwhile the room was filling up. Baron F., wearing his whole wardrobe dating from the coronation of the Emperor Francis the First, Hofrat R., here called *in qualitate* Herr *von* R., with his deaf wife etc., to say nothing of J., who is badly off, his antiquated garments contrasting strangely with the fashionable oddments he wore with them—all these were arriving, and I was conversing with some of the people I knew, who were all very laconic. I was occupied with my thoughts, and only concerned with my Fräulein B. I did not notice that the women were whispering to each other at the end of the room, that this infected the men, that Frau von S. was talking to the Count (Fräulein B. told me all this afterwards), until finally the Count came up to me and led me to a window. "You are aware," he said, "of our odd conventions. The company, I observe, is displeased to see you here. I would not for anything in the world. . . ." "Your Excellency," I interrupted, "I beg a thousand pardons. I should have thought of it before, but I know you will forgive my *faux pas*. I was about to take my leave some time ago, but" I added with a smile as I bowed, "an evil genius held me back." The Count pressed my hand with a sympathy which said more than words. I made my bow to the distinguished company, and took a coach as far as M. to see the sun setting from the top of the hill, and read in my Homer the glorious canto where Ulysses is entertained by the worthy swineherd. This was all delightful.

In the evening I returned home to sup. There were only a few people left in the coffee-room, and they had turned back the table cloth and were throwing dice in a corner. Then Adelin came in, put down his hat, as he glanced at me, came up and said softly, "You were rebuffed?" "*I* was?" I said. "The Count asked you to leave the company." "The Devil take them," I said. "I was glad to get out into the fresh air." "Good," he said, "that you treat it lightly. But I am annoyed. Everybody is talking about it." Now for the first time the matter began to vex me. I thought everyone who looked at me at table did so because he knew about it. This began to rouse my choler.

And now, when I am pitied wherever I go, when I hear those who are jealous of me exclaiming triumphantly that one could see what happened to arrogant fellows who boasted of their modicum of intellect and thought it gave them a right to set themselves above all conventions, and that sort of twaddle—it is enough to make a man stick a knife in his heart. For whatever people may say about independence, I would like to see who can bear scoundrels talking about him when they have him at a disadvantage. If it is only empty talk, oh! then one can easily ignore them.

16 March.

EVERYTHING is combining to provoke me! Today I met Fräulein B. in the avenue. I could not refrain from addressing her, and showing her, as soon as we were some distance from the rest of the company, that I was hurt at her recent behaviour. "Oh! Werther!" she said, in a tone of deep sincerity, "could you thus interpret my confusion, knowing my heart as you do? How I suffered for your sake, from the moment when I entered the the room! I foresaw everything, a hundred times it was on the tip of my tongue to warn you, I knew that Madame von S. and Madame von T., together with their husbands, would rather take their departure than stay in your company, I knew that the Count would not venture to fall out with them—and now all this fuss . . ." "What do you mean?" I asked, and concealed my dismay, for everything that Adelin had told me the day before yesterday coursed through my veins like boiling water at this moment. "How much it has already cost me!" said the sweet creature, with tears in her eyes. I could no longer control myself, was about to throw myself at her feet. "Tell me what you mean," I cried. The tears ran down her cheeks. I was beside myself. She dried them without any attempt at concealment. "You know my aunt," she began. "She was there, and oh! how she opened her eyes! Werther, I endured last night and this morning a sermon about my intercourse with you, and had to listen to you being disparaged, degraded, and was only half able to defend you."

Every word she uttered pierced my heart like a sword. She did not see what a mercy it would have been to hide all this from me, and she now told me all the further gossip there would be, how all the malicious fellows would be triumphant. How from now on they would proclaim that my arrogance and disdain of others, which they had long blamed in me, was now punished and humbled. To hear all this from her lips, Wilhelm, in a tone of sincerest sympathy—I was overcome, and am still raging inwardly. I wish someone would dare to cast it in my teeth, that I might thrust my sword through his body! If I were to see blood I should feel better. Oh! I have taken up a knife a hundred times to let air into my suffocating heart. It is related of a noble species of horses that, when they are frightfully heated and at their last gasp, they instinctively bite open a vein to help them to breathe. I often feel like that. I would like to open a vein and achieve eternal freedom.

24 March.

I HAVE HANDED in my resignation at Court and hope it will be accepted. You will forgive me for not asking your permission first. I *had* to go away, and I already know everything you would say to persuade me to stay, so—sugar the pill for my mother. I cannot help myself so she must put up with it, though I cannot help her either. It will certainly grieve her. To see the brilliant career which was leading her son to a privy councillorship or an embassy suddenly interrupted and the horse put back in its stable! Make of it what you will and add up the possible eventualities which might have made it possible for me to stay, or obliged me to do so. Enough, I am going. And that you may know whither I am going, Prince ***, who relishes my society, is here, and asked me, when he heard of my intention, to accompany him to his estates and spend the beautiful Spring there. He has promised that I shall be left entirely to myself and, since we understand each other up to a certain point, I will try my luck and go with him.

19 April.

For your Information.

I THANK you for your two letters. I did not reply, since I was leaving this letter until my resignation had been accepted at Court, for I feared my mother might apply to the minister and render my purpose difficult. Now, however, it is all over, and I have my discharge. I hardly like to tell you how unwillingly they gave it me, and what the minister has written; you would break out into fresh lamentations. The hereditary prince has sent me a parting gift of twenty-five ducats, with a letter that moved me to tears. So my mother need not send me the money I wrote for recently.

5 May.

I LEAVE here to-morrow, and since the place where I was born is only a few miles away, I would like to see it again, and recall the happy days I used to dream away. I will enter by the very gate from which I drove out with my mother when she left the dear, familiar spot after my father's death, to shut herself up in her unbearable town. Adieu, Wilhelm, you shall have news of my progress.

9 May.

I HAVE fulfilled the pilgrimage to my home with a pilgrim's reverence and have been affected by many an unexpected emotion. I stopped at the great lime tree, a quarter of an hour's journey outside the town on the way to S. I alighted and bade the postillion take the coach on, that I might go on foot to savour each memory anew, vividly, and in my own way. There I stood beneath the lime which used to be the goal and boundary of my walks as a boy. How different the circumstances! Then, in my blissful ignorance, I had yearned to go out into the unknown world, where my heart hoped to find all the nourishment, all the enjoyment of which I so often felt the lack in my bosom. Now I was coming back from the wide world—with oh! how many hopes miscarried, how many plans shattered!—I saw the range of mountains in front of me, that had times without number been the object of my desires. I had sat here for hours at a time, yearning to be there, fervently absorbed in the woods and valleys which appeared before me in an intimate halflight—and then, when the time came to return home, how unwillingly I left the beloved spot! I approached the town, greeted all the old familiar summer-houses, and disliked the new ones as well as all the other changes which had taken place. I went in through the gate and there I found myself again completely. I will not give you all the details, for, charming as they were to me, the record would only be monotonous. I had made up my mind to take a lodging in the market-place, next door to our old house. As I walked along I noticed that the little school, where our childhood had been penned up by an honest old dame, was turned into a shop. I recalled the restlessness, the tears, the mental apathy and heartaches I had endured in that den.—Every step I took was fraught with interest. No pilgrim in the Holy Land comes across so many shrines of pious memory, and the souls of few are so filled with sacred emotion. One more detail that must suffice for a thousand. I went down the river to a certain farm, which used also to be one of my walks, and looked at the places where we boys tried who could make the flat stones rebound most often as we skimmed them along the surface of the water. I remember most vividly how I often stood there and gazed at the stream, the wondrous presentiments with which I followed it, how romantic the country appeared to me to which it was flowing, how I soon found that there were limits to my imagination and yet I had to penetrate further, ever further, until I had completely lost myself in the illimitable distance. Is that not just what the glorious patriarchs felt! When

Ulysses speaks of the immeasurable ocean and the unbounded earth, is not that more true, more human, more fervent, than nowadays when every schoolboy thinks himself a miracle of wisdom because he can repeat that the world is round?

Here I am in the Prince's hunting-box. He is quite agreeable to live with, being simple and sincere. I am often pained, however, when he talks about things that he only knows from hearsay or reading, and always from a second-hand point of view.

And he has more understanding for my intellect and talents than for my heart, which is, after all, my only pride, the sole source of everything, all vigour, all bliss and all misery. Oh! anyone can know what I know.—My heart is my own.

25 May.

I HAD something in my mind about which I was unwilling to tell you anything until it had been put into execution but, now that it has come to nothing, I may just as well do so. I wanted to go to the wars! My heart was long intent on it. It was the chief reason why I came here with the Prince, who is a general in the *** service. I revealed my intention to him during one of our walks, he dissuaded me, and it would have had to be a passion rather than a whim to prevent me listening to his arguments.

11 June.

SAY WHAT you will, I cannot stay any longer. What is the use? I am finding it tedious. The Prince treats me as an equal and yet I do not feel at home. And we have not really anything in common. He is a man of intellect, but of a low order, and I find his conversation no more entertaining than a well-written book. I shall stay another week and then resume my wanderings. The best thing I have done here is my sketching. The Prince has a feeling for Art, though this would be deeper if he were not limited by the abominations of science and the usual terminology. It often makes me gnash my teeth when, upon my introducing with warmth and imagination topics of Nature and Art, he thinks he is doing quite well as he suddenly blunders in with some conventional technical term.

416

18 June.

WHERE AM I going? I will tell you in confidence. I have to remain here another fortnight after all, and then I pretend to myself that I am going to visit the mines in ***. Nothing of the sort, however. I only want to see Lotte again. That is all. And I ridicule my own heart—but shall do what it demands.

29 July.

No, IT IS all right! Everything is all right! I—her husband! Oh! God, Who made me, if Thou hadst granted me that bliss, my whole life would be one continual prayer. I will not complain, and crave pardon for these tears, pardon for my vain desires.— She—my wife! If I had the dearest being under the sun enfolded in my arms—a shudder goes through my whole body, Wilhelm, when Albert embraces her slender waist.

And—ought I to say it? Why not, Wilhelm? She would have been happier with me than with him! Oh! he is not the man to fulfil all the longings of that heart. A certain lack of delicacy, a lack—take it as you will, that his heart does not beat in sympathy at—oh!—at a passage in a beloved book where my heart and Lotte's meet as one. In a hundred other cases, when it happens that we express our feelings at the action of someone else. Dear Wilhelm!—He *does* love her with his whole soul, and what is such a love not worth. . . .

I have been interrupted by an insupportable fellow. My tears are dried. I am distracted. Adieu, dear friend!

4 August.

I AM NOT the only one to suffer thus. All men find their hopes deceived, their expectations betrayed. I visited the good woman who lives by the lime tree. Her eldest boy ran towards me, and his shouts of joy attracted his mother, who looked very downcast. Her first words were, "Good Sir! Alas, my Hans is dead." —He was the youngest of her sons. I was silent.—"And my husband," she continued, "has returned from Switzerland with empty hands, and were it not for some kind people he would have had to go a-begging. He fell ill of a fever on the way." I knew not what to say to her, and gave something to the little one.

She asked me to accept some apples, which I did and left the place of melancholy memory.

---

21 August.

I CHANGE in a flash. Sometimes I find a gleam of joy in life once more, but alas! only for a moment. When I thus lose myself in my dreams, I cannot avoid the thought—'What if Albert were to die! You would, she would—,' and then I pursue the will o' the wisp till it leads me to the verge of abysses before which I shudder back.

When I go out at the town gate, the way I first went when I fetched Lotte to the ball—how different it all was! All, all is over. Not a vestige of the former world, not a throb of the emotion I then felt. I feel like a ghost that has returned to the burnt-out castle which it once built in its princely glory and bequeathed on its death-bed, splendidly furnished, to a beloved son.

---

3 September.

I AM SOMETIMES unable to comprehend how another can, or may love her, when I love her so singleheartedly, so fervently, so completely, and know nothing, am aware of nothing, have nothing but her.

---

6 September.

I HAD a difficult struggle before I was able to make up my mind to put aside the simple blue coat in which I first danced with Lotte, but it grew at last too shabby. I have had a new one made, just like the last, with collar and facings, and another yellow waistcoat and pair of breeches.

But it has not quite the same effect. I do not know—perhaps, with time, I shall grow to like it more.

---

15 September.

IT IS ENOUGH to make one resign oneself to the Devil to see all the hounds that God tolerates on this earth, without sense or feeling for what little there is of value on it. You know the walnut trees beneath which I sat with Lotte at the honest old clergyman's in St., the glorious walnut trees which, God knows, always filled my soul with the greatest content. How intimate and cool they made the courtyard, how glorious their branches were. And the memories they held, back to the good clergymen who had planted them so many years ago. The schoolmaster often mentioned the name of one of them, which he had learned from his grandfather. He is said to have been such a worthy man and his memory was always sacred to me under the trees. I tell you there were tears in the schoolmaster's eyes yesterday when we discussed their having been cut down.—Cut down! The thought makes me frenzied, I could murder the hound who struck the first blow. I, who could pine away with grief if a few trees stood in my courtyard and one of them withered with age—I have to look on at this. But there is one point worth mentioning. What a thing is human feeling! The whole village is muttering, and I hope the minister's wife will feel the difference in the way of butter, eggs and other presents, to show how she has wounded the villagers. For it is she who is to blame, the wife of the new minister (the old one is dead), a scraggy, sickly brute with very good cause to take no interest in the world, since no one takes any in her. An ugly creature who puts forth pretensions to learning, takes a hand in the examination of the canon, works a great deal at the new-fangled, critico-moral reformation of Christianity and shrugs her shoulders at the enthusiasms of Lavater, is quite shattered in health and therefore without joy on God's earth. Only such a creature could find it possible to cut down my walnut trees. I cannot keep cool! Just imagine, the falling leaves make the courtyard dank and dirty, the trees take away the light and, when the nuts are ripe, the boys throw stones at them and that jars her nerves, disturbs the profundity of her meditations when she is pondering the differing views of Kennicott, Semler and Michaelis. When I saw how discontented the villagers were, especially the old ones, I asked why they had suffered it. "When the mayor wants a thing hereabouts," they replied, "what can we do?" But one justice was done at least. The mayor and the parson, who at any rate wanted to make something out of his wife's whims, which don't bring him in much profit, thought of sharing the proceeds, but the revenue-office heard of it and said, "This way please!", and sold the trees to the highest bidder. There they lie! Oh if I were but a Prince! The parson's wife, the mayor and the revenue-office would be—Prince!—Well, if I were a Prince, would I worry about the trees in my country!

10 October.

IF I ONLY look into her black eyes, I am already cured! And what mortifies me is that Albert does not appear to be as happy as he—expected—as I—thought I would be—if—I am not fond of dashes, but it is the only way I can express myself here—and I think it is clear enough.

12 October.

OSSIAN has crowded Homer out of my heart. To what a world this glorious poet has introduced me! To wander over the heath, with the storm wind howling round me, carrying along in the steaming mists the ghosts of ancestors under the light of the moon. To hear from the mountains, amid the roaring of the forest river, the fading groans of spirits in their caves and the laments of the maiden pining with grief by the four moss-covered, grass-grown stones that mark the grave of her noble lover. Then when I find him, the wandering grey bard, who seeks on the broad heath the foot-steps of his fathers, and finds alas! their tombstones, and then gazes lamenting at the evening star which is hiding in the rolling ocean, and ages long gone by re-awaken in the soul of the hero, when the friendly beam shed its light upon the perils of the brave ones and the moon illumined their ship returning wreathed in victory; when I read the deep sorrow on his brow, see the last forlorn hero tottering exhausted to the grave, drinking in ever fresh, grievously glowing joys in the impotent presence of the shades of his departed ones, and looking down on the cold earth and the high waving grass, crying out: "The traveller will come, will come, who knew me in my beauty and will ask, 'Where is the minstrel, Fingal's worthy son?' His foot-step will pass over my grave and he will ask for me upon the earth in vain."—Oh Friend! I would like to draw my sword like a noble armour-bearer and free my lord with one blow from the quivering torment of this slowly receding life, and send my soul to follow the freed demi-god.

420

19 October.

OH! THIS void, this dreadful void within my breast. I often think—if you could but press her once, only once, to your heart, the void would all be filled.

26 October.

YES, I AM growing certain, friend, certain and ever more certain, that the existence of any creature matters little, very little. One of Lotte's friends came to see her, and I went into the next room to find a book, but could not read, so took up a pen to write. I heard them speaking softly, exchanging trifling gossip, news of the town, how one girl had married, another was very sick. "She has a dry cough, the bones are sticking out of her face, she gets fainting fits, I wouldn't give a penny for her life," said the friend. "So and so is also in a bad way," said Lotte. "He has swollen up already," said the other. My vivid imagination set me at the bedsides of these poor people, I saw how reluctantly they turned their backs on this life, how they—and Wilhelm, these ladies were discussing the matter in the way we usually discuss a stranger's death. And when I look round, and see the room, with Lotte's clothes lying about, her ear-rings here on the table, and Albert's papers and the furniture with which I am so familiar, even this ink-pot, and think to myself, "See what you are to this house! All in all. Your friends esteem you. You often make them happy and your heart feels that it could not exist without them; and yet—if you were to go? if you were to leave this circle? would they, and for how long, feel the void which your loss would make in their lot? for how long?"—Oh! man is so transitory that even where he finds the actual certainty of his existence, where he leaves the only true impress of his presence, in the memory, in the soul of those he loves—even there he must be extinguished, must disappear, and oh! how soon!

27 October.

I WOULD often like to tear my breast and dash out my brains at the thought that two mortals can be so little to one other. The love, the joy, the ardour, the rapture that do not come form myself will not be given me by another, and though my whole heart be full of bliss I cannot make another happy if he stands before me cold and limp.

30 October.

IF I HAVE not a hundred times been on the verge of embracing her! The great God knows what it feels like to see so much charm about one and not be able to grasp it. And that is yet the most natural of human instincts. Do not children grasp at everything they see?—And I?

3 November.

GOD KNOWS, I lie down to sleep so often with the wish, sometimes with the hope, that I shall not wake again; and in the morning I open my eyes, see the sun again and am wretched. Oh! that I could be peevish, could shift the blame to the weather, to a third party, to an unsuccessful venture; the intolerable burden of ill-humour would then only half rest upon myself. Woe is me, I feel only too truly that the whole fault is mine alone—not fault! Enough that the source of all my misery lies concealed within myself, as formerly was the source of all my happiness. Am I not still the same who formerly hovered amidst all the abundance of emotion, with a Paradise following on every step, with a heart able to embrace a whole world with love? And this heart is now dead, no more delights flow from it, my eyes are dry, and my faculties, no longer revived by refreshing tears, draw uneasy furrows across my brow. I am suffering much, because I have lost what was the sole delight of my life, the holy vivifying power with which I created worlds around me. It has gone!—When I look out of my window at the distant hill, as the morning sun pierces the mist above it and illumines the tranquil meadows in the valley, and the gentle stream winds towards me between its leafless willows—oh! when this glorious scene appears before me as fixed as a varnished picture and all this rapture is incapable of pumping a single drop of happiness from my heart up into my brain, and my whole churlish self stands before the face of God like a dried-up spring, like a cracked pitcher! I have so often cast myself upon the ground and implored God to send me tears as a husbandman prays for rain, when the sky is brazen overhead and the earth about him is parched.

But oh! I feel that God does not send rain and sunshine at

422

our impetuous bidding, and those times, the memory of which torments me, why were they so happy if not because I patiently awaited His spirit and received with a grateful fervent heart the rapture which He caused to descend upon me!

8 November.

SHE HAS reproached me with my lack of control, and oh! so gently! That I sometimes allow myself to be seduced by a glass of wine into drinking the whole bottle. "Don't do it," she said, "think of Lotte!" "Think!" I said. "Do you need to bid me do that? I think!—or do not think! You are always present to my soul. I sat to-day at the spot where you alighted lately from the coach. . . ." She changed the topic, to stop me pursuing the subject further. Friend, I am lost! She can do with me what she will.

15 November.

I AM GRATEFUL to you, Wilhelm, for your sincere sympathy, for your well-meant advice, and would beg you to be tranquil. Let me endure it to the end; with all my lassitude I have strength enough to see it out. I have respect for religion, as you know, I feel that it is a staff for many a weary soul, refreshment for many who are faint. But—can it, must it then be for everyone? When you look at the great world, you see thousands for whom it has not been, thousands for whom it will not be—preached or not preached—must it then be for me? Does not even the Son of God say that those would be about Him whom His Father has given to Him? Supposing our Father wishes to keep me for Himself, as my heart tells me? I beg you, do not interpret this falsely, do not look for mockery in these innocent words; it is my whole soul that I am baring to you. Otherwise I would rather have remained silent, for I do not willingly waste words about things of which no one knows any more than I do. What is it but the fate of man to endure his lot, to drain his cup?—And if the cup was too bitter for the human lips of the God Who came from Heaven, why should I brag and pretend it tastes sweet to me? And why should I be ashamed, in the dread moment when my whole existence is trembling between being and not being, when the past is gleaming like lightning over the dark abyss of the future, when everything around me is falling away and the world crashing to ruin over my head?—Is it not the voice of the mortal who is thrust wholly in upon himself, insufficient unto himself, plunging headlong into the chasm, which grates from the secret recesses of his vainly upward-striving soul: "My God, My God, why hast Thou forsaken me?" And should I be ashamed to say this, should I stand in dread of the moment when even He did not escape it Who rolls the Heavens together like a cloth?

21 November.

SHE DOES NOT see, she does not feel that she is preparing a poison which will bring us both to grief. And I am voluptuously draining the cup that she is handing me for my destruction. What is the meaning of the kindly glance with which she often—often? —no, not often, but nevertheless sometimes looks at me, the favour with which she receives an involuntary expression of my feeling, the sympathy with my suffering that I see on her brow?

Yesterday, as I was leaving, she gave me her hand and said, "Adieu, dear Werther!" Dear Werther! It was the first time that she called me "dear," and it penetrated to my very marrow. I repeated it to myself a hundred times, and last night, as I was going to bed, as I was chattering to myself about nothing in particular, I suddenly said, "Good night, dear Werther!" and had to laugh at myself afterwards.

24 November.

SHE FEELS what I am suffering. Her gaze went deep into my heart to-day. I found her alone. I said nothing, and she looked at me. And I no longer saw in her the charming beauty, no longer saw the shining of her fine spirit; all that disappeared from before my eyes. The gaze which affected me was far more glorious, full of an expression of the most ardent interest, the sweetest sympathy. Why could I not cast myself at her feet? Why could I not embrace her in reply with a thousand kisses?—She took refuge at the harpsichord, and in a sweet, soft voice breathed harmonious sounds to accompany her playing. Never have I seen her lips so alluring; it was as though they opened thirstily to drink in the sweet tones that welled forth from the instrument, and only the secret echo was returning from her sweet

424

mouth—if I could only tell you what it was like! I no longer resisted; I bowed my head and vowed that I would never venture to imprint a kiss on those lips on which the spirits of Heaven are hovering. And yet—I will—Ha! you see, it stands like a barrier before my soul—this bliss—and then to go down to do penance for my sin—sin?

30 November.

I CANNOT, I cannot regain command of myself. Wherever I go I encounter an apparition which totally deranges me. To-day! Oh fate! Oh humanity!

At noon I went down to the river, I had no desire for food. Everything was so dreary. A damp, cold west wind was blowing from the mountains and the gray storm clouds were being wafted along the valley. From a distance I saw a man in a shabby green coat crawling about among the rocks and appearing to search for herbs. When I came close to him, and the noise I made caused him to turn round, I saw a very interesting physiognomy of which the chief feature was a quiet melancholy, but which otherwise expressed only a good and frank disposition; his black hair was held in two coils by pins, and the rest woven into a thick plait which hung down his back. Since his dress seemed to me to denote a man of inferior rank, I thought he would not take it amiss if I betrayed an interest in his occupation, so I asked him what he was looking for. "I am looking for flowers," he replied with a deep sigh, "and can find none." "This is not the season for them," I said with a smile. "There are so many flowers," he said, coming down towards me. "In my garden there are roses and two kinds of honeysuckle, one of which my father gave me; they grow like weeds; I have been searching for two days and cannot find any. Out there also there are always flowers, yellow and blue and red, and the centaury has a beautiful flower. I cannot find any at all." There seemed to be something queer about this, so I asked him in a roundabout way, "What do you want the flowers for then?" His mouth twitched with an odd wry smile. "If you will not give me away," he said, pressing his finger to his lips, "I have promised to take a nosegay to my sweetheart." "That is fine," I said. "Oh!" he replied, "She has a lot of other things, she is rich." "And yet she would like your nosegay," I said. "Oh!" he

continued, "she has jewels and a crown." "What is her name?"
"If the States General were to pay me," he replied, "I should be
another man. Yes, there was once a time when I was so well off.
Now it is all over with me, now I am. . . ."—a tearful gaze at the
heavens expressed everything. "So you were happy?" I asked.
"Oh! I wish I were so again!" he said, "then I was so well off,
so gay, as happy as a fish in water." "Heinrich!" cried an old
woman who came along the path, "Heinrich, where have you
been? We have looked for you everywhere. Come and eat."
"Is he your son?" I asked, going up to her. "Yes, my poor son,"
she replied. "God has given me a heavy cross to bear." "How
long has he been like this?" I asked. "He has been as quiet as
this for half a year now. Thank God he has got so far! Before
that he was in a frenzy for a whole year, and he lay in chains
in the madhouse. Now he would not harm anybody, and is only
occupied with kings and emperors. He was such a good quiet
boy, who helped to keep me and wrote a good hand; but suddenly he grew melancholy, fell into a violent fever, then into
a frenzy, and now he is as you see him. If I were to tell you,
Sir . . ." I broke in upon her stream of reminiscences by asking
what he meant by the time when he was so happy and well off.
"The crazy fellow," she cried with a smile of compassion. "He
means the time when he was out of his mind; he always praises it.
That was when he was in the madhouse, when he was unaware
of his condition."—I was thunderstruck. I pressed a piece of
money in her hand and rushed away.

"When you were happy!" I cried aloud, as I hastened towards
the town. "Happy as a fish in water.—God in Heaven! hast Thou
made it the fate of man that he is only to be happy when he has
come to his senses and when he loses them again! Poor fellow!
yet how I envy your melancholy, the confusion of mind in which
you are languishing! You set out hopefully to pluck flowers for
your queen—in Winter—and are sad that you can find none,
and cannot comprehend why you can find none. And I—and I
set out without hope or purpose, and return home as I came. You
indulge your fancy of what you would do if the States General
were to pay you. Blissful being, who can impute his lack of
happiness to an earthly obstacle. You do not feel! you do not
feel that your misery springs from your ravaged heart, from
your unhinged brain, and that all the kings on earth cannot
help you."

426

He should perish without hope who mocks a sick man for traveling to the furthermost spring that will only intensify his malady and render his death more painful, who assumes himself superior to an oppressed being when the latter, to rid himself of remorse and the sufferings of the spirit, makes a pilgrimage to the Holy Tomb. Every footprint on an untrodden path is a drop of balsam for the anguished soul, and with every day's toilsome journey he lies down relieved of so much affliction. And can you call that madness—you armchair windbags?—Madness! —Oh God! Thou seest my tears! Why didst Thou, Who createdst man in wretchedness enough, put brothers at his side to rob him of his morsel of wretchedness, the morsel of trust he has in Thee, in Thee, Thou All-loving One? For what is trust in a healing root, in the tears of the vine, but trust in Thee, that Thou hast laid in all the things about us the power to heal and soothe which we need at every step? Father, Whom I do not know! Father, Who didst formerly fill my whole soul and now hast turned away Thy face from me! Call me to Thee! Break Thy silence! Thy silence cannot sustain this thirsting soul—and could a man, a father, be angry whose son returned before his time and fell upon his neck and cried, "I am returned, my father. Be not angry that I have broken off my journey which, according to thy will, I should have prolonged. The world is everywhere the same, for work and toil, reward and joy, but what is that to me? I am only well where thou art, and in thy presence I will suffer and rejoice."—And Thou, dear Heavenly Father, wouldst *Thou* turn him from Thee?

1 December.

WILHELM! the man I wrote to you about, the happy unhappy one, was a clerk in the employ of Lotte's father, and an unhappy passion for her which he nourished, concealed, and then revealed, so that he was dismissed from his office, sent him mad. Feel, fellow, at these dry words, the distraction with which I listened to this story when Albert related it as calmly as you, perhaps, will read it.

4 December.

I BEG OF YOU—you see, it is all over with me—I can bear it all no longer. I sat by her to-day—sat, she played on the harpsichord, various melodies, with such expression! such expression!—what will you?—her little sister sat on my knee and dressed her doll. Tears came into my eyes. I bent my head and caught sight of her wedding ring.—My tears flowed.—And suddenly she played the divine old melody, suddenly, and through my soul there coursed a feeling of solace and memory of all the past, all the occasions when I had heard the song, all the dismal intervals of chagrin and hopes miscarried, and then—I walked up and down the room, my heart suffocating under it all. "For God's sake," I said, going up to her in a violent outburst. "For God's sake, stop!" She ceased playing and gazed at me fixedly. "Werther," she said, with a smile that went to my soul, "Werther, you are very ill, you have taken a dislike to your favourite dishes. Go, I beg you! Calm yourself!" I tore myself away, and—God! Thou seest my misery and wilt put an end to it.

6 December.

How HER FORM pursues me! Waking and dreaming she absorbs my soul. Here, when I close my eyes, here in my forehead, at the focus of inward vision, are her black eyes. Here! I cannot explain it to you. When I close my eyes, they are there, like an ocean, like an abyss they lie before me, in me, absorb my mental faculties.

What is man? The lauded demi-god! Are not his powers deficient just when he has most need of them? And when he soars up in bliss or sinks down in suffering, is he not held back, is he not again restored to cold dull consciousness, just at the moment when he longed to lose himself in the fulness of the infinite?

8 December.

DEAR Wilhelm, my condition is that in which those unhappy beings must have been who were believed to be driven about by evil spirits. I am often possessed by something which is not fear, not craving. It is an unknown inward raging that threatens to tear my breast, that clutches my throat. I am wretched! wretched! And then I wander about the dread nocturnal countryside of this inhuman season.

Last night I was impelled to go out. I had heard in the evening that the stream had overflowed, and all the brooks, and that the whole of my dear valley, from Wahlheim downwards, was inundated. At night, some time after eleven, I hastened out. A dreadful scene. To see the turbulent flood whirling down from the rock in the moonlight over fields, meadows and hedges, and up and down the broad valley a raging sea lashed by the howling wind. When the moon came out again and illumined the black clouds and the booming flood rolled out in front of me in the dreadful glorious reflection, I was overcome by awe and longing. Oh! I faced the abyss with widespread arms and breathed, 'Down! down!', and was immersed in the rapture of hurling down there all my torment and all my suffering, to rage along like the torrent. And oh! I was incapable of raising my foot from the ground to put an end to all my affliction!—My clock has not yet run down—I feel it! Oh Wilhelm! how willingly would I have surrendered all my humanity to tear the clouds apart with the storm wind, to embrace the flood. Ha! Will not perhaps the prisoner one day share this rapture?—

And as I gazed down pensively at a spot where I had rested with Lotte beneath a willow when we were heated with our walk, it was also submerged, and I could hardly make out where the willow was. And I thought of her meadows, and the whole region round her hunting-lodge! how our summer-house was now scattered by the raging stream! And a sunbeam from the past gleamed out as when a captive dreams of herds, meadows and cornfields. I stayed.—I do not blame myself, for I have the courage to die.—I should have. . . . Now I am sitting here like an old woman gleaning wood from hedges and begging bread at doors to prolong and alleviate her wasting, joyless life for yet another moment.

17 December.

WHAT IS THIS, my friend? I start back in terror from myself! Is not my love for her the holiest, purest, most brotherly love? Have I ever borne in my soul a culpable desire?—I will not maintain. . . . and now—dreams! Oh! how true a perception they had when they ascribed such contradictory effects to strange forces! Last night, I shudder to say it, I held her in my arms, clasped her tightly to my bosom and covered her love-lisping lips with unending kisses. My eye swam in the intoxication of hers. God! am I to blame that I even yet feel an ectasy in recalling with all their fervour these glowing joys. Lotte! Lotte!—And it is all over with me! My senses are confused. For a week I have lost my powers of deliberation, my eyes have been filled with tears. I am at ease nowhere and everywhere. I desire nothing, require nothing. It is better that I should go.

THE EDITOR

TO THE READER

IN ORDER to supply the detailed story of our friend's last remarkable days, I am compelled to interrupt his letters by a narration, the material for which I gathered from the mouth of Lotte, Albert, his servant and other witnesses.

Werther's passion had gradually undermined the peace of Albert and his wife. The latter loved her with the tranquil faithfulness of an honourable man, and his amiable intercourse with her was in time subordinated more and more to his profession. To be sure, he did not want to admit to himself the difference which distinguished the present situation from the days when they were betrothed, but he felt a certain inward resentment at Werther's attentions to Lotte, which must have seemed both an interference with his privileges and a silent reproach. This increased the ill-humour which was often generated by overwork in his hampered and badly-paid profession, and, since Werther's situation made him also a depressing companion, the anguish of his heart having consumed his remaining spiritual faculties, his vivacity and his acumen, it was unavoidable that at last Lotte should also be infected and that she fell into a kind of melancholy in which Albert thought he could perceive a growing passion for the lover, and Werther a deep chagrin at the changed demeanour of her husband. The distrust with which the two friends regarded one another rendered their mutual presence very embarrassing to them. Albert avoided his wife's room when Werther was with her, and the latter, noticing it, after some fruitless attempts to keep away from her altogether, seized the opportunity of visiting her when her husband was detained at his office. This gave cause for fresh discontent, their tempers grew more and more exasperated, until at last Albert said rather curtly to his wife that she should at least for people's sake give a different turn to her relations to Werther, and put an end to his too-frequent visits.

It was about this time that the resolve to quit the world had taken shape in the poor youth's soul. It had always been a favourite idea of his, which had occupied him particularly since his return to Lotte.

It was, however, to be no precipitate, rash act; he wanted to take the step with the firmest conviction, with the most tranquil resolution.

His doubts, his struggle with himself, can be seen in a note that is probably the beginning of a letter to Wilhelm, and was found undated among his papers.

Her presence, her fate, her sympathy with mine, press the last tears from my parched brain.

To raise the curtain and step behind, that is all! So why this fear and hesitation?—Because we do not know what it is like behind?—And because there is no return?—And because it is the quality of our mind to forebode confusion and darkness where we know nothing definite.

He could not forget the rebuff at the embassy. He rarely mentioned it, but one could feel imperceptibly that he considered his honour irretrievably outraged, and that the episode had inspired him with a dislike for a profession or political activity. He therefore resigned himself totally to the odd emotional and mental idiosyncrasies with which we are acquainted from his letters, and to a bottomless passion which was bound to cause the eventual extinction of all his vital energies. The eternal monotony of a melancholy attachment to the charming and beloved being whose peace of mind he was upsetting, the tempestuous wearing down of his vitality, without hope or purpose, drove him at last to the dreadful act.

20 December.

I am grateful, Wilhelm, for the affection that has prompted you to accept my remark as you have. Yes, you are right, it is better that I should go. Your suggestion that I should return to you does not please me altogether; at least, I would like to come by a roundabout way, especially as it is to be expected that the frost will last and the roads be good. I am glad that you will come to fetch me, but postpone it for a fortnight until you have received a letter from me with further news. Nothing should be plucked until it is ripe. And a fortnight more or less can do much. Ask my mother to pray for her son, and to forgive all the trouble I have caused her. It was my fate to sadden those to whom I owed happiness. Farewell, my dearest friend. All the blessing of Heaven be upon you! Farewell!

On that very day—it was the Sunday before Christmas—he came to Lotte in the evening, and found her alone. She was occupied in arranging some toys that she had prepared as Christmas presents for her little brothers and sisters. He talked about the pleasure the little ones would experience, and about the times when the unexpected opening of the door and the appearance of a decorated Christmas tree with wax candles, sweetmeats & apples inspired a heavenly ecstasy. "You also," said Lotte, concealing her embarrassment with a sweet smile, "you also are to receive Christmas presents, if you behave properly, a little roll of wax tapers and something else." "And what do you call behaving properly?" he cried. "What am I to do, what can I do, dearest Lotte?" "Thursday evening," she said, "is Christmas Eve, when the children are coming, and my father also, then everyone will receive his present, and you are to come as well—but not before." Werther was taken aback. "I beg of you," she continued, "that is how things are, and I beg you for the sake of my peace of mind, we cannot, we cannot continue like this!"—He turned his eyes away from her, went up and down the room, and muttered, "we cannot continue like this!" between his teeth. Lotte, who perceived the terrible state these words had put him in, tried to divert his thoughts by asking him all manner of questions, but without avail. "No, Lotte," he cried, "I shall not see you again!"—"Why?" she rejoined, "you can, you must see us again, only control yourself. Oh! why were you born with this impetuosity, this persistent passion for everything that you once touch! I beg of you," she continued, taking his hand, "control yourself. Your intellect, your knowledge, your talents—what diverse enjoyments do these not offer you! Be a man. Rid yourself of this melancholy attachment to a person who can do nought but pity you." He grated his teeth and looked at her gloomily. She held his hand. "Only one moment of calm thinking, Werther," she said. "Do you not perceive that you are deceiving yourself, that you are the voluntary cause of your own undoing? Why me, Werther? Just me, who belong to another? Just this? I fear, I fear it is only the impossibility of possessing

me that makes this desire so alluring." He withdrew his hand
from hers, gazing at her with a fixed and angry look. "Clever!"
he cried. "Very clever! Did Albert say that, I wonder? Subtle!
Very subtle!"—"Anyone might say it," she replied. "Is there
then no maiden in the wide world who could fulfil the desires
of your heart? Bring yourself to look for her, and I swear to
you that you will find her. For a long time I have feared for
you and for us the restriction you have imposed upon yourself.
Bring yourself to it! A journey will and must distract you! Seek
and find a worthy object for all your love, then return and let
us enjoy together the happiness of a true friendship."

"That ought to be printed," he said with a cold laugh, "and
recommended to all tutors. Dear Lotte, let me have just a little
repose, and everything will be all right."—"Only this, Werther!
that you do not come back till Christmas Eve."—He was about
to reply, when Albert entered the room. They bade one another
a frigid good evening, and walked up and down the room
together with some embarrassment. Werther began some trifling
conversation, which soon petered out. Albert did the same and
then asked his wife about some commissions and, when he heard
that they had not yet been carried out, returned a sharp answer
that cut Werther to the heart. He wanted to go, could not, and
delayed till eight o'clock. Their irritation and ill-humour with
one another increased more and more until the table was laid and
he took his hat and stick, when Albert, with conventional politeness, invited him to take pot-luck with them.

He arrived at his lodging, took the candle from his servant
who wanted to light him on his way, and went alone to his room,
where he wept aloud, spoke in an excited manner to himself,
strode violently up and down, and finally threw himself, fully
clad, on his bed, where he was found by his man who ventured
about eleven o'clock to go in and ask whether he should take
off his master's boots. This he let him do, and then ordered him
not to come into the room the next morning until he was called.

On Monday morning, the twenty-first of December, he wrote
the following letter to Lotte, which was found sealed on his
writing-desk after his death and brought to her. I will insert it
here at intervals, just as—and this is evident from what happened
—he wrote it.

My mind is made up, Lotte. I intend to die, and I am writing you this
calmly, without romantic exaltation, on the morning of the day when

I shall see you for the last time. When you read this, my dearest, the cool grave will already cover the stiffened remains of the restless, unhappy man who knows no sweeter bliss in the last moments of his life than to converse with you. I have had a terrible night, which has strengthened, has fixed my wavering resolve. I intend to die. When I tore myself away from you yesterday, with my senses in a state of fearful excitement, when it all rushed in upon my heart, and the thought of my hopeless, joyless existence at your side seized hold of me with chill horror—I was hardly able to reach my room, beside myself I fell upon my knees, and oh! God! Thou didst grant me the final boon of bitter tears! A thousand plans, a thousand possibilities coursed through my brain, and at last it was there, firmly, wholly, the one ultimate thought—I intend to die!—I lay down, and this morning, in all the tranquillity of my awakening, it is still firm, still strong in my heart—I intend to die!—It is not despair, but the certainty that I have reached the end, and that I am sacrificing myself for you. Yes, Lotte! Why should I not say it? One of us three must go, and I will be the one. Oh! my dearest, the frenzy has often crept through my torn heart, often—to murder your husband!—You!—Myself! So let it be then!—When you climb up the hill, on a beautiful summer evening, remember me, how I often came thus up the valley, and then gaze across at the churchyard to my grave, as the wind gently waves the grass to and fro in the rays of the setting sun.—I was calm when I began, and now I am weeping like a child when I see it all so vividly.

Towards ten o'clock Werther called his servant, and said to him as he dressed that he was going away in a few days, and his clothes should therefore be turned out and made ready for packing. He also ordered him to ask everywhere for bills to be sent in, to collect some books that had been lent, and to pay two months advance to some poor people to whom he was accustomed to give something every week.

He had his meal brought to his room, and rode out afterwards to the bailiff, whom he did not find at home. He walked pensively up and down the garden, and appeared to want to bury himself at the last moment under all his melancholy memories.

The little ones did not long leave him in peace, but pursued him, sprang up at him, told him that when tomorrow had come, and then another day, and another day after that, they were going to Lotte's to fetch their Christmas presents, and spoke of the wonders that their little imaginations promised them. "Tomorrow!" he cried, "and then another day, and another day after that!" And he kissed them all affectionately, and was about to go

434

when the smallest one tried to whisper something in his ear. He confided to him that his big brothers had written beautiful New Year greetings, so big! one for papa, one for Albert and Lotte, and also one for Herr Werther. They were going to hand them over early on New Year's Day.

This overcame him. He gave each one something, mounted his horse, asked them to give his regards to the old man, and rode away with tears in his eyes.

He reached home towards five, ordered the maid to see to the fire and to keep it going till night time. He told his servant to pack his books and linen in his trunk downstairs and to sew his clothes up in a bale. Then he probably wrote the following passage in his last letter to Lotte.

You do not expect me. You think I shall obey you and not see you again till Christmas Eve. Oh, Lotte! To-day or never again. On Christmas Eve you will hold this letter in your hand and tremble as you moisten it with your sweet tears. I will, I must! Oh! how glad I am that I have made up my mind!

At half past six he went to Albert's house, and found Lotte alone, very alarmed at his visit. She had told her husband in the course of conversation that Werther would not return until Christmas Eve. Soon after he had had his horse saddled, saying he was riding to an official in the neighbourhood with whom he had some business to settle, and had gone out in spite of the inclement weather. Lotte, who knew quite well that he had long postponed this matter and that it would keep him from home all night, understood the pantomime only too well, and was very depressed. She sat alone, her heart was touched, she thought of the past, feeling how precious it had been, and her love for her husband, who now, instead of the promised happiness, was beginning to make her life wretched. Her thoughts came back to Werther. She blamed him, but could not hate him. A mysterious trait had attracted her to him from the beginning of their friendship and now, after so long, after having lived through so many experiences, the impression on her heart was bound to be inextinguishable. Her oppressed heart at last found relief in tears, and she fell into a quiet melancholy in which she became more and more deeply immersed. But how her heart hammered when she heard Werther ascending the steps and asking for her outside! It was too late to say she was not at home, and she had only half recovered from her confusion when he entered the room. "You have not kept your word!" she cried. "I made no promise," was his answer. "Then you should at least have acceded to my request," she said, "it was for both our sakes." As she spoke, she made up her mind to send for some girl friends. These should be witnesses to her conversation with Werther and, since he would have to see them home, she would be able to get rid of him early. He had brought her back some books, and she enquired about some others, trying to keep the conversation on a general level until her friends arrived, when the maid returned and informed her that they both begged to be excused, one of them having some relations visiting her whom she could not send away, and the other not wanting to dress and go out in such wretched weather.

This made her ponder for a few minutes, until the feeling of her innocence roused her pride. She decided to defy Albert's crotchets, and the purity of her heart fortified her, so that she did not, as she at first intended, call her maid into the room but, after she had played a number of minuets on the harpsichord to recover herself and allay the confusion of her heart, sat down calmly on the sofa at Werther's side. "Have you nothing to read?" she said. He had nothing. "In my drawer there," she began, "is your translation of some of the songs of Ossian. I have not read them yet, for I hoped to hear you recite them, but ever since you haven't been fit for anything." He smiled, fetched the songs, a tremor ran through him as he took them in his hand, and his eyes filled with tears as he looked at them. He sat down and read:*

"Star of descending night! fair is thy light in the west! thou liftest thy unshorn head from thy cloud: thy steps are stately on thy hill. What dost thou behold in the plain? The stormy winds are laid. The murmur of the torrent comes from afar. Roaring waves climb the distant rock. The flies of evening are on their feeble wings; the hum of their course is on the field. What dost thou behold, fair light? But thou dost smile and depart. The waves come with joy around thee: they bathe thy lovely hair. Farewell, thou silent beam! Let the light of Ossian's soul arise!

And it does arise in its strength! I behold my departed friends. Their gathering is on Lora, as in the days of other years. Fingal comes

---

* This extract from Ossian's *The Songs of Selma* is here reproduced in the original—(Translator's note).

like a watry column of mist! his heroes are around: and see the bards of song, grey-haired Ullin! stately Ryno! Alpin, with the tuneful voice! the soft complaint of Minona! How are ye changed, my friends, since the days of Selma's feast? when we contended, like gales of spring, as they fly along the hill, and bend by turns the feebly-whistling grass.

Minona came forth in her beauty; with down-cast look and tearful eye. Her hair flew slowly on the blast, that rushed unfrequent from the hill. The souls of the heroes were sad when she raised the tuneful voice. Often had they seen the grave of Salgar, the dark dwelling of white-bosomed Colma. Colma left alone on the hill, with all her voice of song! Salgar promised to come: but the night descended around. Hear the voice of Colma, when she sat alone on the hill!

COLMA

It is night; I am alone, forlorn on the hill of storms. The wind is heard on the mountain. The torrent pours down the rock. No hut receives me from the rain; forlorn on the hill of winds!

Rise, moon! from behind thy clouds. Stars of the night, arise! Lead me, some light, to the place, where my love rests from the chase alone! his bow near him, unstrung: his dogs panting around him. But here I must sit alone, by the rock of the mossy stream. The stream and the wind roar aloud. I hear not the voice of my love! Why delays my Salgar, why the chief of the hill, his promise? Here is the rock, and here the tree! here is the roaring stream! Thou didst promise with night to be here. Ah! whither is my Salgar gone? With thee I would fly, from my father; with thee, from my brother of pride. Our race have long been foes; we are not foes, O Salgar!

Cease a little while, O wind! stream, be thou silent a while! let my voice be heard around. Let my wanderer hear me! Salgar! it is Colma who calls. Here is the tree, and the rock. Salgar, my love! I am here. Why delayest thou thy coming? Lo! the calm moon comes forth. The flood is bright in the vale. The rocks are grey on the steep. I see him not on the brow. His dogs come not before him, with tidings of his near approach. Here I must sit alone!

Who lie on the heath beside me? Are they my love and my brother? Speak to me, O my friends! To Colma they give no reply. Speak to me: I am alone! My soul is tormented with fears! Ah! they are dead! Their swords are red from the fight. O my brother! my brother! why hast thou slain my Salgar? why, O Salgar! hast thou slain my brother? Dear were ye both to me! what shall I say in your praise? Thou wert fair on the hill among thousands! he was terrible in fight. Speak to me; hear my voice; hear me, sons of my love! They are silent; silent for ever! Cold, cold are their breasts of clay! Oh! from the rock on the hill; from the top of the windy steep, speak, ye ghosts of the dead!

437

speak, I will not be afraid! Whither are ye gone to rest? In what cave of the hill shall I find the departed? No feeble voice is on the gale: no answer half-drowned in the storm!

I sit in my grief; I wait for morning in my tears! Rear the tomb, ye friends of the dead. Close it not till Colma come. My life flies away like a dream: why should I stay behind? Here shall I rest with my friends, by the stream of the sounding rock. When night comes on the hill; when the loud winds arise; my ghost shall stand in the blast, and mourn the death of my friends. The hunter shall hear from his booth. He shall fear but love my voice! For sweet shall my voice be for my friends: pleasant were her friends to Colma!

Such was thy song, Minona, softly-blushing daughter of Torman. Our tears descended for Colma, and our souls were sad! Ullin came with his harp! he gave the song of Alpin. The voice of Alpin was pleasant: the soul of Ryno was a beam of fire! But they had rested in the narrow house: their voice had ceased in Selma. Ullin had returned, one day, from the chase, before the heroes fell. He heard their strife on the hill; their song was soft but sad! They mourned the fall of Morar, first of mortal men! His soul was like the soul of Fingal; his sword like the sword of Oscar. But he fell, and his father mourned: his sister's eyes were full of tears, Minona's eyes were full of tears, the sister of car-borne Morar. She retired from the song of Ullin, like the moon in the west, when she foresees the shower, and hides her fair head in a cloud. I touched the harp with Ullin; the song of mourning rose!

RYNO

The wind and the rain are past: calm is the noon of day. The clouds are divided in heaven. Over the green hills flies the inconstant sun. Red through the stony vale comes down the stream of the hill. Sweet are thy murmurs, O stream! but more sweet is the voice I hear. It is the voice of Alpin, the son of song, mourning for the dead! Bent is his head of age; red his tearful eye. Alpin, thou son of song, why alone on the silent hill? why complainest thou, as a blast in the wood; as a wave on the lonely shore?

ALPIN

My tears, O Ryno! are for the dead; my voice for those that have passed away. Tall thou art on the hill; fair among the sons of the vale. But thou shalt fall like Morar; the mourner shall sit on thy tomb. The hills shall know thee no more; thy bow shall lie in thy hall unstrung!

Thou wert swift, O Morar! as a roe on the desert; terrible as a meteor of fire. Thy wrath was as the storm. Thy sword in battle, as lightning in the field. Thy voice was a stream after rain; like thunder on distant hills. Many fell by thy arm; they were consumed in the flames of thy wrath. But when thou didst return from war, how peaceful was thy brow! Thy face was like the sun after rain; like the moon in the silence of night; calm as the breast of the lake when the loud wind is laid.

Narrow is thy dwelling now! dark the place of thine abode! With three steps I compass thy grave, O thou who wast so great before! Four stones, with their heads of moss, are the only memorial of thee. A tree with scarce a leaf, long grass, which whistles in the wind, mark to the hunter's eye the grave of the mighty Morar. Morar! thou art low indeed. Thou hast no mother to mourn thee; no maid with her tears of love. Dead is she that brought thee forth. Fallen is the daughter of Morglan.

Who on his staff is this? who is this, whose head is white with age? whose eyes are red with tears? who quakes at every step? It is thy father, O Morar! the father of no son but thee. He heard of thy fame in war; he heard of foes dispersed. He heard of Morar's renown; why did he not hear of his wound? Weep, thou father of Morar! weep; but thy son heareth thee not. Deep is the sleep of the dead; low their pillow of dust. No more shall he hear thy voice; no more awake at thy call. When shall it be morn in the grave, to bid the slumberer awake? Farewell, thou bravest of men! thou conqueror in the field! but the field shall see thee no more; nor the dark wood be lightened with the splendour of thy steel. Thou has left no son. The song shall preserve thy name. Future times shall hear of thee; they shall hear of the fallen Morar!

The grief of all arose, but most the bursting sigh of Armin. He remembers the death of his son, who fell in the days of his youth. Carmor was near the hero, the chief of the echoing Galmal. Why bursts the sigh of Armin? he said. Is there a cause to mourn? The song comes, with its music, to melt and please the soul. It is like soft mist, that, rising from a lake, pours on the silent vale; the green flowers are filled with dew, but the sun returns in his strength, and the mist is gone. Why art thou sad, O Armin, chief of sea-surrounded Gorma?

Sad! I am! nor small is my cause of woe! Carmor, thou hast lost no son; thou hast lost no daughter of beauty. Colgar the valiant lives; and Annira fairest maid. The boughs of thy house ascend, O Carmor! but Armin is the last of his race. Dark is thy bed, O Daura! deep thy sleep in the tomb! When shalt thou awake with thy songs? with all thy voice of music?

Arise, winds of autumn, arise; blow along the heath! streams of the mountains roar! roar, tempests, in the groves of my oaks! walk through broken clouds, O moon! show thy pale face, at intervals! bring to my mind the night, when all my children fell; when Arindal the mighty fell; when Daura the lovely failed! Daura, my daughter! thou wert fair; fair as the moon on Fura; white as the driven snow; sweet as the breathing gale. Arindal, thy bow was strong. Thy spear was swift in the field. Thy look was like mist on the wave: thy shield, a red cloud in a storm. Armar, renowned in war, came, and sought Daura's love. He was not long refused: fair was the hope of their friends!

Erath, son of Odgal, repined: his brother had been slain by Armar. He came disguised like a son of the sea: fair was his skiff on the wave; white his locks of age; calm his serious brow. Fairest of women, he said, lovely daughter of Armin! a rock not distant in the sea, bears a tree on its side; red shines the fruit afar! There Armar waits for Daura. I come to carry his love! She went; she called on Armar. Nought answered, but the son of the rock, Armar, my love! my love! why tormentest thou me with fear? hear, son of Arnart, hear: it is Daura who calleth thee! Erath the traitor fled laughing to the land. She lifted up her voice; she called for her brother and her father. Arindal! Armin! none to relieve your Daura!

Her voice came over the sea. Arindal my son descended from the hill; rough in the spoils of the chase. His arrows rattled by his side; his bow was in his hand: five dark grey dogs attend his steps. He saw fierce Erath on the shore: he seized and bound him to an oak. Thick wind the thongs of the hide around his limbs; he loads the wind with his groans. Arindal ascends the deep in his boat, to bring Daura to land. Armar came in his wrath, and let fly the grey-feathered shaft. It sung; it sunk in thy heart, O Arindal my son! for Erath the traitor thou diedst. The oar is stopped at once; he panted on the rock and expired. What is thy grief, O Daura, when round thy feet is poured thy brother's blood! The boat is broken in twain. Armar plunges into the sea, to rescue his Daura, or die. Sudden a blast from the hill came over the waves. He sunk, and he rose no more.

Alone, on the sea-beat rock, my daughter was heard to complain. Frequent and loud were her cries. What could her father do? All night I stood on the shore. I saw her by the faint beam of the moon. All night I heard her cries. Loud was the wind; the rain beat hard on the hill. Before morning appeared, her voice was weak. It died away, like the evening-breeze among the grass of the rocks. Spent with grief she expired; and left thee, Armin, alone. Gone is my strength in war! fallen my pride among women! When the storms aloft arise; when the north lifts the wave on high; I sit by the sounding shore, and look on the fatal rock. Often by the setting moon, I see the ghost of my children. Half-viewless, they walk in mournful conference together."

A stream of tears, which gushed from Lotte's eyes and afforded relief to her oppressed heart, interrupted Werther's reading. He threw down the sheets, seized her hand and wept bitterly. Lotte

440

supported herself on her other arm and hid her eyes in her hand-kerchief. The agitation of both of them was terrible. They felt their own misery in the fate of those noble ones, felt it together, and their tears mingled. Werther's lips and eyes burned on Lotte's arms, a tremor ran through her, she tried to withdraw, and all her grief, all her pity lay heavy as lead upon her. She took a deep breath to recover herself and begged him with a sob to continue, begged him with the whole voice of Heaven. Wer-ther trembled, his heart felt as though it would burst, he picked up the sheet and read in a broken voice:*

"Why dost thou awake me, O breath of Spring, thou dost woo me and say: 'I cover thee with the drops of heaven.' But the time of my fading is near, the blast that shall scatter my leaves. To-morrow shall the traveller come; he that saw me in my beauty shall come. His eyes will search the field, but they will not find me."

The whole force of these words deprived the unhappy man of his self-possession. He threw himself at Lotte's feet in utter despair, seized her hands, pressed them against his eyes, against his forehead, and a foreboding of his dreadful intention appeared to flash through her soul. Her mind grew confused, she clasped his hands, pressed them against her breast, bent over him with a sorrowful air, and their burning cheeks touched. They were lost to the world, he twined his arms round her, pressed her to his breast, and covered her trembling, stammering lips with frenzied kisses. "Werther!" she cried in a suffocating voice, turning away her face, "Werther!", and she thrust him away from her breast with a nerveless hand. "Werther!" she cried in a calm tone with noble dignity. He did not resist, released her from his embrace, and threw himself madly at her feet. She got up hastily and, in nervous confusion, trembling between love and anger, she said, "This is the last time, Werther! You shall not see me again." With a look, fraught with love, at the unhappy man, she rushed into the next room and locked the door behind her. Werther stretched his arms out towards her, not daring to hold her back. He lay on the ground, his head on the sofa, and in this attitude he remained for half an hour, until a sound recalled him to himself. It was the maid who wanted to lay the table. He walked up and down the room and, when he saw that he was alone again, went to the door of the cabinet and called gently,

---

* From Ossian's *Berrathon*. (Translator's note).

"Lotte! Lotte! only one word more, in farewell!"—She was silent, he waited—and begged—and waited, then tore himself away and cried, "Farewell, Lotte! Farewell for ever!"

He came to the town gate. The watchmen, who were used to him, let him out without a word. There was a drizzle, half rain half snow, and it was getting on for eleven when he knocked at the gate again. His servant noticed, when Werther returned home, that he was without his hat. He did not venture to say anything and undressed him. Everything was wet. The hat was found afterwards on a rock, on the slope of the hill towards the valley, and it is inconceivable how he managed to climb up there on a wet dark night without falling headlong.

He lay down in bed and slept for many hours. His servant found him writing, when, at his call, he brought in his coffee next morning. He added the following to the letter to Lotte:

For the last time then, for the last time I open these eyes. They are alas! to see the sun no more; it is hidden by a dark and misty day. Mourn then, Nature! thy son, thy friend, thy lover nears his end. Lotte, it is a feeling without compare, and yet it is most akin to a twilight dream, to say to oneself, 'This is the last morning.' The last! Lotte, I have no conception of the word—the last! Do I not stand here in all my strength, and to-morrow I shall lie stretched out and inert on the ground! Die! What does that mean? We are dreaming when we speak of death. I have seen many people die, yet humanity is so limited that it has no conception of the beginning and end of its existence. Still mine, thine! thine! beloved, and the next moment—separated, parted—perhaps for ever.—No, Lotte, no.—How can I pass away, how can you pass away, do we not exist!—Pass away!—What does that mean? It is again a word! an empty sound, that awakes no echo in my heart.—Dead, Lotte! Interred in the cold earth, so narrow, so dark!—There was a girl who was everything to me in my helpless youth; she died, and I followed her corpse and stood beside her grave. As they let down the coffin and pulled up the whirring ropes again from under it, as the first shovelful of earth thudded down and the fearful shell gave back a muffled sound, becoming more and more muffled till it was at last entirely covered—I sank down beside the grave—moved, shaken, in anguish, my soul torn, but I knew not what had happened to me—what will happen to me—Death! The grave! I do not understand the words!

Oh, forgive me! Yesterday! It should have been the last hour of my life. Oh, you angel! for the first time, for the first time there glowed through the depths of my soul, without room for doubt, the feeling of rapture: She loves me! She loves me! The sacred fire that streamed from your lips still burns on mine, a fresh rapturous warmth is in my heart. Forgive me, forgive me.

Oh, I knew that you loved me, knew from the first soulful glances, the first hand pressure, and yet when I went away again, when I saw Albert at your side, I again despaired with feverish doubtings.

Do you remember the flowers you sent me, when you were unable to say a word to me, or give me your hand, at that odious party? Oh! I have knelt in front of them half the night and they put the seal on your love for me. But alas! these impressions faded, as the believer gradually loses the sense of his God's loving kindness which was accorded him with all Heaven's abundance in sacred and visible symbols.

All this is transitory, but no eternity can extinguish the glowing essence that I imbibed yesterday from your lips, that I feel within me. She loves me! This arm has embraced her, these lips have trembled on her lips, this mouth has stammered against hers. She is mine! You are mine! Yes, Lotte, for ever!

And what does it mean, that Albert is your husband? Husband!— That is to say in this world—and in this world it is a sin that I love you, that I would like to snatch you from his arms into mine? A sin? Good! I am punishing myself for it. I have tasted this sin in all its divine rapture, have drunk restoring balsam and strength into my heart. From that moment you were mine! mine, Lotte! I go ahead! to my Father and to yours. To Him I will bring my plaint, and He will solace me till you come and I can fly to you, clasp you, stay with you before the face of the Infinite in an eternal embrace.

This is no dream, no delusion! On the verge of the grave I saw more clearly. We *shall* exist! We shall see one another again! See your mother! I shall see her, find her, and oh! pour out all my heart before her. Your mother, bearing the semblance of yourself.

Towards eleven o'clock Werther enquired of his servant whether Albert had yet returned. The servant said that he had, for he had seen his horse being led. His master then gave him an unsealed note with the following contents:

Would you lend me your pistols for a journey I am about to undertake? Farewell.

Lotte had slept little that night; she was in a state of feverish agitation, and her heart was ravaged with a thousand emotions. In spite of herself, she felt deep within her breast the passion of Werther's embraces, and at the same time she saw with double beauty the days of her artless innocence, of her care-free confidence in herself. She already feared beforehand her husband's gaze and his half-vexed, half-mocking questions, when he should hear of Werther's visit. She had never dissembled, she had never lied, and now she was faced, for the first time, with the unavoidable necessity of doing so. The reluctance, the embarrassment she felt, made the fault all the greater in her eyes, and yet she could neither hate him who was the cause of it nor promise herself never to see him again. She wept till morning, when she sank into a sleep of exhaustion, from which she had hardly risen and dressed when her husband returned, whose presence for the first time she found quite unbearable. For she trembled lest he should discover in her the traces of a sleepless night spent in tears, and this increased her confusion, so that she greeted him with an impetuous embrace which was more expressive of consternation and remorse than passionate delight, thereby attracting the attention of Albert, who asked her curtly, after he had opened some letters and packets, whether anything had happened, whether any one had called. She answered hesitatingly that Werther had been there for an hour on the previous day.—"He chooses his time well," he replied, and went to his study. Lotte remained alone for a quarter of an hour. The presence of her husband, whom she loved and honoured, had made a fresh impression on her heart. She remembered all his kindness, generosity and affection, and reproached herself for having so ill requited them. An obscure impulse made her follow him; she took her work, as she was sometimes wont to do, and went to his room. She asked him whether he needed anything, but he said that he did not and sat down at his desk to write, while she sat down to do her knitting. They had been together for an hour in this way, when Albert began to walk up and down the room. Lotte spoke to him, but he made little or no reply, only sitting down at his desk again, and she fell into a train of melancholy thoughts which were all the more distressing since she tried to hide them and to stay her tears.

The appearance of Werther's boy plunged her in the greatest embarrassment. He handed the note to Albert, who turned coldly to his wife and said, "Give him the pistols."—"I wish him a good journey," he said to the youth. This was like a thunderclap to her. She faltered in an attempt to rise. She could not understand her feelings. Slowly she went to the wall, took them down trembling, wiped off the dust and hesitated, and would have delayed still more if Albert's enquiring glance had not impelled her. She gave the fatal weapons to the boy, without being able

444

to utter a word, and when he had gone she gathered her work together and went to her room in a state of the most inexpressible anguish. Her heart prophesied all sorts of catastrophes. At first she was on the verge of throwing herself at her husband's feet and revealing everything—what had happened on the previous evening, her own fault and forebodings. Then she could not see what would be the advantage of such a step. Least of all could she hope to persuade her husband to go to Werther. The table was laid, and a friend of Lotte's, who only came to make some enquiry but was not allowed by Lotte to leave, made conversation bearable during the meal. They constrained themselves, discussed sundry matters, and were able to forget.

The boy brought the pistols to Werther, who took them from him in a transport of delight when he heard that they had been handed to him by Lotte. He had bread and wine brought in, told the boy to go and have his dinner, and sat down to write.

They have passed through your hands, you have wiped the dust from them, I kiss them a thousand times for you have touched them. Thou, Spirit of Heaven, dost favour my resolve! And you, Lotte, offer me the weapon, you, at whose hands I wished to encounter death and alas! now encounter it! Oh! I made my servant tell me everything—you trembled when you handed them to him, you bade me no farewell!—Alas! Alas!—no farewell! Is it possible that you have closed your heart to me on account of the moment which sealed me to you for ever? Lotte, a thousand years cannot wipe out the impress! And I feel that you cannot hate him who burns for you thus.

After the meal he ordered his boy to finish packing everything, destroyed a number of papers, and went out to settle some small debts. He returned home, went out again beyond the gate, in spite of the rain, as far as the Count's garden, roved about the neighbourhood, came back as night fell, and wrote:

I have seen field, wood and sky for the last time, Wilhelm. I bid you farewell, also! Forgive me, mother! Console her, Wilhelm. God bless you both! My affairs are all in order. Farewell! We shall meet again in happier circumstances.

I have ill rewarded you, Albert, but you will forgive me. I have ruined the peace of your house and sowed distrust between you. Farewell, I am about to make an end. Oh! that my death might restore your happiness! Albert! Albert! Make the angel happy. And may God's blessing rest upon you!

He spent much time turning out his papers during the evening, tore many of them up and threw them in the stove, and sealed a number of packages which he addressed to Wilhelm. They contained small essays and disconnected ideas, several of which I have seen. After having the fire made up and a flask of wine brought in, he sent his servant, who slept some distance away, as did the other domestics, to bed. The boy lay down in his clothes in order to be at hand at an early hour, for his master had told him that the coach horses would be at the door before six.

after eleven.

All is so still around me and my soul so calm. I thank thee, Lord, for these last moments of strength and ardour.

I step to the window, my dearest, and still see some stars shining through the fleeting storm-clouds. No, you will not fall! The Eternal One bears you at his heart, and me. I saw the wheeler stars of Charles's Wain, the loveliest of all the constellations. When I left you at night, as I went out at the gate, it was in front of me. With what intoxication have I so often gazed at it, raised aloft my hands and made it a symbol, a sacred token of the bliss I felt, and still—Oh! Lotte, what is there that does not remind me of you! Are you not about me always! And have I not always, like a child, insatiably, seized every trifle that your saintly hands had touched!

Beloved silhouette! I now return it to you at my death, Lotte, and beg you to hold it in honour. I have pressed a thousand, thousand kisses on it, waved a thousand greetings to it when I went out or returned.

I have left a note for your father entreating him to protect my body. In the churchyard there are two lime trees, at the back in a corner, towards the field, and there I wish to lie. He can and will do this for his friend. Add your entreaties to mine. I will not ask pious Christians to allow their bodies to rest beside that of a poor wretch. Oh! I could wish to be buried by the wayside, or in the lonely valley, that priest and Levite might cross themselves as they passed by the stone which marked the spot, and the Samaritan shed a tear.

Here, Lotte! I do not shudder to take the dread cold cup from which I am to drink the ecstasy of death! It is you who have handed it to me, and I do not fear. All! All! thus are all the desires and hopes of my life fulfilled! To knock so cold, so stiff, at the brazen gate of death.

That I might have been granted the happiness to die for you! To sacrifice myself for you, Lotte! I would die with a stout heart, I would die gladly, if I could restore the tranquillity, the rapture of your life. But alas! it was granted to but few noble souls to shed their blood for those they loved, and by their deaths to kindle for them a new life enhanced an hundredfold.

I wish to be buried in these clothes, Lotte. You have touched and sanctified them. I have asked your father to grant me this favour. My soul will hover over my coffin. Let them not search my pockets. This pink bow which you wore on your bosom, when I met you first among your children—Oh! kiss them a thousand times and tell them the fate of their unhappy friend. The darlings, how they swarm about me. Oh! how I attached myself to you, could not keep away from you from the first moment! Let this bow be buried with me. You gave it me on my birthday! How eagerly I accepted it all!—Alas, I did not think that the way would lead to this!—Be calm! I beg you, be calm!—

They are loaded—it is striking twelve!—So be it then—Lotte! Lotte, farewell! Farewell!

A neighbour saw the flash of the powder and heard the shot, but as everything remained still he paid no more attention.

At six next morning the servant entered with a candle and found his master stretched on the floor, with blood about and the pistol by him. He called to him, seized hold of him, but there was no answer, only a rattling in the throat. He ran for a doctor, for Albert. Lotte heard the bell, all her limbs began to tremble. She woke her husband, they got up, the servant stammered the news amid sobs, Lotte sank to the ground in a swoon in front of Albert.

When the physician arrived, he found the unhappy youth on the floor beyond all hope; his pulse was still beating but all his limbs were paralysed. He had shot himself through the head above the right eye, and his brains were protruding. He was bled in the arm, the blood flowed and he still breathed.

From the blood on the arm of his chair it was concluded that he had committed the deed sitting at his desk. He had then sunk down and twisted convulsively round the chair. He lay on his back in the direction of the window, deprived of strength, fully dressed in boots, blue coat and yellow waistcoat.

The house, the neighbours, the whole town were in a turmoil. Albert entered. Werther had been laid on the bed, his forehead tied up, his face already like that of a dead man, without moving a limb. A dreadful rattling noise still came from his lungs, now faintly, now more loudly; the end was near.

He had only drunk one glass of the wine. *Emilia Galotti* lay open on his desk.

Johann Wolfgang von Goethe

I cannot describe Albert's dismay, Lotte's grief.

The old bailiff came galloping up at the news, and he kissed the dying youth as the hot tears coursed down his cheeks. His eldest sons arrived soon afterwards on foot and sank beside the bed with expressions of the most unrestrained sorrow, kissed his hands and mouth, and the eldest, of whom he had been the most fond, clung to his lips and had to be torn away by force. He died at noon. The presence of the bailiff and the arrangements he made prevented a crowd from assembling. He had him buried towards eleven o'clock at night at the spot that he had chosen. The old man and his sons followed the body. Albert could not. Lotte's life was in danger. He was carried by workmen. There was no pastor present.

From Wilhelm Meister's Apprenticeship

A PRODUCTION OF HAMLET

ONE of the conditions under which our friend had gone upon the stage was not acceded to by Serlo without some limitations. Wilhelm had required that "Hamlet" should be played entire and unmutilated: the other had agreed to this strange stipulation, in so far as it was *possible*. On this point they had many a contest; for as to what was possible or not possible, and what parts of the piece could be omitted without mutilating it, the two were of very different opinions.

Wilhelm was still in that happy season when one cannot understand how, in the woman one loves, in the writer one honors, there should be any thing defective. The feeling they excite in us is so entire, so accordant with itself, that we cannot help attributing the same perfect harmony to the objects themselves. Serlo again was willing to discriminate, perhaps too willing: his acute understanding could usually discern in any work of art nothing but a more or less *im*-perfect whole. He thought, that as pieces usually stood, there was little reason to be chary about meddling with them; that of course Shakespeare, and particularly "Hamlet," would need to suffer much curtailment.

But, when Serlo talked of separating the wheat from the chaff, Wilhelm would not hear of it. "It is not chaff and wheat together," said he: "it is a trunk with boughs, twigs, leaves, buds, blossoms, and fruit. Is not the one there with the others, and by means of them?" To which Serlo would reply, that people did not bring a whole tree upon the table; that the artist was required to present his guests with silver apples in platters of silver. They

Translated by Thomas Carlyle

exhausted their invention in similitudes, and their opinions seemed still farther to diverge.

Our friend was on the borders of despair, when on one occasion, after much debating, Serlo counselled him to take the simple plan,—to make a brief resolution, to grasp his pen, to peruse the tragedy; dashing out whatever would not answer, compressing several personages into one: and if he was not skilled in such proceedings, or had not heart enough for going through with them, he might leave the task to him, the manager, who would engage to make short work with it.

"That is not our bargain," answered Wilhelm. "How can you, with all your taste, show so much levity?"

"My friend," cried Serlo, "you yourself will erelong feel it and show it. I know too well how shocking such a mode of treating works is: perhaps it never was allowed on any theatre till now. But where, indeed, was ever one so slighted as ours? Authors force us on this wretched clipping system, and the public tolerates it. How many pieces have we, pray, which do not overstep the measure of our numbers, of our decorations and theatrical machinery, of the proper time, of the fit alternation of dialogue, and the physical strength of the actor? And yet we are to play, and play, and constantly give novelties. Ought we not to profit by our privilege, then, since we accomplish just as much by mutilated works as by entire ones? It is the public itself that grants the privilege. Few Germans, perhaps few men of any modern nation, have a proper sense of an æsthetic whole:—they praise and blame by passages; they are charmed by passages; and who has greater reason to rejoice at this than actors, since the stage is ever but a patched and piece-work matter?"

"Is!" cried Wilhelm; "but *must* it ever be so? Must every thing that is continue? Convince me not that you are right, for no power on earth should force me to abide by any contract which I had concluded with the grossest misconceptions."

Serlo gave a merry turn to the business, and persuaded Wilhelm to review once more the many conversations they had had together about "Hamlet," and himself to invent some means of properly re-forming the piece.

After a few days, which he had spent alone, our friend returned with a cheerful look. "I am much mistaken," cried he, "if I have not now discovered how the whole is to be managed: nay, I am convinced that Shakespeare himself would have arranged it so, had not his mind been too exclusively directed to the ruling interest, and perhaps misled by the novels which furnished him with his materials."

"Let us hear," said Serlo, placing himself with an air of solemnity upon the sofa: "I will listen calmly, but judge with rigor."

"I am not afraid of you," said Wilhelm: "only hear me. In the composition of this play, after the most accurate investigation and the most mature reflection, I distinguish two classes of objects. The first are the grand internal relations of the persons and events, the powerful effects which arise from the characters and proceedings of the main figures: these, I hold, are individually excellent; and the order in which they are presented cannot be improved. No kind of interference must be suffered to destroy them, or even essentially to change their form. These are the things which stamp themselves deep into the soul, which all men long to see, which no one dares to meddle with. Accordingly, I understand, they have almost wholly been retained in all our German theatres. But our countrymen have erred, in my opinion, with regard to the second class of objects, which may be observed in this tragedy: I allude to the external relations of the persons, whereby they are brought from place to place, or combined in various ways, by certain accidental incidents. These they have looked upon as very unimportant; have spoken of them only in passing, or left them out altogether. Now, indeed, it must be owned, these threads are slack and slender; yet they run through the entire piece, and bind together much that would otherwise fall asunder, and does actually fall asunder, when you cut them off, and imagine you have done enough and more, if you have left the ends hanging.

"Among these external relations I include the disturbances in Norway, the war with young Fortinbras, the embassy to his uncle, the settling of that feud, the march of young Fortinbras to Poland, and his coming back at the end; of the same sort are Horatio's return from Wittenberg, Hamlet's wish to go thither, the journey of Laertes to France, his return, the despatch of Hamlet into England, his capture by pirates, the death of the two courtiers by the letter which they carried. All these circumstances and events would be very fit for expanding and lengthening a novel; but here they injure exceedingly the unity of the piece, particularly as the hero has no plan, and are, in consequence, entirely out of place."

451

"For once in the right!" cried Serlo.

"Do not interrupt me," answered Wilhelm: "perhaps you will not always think me right. These errors are like temporary props of an edifice: they must not be removed till we have built a firm wall in their stead. My project, therefore, is, not at all to change those first-mentioned grand situations, or at least as much as possible to spare them, both collectively and individually; but with respect to these external, single, dissipated, and dissipating motives, to cast them all at once away, and substitute a solitary one instead of them."

"And this?" inquired Serlo, springing up from his recumbent posture.

"It lies in the piece itself," answered Wilhelm, "only I employ it rightly. There are disturbances in Norway. You shall hear my plan, and try it.

"After the death of Hamlet the father, the Norwegians, lately conquered, grow unruly. The viceroy of that country sends his son, Horatio, an old school-friend of Hamlet's, and distinguished above every other for his bravery and prudence, to Denmark, to press forward the equipment of the fleet, which, under the new luxurious king, proceeds but slowly. Horatio has known the former king, having fought in his battles, having even stood in favor with him,—a circumstance by which the first ghost-scene will be nothing injured. The new sovereign gives Horatio audience, and sends Laertes into Norway with intelligence that the fleet will soon arrive; whilst Horatio is commissioned to accelerate the preparation of it: and the Queen, on the other hand, will not consent that Hamlet, as he wishes, should go to sea along with him."

"Heaven be praised!" cried Serlo: "we shall now get rid of Wittenberg and the university, which was always a sorry piece of business. I think your idea extremely good; for, except these two distant objects, Norway and the fleet, the spectator will not be required to *fancy* any thing: the rest he will *see*; the rest takes place before him; whereas, his imagination, on the other plan, was hunted over all the world."

"You easily perceive," said Wilhelm, "how I shall contrive to keep the other parts together. When Hamlet tells Horatio of his uncle's crime, Horatio counsels him to go to Norway in his company, to secure the affections of the army, and return in warlike force. Hamlet also is becoming dangerous to the King and Queen; they find no readier method of deliverance, than to send him in the fleet, with Rosencrantz and Guildenstern to be spies upon him; and, as Laertes in the mean time comes from France, they determine that this youth, exasperated even to murder, shall go after him. Unfavorable winds detain the fleet: Hamlet returns; for his wandering through the churchyard, perhaps some lucky motive may be thought of; his meeting with Laertes in Ophelia's grave is a grand moment, which we must not part with. After this, the King resolves that it is better to get quit of Hamlet on the spot: the festival of his departure, the pretended reconcilement with Laertes, are now solemnized; on which occasion knightly sports are held, and Laertes fights with Hamlet. Without the four corpses, I cannot end the play: no one must survive. The right of popular election now again comes in force; and Hamlet, while dying, gives his vote to Horatio."

"Quick! quick!" said Serlo, "sit down and work the play: your plan has my entire approbation; only let not your zeal evaporate."

WILHELM had already been for some time busied with translating "Hamlet;" making use, as he labored, of Wieland's spirited performance, through which he had first become acquainted with Shakspeare. What had been omitted in Wieland's work he replaced, and had secured a complete version, at the very time when Serlo and he were pretty well agreed about the way of treating it. He now began, according to his plan, to cut out and insert, to separate and unite, to alter, and often to restore; for, satisfied as he was with his own conception, it still appeared to him as if, in executing it, he were but spoiling the original.

When all was finished, he read his work to Serlo and the rest. They declared themselves exceedingly contented with it: Serlo, in particular, made many flattering observations.

"You have felt very justly," said he, among other things, "that some external circumstances must accompany this play, but that they must be simpler than those which the great poet has employed. What takes place without the theatre, what the spectator does not see, but must imagine, is like a background, in front of which the acting figures move. Your large and simple prospect of the fleet and Norway will do much to improve the play; if this were altogether taken from it, we should have but a family scene remaining; and the great idea, that here a kingly house, by internal crimes and incongruities, goes down to ruin, would not be presented with its proper dignity. But if the former background were left standing, so manifold, so fluctuating and confused, it would hurt the impression of the figures."

Wilhelm again took Shakspeare's part; alleging that he wrote for islanders, for Englishmen, who generally, in the distance, were accustomed to see little else than ships and voyages, the coast of France and privateers; and thus what perplexed and distracted others was to them quite natural.

Serlo assented; and both were of opinion, that, as the play was now to be produced upon the German stage, this more serious and simple background was the best adapted for the German mind.

The parts had been distributed before: Serlo undertook Polonius; Aurelia, Ophelia; Laertes was already designated by his name; a young, thick-set, jolly new-comer was to be Horatio; the King and Ghost alone occasioned some perplexity, for both of these no one but Old Boisterous remaining. Serlo proposed to make the Pedant, King; but against this our friend protested in the strongest terms. They could resolve on nothing.

Wilhelm had also allowed both Rosencrantz and Guildenstern to continue in his play. "Why not compress them into one?" said Serlo. "This abbrevation will not cost you much."

"Heaven keep me from all such curtailments!" answered Wilhelm: "they destroy at once the sense and the effect. What these two persons are and do it is impossible to represent by one. In such small matters we discover Shakspeare's greatness. These soft approaches, this smirking and bowing, this assenting wheedling, flattering, this whisking agility, this wagging of the tail, this allness and emptiness, this legal knavery, this ineptitude and insipidity,—how can they be expressed by a single man? There ought to be at least a dozen of these people, if they could be had; for it is only in society that they are any thing; they are society itself; and Shakspeare showed no little wisdom and discernment in bringing in a pair of them. Besides, I need them as a couple that may be contrasted with the single, noble, excellent Horatio."

"I understand you," answered Serlo, "and we can arrange it. One of them we shall hand over to Elmira, Old Boisterous's eldest daughter: it will all be right, if they look well enough;

454

and I will deck and trim the puppets so that it shall be first-rate fun to behold them."

Philina was rejoicing not a little, that she had to act the Duchess in the small subordinate play. "I will show it so natural," cried she, "how you wed a second husband, without loss of time, when you have loved the first immensely. I mean to win the loudest plaudits, and every man shall wish to be the third."

Aurelia gave a frown: her spleen against Philina was increasing every day.

" 'Tis a pity, I declare," said Serlo, "that we have no ballet; else you should dance me a *pas de deux* with your first, and then another with your second husband,—and the first might dance himself to sleep by the measure; and your bits of feet and ankles would look so pretty, tripping to and fro upon the side stage."

"Of my ankles you do not know much," replied she pertly; "and as to my bits of feet," cried she, hastily reaching below the table, pulling off her slippers, and holding them together out to Serlo, "here are the cases of them; and I challenge you to find me more dainty ones."

"I was in earnest," said he, looking at the elegant half-shoes. "In truth, one does not often meet with any thing so dainty."

They were of Parisian workmanship: Philina had received them as a present from the countess, a lady whose foot was celebrated for its beauty.

"A charming thing!" cried Serlo: "my heart leaps at the sight of them."

"What gallant throbs!" replied Philina.

"There is nothing in the world beyond a pair of slippers," said he, "of such pretty manufacture, in their proper time and place, when"—

Philina took her slippers from his hands, crying, "You have squeezed them all! They are far too wide for me!" She played with them, and rubbed the soles of them together. "How hot it is!" cried she, clapping the sole upon her cheek, then again rubbing, and holding it to Serlo. He was innocent enough to stretch out his hand to feel the warmth. "Clip! clap!" cried she, giving him a smart rap over the knuckles with the heel; so that he screamed, and drew back his hand. "That's for indulging in thoughts of your own at the sight of my slippers."

"And that's for using old folk like children," cried the other; then sprang up, seized her, and plundered many a kiss, every one

455

of which she artfully contested with a show of serious reluctance. In this romping, her long hair got loose, and floated round the group; the chair overset; and Aurelia, inwardly indignant at such rioting, arose in great vexation.

Though in this remoulding of "Hamlet" many characters had been cut off, a sufficient number of them still remained,—a number which the company was scarcely adequate to meet.

"If this is the way of it," said Serlo, "our prompter himself must issue from his den, and mount the stage, and become a personage like one of us."

"In his own station," answered Wilhelm, "I have frequently admired him."

"I do not think," said Serlo, "that there is in the world a more perfect artist of his kind. No spectator ever hears him: we upon the stage catch every syllable. He has formed in himself, as it were, a peculiar set of vocal organs for this purpose: he is like a Genius that whispers intelligibly to us in the hour of need. He feels, as if by instinct, what portion of his task an actor is completely master of, and anticipates from afar where his memory will fail him. I have known cases in which I myself had scarcely read my part: he said it over to me word for word, and I played happily. Yet he has some peculiarities which would make another in his place quite useless. For example, he takes such an interest in the plays, that, in giving any moving passage, he does not indeed declaim it, but he reads it with all pomp and pathos. By this ill habit he has nonplussed me on more than one occasion."

"As with another of his singularities," observed Aurelia, "he once left me sticking fast in a very dangerous passage."

"How could this happen, with the man's attentiveness?" said Wilhelm.

"He is so affected," said Aurelia, "by certain passages, that he weeps warm tears, and for a few moments loses all reflection; and it is not properly passages such as we should call affecting that produce this impression on him; but, if I express myself clearly, the *beautiful* passages, those out of which the pure spirit of the poet looks forth, as it were, through open, sparkling eyes, —passages which others at most rejoice over, and which many thousands altogether overlook."

"And with a soul so tender, why does he never venture on the stage?"

"A hoarse voice," said Serlo, "and a stiff carriage, exclude him from it; as his melancholic temper excludes him from society. What trouble have I taken, and in vain, to make him take to me! But he is a charming reader; such another I have never heard; no one can observe like him the narrow limit between declamation and graceful recital."

"The very man!" exclaimed our friend, "the very man! What a fortunate discovery! We have now the proper hand for delivering the passage of 'the rugged Pyrrhus.' "

"One requires your eagerness," said Serlo, "before he can employ every object in the use it was meant for."

"In truth," said Wilhelm, "I was very much afraid we should be obliged to leave this passage out: the omission would have lamed the whole play."

"Well! That is what I cannot understand," observed Aurelia.

"I hope you will erelong be of my opinion," answered Wilhelm. "Shakspeare has introduced these traveling players with a double purpose. The person who recites the death of Priam with such feeling, in the *first* place, makes a deep impression on the prince himself; he sharpens the conscience of the wavering youth: and, accordingly, this scene becomes a prelude to that other, where, in the *second* place, the little play produces such effect upon the King. Hamlet sees himself reproved and put to shame by the player, who feels so deep a sympathy in foreign and fictitious woes; and the thought of making an experiment upon the conscience of his stepfather is in consequence suggested to him. What a royal monologue is that, which ends the second act! How charming it will be to speak it!

> " '*Oh, what a rogue and peasant slave am I!*
> *Is it not monstrous that this player here,*
> *But in a fiction, in a dream of passion,*
> *Could force his soul so to his own conceit,*
> *That, from her working, all his visage wann'd;*
> *Tears in his eyes, distraction in's aspect,*
> *A broken voice, and his whole function suiting*
> *With forms to his conceit? and all for nothing!*
> *For Hecuba!*
> *What's Hecuba to him, or he to Hecuba,*
> *That he should weep for her?*' "

"If we can but persuade our man to come upon the stage," observed Aurelia.

"We must lead him to it by degrees," said Serlo. "At the rehearsal he may read the passage: we shall tell him that an actor whom we are expecting is to play it; and so, by and by, we shall lead him nearer to the point."

Having agreed on this affair, the conversation next turned upon the Ghost. Wilhelm could not bring himself to give the part of the living King to the Pedant, that so Old Boisterous might play the Ghost: he was of opinion that they ought to wait a while; because some other actors had announced themselves, and among these it was probable they would find a fitter man.

We can easily conceive, then, how astonished Wilhelm must have been when, returning home that evening, he found a billet lying on his table, sealed with singular figures, and containing what follows:—

"Strange youth! we know thou art in great perplexity. For thy Hamlet thou canst hardly find men enough, not to speak of ghosts. Thy zeal deserves a miracle: miracles we cannot work, but somewhat marvellous shall happen. If thou have faith, the Ghost shall arise at the proper hour! Be of courage and keep firm! This needs no answer: thy determination will be known to us."

With this curious sheet he hastened back to Serlo, who read and re-read it, and at last declared, with a thoughtful look, that it seemed a matter of some moment; that they must consider well and seriously whether they could risk it. They talked the subject over at some length; Aurelia was silent, only smiling now and then; and a few days after, when speaking of the incident again, she gave our friend, not obscurely, to understand that she held it all a joke of Serlo's. She desired him to cast away anxiety, and to expect the Ghost with patience.

Serlo, for most part, was in excellent humor: the actors that were going to leave him took all possible pains to play well, that their absence might be much regretted; and this, combined with the new-fangled zeal of the others, gave promise of the best results.

His intercourse with Wilhelm had not failed to exert some influence on him. He began to speak more about art: for, after all, he was a German; and Germans like to give themselves account of what they do. Wilhelm wrote down many of their conversations; which, as our narrative must not be so often interrupted here, we shall communicate to such of our readers as feel an interest in dramaturgic matters, by some other opportunity.

In particular, one evening, the manager was very merry in speaking of the part of Polonius, and how he meant to take it up. "I engage," said he, "on this occasion, to present a very meritorious person in his best aspect. The repose and security of this old gentleman, his emptiness and his significance, his exterior gracefulness and interior meanness, his frankness and sycophancy, his sincere roguery and deceitful truth, I will introduce with all due elegance in their fit proportions. This respectable, gray-haired, enduring, time-serving half-knave, I will represent in the most courtly style: the occasional roughness and coarseness of our author's strokes will further me here. I will speak like a book when I am prepared beforehand, and like an ass when I utter the overflowings of my heart. I will be insipid and absurd enough to chime in with every one, and acute enough never to observe when people make a mock of me. I have seldom taken up a part with so much zeal and roguishness."

"Could I but hope as much from mine!" exclaimed Aurelia. "I have neither youth nor softness enough to be at home in this character. One thing alone I am too sure of,—the feeling that turns Ophelia's brain, I shall not want."

"We must not take the matter up so strictly," said our friend. "For my share, I am certain, that the wish to act the character of Hamlet has led me exceedingly astray, throughout my study of the play. And now, the more I look into the part, the more clearly do I see, that, in my whole form and physiognomy, there is not one feature such as Shakspeare meant for Hamlet. When I consider with what nicety the various circumstances are adapted to each other, I can scarcely hope to produce even a tolerable effect."

"You are entering on your new career with becoming conscientiousness," said Serlo. "The actor fits himself to his part as he can, and the part to him as it must. But how has Shakspeare drawn his Hamlet? Is he so utterly unlike you?"

"In the first place," answered Wilhelm, "he is fair-haired."

"That I call far-fetched," observed Aurelia. "How do you infer that?"

"As a Dane, as a Northman, he is fair-haired and blue-eyed by descent."

"And you think Shakspeare had this in view?"

Johann Wolfgang von Goethe

"I do not find it specially expressed; but, by comparison of passages, I think it incontestable. The fencing tires him; the sweat is running from his brow; and the Queen remarks, 'He's fat, and scant of breath.' Can you conceive him to be otherwise than plump and fair-haired? Brown-complexioned people, in their youth, are seldom plump. And does not his wavering melancholy, his soft lamenting, his irresolute activity, accord with such a figure? From a dark-haired young man, you would look for more decision and impetuosity."

"You are spoiling my imagination," cried Aurelia: "away with your fat Hamlets! Do not set your well-fed prince before us! Give us rather any *succedaneum* that will move us, will delight us. The intention of the author is of less importance to us than our own enjoyment, and we need a charm that is adapted for us."

ONE EVENING a dispute arose among our friends about the novel and the drama, and which of them deserved the preference. Serlo said it was a fruitless and misunderstood debate: both might be superior in their kinds, only each must keep within the limits proper to it.

"About their limits and their kinds," said Wilhelm, "I confess myself not altogether clear."

"Who *is* so?" said the other; "and yet perhaps it were worth while to come a little closer to the business."

They conversed together long upon the matter; and, in fine, the following was nearly the result of their discussion:—

"In the novel as well as in the drama, it is human nature and human action that we see. The difference between these sorts of fiction lies not merely in their outward form,—not merely in the circumstance that the personages of the one are made to speak, while those of the other have commonly their history narrated. Unfortunately many dramas are but novels, which proceed by dialogue; and it would not be impossible to write a drama in the shape of letters.

"But, in the novel, it is chiefly *sentiments* and *events* that are exhibited; in the drama, it is *characters* and *deeds*. The novel must go slowly forward; and the sentiments of the hero, by some means or another, must restrain the tendency of the whole to unfold itself and to conclude. The drama, on the other hand, must hasten; and the character of the hero must press forward to the end: it does not restrain, but is restrained. The novel-hero

460

must be suffering,—at least he must not in a high degree be active: in the dramatic one, we look for activity and deeds. Grandison, Clarissa, Pamela, the Vicar of Wakefield, Tom Jones himself, are, if not suffering, at least retarding, personages; and the incidents are all in some sort modelled by their sentiments. In the drama the hero models nothing by himself; all things withstand him; and he clears and casts away the hindrances from off his path, or else sinks under them."

Our friends were also of opinion, that, in the novel, some degree of scope may be allowed to Chance, but that it must always be led and guided by the sentiments of the personages: on the other hand, that Fate, which, by means of outward, unconnected circumstances, carries forward men, without their own concurrence, to an unforeseen catastrophe, can have place only in the drama; that Chance may produce pathetic situations, but never tragic ones; Fate, on the other hand, ought always to be terrible,—and is, in the highest sense, tragic, when it brings into a ruinous concatenation the guilty man, and the guiltless that was unconcerned with him.

These considerations led them back to the play of "Hamlet," and the peculiarities of its composition. The hero in this case, it was observed, is endowed more properly with sentiments than with a character: it is events alone that push him on, and accordingly the play has in some measure the expansion of a novel. But as it is Fate that draws the plan, as the story issues from a deed of terror, and the hero is continually driven forward to a deed of terror, the work is tragic in the highest sense, and admits of no other than a tragic end.

The book-rehearsal was now to take place, to which Wilhelm had looked forward as to a festival. Having previously collated all the parts, no obstacle on this side could oppose him. The whole of the actors were acquainted with the piece: he endeavored to impress their minds with the importance of these book-rehearsals. "As you require," said he, "of every musical performer, that he shall, in some degree, be able to play from the book: so every actor, every educated man, should train himself to recite from the book, to catch immediately the character of any drama, any poem, any tale he may be reading, and exhibit it with grace and readiness. No committing to memory will be of service, if the actor have not, in the first place, penetrated into the sense and spirit of his author: the mere letter will avail him nothing."

Serlo declared that he would overlook all subsequent rehearsals, —the last rehearsal itself,—if justice were but done to these rehearsals from the book. "For, commonly," said he, "there is nothing more amusing than to hear an actor speak of study: it is as if freemasons were to talk of building."

The rehearsal passed according to their wishes; and we may assert, that the fame and favor which our company acquired afterwards had their foundation in these few but well-spent hours.

"You did right, my friend," said Serlo, when they were alone, "in speaking to our fellow-laborers so earnestly; and yet I am afraid they will scarcely fulfil your wishes."

"How so?" asked Wilhelm.

"I have noticed," answered Serlo, "that, as easily as you may set in motion the imaginations of men, gladly as they listen to your tales and fictions, it is yet very seldom that you find among them any touch of an imagination you can call productive. In actors this remark is strikingly exemplified. Any one of them is well content to undertake a beautiful, praiseworthy, brilliant part; and seldom will any one of them do more than self-complacently transport himself into his hero's place, without in the smallest troubling his head whether other people view him so or not. But to seize with vivacity what the author's feeling was in writing; what portion of your individual qualities you must cast off, in order to do justice to a part; how, by your own conviction that you are become another man, you may carry with you the convictions of the audience; how, by the inward truth of your conceptive power, you can change these boards into a temple, this pasteboard into woods,—to seize and execute all this, is given to very few. That internal strength of soul, by which alone deception can be brought about; that lying truth, without which nothing will affect us rightly,—have, by most men, never even been imagined.

"Let us not, then, press too hard for spirit and feeling in our friends. The surest way is first coolly to instruct them in the sense and letter of the play,—if possible, to open their understandings. Whoever has the talent will then, of his own accord, eagerly adopt the spirited feeling and manner of expression; and those who have it not will at least be prevented from acting or reciting altogether falsely. And among actors, as indeed in all cases, there is no worse arrangement than for any one to make pretensions to the spirit of a thing, while the sense and letter of it are not ready and clear to him."

Coming to the first stage-rehearsal very early, Wilhelm found himself alone upon the boards. The appearance of the place surprised him, and awoke the strangest recollections. A forest and village scene stood exactly represented as he once had seen it in the theatre of his native town. On that occasion also, a rehearsal was proceeding; and it was the morning when Mariana first confessed her love to him, and promised him a happy interview. The peasants' cottages resembled one another on the two stages, as they did in nature: the true morning sun, beaming through a half-closed window-shutter, fell upon a part of a bench ill joined to a cottage door; but unhappily it did not now enlighten Mariana's waist and bosom. He sat down, reflecting on this strange coincidence: he almost thought that perhaps on this very spot he would soon see her again. And, alas! the truth was nothing more, than that an afterpiece, to which this scene belonged, was at that time very often played upon the German stage.

Out of these meditations he was roused by the other actors, along with whom two amateurs, frequenters of the wardrobe and the stage, came in, and saluted Wilhelm with a show of great enthusiasm. One of these was in some degree attached to Frau Melina, but the other was entirely a lover of the art, and both were of the kind which a good company should always wish to have about it. It was difficult to say whether their love for the stage, or their knowledge of it, was the greater. They loved it too much to know it perfectly: they knew it well enough to prize the good and to discard the bad. But, their inclination being so powerful, they could tolerate the mediocre; and the glorious joy which they experienced from the foretaste and the aftertaste of excellence surpassed expression. The mechanical department gave them pleasure, the intellectual charmed them; and so strong was their susceptibility, that even a discontinuous rehearsal afforded them a species of illusion. Deficiencies appeared in their eyes to fade away in distance: the successful touched them like an object near at hand. In a word, they were judges such as every artist wishes in his own department. Their favorite movement was from the side-scenes to the pit, and from the pit to the side-scenes; their happiest place was in the wardrobe; their busiest employment was in trying to improve the dress, position, recitation, gesture, of the actor; their liveliest conversation was on the effect produced by him; their most constant effort was to keep him accurate, active, and attentive, to do him service or kindness, and, without squandering, to procure for the company a series of enjoyments. The two had obtained the exclusive privilege of being present on the stage at rehearsals as well as exhibitions. In regard to "Hamlet," they had not in all points agreed with Wilhelm: here and there he had yielded; but, for most part, he had stood by his opinion: and, upon the whole, these discussions had been very useful in the forming of his taste. He showed both gentlemen how much he valued them; and they again predicted nothing less, from these combined endeavors, than a new epoch for the German theatre.

The presence of these persons was of great service during the rehearsals. In particular they labored to convince our players, that, throughout the whole of their preparations, the posture and action, as they were intended ultimately to appear, should always be combined with the words, and thus the whole be mechanically united by habit. In rehearsing a tragedy especially, they said, no common movement with the hands should be allowed: a tragic actor that took snuff in the rehearsal always frightened them; for, in all probability, on coming to the same passage in the exhibition, he would miss his pinch. Nay, on the same principles, they maintained that no one should rehearse in boots, if his part were to be played in shoes. But nothing, they declared, afflicted them so much as when the women, in rehearsing, stuck their hands into the folds of their gowns.

By the persuasion of our friends, another very good effect was brought about: the actors all began to learn the use of arms. Since military parts occur so frequently, said they, can any thing look more absurd than men, without the smallest particle of discipline, trolling about the stage in captains' and majors' uniforms?

Wilhelm and Laertes were the first that took lessons of a subaltern: they continued their practising of fence with the greatest zeal.

Such pains did these two men take for perfecting a company which had so fortunately come together. They were thus providing for the future satisfaction of the public, while the public was usually laughing at their taste. People did not know what gratitude they owed our friends, particularly for performing one service,—the service of frequently impressing on the actor the fundamental point, that it was his duty to speak so loud as to be heard. In this simple matter, they experienced more opposition and repugnance than could have been expected. Most part maintained that they were heard well enough already; some laid the blame upon the building; others said, one could not yell and bellow, when one had to speak naturally, secretly, or tenderly.

Our two friends, having an immeasurable stock of patience, tried every means of undoing this delusion, of getting round this obstinate self-will. They spared neither arguments nor flatteries; and at last they reached their object, being aided not a little by the good example of Wilhelm. By him they were requested to sit down in the remotest corners of the house, and, every time they did not hear him perfectly, to rap on the bench with a key. He articulated well, spoke out in a measured manner, raised his tones gradually, and did not overcry himself in the most vehement passages. The rapping of the key was heard less and less every new rehearsal: by and by the rest submitted to the same operation, and at last it seemed rational to hope that the piece would be heard by every one in all the nooks of the house.

From this example we may see how desirous people are to reach their object in their own way; what need there often is of enforcing on them truths which are self-evident; and how difficult it may be to reduce the man who aims at effecting something to admit the primary conditions under which alone his enterprise is possible.

THE NECESSARY preparations for scenery and dresses, and whatever else was requisite, were now proceeding. In regard to certain scenes and passages, our friend had whims of his own, which Serlo humored, partly in consideration of their bargain, partly from conviction, and because he hoped by these civilities to gain Wilhelm, and to lead him according to his own purposes the more implicitly in time to come.

Thus, for example, the King and Queen were, at the first audience, to appear sitting on the throne, with the courtiers at the sides, and Hamlet standing undistinguished in the crowd. "Hamlet," said he, "must keep himself quiet: his sable dress will sufficiently point him out. He should rather shun remark than seek it. Not till the audience is ended, and the King speaks with him as with a son, should he advance, and allow the scene to take its course."

A formidable obstacle still remained, in regard to the two pictures which Hamlet so passionately refers to in the scene with his mother. "We ought," said Wilhelm, "to have both of them visible, at full length, in the bottom of the chamber, near the main door; and the former king must be clad in armor, like the Ghost, and hang at the side where it enters. I could wish that the figure held its right hand in a commanding attitude, were somewhat turned away, and, as it were, looked over its shoulder, that so it might perfectly resemble the Ghost at the moment when he issues from the door. It will produce a great effect, when at this instant Hamlet looks upon the Ghost, and the Queen upon the picture. The stepfather may be painted in royal ornaments, but not so striking."

There were several other points of this sort, about which we shall, perhaps, elsewhere have opportunity to speak.

"Are you, then, inexorably bent on Hamlet's dying at the end?" inquired Serlo.

"How can I keep him alive," said Wilhelm, "when the whole play is pressing him to death? We have already talked at large on that matter."

"But the public wishes him to live."

"I will show the public any other complaisance; but, as to this, I cannot. We often wish that some gallant, useful man, who is dying of a chronical disease, might yet live longer. The family weep, and conjure the physician; but he cannot stay him: and no more than this physician can withstand the necessity of nature, can we give law to an acknowledged necessity of art. It is a false compliance with the multitude, to raise in them emotions which they *wish*, when these are not emotions which they *ought*, to feel."

"Whoever pays the cash," said Serlo, "may require the ware according to his liking."

"Doubtless, in some degree," replied our friend; "but a great public should be reverenced, not used as children are, when pedlers wish to hook the money from them. By presenting excellence to the people, you should gradually excite in them a taste and feeling for the excellent; and they will pay their money with double satisfaction when reason itself has nothing to object against this outlay. The public you may flatter, as you do a well-beloved child, to better, to enlighten, it; not as you do a pampered child of quality, to perpetuate the error you profit from."

In this manner various other topics were discussed relating to the question, What might still be changed in the play, and what must of necessity remain untouched? We shall not enter farther on those points at present; but, perhaps, at some future time we may submit this altered "Hamlet" itself to such of our readers as feel any interest in the subject.

The main rehearsal was at length concluded: it had lasted very long. Serlo and Wilhelm still found much to care for: notwithstanding all the time which had already been consumed in preparation, some highly necessary matters had been left to the very last moment.

Thus, the pictures of the kings, for instance, were not ready: and the scene between Hamlet and his mother, from which so powerful an effect was looked for, had a very helpless aspect, as the business stood; for neither Ghost nor painted image of him was at present forthcoming. Serlo made a jest of this perplexity: "We should be in a pretty scrape," said he, "if the Ghost were to decline appearing, and the guard had nothing to fight with but the air, and our prompter were obliged to speak the spirit's part from the side-scenes."

"We will not scare away our strange friend by unbelief," said Wilhelm: "doubtless at the proper season he will come, and astonish us as much as the spectators."

"Well, certainly," said Serlo, "I shall be a happy man to-morrow night, when once the play will have been acted. It costs us more arrangement than I dreamed of."

"But none of you," exclaimed Philina, "will be happier than I, little as my part disturbs me. Really, to hear a single subject talked of forever and forever, when, after all, there is nothing to come of it beyond an exhibition, which will be forgotten like so many hundred others, this is what I have not patience for. In Heaven's name, not so many *pros* and *cons!* The guests you entertain have always something to object against the dinner; nay, if you could hear them talk of it at home, they cannot understand how it was possible to undergo so sad a business."

"Let me turn your illustration, pretty one, to my own advantage," answered Wilhelm. "Consider how much must be done by art and nature, by traffickers and tradesmen, before an entertainment can be given. How many years the stag must wander in the forest, the fish in the river or the sea, before they can deserve to grace our table! And what cares and consultations with her cooks and servants has the lady of the house submitted to! Observe with what indifference the people swallow the production of the distant vintager, the seaman, and the vintner, as if it were a thing of course. And ought these men to cease from laboring, providing, and preparing; ought the master of the house to cease from purchasing and laying up the fruit of their exertions,—because at last the enjoyment it affords is transitory? But no enjoyment can be transitory; the impression which it leaves is permanent: and what is done with diligence and effort communicates to the spectator a hidden force, of which we cannot say how far its influence may reach."

" 'Tis all one to me," replied Philina: "only here again I must observe, that you men are constantly at variance with yourselves. With all this conscientious horror at curtailing Shakespeare you have missed the finest thought there was in 'Hamlet'!"

"The finest?" cried our friend.

"Certainly the finest," said Philina: "the prince himself takes pleasure in it."

"And it is?" inquired Serlo.

"If you wore a wig," replied Philina, "I would pluck it very coolly off you; for I think you need to have your understanding opened."

The rest began to think what she could mean: the conversation paused. The party arose; it was now grown late; they seemed about to separate. While they were standing in this undetermined mood, Philina all at once struck up a song, with a very graceful, pleasing tune:—

> *"Sing me not with such emotion,*
> *How the night so lonesome is:*
> *Pretty maids, I've got a notion*
> *It is the reverse of this.*
>
> *For as wife and man are plighted,*
> *And the better half the wife;*
> *So is night to day united:*
> *Night's the better half of life.*

Can you joy in bustling daytime,
  Day when none can get his will?
It is good for work, for haytime;
  For much other it is ill.

But when, in the nightly glooming,
  Social lamp on table glows,
Face for faces dear illuming,
  And such jest and joyance goes;

When the fiery, pert young fellow,
  Wont by day to run or ride,
Whispering now some tale would tell O,
  All so gentle by your side;

When the nightingale to lovers
  Loving her songlet sings,
Which for exiles and sad rovers
  Like mere woe and wailing rings,—

With a heart how lightsome feeling,
  Do ye count the kindly clock,
Which twelve times deliberate pealing,
  Tells you none to-night shall knock!

Therefore, on all fit occasions,
  Mark it, maidens, what I sing:
Every day its own vexations,
  And the night its joys, will bring."

She made a slight courtesy on concluding, and Serlo gave a loud "Bravo!" She scuttled off, and left the room with a teehee of laughter. They heard her singing and skipping as she went down-stairs.

Serlo passed into another room: Wilhelm bade Aurelia good-night; but she continued looking at him for a few moments, and said,—

"How I dislike that woman! Dislike her from my heart, and to her very slightest qualities! Those brown eyelashes, with her fair hair, which our brother thinks so charming, I cannot bear to look at; and that scar upon her brow has something in it so repulsive, so low and base, that I could recoil ten paces every time I meet her. She was lately telling as a joke, that her father, when she was a child, threw a plate at her head, of which this is the mark. It is well that she is marked in the eyes and brow, that those about her may be on their guard."

Wilhelm made no answer; and Aurelia went on, apparently with greater spleen,—

"It is next to impossible for me to speak a kind, civil word to her, so deeply do I hate her, with all her wheedling. Would that we were rid of her! And you, too, my friend, have a certain complaisance for the creature, a way of acting towards her, that grieves me to the soul,—an attention which borders on respect; which, by Heaven! she does not merit."

"Whatever she may be," replied our friend, "I owe her thanks. Her upbringing is to blame: to her natural character I would do justice."

"Character!" exclaimed Aurelia; "and do you think such a creature has a character? O you men! It is so like you! These are the women you deserve!"

"My friend, can you suspect me?" answered Wilhelm. "I will give account of every minute I have spent beside her."

"Come, come," replied Aurelia: "it is late, we will not quarrel. All like each, and each like all! Good-night, my friend! Good-night, my sparkling bird-of-paradise!"

Wilhelm asked how he had earned this title.

"Another time," cried she; "another time. They say it has no feet, but hovers in the air, and lives on ether. That, however, is a story, a poetic fiction. Good-night! Dream sweetly, if you are in luck!"

She proceeded to her room; and he, being left alone, made haste to his.

Half angrily he walked along his chamber to and fro. The jesting but decided tone of Aurelia had hurt him: he felt deeply how unjust she was. Could he treat Philina with unkindness or ill-nature? She had done no evil to him; but, for any love to her, he could proudly and confidently take his conscience to witness that it was not so.

On the point of beginning to undress, he was going forward to his bed to draw aside the curtains, when, not without extreme astonishment, he saw a pair of women's slippers lying on the floor before it. One of them was resting on its sole, the other on its edge. They were Philina's slippers: he recognized them but too well. He thought he noticed some disorder in the curtains; nay, it seemed as if they moved. He stood, and looked with unaverted eyes.

A new impulse, which he took for anger, cut his breath: after a short pause, he recovered, and cried in a firm tone,—

"Come out, Philina! What do you mean by this? Where is your sense, your modesty? Are we to be the speech of the house to-morrow?"

Nothing stirred.

"I do not jest," continued he: "these pranks are little to my taste."

No sound! No motion!

Irritated and determined, he at last went forward to the bed, and tore the curtains asunder. "Arise," said he, "if I am not to give you up my room to-night."

With great surprise, he found his bed unoccupied; the sheets and pillows in the sleekest rest. He looked around: he searched and searched, but found no traces of the rouge. Behind the bed, the stove, the drawers, there was nothing to be seen: he sought with great and greater diligence; a spiteful looker-on might have believed that he was seeking in the hope of finding.

All thought of sleep was gone. He put the slippers on his table; went past it, up and down; often paused before it; and a wicked sprite that watched him has asserted that our friend employed himself for several hours about these dainty little shoes; that he viewed them with a certain interest; that he handled them and played with them; and it was not till towards morning that he threw himself on the bed, without undressing, where he fell asleep amidst a world of curious fantasies.

He was still slumbering, when Serlo entered hastily. "Where are you?" cried he: "still in bed? Impossible! I want you in the theatre: we have a thousand things to do."

THE FORENOON and the afternoon fled rapidly away. The playhouse was already full: our friend hastened to dress. It was not with the joy which it had given him when he first essayed it, that he now put on the garb of Hamlet: he only dressed that he might be in readiness. On his joining the women in the stage-room, they unanimously cried that nothing sat upon him right; the fine feather stood awry; the buckle of his belt did not fit:

they began to slit, to sew, and piece together. The music started: Philina still objected somewhat to his ruff; Aurelia had much to say against his mantle. "Leave me alone, good people," cried he: "this negligence will make me liker Hamlet." The women would not let him go, but continued trimming him. The music ceased. the acting was begun. He looked at himself in the glass, pressed his hat closer down upon his face, and retouched the painting of his cheeks.

At this instant somebody came rushing in, and cried, "The Ghost! the Ghost!"

Wilhelm had not once had time all day to think of the Ghost, and whether it would come or not. His anxiety on that head was at length removed, and now some strange assistant was to be expected. The stage-manager came in, inquiring after various matters: Wilhelm had not time to ask about the Ghost; he hastened to present himself before the throne, where King and Queen, surrounded with their court, were already glancing in all the splendors of royalty, and waiting till the scene in front of them should be concluded. He caught the last words of Horatio, who was speaking of the Ghost, in extreme confusion, and seemed to have almost forgotten his part.

The intermediate curtain went aloft, and Hamlet saw the crowded house before him. Horatio, having spoken his address, and been dismissed by the King, pressed through to Hamlet; and, as if presenting himself to the Prince, he said, "The Devil is in harness: he has put us all in fright."

In the mean while, two men of large stature, in white cloaks and capouches, were observed standing in the side-scenes. Our friend, in the distraction, embarrassment, and hurry of the moment, had failed in the first soliloquy; at least, such was his own opinion, though loud plaudits had attended his exit. Accordingly, he made his next entrance in no pleasant mood, with the dreary wintry feeling of dramatic condemnation. Yet he girded up his mind, and spoke that appropriate passage on the "rouse and wassail," the "heavy-headed revel" of the Danes, with suitable indifference; he had, like the audience, in thinking of it, quite forgotten the Ghost; and he started, in real terror, when Horatio cried out, "Look, my lord! it comes!" He whirled violently round; and the tall, noble figure, the low, inaudible tread, the light movement in the heavy-looking armor, made such an impression on him, that he stood as if transformed to stone, and could utter only in a half-voice his "Angels and ministers of grace defend us!" He glared at the form, drew a deep breathing once or twice, and pronounced his address to the Ghost in a manner so confused, so broken, so constrained, that the highest art could not have hit the mark so well.

His translation of this passage now stood him in good stead. He had kept very close to the original, in which the arrangement of the words appeared to him expressive of a mind confounded, terrified, and seized with horror:—

> " '*Be thou a spirit of health, or goblin damn'd,*
> *Bring with thee airs from heaven, or blasts from hell,*
> *Be thy intents wicked, or charitable,*
> *Thou com'st in such a questionable shape,*
> *That I will speak to thee: I'll call thee Hamlet,*
> *King, father, royal Dane: oh, answer me!* '"

A deep effect was visible in the audience. The Ghost beckoned, the Prince followed him amid the loudest plaudits.

The scene changed: and, when the two had re-appeared, the Ghost, on a sudden, stopped, and turned round; by which means Hamlet came to be a little too close upon it. With a longing curiosity, he looked in at the lowered visor; but except two deep-lying eyes, and a well-formed nose, he could discern nothing. Gazing timidly, he stood before the Ghost; but when the first tones issued from the helmet, and a somewhat hoarse, yet deep and penetrating, voice, pronounced the words, "I am thy father's spirit," Wilhelm, shuddering, started back some paces; and the audience shuddered with him. Each imagined that he knew the voice: Wilhelm thought he noticed in it some resemblance to his father's. These strange emotions and remembrances, the curiosity he felt about discovering his secret friend, the anxiety about offending him, even the theatric impropriety of coming too near him in the present situation, all this affected Wilhelm with powerful and conflicting impulses. During the long speech of the Ghost, he changed his place so frequently, he seemed so unsettled and perplexed, so attentive and so absent-minded, that his acting caused a universal admiration, as the Spirit caused a universal horror. The latter spoke with a feeling of melancholy anger, rather than of sorrow; but of an anger spiritual, slow, and inexhaustible. It was the mistemper of a noble soul, that is severed from all earthly things, and yet devoted

473

to unbounded woe. At last he vanished, but in a curious manner; for a thin, gray, transparent gauze arose from the place of descent, like a vapor, spread itself over him, and sank along with him.

Hamlet's friends now entered, and swore upon the sword. Old Truepenny, in the mean time, was so busy under ground, that, wherever they might take their station, he was sure to call out right beneath them, "Swear!" and they started, as if the soil had taken fire below them, and hastened to another spot. On each of these occasions, too, a little flame pierced through at the place where they were standing. The whole produced on the spectators a profound impression.

After this, the play proceeded calmly on its course: nothing failed; all prospered; the audience manifested their contentment, and the actors seemed to rise in heart and spirits every scene.

THE CURTAIN fell, and rapturous applauses sounded out of every corner of the house. The four princely corpses sprang aloft, and embraced each other. Polonius and Ophelia likewise issued from their graves, and listened with extreme satisfaction, as Horatio, who had stepped before the curtain to announce the following play, was welcomed with the most thundering plaudits. The people would not hear of any other play, but violently required the repetition of the present.

"We have won," cried Serlo, "and so not another reasonable word this night! Every thing depends on the first impression: we should never take it ill of any actor, that, on occasion of his first appearance, he is provident, and even self-willed."

The box-keeper came, and delivered him a heavy sum. "We have made a good beginning," cried the manager, "and prejudice itself will now be on our side."

From Wilhelm Meister's Travels

THE NEW MELUSINA

R ESPECTED gentlemen! Being aware that preliminary speeches and introductions are not much to your taste, I shall without further talk assure you, that, in the present instance, I hope to fulfill your commission moderately well. From me has many a true history gone forth already, to the high and universal satisfaction of hearers; but to-day I may assert, that I have one to tell which far surpasses the former, and which, though it happened to me several years ago, still disquiets me in recollecting it, nay, still gives hope of some further development.

By way of introduction, let me confess, that I have not always so arranged my scheme of life as to be certain of the next period in it, or even of the next day. In my youth, I was no first-rate economist, and often found myself in manifold perplexity. At one time I undertook a journey, thinking to derive good profit in the course of it; but the scale I went upon was too liberal: and after having commenced my travel with extra-post, and then prosecuted it for a time in the diligence, I at last found myself obliged to front the end of it on foot.

Like a gay young blade, it had been from of old my custom, on entering any inn, to look round for the landlady, or even the cook, and wheedle myself into favor with her; whereby, for most part, my shot was somewhat reduced.

One night at dusk, as I was entering the post-house of a little town, and purposing to set about my customary operations, there came a fair double-seated coach with four horses rattling up to the door behind me. I turned round, and observed in it a young lady, without maid, without servants. I hastened to open the carriage for her, and to ask if I could help her in any thing. On

Translated by Thomas Carlyle

stepping out, a fair form displayed itself; and her lovely countenance, if you looked at it narrowly, was adorned with a slight shade of sorrow. I again asked if there was aught I could do for her. "Oh, yes!" said she, "if you will lift that little box carefully, which you will find standing on the seat, and bring it in; but I beg very much of you to carry it with all steadiness, and not to move or shake it in the least." I took out the box with great care: she shut the coach-door; we walked up-stairs together, and she told the servants that she was to stay here for the night.

We were now alone in the chamber: she desired me to put the box on the table, which was standing at the wall; and as, by several of her movements, I observed that she wished to be alone, I took my leave, reverently but warmly kissing her hand.

"Order supper for us two," said she then: and you may well conceive with what pleasure I executed the commission; scarcely deigning, in my pride of heart, to cast even a side-look on landlady and menials. With impatience I expected the moment that was to lead me back to her. Supper was served: we took our seats opposite each other; I refreshed my heart, for the first time during a considerable while, with a good meal, and no less with so desirable a sight beside me: nay, it seemed as if she were growing fairer and fairer every moment.

Her conversation was pleasant, yet she carefully waived whatever had reference to affection and love. The cloth was removed: I still lingered, I tried all sorts of manœuvres to get near her, but in vain; she kept me at my distance, by a certain dignity which I could not withstand: nay, against my will, I had to part from her at a rather early hour.

After a night passed in waking or unrestfully dreaming, I rose early, inquired whether she had ordered horses; and, learning that she had not, I walked into the garden, saw her standing dressed at the window, and hastened up to her. Here, as she looked so fair, and fairer than ever, love, roguery, and audacity all at once started into motion within me: I rushed towards her, and clasped her in my arms. "Angelic, irresistible being," cried I, "pardon! but it is impossible!"—With incredible dexterity she whisked herself out of my arms, and I had not even time to imprint a kiss on her cheek. "Forbear such outbreakings of a sudden foolish passion," said she, "if you would not scare away a happiness which lies close beside you, but which cannot be laid hold of till after some trials."

476

"Ask of me what thou pleasest, angelic spirit!" cried I, "but do not drive me to despair." She answered, with a smile, "If you mean to devote yourself to my service, hear the terms. I am come hither to visit a lady of my friends, and with her I purpose to continue for a time: in the meanwhile, I could wish that my carriage and this box were taken forward. Will you engage with it? You have nothing to do but carefully to lift the box into the carriage and out, to sit down beside it, and punctually take charge that it receive no harm. When you enter an inn, it is put upon a table, in a chamber by itself, in which you must neither sit nor sleep. You lock the chamber-door with this key, which will open and shut any lock, and has the peculiar property, that no lock shut by it can be opened in the interim."

I looked at her; I felt strangely enough at heart; I promised to do all, if I might hope to see her soon, and if she would seal this hope to me with a kiss. She did so, and from that moment I had become entirely her bondman. I was now to order horses, she said. We settled the way I was to take, the places where I was to wait, and expect her. She at last pressed a purse of gold into my hand, and I pressed my lips on the fair hand that gave it me. She seemed moved at parting; and, for me, I no longer knew what I was doing or was to do.

On my return from giving my orders, I found the room-door locked. I directly tried my master-key, and it performed its duty perfectly. The door flew up: I found the chamber empty, only the box standing on the table where I had laid it.

The carriage drove up: I carried the box carefully down with me, and placed it by my side. The hostess asked, "But where is the lady?" A child answered, "She is gone into the town." I nodded to the people, and rolled off in triumph from the door which I had last night entered with dusty gaiters. That in my hours of leisure I diligently meditated on this adventure, counted my money, laid many schemes, and still now and then kept glancing at the box, you will readily imagine. I posted right forward, passed several stages without alighting, and rested not till I had reached a considerable town, where my fair one had appointed me to wait. Her commands had been pointedly obeyed, —the box always carried to a separate room, and two wax candles lighted beside it; for such, also, had been her order. I would then lock the chamber, establish myself in my own, and take such comfort as the place afforded.

For a while I was able to employ myself with thinking of her, but by degrees the time began to hang heavy on my hands. I was not used to live without companions: these I soon found, at *tables-d'hôte*, in coffee-houses, and public places, altogether to my wish. In such a mode of living, my money began to melt away; and one night it vanished entirely from my purse in a fit of passionate gaming, which I had not had the prudence to abandon. Void of money, with the appearance of a rich man, expecting a heavy bill of charges, uncertain whether and when my fair one would again make her appearance, I felt myself in the deepest embarrassment. Doubly did I now long for her, and believe, that, without her and her gold, it was quite impossible for me to live.

After supper, which I had relished very little, being forced for this time to consume it in solitude, I took to walking violently up and down my room: I spoke aloud to myself, cursed my folly with horrid execrations, threw myself on the floor, tore my hair, and indeed behaved in the most outrageous fashion. Suddenly, in the adjoining chamber where the box was, I heard a slight movement, and then a soft knocking at the well-bolted door, which entered from my apartment. I gather myself, grope for my master-key; but the door-leaves fly up of themselves, and in the light of those burning wax candles enters my beauty. I cast myself at her feet, kiss her robe, her hands; she raises me; I venture not to clasp her, scarcely to look at her, but candidly and repentantly confess to her my fault. "It is pardonable," said she: "only it postpones your happiness and mine. You must now make another tour into the world before we can meet again. Here is more money," continued she, "sufficient if you husband it with any kind of reason. But, as wine and play have brought you into this perplexity, be on your guard in future against wine and women, and let me hope for a glad meeting when the time comes."

She retired over the threshold; the door-leaves flew together: I knocked, I entreated; but nothing further stirred. Next morning, while presenting his bill, the waiter smiled, and said, "So we have found out at last, then, why you lock your door is so artful and incomprehensible a way, that no master-key can open it. We supposed you must have much money and precious ware laid up by you: but now we have seen your treasure walking downstairs; and, in good truth, it seemed worthy of being well kept."

To this I answered nothing, but paid my reckoning, and mounted with my box into the carriage. I again rolled forth into the world, with the firmest resolution to be heedful in future of the warning given me by my fair and mysterious friend. Scarcely, however, had I once more reached a large town, when forthwith I got acquainted with certain interesting ladies, from whom I absolutely could not tear myself away. They seemed inclined to make me pay dear for their favor: for, while they still kept me at a certain distance, they led me into one expense after the other; and I, being anxious only to promote their satisfaction, once more ceased to think of my purse, but paid and spent straightforward, as occasion needed. But how great was my astonishment and joy, when, after some weeks, I observed that the fulness of my store was not in the least diminished, that my purse was still as round and crammed as ever! Wishing to obtain more strict knowledge of this pretty quality, I set myself down to count: I accurately marked the sum, and again proceeded in my joyous life as before. We had no want of excursions by land, and excursions by water; of dancing, singing, and other recreations. But now it required small attention to observe that the purse was actually diminishing, as if by my cursed counting I had robbed it of the property of being uncountable. However, this gay mode of existence had been once entered on: I could not draw back, and yet my ready money soon verged to a close. I execrated my situation; upbraided my fair friend for having so led me into temptation; took it as an offence that she did not again show herself to me; renounced in my spleen all duties towards her; and resolved to break open the box, and see if peradventure any help might be found there. I was just about proceeding with my purpose: but I put it off till night, that I might go through the business with full composure; and, in the mean time, I hastened off to a banquet, for which this was the appointed hour. Here again we got into a high key: the wine and trumpet-sounding had flushed me not a little, when by the most villainous luck it chanced, that, during the dessert, a former friend of my dearest fair one, returning from a journey, entered unexpectedly, placed himself beside her, and, without much ceremony, set about asserting his old privileges. Hence, very soon arose ill-humor, quarrelling, and battle: we plucked out our spits, and I was carried home half dead of several wounds.

The surgeon had bandaged me and gone away; it was far in

the night; my sick-nurse had fallen asleep; the door of the side-room went up; my fair, mysterious friend came in, and sat down by me on the bed. She asked how I was. I answered not, for I was faint and sullen. She continued speaking with much sympathy: she rubbed my temples with a certain balsam, whereby I felt myself rapidly and decidedly strengthened,—so strengthened that I could now get angry and upbraid her. In a violent speech I threw all the blame of my misfortune on her; on the passion she had inspired me with; on her appearing and vanishing; and the tedium, the longing, which, in such a case, I could not but feel. I waxed more and more vehement, as if a fever had been coming on; and I swore to her at last, that if she would not be mine, would not now abide with me and wed me, I had no wish to live any longer: to all which I required a peremptory answer. As she lingered and held back with her explanation, I got altogether beside myself, and tore off my double and triple bandages in the firmest resolution to bleed to death. But what was my amazement when I found all my wounds healed, my skin smooth and entire, and this fair friend in my arms!

Henceforth we were the happiest pair in the world. We both begged pardon of each other without either of us rightly knowing why. She now promised to travel on along with me; and soon we were sitting side by side in the carriage, the little box lying opposite us on the other seat. Of this I had never spoken to her, nor did I now think of speaking, though it lay there before our eyes: and both of us, by tacit agreement, took charge of it, as circumstances might require; I, however, still carrying it to and from the carriage, and busying myself, as formerly, with the locking of the doors.

So long as aught remained in my purse I had continued to pay; but, when my cash went down, I signified the fact to her. "That is easily helped," said she, pointing to a couple of little pouches fixed at the top, to the sides of the carriage. These I had often observed before, but never turned to use. She put her hand into the one, and pulled out some gold pieces, as from the other some coins of silver; thereby showing me the possibility of meeting any scale of expenditure which we might choose to adopt. And thus we journeyed on from town to town, from land to land, contented with each other and with the world; and I fancied not that she would again leave me, the less so that for some time she had evidently been as loving wives wish to be, a circumstance by which our happiness and mutual affection was increased still further. But one morning, alas! she could not be found; and as my actual residence, without her company, became displeasing, I again took the road with my box, tried the virtue of the two pouches, and found it still unimpaired.

My journey proceeded without accident. But if I had hitherto paid little heed to the mysteries of my adventure, expecting a natural solution of the whole, there now occurred something which threw me into astonishment, into anxiety, nay, into fear. Being wont, in my impatience for change of place, to hurry forward day and night, it was often my hap to be travelling in the dark, and, when the lamps by any chance went out, to be left in utter obscurity. Once, in the dead of such a night, I had fallen asleep; and on awakening I observed the glimmer of a light on the covering of my carriage. I examined this more strictly, and found that it was issuing from the box, in which there seemed to be a chink, as if it had been chapped by the warm and dry weather of summer, which was now come on. My thoughts of jewels again came into my head: I supposed there must be some carbuncle lying in the box, and this point I forthwith set about investigating. I postured myself as well as might be, so that my eye was in immediate contact with the chink. But how great was my surprise when a fair apartment, well lighted, and furnished with much taste and even costliness, met my inspection; just as if I had been looking down through the opening of a dome into a royal saloon! A fire was burning in the grate, and before it stood an arm-chair. I held my breath, and continued to observe. And now there entered from the other side of the apartment a lady with a book in her hand, whom I at once recognized for my wife; though her figure was contracted into the extreme of diminution. She sat down in the chair by the fire to read; she trimmed the coals with the most dainty pair of tongs; and, in the course of her movements, I could clearly perceive that this fairest little creature was also in the family way. But now I was obliged to shift my constrained posture a little; and the next moment, when I bent down to look in again, and convince myself that it was no dream, the light had vanished, and my eye rested on empty darkness.

How amazed, nay, terrified, I was, you may easily conceive. I started a thousand thoughts on this discovery, and yet in truth could think nothing. In the midst of this I fell asleep, and on awakening I fancied that it must have been a mere dream: yet I felt myself in some degree estranged from my fair one; and, though I watched over the box but so much the more carefully, I knew not whether the event of her re-appearance in human size was a thing which I should wish or dread.

After some time she did actually re-appear. One evening in a white robe she came gliding in; and, as it was just then growing dusky in my room, she seemed to me taller than when I had seen her last: and I remembered having heard that all beings of the mermaid and gnome species increased in stature very perceptibly at the fall of night. She flew as usual to my arms, but I could not with right gladness press her to my obstructed breast.

"My dearest," said she, "I now feel, by thy reception of me, what, alas! I already knew too well. Thou hast seen me in the interim; thou art acquainted with the state in which, at certain times, I find myself: thy happiness and mine is interrupted,—nay, it stands on the brink of being annihilated altogether. I must leave thee, and I know not whether I shall ever see thee again." Her presence, the grace with which she spoke, directly banished from my memory almost every trace of that vision, which, indeed, had already hovered before me as little more than a dream. I addressed her with kind vivacity, convinced her of my passion, assured her that I was innocent, that my discovery was accidental, —in short, I so managed it that she appeared composed, and endeavored to compose me.

"Try thyself strictly," said she, "whether this discovery has not hurt thy love; whether thou canst forget that I live in two forms beside thee; whether the diminution of my being will not also contract thy affection."

I looked at her; she was fairer than ever: and I thought within myself, Is it so great a misfortune, after all, to have a wife who from time to time becomes a dwarf, so that one can carry her about with him in a casket? Were it not much worse if she became a giantess, and put her husband in the box? My gayety of heart had returned. I would not for the whole world have let her go. "Best heart," said I, "let us be and continue ever as we have been. Could either of us wish to be better? Enjoy thy conveniency, and I promise thee to guard the box with so much the more faithfulness. Why should the prettiest sight I have ever seen in my life make a bad impression on me? How happy would lovers be, could they but procure such miniature pictures! And, after all, it was but a picture, a little sleight-of-hand deception. Thou art trying and teasing me, but thou shalt see how I will stand it."

"The matter is more serious than thou thinkest," said the fair one: "however, I am truly glad to see thee take it so lightly; for much good may still be awaiting us both. I will trust in thee, and for my own part do my utmost: only promise me that thou wilt never mention this discovery by way of reproach. Another prayer likewise I most earnestly make to thee: Be more than ever on thy guard against wine and anger."

I promised what she required; I could have gone on promising to all lengths: but she herself turned aside the conversation, and thenceforth all proceeded in its former routine. We had no inducement to alter our place of residence: the town was large, the society various; and the fine season gave rise to many an excursion and garden festival.

In all such amusements the presence of my wife was welcome, nay, eagerly desired, by women as well as men. A kind, insinuating manner, joined with a certain dignity of bearing, secured to her on all hands praise and estimation. Besides, she could play beautifully on the lute, accompanying it with her voice; and no social night could be perfect unless crowned by the graces of this talent.

I will be free to confess that I never cared much for music: on the contrary, it has always rather had a disagreeable effect on me. My fair one soon noticed this: and accordingly, when by ourselves, she never tried to entertain me by such means: in return, however, she appeared to indemnify herself while in society, where, indeed, she always found a crowd of admirers.

And now, why should I deny it? our late dialogue, in spite of my best intentions, had by no means sufficed to settle the matter within me: on the contrary, my temper of mind had by degrees got into the strangest tune, almost without my being conscious of it. One night, in a large company, this hidden grudge broke loose, and, by its consequences, produced to myself the greatest damage.

When I look back on it now, I, in fact, loved my beauty far less after that unlucky discovery: I was also growing jealous of her,—a whim that had never struck me before. This night at table, I found myself placed very much to my mind beside my two neighbors, a couple of ladies, who, for some time, had appeared to me very charming. Amid jesting and soft small talk, I was not sparing of my wine; while, on the other side, a pair of musical *dilettanti* had got hold of my wife, and at last contrived to lead the company into singing separately, and by way of chorus. This put me into ill-humor. The two amateurs appeared to me impertinent; the singing vexed me; and when, as my turn came, they even requested a solo-strophe from me, I grew truly indignant: I emptied my glass, and set it down again with no soft movement.

The grace of my two fair neighbors soon pacified me, but there is an evil nature in wrath when once it is set a-going. It went on fermenting within me, though all things were of a kind to induce joy and complaisance. On the contrary, I waxed more splenetic than ever when a lute was produced, and my fair one began fingering it and singing, to the admiration of all the rest. Unhappily a general silence was requested. So, then, I was not even to talk any more; and these tones were going through me like a toothache. Was it any wonder that, at last, the smallest spark should blow up the mine?

The songstress had just ended a song amid the loudest applauses, when she looked over to me; and this truly with the most loving face in the world. Unluckily, its lovingness could not penetrate so far. She perceived that I had just gulped down a cup of wine, and was pouring out a fresh one. With her right forefinger she beckoned to me in kind threatening. "Consider that it is wine!" said she, not louder than for myself to hear it. "Water is for mermaids!" cried I. "My ladies," said she to my neighbors, "crown the cup with all your gracefulness, that it be not too often emptied."—"You will not let yourself be tutored?" whispered one of them in my ear. "What ails the dwarf?" cried I, with a more violent gesture, in which I overset the glass. "Ah, what you have spilt!" cried the paragon of women; at the same time twanging her strings, as if to lead back the attention of the company from this disturbance to herself. Her attempt succeeded; the more completely as she rose to her feet, seemingly that she might play with greater convenience, and in this attitude continued preluding.

At sight of the red wine running over the tablecloth, I returned to myself. I perceived the great fault I had been guilty of, and it cut me through the very heart. Never till now had music had an effect on me: the first verse she sang was a friendly good-night

484

to the company, here as they were, as they might still feel themselves together. With the next verse they became as if scattered asunder: each felt himself solitary, separated, no one could fancy that he was present any longer. But what shall I say of the last verse? It was directed to me alone, the voice of injured love bidding farewell to moroseness and caprice.

In silence I conducted her home, foreboding no good. Scarcely, however, had we reached our chamber, when she began to show herself exceedingly kind and graceful,—nay, even roguish: she made me the happiest of all men.

Next morning, in high spirits and full of love, I said to her "Thou hast so often sung, when asked in company; as, for example, thy touching farewell song last night. Come now, for my sake, and sing me a dainty, gay welcome to this morning hour, that we may feel as if we were meeting for the first time."

"That I cannot do, my friend," said she seriously. "The song of last night referred to our parting, which must now forthwith take place; for I can only tell thee, the violation of thy promise and oath will have the worst consequences for us both: thou hast scoffed away a great felicity; and I, too, must renounce my dearest wishes."

As I now pressed and entreated her to explain herself more clearly, she answered, "That, alas! I can well do; for, at all events, my continuance with thee is over. Hear, then, what I would rather have concealed to the latest times. The form under which thou sawest me in the box is my natural and proper form; for I am of the race of King Eckwald, the dread sovereign of the dwarfs, concerning whom authentic history has recorded so much. Our people are still, as of old, laborious and busy, and therefore easy to govern. Thou must not fancy that the dwarfs are behindhand in their manufacturing skill. Swords which followed the foe, when you cast them after him; invisible and mysteriously binding chains; impenetrable shields, and such like ware, in old times,—formed their staple produce. But now they chiefly employ themselves with articles of convenience and ornament, in which truly they surpass all people of the earth. I may well say, it would astonish thee to walk through our workshops and warehouses. All this would be right and good, were it not that with the whole nation in general, but more particularly with the royal family, there is one peculiar circumstance connected."

She paused for a moment, and I again begged further light on

485

these wonderful secrets; which, accordingly, she forthwith proceeded to grant.

"It is well known," said she, "that God, so soon as he had created the world, and the ground was dry, and the mountains were standing bright and glorious, that God, I say, thereupon, in the very first place, created the dwarfs, to the end that there might be reasonable beings also, who, in their passages and chasms, might contemplate and adore his wonders in the inward parts of the earth. It is further well known, that this little race by degrees became uplifted in heart, and attempted to acquire the dominion of the earth; for which reason God then created the dragons, in order to drive back the dwarfs into their mountains. Now, as the dragons themselves were wont to nestle in the large caverns and clefts, and dwell there; and many of them, too, were in the habit of spitting fire, and working much other mischief,—the poor little dwarfs were by this means thrown into exceeding straits and distress: so that, not knowing what in the world to do, they humbly and fervently turned to God, and called to him in prayer, that he would vouchsafe to abolish this unclean dragon generation. But though it consisted not with his wisdom to destroy his own creatures, yet the heavy sufferings of the poor dwarfs so moved his compassion, that anon he created the giants, ordaining them to fight these dragons, and, if not root them out, at least lessen their numbers.

"Now, no sooner had the giants got moderately well through with the dragons, than their hearts also began to wax wanton: and, in their presumption, they practised much tyranny, especially on the good little dwarfs, who then once more in their need turned to the Lord; and he, by the power of his hand, created the knights, who were to make war on the giants and dragons, and to live in concord with the dwarfs. Hereby was the work of creation completed on this side; and it is plain, that henceforth giants and dragons, as well as knights and dwarfs, have always maintained themselves in being. From this, my friend, it will be clear to thee that we are of the oldest race on the earth,—a circumstance which does us honor, but at the same time brings great disadvantage along with it.

"For as there is nothing in the world than can endure forever, but all that has once been great must become little and fade, it is our lot, also, that, ever since the creation of the world, we have been waning, and growing smaller,—especially the royal

486

family, on whom, by reason of their pure blood, this destiny presses with the heaviest force. To remedy this evil, our wise teachers have many years ago devised the expedient of sending forth a princess of the royal house from time to time into the world, to wed some honorable knight, that so the dwarf progeny may be refected, and saved from entire decay."

Though my fair one related these things with an air of the utmost sincerity, I looked at her hesitatingly; for it seemed as if she meant to palm some fable on me. As to her own dainty lineage I had not the smallest doubt; but that she should have laid hold of me in place of a knight occasioned some mistrust, seeing I knew myself too well to suppose that my ancestors had come into the world by an immediate act of creation.

I concealed my wonder and scepticism, and asked her kindly, "But tell me, my dear child, how hast thou attained this large and stately shape? For I know few women that in richness of form can compare with thee."—"Thou shalt hear," replied she. "It is a settled maxim in the council of the dwarf kings, that this extraordinary step be forborne as long as it possibly can; which, indeed, I cannot but say is quite natural and proper. Perhaps they might have hesitated still longer had not my brother, born after me, come into the world so exceedingly small that the nurses actually lost him out of his swaddling-clothes; and no creature yet knows whither he is gone. On this occurrence, unexampled in the annals of dwarfdom, the sages were assembled; and, without more ado, the resolution was taken, and I sent out in quest of a husband."

"The resolution!" exclaimed I, "that is all extremely well. One can resolve, one can take his resolution; but, to give a dwarf this heavenly shape, how did your sages manage that?"

"It had been provided for already," said she, "by our ancestors. In the royal treasury lay a monstrous gold ring. I speak of it as it then appeared to me, when I saw it in my childhood; for it was this same ring which I have here on my finger. We now went to work as follows.

"I was informed of all that awaited me, and instructed what I had to do and to forbear. A splendid palace, after the pattern of my father's favorite summer residence, was then got ready,— a main edifice, wings, and whatever else you could think of. It stood at the entrance of a large rock-cleft, which it decorated in the handsomest style. On the appointed day our court moved thither, my parents, also, and myself. The army paraded; and four and twenty priests, not without difficulty, carried on a costly litter the mysterious ring. It was placed on the threshold of the building, just within the spot where you entered. Many ceremonies were observed; and, after a pathetic farewell, I proceeded to my task. I stepped forward to the ring, laid my finger on it, and that instant began perceptibly to wax in stature. In a few moments I had reached my present size, and then I put the ring on my finger. But now, in the twinkling of an eye, the doors, windows, gates, flapped to; the wings drew up into the body of the edifice; instead of a palace stood a little box beside me, which I forthwith lifted, and carried off with me, not without a pleasant feeling in being so tall and strong. Still, indeed, a dwarf to trees and mountains, to streams, and tracts of land, yet a giant to grass and herbs, and, above all, to ants, from whom we dwarfs, not being always on the best terms with them, often suffer considerable annoyance.

"How it fared with me on my pilgrimage, I might tell thee at great length. Suffice it to say I tried many, but no one save thou seemed worthy of being honored to renovate and perpetuate the line of the glorious Eckwald."

In the course of these narrations my head had now and then kept wagging, without myself having absolutely shaken it. I put several questions, to which I received no very satisfactory answers: on the contrary, I learned, to my great affliction, that after what had happened, she must needs return to her parents. She had hopes still, she said, of getting back to me: but, for the present, it was indispensably necessary to present herself at court; as otherwise, both for her and me, there was nothing but utter ruin. The purses would soon cease to pay, and who knew what all would be the consequences?

On hearing that our money would run short, I inquired no further into consequences; I shrugged my shoulders; I was silent, and she seemed to understand me.

We now packed up, and got into our carriage, the box standing opposite us; in which, however, I could still see no symptoms of a palace. In this way we proceeded several stages. Post-money and drink-money were readily and richly paid from the pouches to the right and left, till at last we reached a mountainous district; and no sooner had we alighted here than my fair one walked forward, directing me to follow her with the box. She led me by rather steep paths to a narrow plot of green ground, through which a clear brook now gushed in little falls, now ran in quiet windings. She pointed to a little knoll, bade me set the box down there, then said, "Farewell! Thou wilt easily find the way back; remember me; I hope to see thee again."

At this moment I felt as if I could not leave her. She was just now in one of her fine days, or, if you will, her fine hours. Alone with so fair a being, on the greensward, among grass and flowers, girt in by rocks, waters murmuring round you, what heart could have remained insensible! I came forward to seize her hand, to clasp her in my arms; but she motioned me back, threatening me, though still kindly enough, with great danger if I did not instantly withdraw.

"Is there not any possibility," exclaimed I, "of my staying with thee, of thy keeping me beside thee?" These words I uttered with such rueful tones and gestures, that she seemed touched by them, and after some thought confessed to me that a continuance of our union was not entirely impossible. Who happier than I! My importunity, which increased every moment, compelled her at last to come out with her scheme, and inform me, that if I, too, could resolve on becoming as little as I had once seen her, I might still remain with her, be admitted to her house, her kingdom, her family. The proposal was not altogether to my mind, yet at this moment I positively could not tear myself away: so, having already for a good while been accustomed to the marvellous, and being at all times prone to bold enterprises, I closed with her offer, and said she might do with me as she pleased.

I was thereupon directed to hold out the little finger of my right hand: she placed her own against it; then, with her left hand, she quite softly pulled the ring from her finger, and let it run along mine. That instant I felt a violent twinge on my finger: the ring shrunk together, and tortured me horribly. I gave a loud cry, and caught round me for my fair one; but she had disappeared. What state of mind I was in during this moment, I find no words to express: so I have nothing more to say but that I very soon, in my miniature size, found myself beside my fair one in a wood of grass-stalks. The joy of meeting after this short yet most strange separation, or, if you will, of this re-union without separation, exceeds all conception. I fell on her neck: she replied to my caresses, and the little pair was as happy as the large one.

With some difficulty we now mounted a hill: I say difficulty, because the sward had become for us an almost impenetrable forest. Yet at length we reached a bare space; and how surprised was I at perceiving there a large, bolted mass, which, erelong, I could not but recognize for the box, in the same state as when I had set it down.

"Go up to it, my friend," said she, "and do but knock with the ring: thou shalt see wonders." I went up accordingly; and no sooner had I rapped, than I did, in fact, witness the greatest wonder. Two wings came jutting out; and at the same time there fell, like scales and chips, various pieces this way and that: while doors, windows, colonnades, and all that belongs to a complete palace, at once came into view.

If ever you have seen one of Röntgen's desks,—how, at one pull, a multitude of springs and latches get in motion, and writing-board and writing materials, letter and money compartments, all at once, or in quick succession, start forward,—you will partly conceive how this palace unfolded itself, into which my sweet attendant now introduced me. In the large saloon I directly recognized the fireplace which I had formerly seen from above, and the chair in which she had then been sitting. And, on looking up, I actually fancied I could still see something of the chink in the dome, through which I had peeped in. I spare you the description of the rest: in a word, all was spacious, splendid, and tasteful. Scarcely had I recovered from my astonishment, when I heard afar off a sound of military music. My better half sprang up, and with rapture announced to me the approach of his Majesty her father. We stepped out to the threshold, and here beheld a magnificent procession moving towards us from a considerable cleft in the rock. Soldiers, servants, officers of state, and glittering courtiers, followed in order. At last you observed a golden throng, and in the midst of it the king himself. So soon as the whole procession had drawn up before the palace, the king, with his nearest retinue, stepping forward. His loving daughter hastened out to him, pulling me along with her. We threw ourselves at his feet: he raised me very graciously; and, on coming to stand before him, I perceived, that in this little world I was still the most considerable figure. We proceeded together to the palace, where his Majesty, in presence of his whole court, was pleased to welcome me with a well-studied oration, in which he expressed his surprise at finding us here, acknowledged me as his son-in-law, and appointed the nuptial ceremony to take place on the morrow.

A cold sweat went over me as I heard him speak of marriage; for I dreaded this even more than music, which had, of old, appeared to me the most hateful thing on earth. Your music-makers, I used to say, enjoy at least the conceit of being in unison with each other, and working in concord; for when they have tweaked and tuned long enough, grating our ears with all manner of screeches, they believe in their hearts that the matter is now adjusted, and one instrument accurately suited to the other. The band-master himself is in this happy delusion; and so they set forth joyfully, though still tearing our nerves to pieces. In the marriage state, even this is not the case; for although it is but a duet, and you might think two voices, or even two instruments, might in some degree be attuned to each other, yet this happens very seldom: for while the man gives out one tone, the wife directly takes a higher one, and the man again a higher; and so it rises from the chamber to the choral pitch, and farther and farther, till at last not even wind-instruments can reach it. And now, as I loathe harmonical music, it cannot be surprising that disharmonical should be a thing which I cannot endure.

Of all the festivities in which the day was spent, I shall and can not give an account; for I paid small heed to them. The sumptuous victuals, the generous wine, the royal amusements, I could not relish. I kept thinking and considering what I was to do. Here, however, there was but little to be considered. I determined, once for all, to take myself away, and hide somewhere. Accordingly, I succeeded in reaching the chink of a stone, where I intrenched and concealed myself as well as might be. My first care after this was to get the unhappy ring off my finger,—an enterprise, however, which would by no means prosper; for, on the contrary, I felt that every pull I gave, the metal grew straiter, and cramped me with violent pains, which again abated so soon as I desisted from my purpose.

Early in the morning I awoke (for my little person had slept, and very soundly), and was just stepping out to look farther about me, when I felt a kind of rain coming on. Through the grass, flowers, and leaves, there fell, as it were, something like sand and grit in large quantities; but what was my horror when the whole of it became alive, and an innumerable host of ants rushed down on me! No sooner did they observe me than they made an attack on all sides; and, though I defended myself stoutly and gallantly enough, they at last so hemmed me in, so nipped and pinched me, that I was glad to hear them calling to surrender. I surrendered instantly and wholly, whereupon an ant of respectable stature approached me with courtesy, nay, with reverence, and even recommended itself to my good graces. I learned that the ants had now become allies of my father-in-law, and by him been called out in the present emergency, and commissioned to fetch me back. Here, then, was little I in the hands of creatures still less. I had nothing for it but looking forward to the marriage; nay, I must now thank Heaven if my father-in-law were not wroth, if my fair one had not taken the sullens.

Let me skip over the whole train of ceremonies: in a word, we were wedded. Gayly and joyously as matters went, there were, nevertheless, solitary hours in which you were led astray into reflection; and now there happened to me something which had never happened before,—what, and how, you shall learn.

Every thing about me was completely adapted to my present form and wants: the bottles and glasses were in a fit ratio to a little toper,—nay, if you will, better measure in proportion than with us. In my tiny palate the dainty tidbits tasted excellently; a kiss from the little mouth of my spouse was still the most charming thing in nature; and I will not deny that novelty made all these circumstances highly agreeable. Unhappily, however, I had not forgotten my former situation. I felt within me a scale of by-gone greatness, and it rendered me restless and cheerless. Now, for the first time, did I understand what the philosophers might mean by their ideal, which they say so plagues the mind of man. I had an ideal of myself, and often in dreams I appeared as a giant. In short, my wife, my ring, my dwarf figure, and so many other bonds and restrictions, made me utterly unhappy; so that I began to think seriously about obtaining my deliverance.

Being persuaded that the whole magic lay in the ring, I resolved on filing this asunder. From the court-jeweller, accordingly, I borrowed some files. By good luck I was left-handed; as, indeed, throughout my whole life I had never done aught in the right-handed way. I stood tightly to the work: it was not small; for the golden hoop, so thin as it appeared, had grown proportionately thicker in contracting from its former length. All vacant hours I privately applied to this task; and at last, the metal being nearly through, I was provident enough to step out of doors. This was a wise measure; for all at once the golden hoop started sharply from my finger, and my frame shot aloft with such violence that I actually fancied I should dash against the sky: and, at all events, I must have bolted through the dome of our palace,—nay, perhaps, in my new awkwardness, have destroyed this summer residence altogether.

Here, then, was I standing again,—in truth, so much the larger, but also, as it seemed to me, so much the more stupid and helpless. On recovering from my stupefaction, I observed the royal strong-box lying near me, which I found to be moderately heavy, as I lifted it, and carried it down the footpath to the next stage, where I directly ordered horses and set forth. By the road I soon made trial of the two side-pouches. Instead of money, which appeared to be run out, I found a little key: it belonged to the strong-box, in which I got some moderate compensation. So long as this held out, I made use of the carriage: by and by I sold it, and proceeded by the diligence. The strong-box, too, I at length cast from me; having no hope of its ever filling again. And thus in the end, though after a considerable circuit, I again returned to the kitchen-hearth, to the landlady and the cook, where you were first introduced to me.

From Elective Affinities

THE TWO STRANGE CHILDREN

TWO children of neighboring families, a boy and a girl, of an age which would suit well for them at some future time to marry, were brought up together with this agreeable prospect, and the parents on both sides, who were people of some position in the world, looked forward with pleasure to their future union.

It was too soon observed, however, that the purpose seemed likely to fail; the dispositions of both children promised everything which was good, but there was an unaccountable antipathy between them. Perhaps they were too much like each other. Both were thoughtful, clear in their wills, and firm in their purposes. Each separately was beloved and respected by his or her companions, but whenever they were together they were always antagonists. Forming separate plans for themselves, they only met mutually to cross and thwart one another; never emulating each other in pursuit of one aim, but always fighting for a single object. Good natured and amiable everywhere else, they were spiteful and even malicious whenever they came in contact.

This singular relation first showed itself in their childish games, and it continued with their advancing years. The boys used to play at soldiers, divide into parties, and give each other battle, and the fierce haughty young lady set herself at once at the head of one of the armies, and fought against the other with such animosity and bitterness that the latter would have been put to a shameful flight, except for the desperate bravery of her own particular rival, who at last disarmed his antagonist and took her prisoner; and even then she defended herself with so much fury that to save his eyes from being torn out, and at the same time

Translated by D. W. Niles

not to injure his enemy, he had been obliged to take off his silk handkerchief and tie her hands with it behind her back.

This she never forgave him: she made so many attempts, she laid so many plans to injure him, that the parents, who had been long watching these singular passions, came to an understanding together and resolved to separate these two hostile creatures, and sacrifice their favorite hopes.

The boy shot rapidly forward in the new situation in which he was placed. He mastered every subject which he was taught. His friends and his own inclination chose the army for his profession, and everywhere, let him be where he would, he was looked up to and beloved. His disposition seemed formed to labor for the well-being and the pleasure of others; and he himself, without being clearly conscious of it, was in himself happy at having got rid of the only antagonist which nature had assigned to him.

The girl, on the other hand, became at once an altered creature. Her growing age, the progress of her education, above all, her own inward feelings, drew her away from the boisterous games with boys in which she had hitherto delighted. Altogether she seemed to want something; there was nothing anywhere about her which could deserve to excite her hatred, and she had never found any one whom she could think worthy of her love.

A young man, somewhat older than her previous neighbor-antagonist, of rank, property, and consequence, beloved in society, and much sought after by women, bestowed his affections upon her. It was the first time that friend, lover, or servant had displayed any interest in her. The preference which he showed for her above others who were older, more cultivated, and of more brilliant pretensions than herself, was naturally gratifying; the constancy of his attention, which was never obtrusive, his standing by her faithfully through a number of unpleasant incidents, his quiet suit, which was declared indeed to her parents, but which as she was still very young he did not press, only asking to be allowed to hope; all this engaged him to her, and custom and the assumption in the world that the thing was already settled, carried her along with it. She had so often been called his bride that at last she began to consider herself so, and neither she nor any one else ever thought any further trial could be necessary before she exchanged rings with the person who for so long a time had passed for her bridegroom.

The peaceful course which the affair had all along followed was not at all precipitated by the betrothal. Things were allowed to go on both sides just as they were; they were happy in being together, and they could enjoy to the end the fair season of the year as the spring of their future more serious life.

The absent youth had meanwhile grown up into everything which was most admirable. He had obtained a well-deserved rank in his profession, and came home on leave to visit his family. Towards his fair neighbor he found himself again in a natural but singular position. For some time past she had been nourishing in herself such affectionate family feelings as suited her position as a bride; she was in harmony with everything about her; she believed that she was happy, and in a certain sense she was so. Now first for a long time something again stood in her way. It was not to be hated—she had become incapable of hatred. Indeed the childish hatred, which had in fact been nothing more than an obscure recognition of inward worth, expressed itself now in a happy astonishment, in pleasure at meeting, in ready acknowledgments, in a half willing, half unwilling, and yet irresistible attraction; and all this was mutual. Their long separation gave occasion for longer conversations; even their old childish foolishness served, now that they had grown wiser, to amuse them as they looked back; and they felt as if at least they were bound to make good their petulant hatred by friendliness and attention to each other—as if their first violent injustice to each other ought not to be left without open acknowledgment.

On his side it all remained in a sensible, desirable moderation. His position, his circumstances, his efforts, his ambition, found him so abundant an occupation, that the friendliness of this pretty bride he received as a very thankworthy present; but without, therefore, even so much as thinking of her in connection with himself, or entertaining the slightest jealousy of the bridegroom, with whom he stood on the best possible terms.

With her, however, it was altogether different. She seemed to herself as if she had awakened out of a dream. Her fightings with her young neighbor had been the beginnings of an affection; and this violent antagonism was no more than an equally violent innate passion for him, first showing under the form of opposition. She could remember nothing else than that she had always loved him. She laughed over her martial encounter with him with weapons in her hand; she dwelt upon the delight of her feelings when he disarmed her. She imagined that it had given her the greatest happiness when he bound her; and whatever she had done afterwards to injure him, or to vex him, presented itself to her as only an innocent means of attracting his attention. She cursed their separation. She bewailed the sleepy state into which she had fallen. She execrated the insidious lazy routine which had betrayed her into accepting so insignificant a bridegroom. She was transformed—doubly transformed, forwards or backwards, which ever way we like to take it.

She kept her feelings entirely to herself; but if any one could have divined them and shared them with her, he could not have blamed her; for indeed the bridegroom could not sustain a comparison with the other as soon as they were seen together. If a sort of regard to the one could not be refused, the other excited the fullest trust and confidence. If one made an agreeable acquaintance, the other we should desire for a companion; and in extraordinary cases, where higher demands might have to be made on them, the bridegroom was a person to be utterly despaired of, while the other would give the feeling of perfect security.

There is a peculiar innate tact in women which discovers to them differences of this kind; and they have cause as well as occasion to cultivate it.

The more the fair bride was nourishing all these feelings in secret, the less opportunity there was for any one to speak a word which could tell in favor of her bridegroom, to remind her of what her duty and their relative position advised and commanded—indeed, what an unalterable necessity seemed now irrevocably to require; the poor heart gave itself up entirely to its passion.

On one side she was bound inextricably to the bridegroom by the world, by her family, and by her own promise; on the other, the ambitious young man made no secret of what he was thinking and planning for himself, conducting himself, towards her no more than a kind but not at all a tender brother, and speaking of his departure as immediately impending; and now it seemed as if her early childish spirit woke up again in her with all its spleen and violence, and was preparing itself in its distemper, on this higher stage of life, to work more effectively and destructively. She determined that she would die to punish the once hated, and now so passionately loved, youth for his want of interest in her; and as she could not possess himself, at least she would wed herself for ever to his imagination and to his repentance. Her dead image should cling to him, and he should never be free from it. He should never cease to reproach himself for not having understood, not examined, not valued her feelings toward him.

This singular insanity accompanied her wherever she went. She kept it concealed under all sorts of forms; and although people thought her very odd, no one was observant enough or clever enough to discover the real inward reason.

In the mean time, friends, relations, acquaintances had exhausted themselves in contrivances for pleasure parties. Scarcely a day had passed, but something new and unexpected was set on foot. There was hardly a pretty spot in the country round which had not been decked out and prepared for the reception of some merry party. And now our young visitor before departing wished to do his part as well, and invited the young couple, with a small family circle, to an expedition on the water. They went on board a large beautiful vessel dressed out in all its colors,—one of the yachts which had a small saloon and a cabin or two besides, and are intended to carry with them upon the water the comfort and conveniences of land.

They set out upon the broad river with music playing. The party had collected in the cabin, below deck, during the heat of the day, and were amusing themselves with games. Their young host, who could never remain without doing something, had taken charge of the helm, to relieve the old master of the vessel, and the latter had lain down and was fast asleep. It was a moment when the steerer required all his circumspectness, as the vessel was nearing a spot where two islands narrowed the channel of the river, while shallow banks of shingle stretching off, first on one side and then on the other, made the navigation difficult and dangerous. Prudent and sharp-sighted as he was, he thought for a moment that it would be better to wake the master; but he felt confident in himself, and he thought he would venture and make straight for the narrows. At this moment his fair enemy appeared upon deck with a wreath of flowers in her hair. "Take this to remember me by," she cried out. She took it off and threw it to the steerer. "Don't disturb me," he answered quickly, as he caught the wreath; "I require all my powers and all my attention now." "You will never be disturbed by me any more," she cried;

498

"you will never see me again." As she spoke, she rushed to the forward part of the vessel, and from thence she sprang into the water. Voice upon voice called out, "Save her, save her, she is sinking!" He was in the most terrible difficulty. In the confusion the old ship-master woke, and tried to catch the rudder, which the young man bid him take. But there was no time to change hands. The vessel stranded; and at the same moment, flinging off the heaviest of his upper graments, he sprang into the water and swam towards his beautiful enemy. The water is a friendly element to a man who is at home in it, and who knows how to deal with it; it buoyed him up, and acknowledged the strong swimmer as its master. He soon overtook the beautiful girl, who had been swept away before him; he caught hold of her, raised her and supported her, and both of them were carried violently down by the current, till the shoals and islands were left far behind, and the river was again open and running smoothly. He now began to collect himself; they had passed the first immediate danger, in which he had been obliged to act mechanically without time to think; he raised his head as high as he could to look about him; and then swam with all his might to a low bushy point, which ran out conveniently into the stream. There he brought his fair burden to dry land, but he could find no signs of life in her; he was in despair, when he caught sight of a trodden path leading among the bushes. Again he caught her up in his arms, hurried forward, and presently reached a solitary cottage. There he found kind, good people—a young married couple; the misfortunes and the dangers explained themselves instantly; every remedy he could think of was instantly applied; a bright fire blazed up: woollen blankets were spread on a bed, counterpane, cloaks, skins, whatever there was at hand which would serve for warmth, were heaped over her as fast as possible. The desire to save life overpowered, for the present, every other consideration. Nothing was left undone to bring back to life the beautiful half-torpid, naked body. It succeeded; she opened her eyes! her friend was before her; she threw her heavenly arms about his neck. In this position she remained for a time; and then a stream of tears burst out and completed her recovery. "Will you forsake me," she cried, "now when I find you again thus?" "Never," he answered, "never," hardly knowing what he said or did. "Only consider yourself," she added; "take care of yourself, for your sake and for mine."

She now began to collect herself, and for the first time recollected the state in which she was; she could not be ashamed before her darling, before her preserver; but she gladly allowed him to go, that he might take care of himself; for the clothes which he still wore were wet and dripping.

Their young hosts considered what could be done. The husband offered the young man, and the wife offered the fair lady, the dresses in which they had been married, which were hanging up in full perfection, and sufficient for a complete suit, inside and out, for two people. In a short time our pair of adventurers were not only equipped, but in full costume. They looked most charming, gazed at one another, when they met, with admiration, and then with infinite affection, half laughing at the same time at the quaintness of their appearance, they fell into each other's arms.

The power of youth and the quickening spirit of love in a few moments completely restored them; and there was nothing wanted but music to have set them both off dancing.

To have found themselves brought from the water on dry land, from death into life, from the circle of their families into a wilderness, from despair into rapture, from indifference to affection and to love, all in a moment: the head was not strong enough to bear it; it must either burst, or go distracted; or if so distressing an alternative were to be escaped, the heart must put out all its efforts.

Lost wholly in each other, it was long before they recollected the alarm and anxiety of those who had been left behind; and they themselves, indeed, could not well think, without alarm and anxiety, how they were again to encounter them. "Shall we run away? shall we hide ourselves?" said the young man. "We will remain together," she said, as she clung about his neck.

The peasant having heard them say that a party was aground on the shoal, had hurried down, without stopping to ask another question, to the shore. When he arrived there, he saw the vessel coming safely down the stream. After much labor it had been got off; and they were now going on in uncertainty, hoping to find their lost ones again somewhere. The peasant shouted and made signs to them, and at last caught the attention of those on board; then he ran to a spot where there was a convenient place for landing, and went on signalling and shouting till the vessel's head was turned toward the shore; and what a scene there was for them when they landed. The parents of the two betrothed

first pressed on the banks; the poor loving bridegroom had almost
lost his senses. They had scarcely learnt that their dear children
had been saved, when in their strange disguise the latter came
forward out of the bushes to meet them. No one recognized
them till they were come quite close. "Who do I see?" cried the
mothers. "What do I see?" cried the fathers. The preserved ones
flung themselves on the ground before them. "Your children,"
they called out; "a pair." "Forgive us!" cried the maiden. "Give
us your blessing!" cried the young man. "Give us your blessing!"
they cried both, as all the world stood still in wonder. Your
blessing! was repeated the third time; and who would have been
able to refuse it?

TRAVEL SKETCHES

From Travels in Italy

PHILIP NERI, THE HUMOROUS SAINT

PHILIP NERI, born in Florence 1515, presents himself to us from childhood as a docile well-behaved boy of powerful natural endowments. There is, happily, a likeness of him as such preserved in Fidanza's *Teste Scelte*, tom. v. plate 31. A trimmer, sounder, more open, and more upright-minded little fellow is not to be conceived. As scion of a noble family, he is instructed in all that is good and worth knowing according to the sense of the time, and is at last sent to Rome to complete his studies, at what age is not said. Here he develops himself to the full measure and stature of a youth; is distinguished by his handsome countenance, his profusion of locks. He is at once attractive and reserved; grace and dignity blend in his every feature, in his every movement.

Here, in the saddest of times, after the atrocious plunder of the city, following the example of many noble men, he gives himself entirely over to exercises of piety, and with the increasing force of his fresh youth his enthusiasm also increases. We hear of his unintermitting attendance at church, especially at the seven head churches, of his fervent prayers importuning succour, of his assiduous confession and participation in the Lord's Supper, of his wrestling in agony of soul after spiritual conquests. In one such enthusiastic moment he throws himself on the steps of the altar and breaks two ribs, an accident which—the ribs being badly healed—entails on him live-long palpitation of the heart, and occasions an intensification of his feelings.

Young men gather around him to engage actively in works of piety and morals, displaying indefatigable zeal in caring for the poor and in nursing the sick, labours which apparently take the precedence of their studies. In all probability they turn the re-

Translated by Rev. A. J. W. Morrison and Charles Nisbet

mittances they get from home to purposes of charity; they are ever ready to give, to help others, retaining nothing for themselves. Neri himself later on expressly refuses all aid from his adherents, in order that they may apply to the benefit of the needy whatever beneficence may offer to their hands, to the degree even of pinching themselves.

Such pious actions testified, however, to too fervent a heart for the actors not to seek mutual edification of soul and sentiment on the most important subjects. The little company had yet no meeting place of their own, but sought the privilege of congregating now in this cloister, now in that, where rooms suitable to such purposes were readily to be had. After short silent prayer, some text of the Holy Scriptures was read over when one and another would hold a brief discourse in the way of exposition or application. They would then deliberate together on the subject, a deliberation having reference entirely to immediate practice; everything of the nature of dialectics and hair-splitting being wholly forbidden. The rest of the day was continually devoted to the careful watching over the sick, to service in hospitals, to the assistance of the poor and needy.

The relations prevailing in such a religious body being altogether free and no express restrictions whatever imposed, every man being at liberty to go or come, the number of adherents to the body exceedingly increased, while the meetings above described grew both in earnestness and magnitude. Chapters from the lives of the Saints were now also read, and passages from the fathers of the church and from church history consulted, after which four of the assembly had the right and duty to deliver their thoughts, each for half an hour.

Such pious, daily, familiar, practical treatment of the highest affairs of the soul excited ever more attention not only among persons individually, but even among whole bodies. The meetings were transferred to sidewalks and unoccupied spaces of this and that church, the attendance increased; the order of the Dominicans showed itself specially disposed to this mode of edification, and attached itself in large numbers to the flock, which was becoming an ever more potent entity, and which, through the energy and exalted mind of its leader, always steadfastly held its own, and though tried by much opposition continued to advance in its proper course.

Seeing, however, that, in accordance with the high sense of

the excellent head of this movement, all speculation was banned and all the activity of the members was regulated and directed immediately to life, and seeing, moreover, that life necessarily implies some measure of satisfaction or even exuberance in the form of gladness, mirth, jollity, the leader of the new band was quite equal to the occasion and knew how to gratify the innocent wants and wishes of his adherents in this direction. On the entrance of Spring, he led them to San Onofrio which, standing high and broad, offered the pleasantest situation at such a season. Here, while everything around them heaved with young and lusty life, after silent prayers, a young boy stepped forth and recited a sermon he had learnt by heart. Prayers followed, and now, by way of conclusion, a choir of singers invited for the purpose sent forth their joyous and impressive strains, an entertainment which was all the more charming that in that age music was little diffused and little cultivated, and that here, perhaps, for the first time religious singing was heard in the open air.

Steadily developing in this manner, the congregation grew in numbers and significance. The Florentines constrained their townsmen to take possession of the cloister San Girolamo, which was dependent on them, where the new body throve and prospered under the influence of the same earnest spirit, till at last the Pope presented them as their peculiar property with a cloister near the Piazza Navona, which being built up anew from its foundation was able to accommodate a large number of pious fellow-worshippers. There was, however, no change made in the former constitution, but the main feature in the movement still continued to be the endeavour to bring the Word of God, that is, holy noble sentiments, into intimate fellowship with the common sense of men, with their common daily life. People assembled afterwards as before, prayed, read a text, uttered their thoughts about it, prayed and were at last regaled by music. What at that time happened frequently, nay, every day, now happens on Sundays, and the traveller who has made the familiar acquaintance of the pious founder will, when opportunity offers, attend the innocent services of the place and will assuredly be in no little degree edified, should he on such occasion allow all that we have above communicated, and shall next communicate in connection with the foundation of the cloister, to hold sway in his heart and mind.

We have now to call to remembrance how this whole institute was ever yet in vital contact with the world. Few of their number had devoted themselves to the special office of the priesthood, and there were only so many consecrated clergymen among them as were required to hear confession and perform the sacrifice of the mass. Philip Neri himself had thus reached his 36th year without seeking consecration. In his unpriestly state he appears to have felt himself freer and much more independent than he would have been had he, fettering himself with Church bands, become a highly honoured yet restricted member of the great hierarchy.

The higher authorities downwards were, however, not satisfied with this state of things. His father confessor made it a point of conscience for him to accept ordination and enter the priesthood. And so, indeed, was it at last brought about. By good policy, the Church now included within its jurisdiction a man who, hitherto of independent mind, had sought to unite the sacred with the profane, the aspirations of virtue with the common every-day concerns of life. This change, however, the transition, namely, to the priesthood, seems not to have in the least affected his external behaviour.

He only practices more strictly than ever every kind of self-renunciation and, in wretched outward circumstances, lives with others in a wretched little cloister. He gives, for example, during a season of great scarcity, the bread allowed him to another more needy than he, and continues to serve the unfortunate.

On his inward disposition, however, the priesthood exercises a remarkable, intensifying influence. The duty laid on him to perform mass transports him into an enthusiasm, an ecstasy in which the natural man, hitherto so prominent, is wholly lost. He hardly knows whither he advances, he staggers on the way to and before the altar. On elevating the Host on high he cannot bring his arms down again; it appears as though an invisible power drew him up. He trembles and shudders on pouring the wine into the cup, and when, after the transubstantiation of this element, he is to partake, he revels in a religious intoxication wonderful and unspeakable. For very passion he bites the cup, while he thinks how mysteriously he is sipping the blood of the body he had shortly before greedily devoured. This transport over, we still find him a man, ecstatic and wonderful no doubt, yet always in the highest degree sensible and practical.

Such a youth, such a man, of so lively temperament and exercising his powers in such an extraordinary manner, could not but appear a strange problem to men, and by reason of his very virtues become occasionally an object of offence and hostility. Probably he had been made frequently to experience this in the course of his former life, but, after his priestly consecration, when hemmed and straitened as a species of guest in a poor cloister, he still seeks verge and scope for himself, adversaries start up openly, pursuing him unrelentingly with mockery and derision.

We, however, go a step further and say that he was a highly eminent man, who yet endeavoured to subdue the lordly disposition native to one of his stamp, and to veil the splendour of his ascendancy in self-denial, outward deprivations, works of beneficence, humility and apparent shame. To appear like a fool to the world that he might the more exclusively dedicate himself to God and divine things was his life-long principle by which alone he sought to train himself and his disciples.

The maxim of St. Bernhard,

> *Spernere mundum,*
> *Spernere neminem,*
> *Spernere se ipsum,*
> *Spernere se sperni,**

appears to have wholly penetrated him, or rather to have redeveloped itself afresh in him.

Similarity of aim and of situation necessitates similarity of principles. Indisputably, men of the loftiest self-respect alone can adopt such principles of practical conduct. They alone it is, who, perceiving beforehand how this world can never but hate and oppose anything of the nature of good and great, make up their minds at the outset for the very worst, and eagerly drink to the dregs every possible cup of bitterness before it is offered to their hands. The accounts which come down to us regarding the unlimited and unintermitting trials to which he subjected his disciples exasperate the patience of every man disposed to the enjoyment of life, just as they must have overwhelmed everyone on whom they were imposed with anguish if not utter despair. Not every one, therefore, who aspired to the position of discipleship was able to stand the fiery trial.

---

* (Contemn the world, contemn no man, contemn yourself, contemn contempt.)

Johann Wolfgang von Goethe

Before, however, entering on such wonderful accounts, which the reader might not find altogether to his mind, we will rather turn once more to those great qualities in him, admitted and highly praised by his contemporaries. Knowledge and culture he derived, they say, immediately from nature rather than from any stated course of instruction and education: all that other people acquire by patient toil came to him as by inspiration. He further possessed the great gift of discerning spirits, of rightly estimating the qualities and capacities of other men. With the most remarkable penetration his mind also pierced into the events of the world, divining the sequences of things, so that people could not help ascribing to him the spirit of prophecy. He was, moreover, endowed with a mighty power of attraction (*attrattiva*, as the Italians beautifully express it), a power which fascinated not men alone but also animals. The dog of a friend, for example, who came to see him, at once attached itself to Neri, refusing to own its first master or be enticed home with him, though all kinds of allurements were tried, but, held fast by the spell of the eminent man, it would not be separated from him, and after many years ended its life in the bedroom of the master of his choice. This gives us occasion to come back to those tests imposed on Neri's disciples and to which this creature itself contributed. It is a well-known fact that to lead or carry a dog was in the middle ages generally and probably also in Rome regarded as the lowest degradation. The pious man was, therefore, in the habit of leading his dog about through the town by a chain. His disciples also had to carry it through the streets in their arms, subjecting themselves to the ridicule and derision of the crowd.

He further laid on his disciples and fellow-worshippers other outward indignities. A young Roman prince, for example, who solicited the honour of becoming a member of the order, was directed to go the round of the streets of Rome with a fox's tail fastened behind him, and his refusal to do this lost him admission into the society. Another he sent through the town without a coat, and a third with the sleeves torn in pieces. A nobleman, compassionating the latter, offered him a pair of new sleeves which he refused; whereupon by command of his master he had to go and accept them thankfully, and wear them. On the building of the new church Neri compelled his disciples to act as day-labourers and supply the materials to the workmen's hands.

In like manner he knew how to thwart and spoil every grain

510

of spiritual complacency a man might feel in himself. If a young man, for example, were getting on well in his sermon, and seemed to find some satisfaction in his own oratory, Neri would interrupt him in the middle of a word, and send up in his place to continue the discourse some less-qualified scholar who, however, from the unexpected stimulus, would deliver himself extemporaneously in a more successful manner than he had ever done before.

Let one transplant himself into the second half of the sixteenth century, and the desolate fermenting state in which Rome appeared under different Popes, and it will be readily comprehended how mighty and effective such a course of doctrine and discipline must have been, imparting as it did to the inward will of man, by means of affection and fear, self-surrender and obedience, the great power of sustaining itself against all outward calamities, of asserting itself against all contingencies, enabling even the man of sober reason and understanding to renounce absolutely all the habitudes and conveniences to which he had been accustomed.

On account of the special grace investing it, the reader will not grudge our repeating here the account which has been already referred to of one remarkable test to which Neri subjected a lady. The Holy Father was informed of a wonder-working nun residing in a cloister in the country. Our friend receives the commission to make a thorough examination into an affair of so much moment for the Church. To execute the commission Neri mounts a mule, but returns much sooner than the Holy Father had expected. He meets his astonished Spiritual Chief with the following words: "Holiest Father, she does no wonders, for the first Christian virtue is wanting to her, humility. From the foul roads and weather, I arrive at the cloister in a bad plight, have her called before me in your name; she appears; and instead of greeting her I reach her my bespattered boot to pull off. She shrinks back aghast, and scornfully replies to the service I was imposing on her, 'What did I take her for? She was the servant of the Lord, but not of everyone who came there to treat her like a menial.' I quietly get up, remount my beast, stand now before you, and am convinced you will need no further proof." The Pope smiling acquiesced, and probably the nun was forbidden doing any more wonders.

If, however, he allowed himself to subject others to such proofs, he himself had to submit to similar trials at the hands of others of kindred mind who had elected the same course of self-denial.

A mendicant monk, who was already in the opinions of men invested with an odour of sanctity, meets him in the most frequented street and offers him a drink from the wine-bottle he providently carries about with him. Without a moment's hesitation, Neri, bending back his head, sets the flask frankly to his mouth, while the people round burst into jeers and laughter at seeing two pious men quaffing to each other in such a style. Philip Neri, who, in spite of his piety and resignation, might not altogether have relished the brimmer given him in such a way, thereupon said: "You have put me to the trial, it is now my turn," and with that he pressed his four-cornered cap on the bald head of his friend, who, now likewise made a laughing-stock of, went his way in all composure, saying: "If any one takes it from my head you are welcome to it." Neri took it from him, and they parted.

No doubt to venture on such things and yet accomplish the greatest moral results required a man like Philip Neri, whose actions were very often to be regarded as wonders. As confessor he made himself dreaded, and therefore worthy of the greatest confidence; he disclosed to his confessing children sins they concealed and faults which had escaped their notice. His fervent ecstatic prayer, as something supernatural, set the people around him in astonishment, in a state in which men think they perceive by their senses that which is but the illusion of an excited imagination, till at last miracle, nay impossibility, related and re-related, is accepted in all good faith as an actual sensible reality. This will explain the report how several times during the sacrifice of mass he was seen lifted up before the altar, and how, while on his knees praying for the recovery of one dangerously ill, he was observed rising aloft till his head nearly touched the ceiling.

In a state in which feeling and imagination so entirely predominate, it is not to be wondered at if fiendish demons should also come into play. Among the crumbling walls of the Antonine baths the pious man once spies a monster hopping about in apish deformity, but which at his command immediately vanishes between the ruins and fissures. More important, however, is the way in which Neri deals with his disciples when they rapturously repeat to him the gracious manifestations deigned them by the mother of God and other saints. Well knowing that these imaginations are generally the result of spiritual self-conceit, the worst and most obdurate of mental evils, he assures them that behind the heavenly radiance and beauty lay concealed a devilish hateful deformity. On the return of the lovely Virgin they are, therefore, by his command to spit right into her face, and on their doing so the devil's face is at once revealed.

The great man may have been led to the adoption of such tactics from calculation, or, what is more probable, from deep instinct, assured that the image which was the creation of fantastic love and longing would through the antidote of hate and contempt immediately transform itself into a grimace.

No doubt, too, he was guided in the election of such a strange discipline by his extraordinary gifts which ever consciously conjoined the physical and the spiritual, which ever divined their inevitable inter-relation (so that seeing the physical he knew the thought which alone determined it, and having a thought knew the external embodiment which was alone possible to it): I refer to his fore-feeling of a person approaching though yet unseen, his presentiment of distant events, his consciousness of the thoughts of a person standing before him, the irresistible transfusion of his own thoughts into the minds of others.

Such and similar gifts are distributed among men; many a one can boast of having been able to exercise them on one and another occasion. The ever-living presence, however, of such powers, the ability to exercise at all times such astounding influence is for ever impossible in an age in which men are only so many fractions and their mechanical achievements only show big in the gross. Such qualifications as these of Neri perhaps necessarily imply a century in which the mental and bodily powers are undivided, in immediate conjunction and in their greatest energy.

Let us, however, consider such a nature longing intensely after independent, unrestricted spiritual activity, and how it must feel itself cramped by the strict encompassing bands of the Roman Church.

The achievements of the Holy Xavier among the idolatrous heathen may well at that time have caused great sensation in Rome. Excited by the news, Neri and some of his friends likewise felt themselves attracted to the so-called Indies and desired the papal permission to repair thither. The confessor, however, having probably received good instructions from upper quarters, dissuaded them from such an enterprise, representing that godly men, intent on the reformation of their fellows and on the spread of religion, would find an adequate India in Rome, and a wide enough field there for their activity. They were also informed of some great calamity impending the great city, the three wells before the gate of St. Sebastian having for some time run thick and bloody, an infallible sign of misfortune. Whether therefore appeased by this means or no, the worthy Neri and his company resolved on confining their beneficent wonder-working endeavours within the town of Rome, it is at all events certain that in this sphere they continued from year to year to grow in the confidence and respect of the great and the humble, the old and the young.

Let one now think of the strange complication of human nature in which are united the most opposing contrasts; material and spiritual, common and uncommon, repulsive and charming, sectarian and universal, and so on to the end of the long list: let one think of such a conflict enacting itself in an eminent man, and how his understanding becomes confused through the incomprehensible which forces itself on him, how his imagination frees herself from all trammels, how his faith adds wings to her aspirations, and how his superstition is kept in countenance, till at length the natural state comes into immediate contact, nay, into union with the unnatural—with these considerations let one pass to the diffuse life which has been handed down to us of this man, and it will be readily comprehended what an influence he must have come to wield in the course of almost a century of uninterrupted, unrelaxing activity in such a large arena, amid a vast raw element. The high opinion in which he was held extended so far that not only did people draw matter of instruction, salvation and blissful sentiment from the sanity and healthful vigour that were in him, but his very errors and diseases were looked up to with reverence, as symptoms of his inward relation to God and the divine nature. We may now comprehend the fact that while in life he was ever approaching nearer and nearer the honour of sainthood, and that at his death this dignity was but the confirmation of the thought and feeling of his contemporaries.

When, therefore, shortly after his decease, which was accompanied by still greater wonders than his life, the question was addressed to Clement VIII., whether a beginning might be made with the examination—the so-called suit which precedes canonization—the answer was returned: "I have ever considered him a saint, and have accordingly no objection to the Church proclaiming and presenting him as such to all believers."

It may further be deemed worthy of attention that, in the long series of years measured out to him, he lived through the reigns of fifteen Popes, having been born in the time of Leo X., and having ended his days under Clement VIII. He, therefore, presumed to assert an independent position in relation to the Pope himself, and though conforming, as a member of the Church, to her general ordinances he would not yet hold himself bound in particulars, but would speak even with an authoritative voice to the supreme head of Christendom. In this way he entirely declined the dignity of Cardinal, and in his *chiesa nuova*, like a refractory knight in an old castle, he did not feel abashed to display his petulance towards his sovereign. The character of these relations, however, in the curious shape it came to assume at the end of the sixteenth century, after the rougher times which had just gone by, cannot be presented in a manner more obvious to the senses, or more impressive to the mind than it is seen in a memorial, which Neri, shortly before his death, addressed to the new Pope Clement VIII., and on which an equally wonderful resolution followed.

There is here disclosed to us, in a way not to be described, the relation of a man, almost an octogenarian, and nearing the rank of a saint, to the sovereign head of the Roman Catholic Church, a man in himself of considerable merit, able and most highly respected during his reign of several years.

MEMORIAL OF PHILIP NERI TO CLEMENT VIII

"Holiest Father! And what sort of person am I then, that the Cardinals come to visit me, and yesterday evening in particular the Cardinals of Florence and Cusano? And because I needed a little bit of manna in some leaves, the said Cardinal of Florence had two ounces from San Spirito fetched to me, the Cardinal having sent a large quantity of it to that hospital. He also stayed with me two hours into the night, and said so much good of your Holiness, much more than seemed to me warranted; for, as you are Pope, you should be humility itself. Christ came at seven o'clock in the night to incorporate himself with me, and your Holiness might surely, also, once come to our church. Christ is Man and God, and visits me very frequently. Your Highness is but a mere man, born of a holy and upright man; *He*, however, of God the Father. The mother of your holiness is Signora Agnesina, a very God-fearing lady, but *His* the virgin of all virgins. What had I not all to tell you, if I were only to give free vent to my gall!

515

Johann Wolfgang von Goethe

"I bid your Holiness to do my will in respect of a maiden I will convey to Torre de' Specchi. She is the daughter of Claudio Neri, to whom your Holiness promised that you would protect his children, and let me remind you it is becoming in a Pope to keep his word. Commit, therefore, the said business to my hands, and in such a way that I may be able to avail myself of your name, if necessary; all the more that I know the maiden's will, and am certain she is acting under divine inspiration. And with the greatest humility due from me I kiss the holiest feet."

AUTOGRAPH RESOLUTION OF THE POPE, WRITTEN BENEATH THE MEMORIAL

"The Pope says that the above paper in the first part of it manifests somewhat of the spirit of vanity, inasmuch as it is intended to show him that the Cardinals visit you so frequently, if, perhaps, it is not also signified thereby, that these dignitaries, as is right well known, are spiritually minded. As to his not coming to see you, he says that your reverence does not deserve it, seeing that you would not be pleased to accept the cardinalate, which was so often offered you. With respect to the command, He is content that you, with your usual love of hectoring, give a sharp reprimand to those good mothers who do not act in accordance with your mind. He now commands you that you take care not to hear confession without his permission. Does, however, our Lord come to visit you? then pray for us, and for the most pressing necessities of Christendom."

At the beginning of the sixteenth century, the spirit of plastic art had completely raised itself out of the barbarism of the middle ages, and had attained to happy free-minded achievements. Those provinces, however, in the high domain of human nature distinguished as understanding, reason, religion, by no means enjoyed free expansion. In the North, a cultivated human sense combatted the gross assumptions of a superannuated tradition; unfortunately words and rational arguments did not suffice, recourse was had to arms. Thousands upon thousands who sought the salvation of their soul in the way spontaneously, purely and integrally suggested and commanded them were cruelly put to death and stripped of their estates.

In the South itself the fairer and nobler spirits endeavoured to free themselves from the yoke of the all-dominating Church, and in our opinion, Philip Neri is an experiment as to how a man might be at once pious, to the degree even of becoming a saint, and yet not submit himself to the sole sovereignty of the Roman

516

Pontiff. No doubt Neri finds in the very element domineered over by the Roman Church satisfaction for his feelings and imaginations; to separate himself entirely from her is therefore impossible for him. How long, however, does he hesitate before joining himself to the priesthood; how he frees himself from all ecclesiastical use and wont, and how he endeavours to render doctrine cheerful and efficiently practical as all real things are; life intelligent and moral, as it must be, if it is not to be illusive and insignificant!

The decided contempt he showed for the Cardinal's hat, to the degree even of offending the Pope, testifies to his aspiration after freedom. Then, the whimsical correspondence with which we close our notice, a correspondence displaying on Neri's part an audacious humour rising to the comic, gives us a vivid illustration of his personality, and in some measure also of the century the extraordinary man almost filled up by his life. It appeared to us in the highest degree remarkable to encounter a saint, a contemporary of the world-child Cellini, likewise a Florentine, to whose memory we have devoted so much attention. The parallel and contrast between the two men would, however, require to be elaborated at greater length, and perhaps some other significant figures of the time to be delineated, in order to present a living image of the period. May, however, the few strokes we have here drawn of a pious, noble enthusiasm serve to induce, in the meantime, some instructive comparisons!

THE ROMAN CARNIVAL

IN UNDERTAKING a description of the Roman Carnival, we cannot but fear the objection being raised that such a festival is a subject not properly admitting of description. So vast a throng of sensible objects would, it may be represented, require to pass in review immediately before the eye—would require to be personally seen and comprehended in his own way by each person wishing to obtain any idea of it.

This objection becomes all the more serious when we have ourselves to confess, that to the stranger viewing it for the first time, especially if he is disposed and qualified only to *see* it with

Translated by Rev. A. J. W. Morrison and Charles Nisbet

his bodily eyes, the Roman Carnival affords neither an integral nor a joyous impression—is neither a particular gratification to the eye nor an exhilaration to the spirits.

The long and narrow street in which innumerable people lurch hither and thither, is is impossible to survey; it is scarcely possible to distinguish anything within the limits of the tumult which your eye can grasp. The movement is monotonous, the noise stupefying, the days of the festival close with no sense of satisfaction. These misgivings, however, are soon dissipated when we enter into a more minute explanation, and indeed the reader will have to decide for himself at the end, whether our description justifies our attempt.

The Roman Carnival is a festival which, in point of fact, is not given to the people, but which the people give themselves.

The state makes little preparations, and but a small contribution to it. The merry round revolves of itself, and the police regulate the spontaneous movement with but a slack hand.

Here is no festival to dazzle the eyes of the spectator, like the many Church festivals of Rome; here are no fireworks affording the on-looker from St. Angelo a single overwhelming spectacle; here is no illumination of St. Peter's Church and dome, attracting and delighting a great concourse of strangers from all lands; here is no brilliant procession on whose approach the people are required to worship with awe. On the contrary, all that is here given is rather a simple sign that each man is at liberty to go fooling to the top of his bent, and that all licence is permissible short of blows and stabs.

The difference between high and low seems for the time being abolished, every one makes up to every one, every one treats with levity whatever he meets, and the mutual license and wantonness is kept in balance only by the universal good humour.

In these holidays the Roman exults, down to our times, that the birth of Christ, though able indeed to postpone for some weeks, was not adequate to abolishing the feast of the Saturnalia and its privileges.

It shall be our endeavour to bring the riot and merriment of these days clearly before the imagination of our readers. We flatter ourselves we shall be of service to such persons as have once been present at the Roman Carnival, and would like to entertain themselves with a vivid remembrance of it, as also to those who still contemplate a journey thither, and whom these few leaves may provide a pleasing perspective of an over-thronged and tumultuous merry-making.

The Corso

The Roman Carnival collects in the Corso. This street limits and determines the public celebration of these days. Anywhere else it would be a different sort of festival, and we have therefore first of all to describe the Corso.

Like several long streets of Italian towns, it derives its name from the horse-races which conclude the entertainment of each Carnival evening, and with which too, in other places, other festivals, such as that of the patron saint or the consecration of a church, are ended.

The street runs in a straight line from the Piazza del Popolo to the Piazza di Venezia; about three thousand five hundred paces long, and enclosed by high, mostly splendid buildings. Its breadth is not proportionate to its length, nor to the height of its edifices. The pavements for foot passengers take up on both sides from six to eight feet. The space in the middle for carriages is at most places from twelve to fourteen feet wide, and therefore, as will be readily calculated, allows but three vehicles at the most to drive abreast.

The obelisk on the Piazza del Popolo is, during the Carnival, the extreme limit of this street at the lower end, the Venetian Palace at the upper.

Driving in the Corso

On all Sundays and festival days of the year the Roman Corso is a scene of animation. The Romans of wealth and distinction take their drives here an hour or an hour and a half before nightfall in a long continuous line. The carriages start from the Venetian Palace, keeping the left side, and in fine weather they pass the obelisk, drive through the gate, on to the Flaminian way, sometimes as far as Ponte Molle.

On returning at an earlier or later hour, they keep the other side, so that the two lines of carriages pass each other in opposite directions in the best order.

Ambassadors have the right of driving up and down between the rows; this distinction was also allowed the Pretender, who stayed in Rome under the name of Duke of Albania.

The moment, however, the bells have sounded night this order is interrupted. Each one turns the way it pleases him, seeking his nearest road home, often to the inconvenience of many other equipages, which get impeded and stopped in the narrow space.

The evening drive, which is a brilliant affair in all great Italian towns, and is imitated in each small town, if only with a few coaches, attracts many foot passengers into the Corso; each one coming to see or to be seen.

The Carnival, as we may soon more particularly observe, is, in fact, but a continuation or rather the climax of the usual Sunday and festival-day recreations; it is nothing eccentric, nothing foreign, nothing unique, but attaches itself quite naturally to the general Roman style of living.

CLIMATE, CLERICAL DRESS

Just as little strange will appear to us a multitude of masks in the open air, seeing we are accustomed the whole year through to so many striking scenes of life under the bright glad heaven.

On the occasion of every festival the outspread tapestries, the scattered flowers, the painted cloths stretched above your head, transform the streets into great salons and galleries.

No corpse is brought to the grave without the accompaniment of the masked fraternities. The many monks' dresses habituate the eye to strange and peculiar figures. It indeed looks like Carnival the whole year round, the abbots in their black dress appearing among the other clerical masks to represent the more noble *tabarros* (cloaks).

COMMENCEMENT

With the beginning of the new year the playhouses are opened, and the Carnival has taken its start. Here and there in the boxes you notice a beauty, in the character of an officer, displaying to the people her epaulettes with the greatest self-complacency. The driving in the Corso becomes more thronged. The general expectancy, however, is directed to the last eight days.

PREPARATIONS FOR THE CONCLUDING DAYS

Many preparations announce to the public the approach of the paradisiacal hours.

The Corso, one of the few streets in Rome which are kept clean the whole year, gets now more carefully swept and tidied up. People are busy seeing that the small basalt blocks, square-hewn, pretty and uniform, of which the beautiful pavement consists, are in proper trim, any which are in any degree worn being removed and replaced by new basalt wedges.

Besides this you observe living indications of the near approaching event. Each Carnival evening, as we have noticed, closes with a horse-race. The horses kept for racing are mostly little, and, on account of the foreign extraction of the best of them, are called "Barberi."

A racing horse, in a covering of white linen, closely fitted to the head, neck and body, and adorned with bright ribbons at the seams, is brought in front of the obelisk to the spot whence later on he is to start. He is trained to stand still for some time with his head directed to the Corso. He is next led gently along the street, and at the Venetian Palace is treated to some oats, to make him feel the greater inducement to speed swiftly to that place.

As this practice is repeated with most of the horses, to the number often of from fifteen to twenty, and this performance is always attended by a number of merry noisy boys, a foretaste is thus given to the inhabitants of the greater uproar and jubilee shortly to follow.

Formerly the first Roman houses kept race-horses in their mews, and it was deemed an honour to a house for one of its horses to have carried off a prize. Bets were laid, and the victory celebrated by a feast. Latterly, however, this fancy has much declined, and the desire to acquire reputation by horses has percolated down into the middle, nay into the lowest class of the people.

From those earlier times, probably, has been handed down the custom that a troop of riders, accompanied by trumpeters, go about through the whole of Rome exhibiting the prizes, and riding into the grounds of distinguished houses, where, after discoursing some trumpet air, they receive a gratuity.

The prize consists of a piece of gold or silver brocade, about three and a half ells long by not quite an ell broad, which, being attached to a piebald pole, is made to wave in the air. On its lower end is worked cross-wise the picture of some running horses.

This prize is called *Palio*, and as many days as the Carnival lasts so many of these quasi-standards are displayed by the procession just mentioned along the streets of Rome.

Meanwhile the Corso begins to alter its appearance. The obelisk now becomes the limit of the street. In front of it a grand stand is erected, with many rows of seats ranged above each other, and looking right into the Corso. Before this scaffold the lists are set up between which the horses must be brought out to run.

On both sides, moreover, great scaffolds are built, attached to the first houses of the Corso, the street in this way being continued into the square. On both sides of the lists stand small, raised and covered boxes for the persons who are to regulate the running of the horses.

Up the Corso you see further scaffolds raised in front of many houses. The squares of St. Carlo and of the Antoninus Column are separated by palings from the street, and everything sufficiently betokens that the whole celebration shall and will be confined within the long and narrow Corso.

Lastly the middle of the street is strewn with *puzzolane*, that the competing horses may not so easily slip on the smooth hard street.

SIGNAL FOR THE COMPLETE CARNIVAL LICENCE

In this way expectation is every day fed and kept on the strain till at last a bell from the Capitol, shortly after noon, announces that people are now at full liberty to go fooling under the bright heaven.

Immediately on hearing it the serious Roman, who has been watchful the whole year round against falling into any slip, doffs his earnestness and gravity.

The bricklayers, who have been thumping away up to the last minute, pack up their tools and make merry over the end of their labour. All balconies, all windows are gradually hung with tapestries; on the raised pavements on both sides chairs are set out; the tenants of smaller houses and all children are in the street, which now ceases to be a street, and resembles rather a large festive salon, a vast adorned gallery.

SUPERINTENDENCE

While the Corso grows ever more animated, and among the many persons walking in their usual dresses a Punchinello here and there shows himself, the military have mustered in front of the Porta del Popolo. Led by the general on horseback, in good order and new uniform, with clanging music, they march up the Corso, and at once occupy all the entrances to it, appoint a couple of guards to the principal places, and assume the oversight of the whole festivity.

The lenders of chairs and scaffolds now call diligently to the passers-by, "Luoghi! Luoghi, Padroni! Luoghi!" ("Places, gentlemen, places!")

MASKS

The masks now begin to multiply. Young men, dressed in the holiday attire of the women of the lowest class, exposing an open breast and displaying an impudent self-complacency, are mostly the first to be seen. They caress the men they meet, allow themselves all familiarities with the women they encounter, as being persons the same as themselves, and for the rest do whatever humour, wit or wantonness suggest.

Among other things, we remember a young man, who played excellently the part of a passionate, brawling, untameable shrew, who went scolding the whole way along the Corso, railing at every one she came across, while those accompanying her took all manner of pains to reduce her to quietness.

Here comes a Punchinello, running with a large horn attached to bright cords dangling about his haunches. By a slight motion, while entertaining himself with the women, he contrives to assume the impudent shape of the old god of the gardens in holy Rome, and his insolence excites more mirth than indignation. Here comes another of like kidney, but more modest and placid, bringing his fair half along with him.

The women having just as much a mind to don the breeches as the men the petticoats, the fairer sex show no contempt for the favourite costume of Punchinello; and in this hermaphrodite figure, it must be allowed, they often show themselves in the highest degree charming.

With rapid steps, declaiming as before a Court of justice, an advocate pushes through the crowd. He bawls up at the windows, lays hold of passers-by masked or unmasked, threatens every person with a process, impeaches this man in a long narration with ridiculous crimes, and specifies to another the list of his debts. He rates the women for their coquetries, the girls for the number of their lovers. He appeals by way of proof to a book he carries about with him, producing documents as well, and setting everything forth with a shrill voice and fluent tongue. It is his aim to expose and confound every one. When you fancy he is at an end he is only beginning, when you think he is leaving he turns back. He flies at one without addressing him, he seizes hold of the other who is already past. Should he come across a brother of his profession, the folly rises to its height.

However, they cannot attract the attention of the public for a long time simultaneously. The maddest impression is swallowed up in repetition and multiplicity.

The quakers make if not so much noise, yet at least as great a sensation as the advocates. The quaker masks appear to have grown so general, on account of the easiness with which old-fashioned pieces of dress can be procured at the second-hand goods' stalls.

The main requirements in reference to these quaker masks is that the dress be old fashioned, yet in good preservation and of fine stuff. You seldom see one in other dress than velvet or silk, his vest being brocaded or laced, and, like the original, he must be of full body. His face is in a full mask with puffed cheeks and small eyes; his wig has odd pig-tails dangling to it; his hat is small and mostly bordered.

This figure, plainly, comes very near the *Buffo caricato* of the comic operas, and as the latter mostly represents a silly, enamoured gull, the quakers show themselves in the character of tasteless dandies. They hop about on their toes with great agility, and carry about large black rings without glass to serve them in the way of opera glasses, and with which they peer into every carriage, and gaze up at all windows. Usually they make a stiff deep bow, and, especially on meeting each other, express their joy by hopping several times straight up in the air, uttering at the same time a shrill, piercing, inarticulate cry, in which the consonants "brr" prevail.

You may often hear this note of salutation sounded by a quaker, and taken up by those of his persuasion next him, till in a short time the whole Corso is rent by their screams.

Wanton boys, again, blow into large twisted shells, assailing the ear with intolerable sounds.

What with the narrowness of the space and the similarity of the masks—for at all hours of the day there may be some hundreds of Punchinellos and about a hundred quakers running up and down the Corso—you soon perceive that few can have the intention of exciting a sensation or attracting attention to themselves. Any bent on that object would have to appear at an early hour in the Corso. Each one is much more intent on amusing himself, on giving free vent to his follies, and enjoying to the full the license of these days.

The girls and women, in particular, devise methods of their own for merry-making. Every one of them hates above everything to stay indoors, and, having but little money to expend on a mask, they are inventive enough to devise all sorts of ways for disguising rather than adorning themselves.

The masks of beggars, male and female, are very easy to assume; beautiful hair is the first requirement, then a perfectly white mask, an earthen pipkin held by a coloured cord, a staff and a hat in the hand. With humble demeanour they step under the windows, bow before each person, receiving for alms sweets, nuts or other like dainty.

Others take it still easier, and, wrapping themselves up in cloaks, or appearing in a nice house-dress, their faces alone being masked, they go about for the most part without male attendants, carrying as their offensive and defensive weapon a small besom composed of cane-branches in blossom, which they in part use to ward off pestilent fellows, in part to flourish wantonly in the faces of acquaintances and strangers whom they meet without masks.

When four or five girls have once caught a man on whom they have designs, there is no deliverance for him. The throng prevents his escape, and let him turn how he will the besom is under his nose. To defend himself in earnest against such provocations would be a very dangerous experiment, seeing the masks are inviolate and under the special protection of the watch.

525

In the same way the usual dresses of all classes are made to serve as masks. Grooms with their big brushes fall to rubbing down any back they take a fancy to. Drivers offer their services with their usual importunity. Pretty, on the other hand, are the masks of the country girls, the Frascati maidens, fishers, Neapolitan watermen, Neapolitan bailiffs and Greeks.

Occasionally a theatrical mask is imitated. Some people again take little trouble about a mask, folding themselves up in tapestry or linen cloths, which they tie over the head.

A white figure is in the habit of stepping in the road of others, and hopping before them, by way of representing a ghost. Others distinguish themselves by odd combinations. The tabarro, however, as being the least distinctive, is deemed the noblest mask.

Witty and satirical masks are very rare, for these have a particular purpose in view, and aim at being particularly noticed. Yet I once saw a Punchinello in the character of a cuckold. The horns were moveable, the wearer being able to draw them out and in like those of a snail. When he stopped before the window of a newly married couple, and slipped out only the faint tip of one horn, or stepping up to another window shot out both horns to their utmost length, vigorously ringing the bells attached to their ends, the public in a moment gave merry attention and often laughed loudly.

A wizard mingles among the crowd, shows the people a book with numbers, and reminds them of their passion for lotteries.

One stands in the throng with two faces, so that you are at a loss to distinguish the front from the back of him, whether he is coming towards you or going from you.

Nor must the stranger feel any ill-humour, should he in these days find himself made the subject of jest. The long clothes of the native of the North, his large buttons, his curious round hat strike the fancy of the Romans, who therefore take the foreigner for a mask.

The foreign painters, particularly those given to the study of landscapes and buildings, and who are to be found sitting everywhere in public places in Rome drawing, are studiously caricatured and show themselves very busy with large portfolios, long surtouts, and colossal pencils.

The German journeymen-bakers in Rome, who are often

found drunk, are represented in their own or in a somewhat ornamental costume, staggering about with a bottle of wine.

We remember but one satirical mask. It had been proposed to raise an obelisk in front of the Church of Trinità dei Monti. The proposal, however, was not popular, partly because the place for its erection was very confined and partly because, for the sake of raising it to a certain height, it would be necessary to build a very high pedestal. It therefore occurred to one satirical wit to carry, by way of head-piece, an enormous white pedestal, crowned by an extremely small reddish obelisk. On the pedestal were large characters, the sense of which was guessed perhaps by only a few people.

CARRIAGES

While the masks are multiplying, the coaches gradually drive into the Corso in the order we have above described when speaking of the driving on Sundays and other holidays, with the difference only that the carriages coming from the Venetian Palace along the left-hand side of the street stop short at the point where the street now terminates, and then turning drive up on the other side.

We have already pointed out that, deducting the space appropriated for the foot pavements, the ground left in the middle of the Corso is at most places hardly more than the breadth of three carriages.

The foot pavements on each side are all blocked with scaffolds, or occupied with chairs, where many spectators are already seated. Alongside of the scaffolds and chairs there is a never-failing stream of carriages moving up or drifting down. The foot-passengers are therefore restricted to the interval between the carriage lines, of eight feet at most. Each one pushes and elbows his way about as best he can, and from all the windows and balconies a thronged populace looks down on a thronged populace.

In the first days of the Carnival only the ordinary carriages are to be seen, each person reserving for the following days anything ornamental or magnificent he has to bring out. Towards the end of the Carnival the more open carriages make their appearance, seating some six persons. Two ladies sit on raised seats opposite each other, displaying their whole figures; four gentlemen occupy the remaining four seats. Coachmen and servants are all in masks, the horses, too, being arrayed in gauze and flowers.

You often see a beautiful white poodle dog decked in rosy ribbons between the coachman's feet, while bells jingle from the horses' trappings; and the display rivets the attention of the public for a few moments.

As may be readily supposed, only beautiful women will mount a seat where they are so much in the eyes of the whole world, and only the fairest of the fair will there appear with unmasked face. When such a queen of beauty takes the Corso, crowning the slow-paced carriage, she becomes the cynosure of all eyes, and from many sides she may hear the words of admiration addressed to her, "O quanto è bella!"

In earlier times, these equipages are said to have been more numerous and more costly, being also rendered more interesting by mythological and allegorical representations. Lately, however, for whatever reason, the more distinguished folk appear to be lost in the mass, being more intent on enjoyment than on showing themselves better than others.

The more the Carnival advances towards its termination, the more splendid do the equipages become.

Even seriously disposed people, who sit themselves without masks in their carriages, permit their coachman and servants to wear them. The coachmen usually select a female dress, and in the last days of the Carnival women alone appear to drive the horses. They are often prettily, nay charmingly dressed. A squat ugly fellow, on the other hand, in the tip-top of fashion, with high frisure and feathers, makes a striking caricature, and as the beauties above referred to have to hear their praises sounded, so must he swallow the affront, when some one steps up to him and shouts, "O fratello mio, che brutta puttana sei!" (Oh, my brother, what an ugly drab you are!)

It is a common thing for the coachman if he comes across one or two of his female friends in the crowd, to lift them up on to the box. They sit beside him, generally in men's clothes, and then the neat little punchinello-legs, with small feet and high heels, often play antics with the heads of the passers-by.

The servants act in a similar style, taking up their male and female friends at the back of the carriage, and all that is left now

528

is a place on the boot, as is the fashion in the case of English country coaches.

The masters and mistresses seem well pleased to see their carriages thoroughly packed; everything is permitted: everything is proper in these days.

CROWDS

Let us now glance at the long, narrow street, where from all balconies and windows thronged on-lookers, standing above long dependent bright cloths, gazing down on scaffolds packed with spectators, and on long lines of chairs on both sides of the street. Between the two lines of chairs crawl two lines of carriages. Between the two carriage lines, again, is a space capable of accommodating a third line of carriages, but which is now wholly occupied by people not walking but elbowing and jostling hither and thither. All precautions are taken to keep the coaches a little apart from each other, to prevent collision in case of a block. Many of the passengers, however, for the sake of a little air, venture to slip out of the throng into the narrow spaces between the wheels of the preceding and the horses of the succeeding carriages, and the greater the danger and difficulty to the walkers, the more do their wantonness and boldness seem to increase.

Most of the foot-passengers moving between the two carriage lines, to avoid danger to limbs and dress, carefully leave an interval between themselves and the wheels and axles of the coaches. Whoever, then, is tired of dragging along with the slow dense mass, and has the courage to do so, may slip into the vacant line between the wheels and the foot-passengers—between the danger and the avoider of it—and may thus in a short time trip over a long stretch of road, till he stumbles against some new obstacle.

Our narrative seems already to trespass the bounds of credibility, and we should scarcely venture any farther were it not for the many people who have been present at the Carnival, and who can vouch for the perfect accuracy of our statements; and were the Carnival not a yearly festival which may in future be visited with our book in hand.

For what will our readers now say, when we assure them that

all we have above related is but, as it were, the first stage of the throng, tumult, uproar, and riot?

PROCESSION OF THE GOVERNOR AND SENATOR

While the coaches push slowly forwards, and at every block come to a stand-still, the foot-passengers have no few inconveniences to put up with.

The Pope's guard ride up and down individually among the throng to clear the occasional disorders and interruptions, and in endeavouring to get out of the way of the coach-horses, the foot-passenger only bobs up against the head of a saddle-horse. That, however, is not the worst of it.

The Governor drives in a large state-carriage with a retinue of several coaches along the interval between the two rows of other coaches. The Pope's guard and the servants who go in front warn the people to clear out of the way, this procession taking up for the moment the whole space shortly before occupied by the foot-passengers. The people jam themselves as best they can between the other carriages, and by hook or crook contrive to get to one side or the other. And as water when a ship cuts through it is parted only for a moment, at once commingling again behind the rudder, so the mass of masked and other foot-passengers at once re-unites behind the procession. Soon again, however, the straitened crowd is disturbed by some new movement.

The Senator advances with a similar procession. His great state-carriage and the carriages of his retinue swim as on the heads of the compressed crowd, and while every man, be he native or foreigner, is captivated and enchanted by the amiability of the present Senator, Prince Rezzonico, the Carnival is perhaps the only occasion when people wish him well out of their sight.

While these two processions of the heads of justice and police in Rome penetrated only the first day through the Corso for the sake of formally opening the Carnival, the Duke of Albania drove daily along the same route to the great inconvenience of the crowd; reminding Rome, the old ruler of kings, during a time of universal mummery, of the farce of his kingly pretensions.

The ambassadors, who had the same privilege of driving as he, used it sparingly and with humane discretion.

THE BEAU MONDE AT THE RUSPOLI PALACE

The free circulation of the Corso is, however, liable to interruptions and blocks other than those caused by these processions. At the Ruspoli Palace and its neighbourhood, where the street is not wider but the foot-pavements stand higher than elsewhere, the *beau monde* have taken possession of all the chairs. The fairest ladies of the middle-class charmingly masked, and waited upon by their friends, display their graces to the inquisitive eye of the passers-by. Whoever comes near them lingers to contemplate the fair rows, and each one endeavours, among the many male figures arrayed there, to single out the female ones, and in a pretty officer, perhaps, to discover the object of his longing. At this spot the movement first comes to a stand; the coaches stay as long as possible in this neighbourhood, and as one must come to a standstill at last, one prefers to remain in this pleasant society.

COMFITS

Hitherto our description has conveyed the idea of but a straitened or distressed situation. Now, however, we must relate how the compressed merriment is set in liveliest agitation by a petty warfare, carried on mostly in the way of jest, but often assuming an all-too-serious aspect.

Probably some time or other a fair one, to attract the notice of her passing friend amid all the hubbub and mummery, threw at him some sugared caraways, when, of course, nothing was more natural than that he should turn round and recognise his roguish fair one. This, at all events, has now grown a universal habit, and after a volley one often sees two friendly faces salute each other. Yet partly from economy, and partly from the abuse of the practice, genuine sweets are less used, and a cheaper and more plentiful stuff is demanded.

It has come to be a trade to carry about, among the crowd, for sale in large baskets gypsum trochisks, made by means of a funnel, and having the appearance of sugar plums.

No man is safe from an attack; every one is, therefore, in a state of defence; and so, in wantonness or otherwise, there arises, now here, now there, a species of duel, skirmish, or battle. Foot-passengers, coach-drivers, spectators at windows, in stands, and on chairs, join in, reciprocally charging and defending.

The ladies have gilded and silver-plated little baskets full of these comfits, and their attendants stand sturdily to defend the fair ones. With their coach-windows dropped down the inmates await an onset. People jest with their friends, and defend themselves obstinately against strangers.

Nowhere, however, is this combat more earnest and general than in the neighbourhood of the Ruspoli Palace. All maskers who have places there are provided with baskets, bags, or handkerchiefs held by the four corners. They attack more than they are attacked. No coach passes with impunity, without suffering at the hands of some or other maskers. No foot-passenger is secure from them. An abbot in black dress becomes a target for missiles on all hands; and seeing that gypsum and chalk always leave their mark wherever they alight, the abbot soon gets spotted all over with white and grey. Often these affrays grow serious and general, and with astonishment you see how envy and personal hatred vent themselves in this way.

All unobserved a masked figure slips up, and with a handful of comfits pelts one of the first beauties so violently and unerringly that the masked face rattles, and the fair neck is marked. Her attendants on both sides are kindled into fury; with the contents of their baskets and bags they storm impetuously on the assailant. He is, however, too well masked and harnessed to suffer from the repeated discharges. The more invulnerable he is, the bolder he plies his onslaught. The defenders protect the lady with their tabarros. The assailant in the brunt of the battle assaults the neighbours too, and what with rudeness and violence generally offends every one, so that the surrounding people join issue and do not spare their comfits or the heavier ammunition, chiefly sugar almonds, that they have in reserve for such cases. At last, overpowered on all sides and with his shot all spent, the assailant is obliged to beat a retreat.

Usually, one does not commit himself to such an adventure without a second to reinforce him with ammunition. The men, too, who drive a trade with gypsum comfits, generally hasten to the scene of such an engagement, ready to weigh out shot from their baskets to any number of pounds.

We have ourselves witnessed a battle of this kind, when the combatants, from want of other ammunition, threw their gilt baskets at each other's heads, and could not be prevailed on by the watch, who suffered from the discharges, to desist from further warfare.

Assuredly, many of these frays would end in stabbings, did not the wound-up *corde*, the well-known instrument of Italian police, at several corners, remind people at all moments in the midst of their frolics how dangerous it would be for them to have recourse to dangerous weapons.

Innumerable are these frays, and generally more in the way of jest than earnest.

Here comes, for example, an open carriage, full of Punchinellos, towards Ruspoli. They intend while passing by the onlookers to hit them all one after the other. Unfortunately, however, the throng is too great, and the carriage is brought to a halt in the middle. All the surrounding people are at once animated by one purpose, and from all sides hail-showers descend on the coach. The Punchinellos in the carriage spend all their ammunition, and for a long time are exposed to a cross-fire from all sides, till in the end the coach looks all covered over with snow and hail, in which state, amid universal ridicule and cries of indignation, it slowly moves off.

DIALOGUE AT THE UPPER END OF THE CORSO

While in the middle of the Corso these lively and violent games occupy a large part of the fair sex, another part of the public finds at the upper end of the Corso another species of entertainment.

Not far from the French Academy appears, unexpectedly issuing from among the onlooking maskers on a scaffold, a so-called Capitano of the Italian Theatre, in Spanish dress, with feathered hat and large gloves, and begins in emphatic tones to relate his great deeds by land and water. He does not proceed far in his narrative till another Punchinello takes up a position over against him, suggests doubts and objections in reference to his statements, and while appearing to take all in good faith by the puns and platitudes he interjects he brings the great achievements of the hero into ridicule.

Here, too, each passer-by stands still to listen to the lively altercation.

Johann Wolfgang von Goethe

KING OF THE PUNCHINELLOS

A new procession often increases the throng. A dozen Punchinellos choose a king, crown him, put a sceptre in his hand, attend him with music, and, in an ornamental little carriage, lead him up the Corso amid loud cries. All Punchinellos spring up to it as the procession advances, increase the train, and with shouting and brandishing of hats make room for it.

You then observe for the first time how each one endeavours to diversify these universal masks. One wears a wig, the other a woman's hood over his black face, the third for a cap has a cage stuck on his head with a pair of birds in it dressed as abbot and dame, hopping about on the perches.

SIDE STREETS

The frightful crush we have endeavoured to the best of our ability to bring before the eyes of the readers drives, of course, a crowd of maskers out of the Corso into the neighbouring streets. There lovers walk more quietly and confidentially together, while madcaps find more scope there for their escapades.

A body of men, in the Sunday dress of the common people, in short doublets with gold-laced vests under them, the hair gathered up in a long descending net, walk up and down with young men disguised as women. One of the women appears to be far advanced in the family way; they walk quietly up and down. All at once the men begin to quarrel; a lively exchange of words arises; the women thrust themselves into the affair; the brawl grows from bad to worse. At last the combatants draw large knives of silvered pasteboard and fall foul of each other. The women, with dreadful cries, rush in to keep them apart, one being pulled in this direction, another in that. The onlookers join in the affair as though it were all in earnest, and try to bring each party to reason.

Meanwhile, the woman who is far gone in the family way falls ill from the shock. A chair is brought. The other women run to her assistance. Her appearance is pitiable, and before you are aware of it, she brings to the world some unshapely brat, to the great merriment of the spectators. The play is over, and the troop move on to some other place to repeat the same, or produce another like farce.

534

The Roman, who is continually hearing stories of murder, is disposed on every occasion to play with ideas of murder. The very children have a game they call *chiesa*, corresponding with our "Frischauf in allen Ecken." Properly, however, it represents a murderer who seeks refuge on the step of a church. The others represent the constables who in all ways endeavour to catch him without, however, daring to touch the place of refuge.

In the side streets, especially the Strada Babuina, and the Spanish Place, the mirth goes on with equal liveliness.

The quakers, too, come in flocks, the more freely to display their finery. They have a manœuvre which makes every one laugh. They come marching, twelve at a time, perfectly straight on tip-toe, in short and rapid steps, forming an entirely even front. When they come to a square, wheeling to right or left, they all at once form a column and now trip away behind each other. All at once, again, with a right turn they are restored to their former order; then, before you know where you are, again left turn. The column is shoved as if on a spit into a doorway, and the fools have disappeared.

EVENING

Now, evening approaches and everything that has life presses ever more into the Corso. The coaches have already been long at a standstill, nay, sometimes two hours before nightfall no carriage can any longer move from the spot.

The Pope's guard and the watchmen are now busy getting all carriages as far as possible away from the middle, and into a perfectly straight row, and with all the multitudinous crowding no little disorder and irritation are occasioned. Everywhere there is kicking, pushing, and pulling. A horse kicking, those behind necessarily back out of the way, and a carriage with its horses is fairly squeezed into the middle. Straightway descend on the carriage the opprobrium of the guard, the curses and threatenings of the watch.

No use for the unlucky coachman to accomplish apparent impossibilities; imprecations and threats assail him. If he cannot fall in again he must without any fault of his own away into the nearest side street. Ordinarily, the side streets are themselves chokeful of carriages which have arrived too late, and could no longer get into the line, because the circulation was already stopped.

Preparations for the Race

The moment of the horse-race is drawing ever nearer, a moment on which the minds of so many thousands of men are strained.

The lenders of chairs, the erectors of scaffolds are now more importunate than ever with their cries "Luoghi! Luoghi avanti! Luoghi nobili! Luoghi Padroni!" It is their pressing interest that in the last moments the places they have to dispose of be all taken even though at a less charge.

And fortunate it is that there is still a vacant chair here and there. For the General, with a part of the guard, now rides down the Corso between the two rows of coaches, sweeping away the foot-passengers from the only space that yet remained to them. Each one then looks out for a chair, a place on a scaffold, on a coach, between the carriages, or at a friend's window, every one of which is now running over with spectators.

Meanwhile, the place in front of the obelisk is entirely cleared of the people, and affords perhaps one of the finest sights in the present world.

The three façades, hung with carpets, of the above-described grand stands enclose the place. Many thousands of heads look forth, ranged in row above row, giving the picture of an ancient amphitheatre or circus. Above the central scaffold towers up in the air the whole height of the obelisk, the scaffold covering but the pedestal. Here you first become aware of its prodigious height, serving as it does by way of measure of the vast human mass. The open space gives the eye a refreshing sense of rest.

The General now comes down the Corso, as a sign that the place is all cleared, and behind him the guard allow no man to step out of the row of the coaches. He takes a place in one of the boxes.

The Race

The order of the horses having been determined by lot, they are led by dressed-out grooms into the lists behind the rope. They have no covering of any kind on the body. Here and there spiked balls are attached to them by cords, and the place where they will be spurred is protected by leather till the moment of starting. Large sheets of tinsel are stuck over them. When brought into the lists they are, mostly, wild and impatient, and it needs all the grooms' strength and tact to keep them in.

Their eagerness for the race makes them intractable; the presence of so many people makes them shy. They often toss their heads over into the neighbouring list and over the rope, and this movement and disorder intensify every moment the eager expectancy of the spectators.

The grooms are on the alert to the utmost degree, because at the moment of the start the skill of the man letting off the horse, as also accidental circumstances, tell greatly to the advantage of one horse or the other.

At last the rope falls, and the horses are off.

On the open square they endeavour to get ahead of each other, but when once they come into the narrow space between the two rows of coaches nearly all competition is useless.

One pair are generally in front, straining every muscle. Notwithstanding the scattered gravel fire strikes from the ground, the manes fly, the tinsel rustles, and you hardly catch a glance of them, when they are again out of sight. The rest of the horses impede each other, pushing and driving; and sometimes one clears the cavalcade and away, though late, after the other two, the riven pieces of tinsel fluttering over the forsaken track. Soon the horses are all vanished, the people reunite from both sides and again fill up the race-ground.

Other grooms await the arrival of the horses at the Venetian Palace. They contrive to catch and hold them fast in an enclosed place. The prize is awarded to the victor.

The holiday thus ends with an overpowering momentary sensation, swift as lightning; on which thousands of people have been strained for a considerable time, though most of them would be at a loss to explain the ground either of their expectation or of their gratification.

From the above description it may easily be inferred that this sport is apt to become dangerous both for animals and men. We will cite only a few instances. With the narrow passage between the carriages a back-wheel may readily project a little outwards, leaving, perhaps, a somewhat wider space behind it. In this case a horse racing past, and sore pressed by the other horses, will in all likelihood take advantage of the piece of ground left vacant, when almost inevitably he will stumble on the projecting wheel.

We have ourselves seen a case in which a horse in such a plight fell from the shock, the next three horses chasing up behind tumbled over the first, while the last horses happily cleared those that were fallen and continued their career.

A horse falling in this way is often killed on the spot, and not seldom spectators also receive mortal injuries. A great mischief may also arise when the horses suddenly turn about.

It has sometimes happened that malignant, envious people, on seeing a horse a long way ahead of his competitors, have shaken their cloaks in his eyes, and by this action have caused him to turn about and run to one side. Still worse is it when the grooms at the Venetian Square have not succeeded in catching the horses. They, then, irresistibly face round, and, the race-course being wholly refilled with the crowd, many accidents are occasioned that are either not heard of or unheeded.

An End of Order

The horses generally do not leave the ground till the night has set in. As soon as they have reached the Venetian Palace, little mortars are let off. This signal is repeated in the middle of the Corso, and given for the last time in the neighbourhood of the obelisk.

At this moment the watch leave their posts, the order of the coaches is no longer kept, and assuredly even for the spectator who looks down tranquilly on all from his window, this is an anxious and vexatious moment, and a few remarks regarding it will not be out of place.

We have already observed above that the fall of night, which is decisive of so much in Italy, breaks up the usual drives on Sundays and festival days. There are no watch and no guards, but it is an old custom, an universal convention, that people drive up and down in the order we have described. So soon, however, as Ave Maria is rung, no one will give up his right of turning about at any time and in any way he pleases. The driving during Carnival on the Corso being subject to the same laws, though the crowding and other circumstances make a great difference, no one will give up his right to abandon the established order.

When we look to the prodigious throng, and see the race-course, which had been cleared but for a moment, again inun-

538

dated in a trice with people, it would seem only reasonable that each equipage should seek in due order the nearest side street and hasten home.

But as soon as the signal has been given, some carriages press into the middle of the street, jamming and confusing the foot-passengers; and as the one coach fancies a drive-up, the other a drive-down, in the narrow space, the two block up each other's way, and often prevent the more reasonable people who have kept the rank from making the least progress.

Let a returning horse now come upon such a complication, and danger, mischief, and vexation increase on all sides.

NIGHT

And yet, later on, all this muddle and confusion are for the most part happily cleared up. Night has fallen, and each one wishes himself the happiness of a little rest.

THEATRES

All face-masks are from this moment removed, and a great part of the public hasten to the theatre. Only in the boxes you may still see tabarros and ladies in mask-dresses. The whole pit appears again in ordinary costume.

The Aliberti and Argentina theatres give grave operas, with intercalated ballets; Valle and Capranica comedies and tragedies, with comic operas for interlude. Pace imitates them, though imperfectly; and so down to puppet-shows and rope-dancing booths there is a wide range of subordinate theatres.

The great Tordenone theatre, which was once burnt down and on being re-built immediately fell in, unfortunately no longer entertains the people with its blood-and-thunder tragedies and other wondrous representations.

The passion of the Romans for the theatre is great, and was formerly in the Carnival time still more ardent, because only at that season could it be gratified. At present there is at least one play-house open in summer and autumn as well as winter, and the public can in some measure satisfy its desires in this respect the greater part of the year.

It would lead us too far away from the purpose on hand were we to give a circumstantial description of the theatres and their idiosyncracies. Our readers will remember our treatment of this subject at another place.

FESTINE

We shall, likewise, have little to relate about the so-called "Festine." They are great mask-balls occasionally given in the beautifully illuminated Aliberti theatre.

Here, too, tabarros have the reputation of being the most becoming mask both for gentlemen and ladies, and the whole salon is filled with black figures, a few character-masks being sprinkled among them.

All the greater curiosity, therefore, is excited when a few noble figures appear displaying, what is a rather rare sight, masks taken from various art-epochs and imitating in a masterly way various statues preserved in Rome. In this manner are shown Egyptian Gods, Priestesses, Bacchus and Ariadne, the Tragic Muse, the Historical Muse, a Town, Vestals, a Consul; all being in accordance with the costume more or less happily carried out.

DANCES

The dances during these holidays are generally in long rows according to English fashion. The only difference is that in their few rounds they mostly express pantomimically some characteristic action or other. For example, two lovers have a fall out, then a reconciliation; they part, and meet again.

The Romans, through these pantomimic ballets, are accustomed to strongly marked gesticulation. In their social dances, too, they love an expression which would appear to us exaggerated and affected. No one will readily engage in dancing who has not learned it artistically. The minuet, in particular, is looked upon as a work of art, and represented, so to say, by but a few couples. A couple doing a performance of this kind is quite enclosed by the rest of the company, who watch their movements with admiration, and at the end shower their applauses on them.

MORNING

If the fashionable world amuses itself in this fashion till morning, in the Corso people are busy at break of day cleaning and sorting it. Particular attention is paid to the equal and clean dispersion of the puzzolane in the middle of the street.

It is not long before the grooms bring the race-horse, which yesterday showed the worst behaviour, before the obelisk. A little boy is mounted on it and another rider with a whip lashes it from behind, making it speed to the goal at its swiftest pace.

About two o'clock in the afternoon, after the bell has rung out the signal, there begins anew each day the round of the festival as already described. The walkers direct their steps to the Corso; the watch march up; balconies, windows, scaffolds are again hung with tapestries; the maskers multiply and give vent to their follies; the coaches drive up and down; the street is more or less thronged, according as weather or other circumstances are favourable or unfavourable. Towards the end, the Carnival naturally increases in spectators, masks, carriages, dresses, and noise. Nothing, however, which precedes comes at all near to the throng and excesses of the last day and evening.

LAST DAY

Generally by two hours before night-fall the rows of coaches are entirely at a standstill. No carriage can any longer move from the spot, nor can any in the side streets squeeze in. The scaffolds and chairs are filled at an earlier hour, although the places are let out dearer. Every one seeks to secure a place at the earliest moment, and people await the running of the horses with more intense longing than ever.

At last this moment also flies by. The signal is given that the festival is at an end. Neither carriage, nor masker, nor spectator, however, shifts ground.

All is quiet, all hushed, while the dusk gently deepens.

MOCCOLI

Hardly have the shades of night crept over the narrow and lofty street when lights are seen shining forth here and there, at the windows, and on the scaffolds; in a short time the circulation of light has proceeded so far that the whole street is luminous with burning wax-tapers.

The balconies are adorned with transparent paper-lanterns. Each person holds his taper out of the window; all scaffolds are

541

illuminated. The inside of the coaches, from whose roofs hang down small crystal chandeliers shedding light on the company, are very pretty, while in other carriages ladies, with bright tapers in their hands, seem to invite outsiders to contemplate their beauty.

The servants stick little tapers on the edges of the coach-roof. Open carriages appear with bright paper-lanterns, Many of the foot-passengers display high light-pyramids on their heads; others have their lights stuck on reeds fastened together, which often attain, with the rod, to a height of two or three stories.

It is now incumbent on every one to carry a taper in his hand, and the favourite imprecation of the Romans, "Sia ammazzato!" (Be murdered!) is heard from all ends and corners. "Sia ammazzato chi non porta moccolo!" (Murder to him who does not carry a taper!) you hear one calling out to the other, while at the same time trying to blow out his neighbour's taper. What with kindling and blowing out lights and the uncontrollable cry, "Sia ammazzato!" life and bustle and mutual interest pervade the prodigious crowd.

No matter whether the person next you is an acquaintance or a stranger, you equally try to blow out his light, and on his rekindling it to blow it out again. And the stronger the bellowing, "Sia ammazzato!" reverberates from all sides, the more does the expression lose its dreadful meaning, the more you forget you are in Rome, in a place where for a trifle such an imprecation might speedily be given effect to.

In time the expression loses all trace of horror. And as in other languages curses and disparaging phrases are often used as interjections of admiration and joy, so in Italian you often hear this evening "Sia ammazzato!" employed as watch-word, as cry of joy, as refrain for all jests, banterings, and compliments.

Thus we hear jestingly, "Sia ammazzato il Signore Abbate che fa l'amore!" (Be murdered the abbot who is making love!) Or one calls to his intimate friend passing by, "Sia ammazzato il Signore Filippo!" Or, in the way of flattery and compliment, "Sia ammazzato la bella Principessa!" "Sia ammazzato la Signora Angelica, la prima pittrice del secolo!" (Be murdered Signora Angelica, the first painter of the age!)

All these phrases are sung out swiftly and impetuously, with a long drawl on the penultimate or antepenultimate. Amid all this never-ceasing cry the blowing-out and kindling of tapers

542

go on constantly. Whomsoever you meet in the house, on the stairs, whether you are in a room with company, or see your neighbour when looking out from your window, you everywhere endeavour to get the advantage of him in blowing out his light.

All ages and classes contend furiously with each other. They jump on the steps on each other's coaches. No pendant light, hardly a lantern is safe. The boy blows out his father's flame and never ceases crying, "Sia ammazzato il Signore Padre!" All in vain for the father to scold him for his impudence; the boy asserts the freedom of the evening, and only the more savagely murders his father. The tumult, while growing fainter on both ends of the Corso, becomes the more uncontrollable in the centre, so that at last there arises a crush past all conception; past the power of the liveliest memory to realise again.

No one dares move from the place where he stands or sits. The heat of such a throng of people, of so many lights, the smoke of tapers ever blown out and ever rekindled, the infinitude of cries from so many men who bellow the more the less they can move a limb—all this, at last, makes the most robust senses giddy. It appears impossible that many accidents should not happen; that the coach-horses should not get wild; that many persons should not get crushed, squeezed, or otherwise hurt.

And yet, as each one ultimately longs more or less to get away, striking into the nearest lane he can reach, or seeking free air and relief in the nearest square, the mass of people is gradually broken up, dissolving from the ends of the street towards the middle, and this festival of general unrestrained licence, these modern Saturnalia close with a universal stupefaction.

The common people now hasten to feast till midnight on a well-prepared banquet of meat soon to be forbidden, while the more elegant world betakes itself to the play-houses to bid farewell to greatly curtailed pieces. At last the stroke of midnight puts an end to these pleasures also.

ASH-WEDNESDAY

And so vanishes the extravagant festival like a dream, like a tale—leaving, perhaps, less trace in the soul of the actors than remains in the minds of our readers to whom we have presented the whole in its connection.

If during the course of these follies the rude Punchinello has reminded us, though unbecomingly, of the joys of love to which we owe our existence, if a Baubo on the open square has desecrated the secrets of woman in child-bearing, if so many kindled tapers have put us in mind of the end of the holiday, we may in the midst of so much nonsense have had our attention drawn by means of these symbols to the most important scenes in our life.

Still more does the narrow, long, densely-packed street suggest to us the ways of the world, where each spectator and actor, with natural face or under mask, from balcony or scaffold, sees but a short distance before and around him, makes progress in coach or on foot only step by step, is rather pushed than walks, is detained more perforce than of free will, endeavours with all zeal to attain a better and less confined position only to find himself in new embarrassments, till at last he is crushed out of the way.

Might we continue a more serious style of speech than the subject seems to allow, we should remark that the intensest and highest pleasures appear to us like the fleeting coursers but for a moment, rustling past us and leaving hardly any trace on our mind; that freedom and equality can only be enjoyed in the tumult of folly; and that the greatest pleasure only powerfully allures when it trenches upon danger, and tempts us by the offer of bitter-sweet gratifications in its vicinity.

In this way, without premeditation, we should have concluded our Carnival, too, with Ash-Wednesday reflections. Not that we would cast any shade of sadness on our readers. On the contrary, seeing that life as a whole, like the Roman Carnival, stretches far beyond our ken, and is full of troubles and vexations, we would desire that every one should with us be reminded by this careless crowd of maskers of the importance of every momentary, and often apparently trivial enjoyment of life.

AUTOBIOGRAPHICAL WRITING

From Poetry and Truth

Book III

FRANKFURT UNDER FRENCH OCCUPATION

AT THAT time the general interchange of personal good wishes made the city very lively on New Year's day. People who as a rule found it difficult to leave home, donned their best clothes, that for the nonce they might show friendliness and civility to their friends and patrons. The festivities at my grand-father's house on this day were a particularly welcome treat to us children. Early dawn found the grandchildren already assembled there to hear the drums, oboes, clarinets, trumpets, and horns played upon by the military, the town musicians, and whoever else contributed to the music. The New Year's gifts, sealed and addressed, were distributed by us children among the humbler well wishers, and, as the day advanced, the number of those of higher rank increased. The relations and intimate friends appeared first, then the subordinate officials; even the gentlemen of the Council did not fail to pay their respects to the *Schultheiss*, and a select number were entertained in the evening in rooms which were hardly ever opened throughout the year. The cakes, biscuits, marchpane, and sweet wine had the greatest charm for the children, and, besides, the *Schultheiss* and the two Burgomasters were annually presented by certain institutions with some silver plate, which was then bestowed upon the grand-children and godchildren in regular order. In fine, this miniature festival was not without any of those attributes which usually glorify the greatest.

The New Year's day of 1759 approached, as welcome and delightful to us children as any preceding one, but full of anxiety and foreboding to older persons. It is true we had become accus-

Translated by John Oxenford and Rev. A. J. W. Morrison; revised by Minna Steele Smith tomed to the marching through of French troops: it was a common occurrence, but had been most frequent in the last days of the past year. According to the ancient usage of an imperial town, the warder of the chief tower sounded his trumpet whenever troops approached, and on this New Year's day he never left off at all, which was a sign that large bodies of men were in motion on several sides. They did, as a matter of fact, march through the city in great masses on this day, and the people ran to see them pass by. At other times we had been used to see them march through in small detachments, but now they gradually increased in size without anyone's being able or willing to hinder it. In short, on the 2nd of January, after a column had come through Sachsenhausen over the bridge, through the Fahrgasse, as far as the Police Guard House—it halted, overpowered the small detachment which escorted it, took possession of the Guard House just mentioned, marched down the Zeil, and, after a slight resistance, forced the main guard also to yield. In a moment the peaceful streets were transformed into a scene of war. The troops remained and bivouacked there, until quarters were assigned them by regular billeting.

This unexpected burden, unheard of for years past, weighed heavily upon the ease-loving citizens, and to none could it have been more irksome than to my father, who was obliged to take foreign soldiers into his barely finished house, to give up to them his well-furnished reception rooms, which were usually kept shut up, and to hand over to the tender mercies of strangers all that he had been accustomed to arrange and manage with such care. Siding as he did with the Prussians, he was now to find himself besieged in his own chambers by the French;—it was, according to his way of thinking, the greatest misfortune that could happen to him. If it had only been possible for him to take the matter more easily, he might have saved himself and us many sad hours, since he spoke French well and could deport himself with dignity and grace in daily life. For it was the King's Lieutenant who was quartered on us, and although he was a military official, it was only civil matters, such as disputes between soldiers and citizens and questions of debt and quarrels that he had to settle. This was the Count Thorane, a native of Grasse in Provence, not far from Antibes; a tall, thin, grave figure, with a face much disfigured by the smallpox, black fiery eyes, and a dignified, self-contained demeanour. His very first entrance was propitious for the inmates of the house. The various apartments were discussed, some of which were to be given up and others retained by the family; and when the Count heard a picture-room mentioned, although it was already dark, he immediately requested permission to give at least a hasty look at the pictures by candlelight. He took extreme pleasure in these things, behaved in the most courteous manner to my father who accompanied him, and when he heard that the majority of the artists were still living and resident in Frankfort and its neighbourhood, he assured us that he desired nothing more than to make their acquaintance as soon as possible, and to employ them.

But even this sympathy in respect to art could not change my father's feelings nor soften his inflexibility. He acquiesced in what he could not prevent, but remained aloof and inactive, and the unwonted state of things around him was intolerable to him, even to the veriest trifle.

Count Thorane, meanwhile, behaved in an exemplary manner. He would not even have his maps nailed on the walls, for fear of injuring the new hangings. His servants were capable, quiet, and orderly; but, seeing that he was never left in peace all day long and part of the night, one complainant quickly following another, persons under arrest being brought in and led out, and all officers and adjutants being admitted to his presence; seeing, furthermore, that the Count kept open table every day; naturally the moderate-sized house, planned only for a family, and with but one open staircase running from top to bottom, was pervaded with a movement and a buzzing like that in a beehive, although everything was under ordered, thoughtful, and strict control.

As mediator between the irritable master of the house—who became daily more of a hypochondriac and a burden to himself —and his well-meaning, but grave and precise military guest, there was, fortunately, an easy-going interpreter, a handsome, corpulent, cheerful man, who was a citizen of Frankfort, spoke French well, could adapt himself to all circumstances, and only made a jest of many little annoyances. Through him my mother had sent a representation to the Count of the situation in which she was placed, owing to her husband's state of mind. He described the situation with great skill—explaining that the new house was still in some disorder, that the owner was naturally

549

reserved and occupied with the education of his family, with much more to the same effect; and the Count, who on his part took the greatest pride in absolute justice, integrity, and honourable conduct, resolved here also to behave in an exemplary manner to those upon whom he was quartered, and, in fact, never swerved from this resolution in spite of changing circumstances during the several years he stayed with us.

My mother possessed some knowledge of Italian, a language not altogether unknown to any of the family; she therefore resolved to learn French immediately. Accordingly the interpreter, for whose child she had stood godmother during these stormy times, and who, in consequence of this family connection, took a redoubled interest in our house, devoted every spare moment to his child's godmother—for he lived directly opposite —and in particular, he taught her those phrases which she would be obliged to use in her personal intercourse with the Count. This succeeded admirably. The Count was flattered by the pains taken by the mistress of the house at her years, and as he had a cheerful, witty vein in his character, and liked to exhibit a certain dry gallantry, a most friendly relation arose between them, and when godmother and father made common cause, they could obtain whatever they wanted from him.

As I said before, if it had been possible to cheer up my father, this altered state of things would have troubled us but little. The Count practised the severest disinterestedness; he even declined gifts to which his position entitled him; he rejected angrily the most trifling present which might have looked like a bribe, and even punished the giver. His servants were most strictly forbidden to put the proprietor of the house to the least expense. On the other hand, we children were bountifully supplied from the dessert. To give an idea of the simplicity of those times, I must take this opportunity of mentioning that my mother grieved us excessively one day by throwing away the ices which had been sent us from the table, because she would not believe it possible for the stomach to bear real ice, however sugary.

Besides these dainties, which we gradually learned to enjoy and to digest quite well, it was very agreeable for us children to be in some measure released from fixed hours of study and strict discipline. My father's ill-humour increased, he could not resign himself to the inevitable. How he tormented himself, my mother, the interpreter, the Councillors, and all his friends, only to rid him of the Count! In vain they represented to him that under existing circumstances the presence of such a man in the house was an actual benefit, and that the removal of the Count would be followed by a constant succession of officers or of privates. None of these arguments had any effect. To him the present seemed so intolerable, that his indignation prevented his conceiving anything worse that might follow.

In this way his activity, which he had been used chiefly to expend upon us, was crippled. He no longer showed the same strictness in setting our tasks, and we tried to gratify our curiosity for military and other public proceedings as much as possible, not only at home, but also in the streets, which was the more easily done, as the front door, open day and night, was guarded by sentries who paid no attention to the running in and out of restless children.

The many affairs which were settled before the tribunal of the Royal Lieutenant had a charm of their own from his making it a point to give some witty, ingenious, or lively turn to his decisions. His verdict was strictly just, his manner of expressing it whimsical and piquant. He seemed to have taken the Duke of Ossuña as his model. Scarcely a day passed in which the interpreter did not tell some anecdote or other of this kind to amuse us and my mother. With his love of fun, he had made a little collection of such Solomonian decisions; but I only retain a general impression, and cannot recall any particular instance.

By degrees we became better acquainted with the unusual character of the Count. He was perfectly aware of his own peculiarities, and as there were times in which he was seized with a sort of dejection, hypochondria, or whatever we may call the evil demon, he used to retire into his room at such hours, which often lengthened into days, would see no one but his valet, and even in urgent cases could not be prevailed upon to admit anyone to his presence. But as soon as the evil spirit had left him, he appeared as before, kind, cheerful, and busy. It might be inferred from the talk of his valet, St. Jean, a merry, good-natured, thin little man, that in his earlier years, while dominated by this mood, he had been the cause of great suffering: and that therefore he had formed a serious resolve to avoid similar aberrations in his present important position, exposed to the eyes of all the world.

Johann Wolfgang von Goethe

During the very first days of the Count's residence with us, all the Frankfort artists, such as Hirt, Schütz, Trautmann, Nothnagel, and Juncker, were summoned by him. They showed their finished pictures, and the Count bought those that were for sale. My pretty, light gable-room in the roof was given up to him, and immediately turned into a cabinet and studio, for he intended to keep all the artists at work for a long time, especially Seekatz of Darmstadt, whose art greatly pleased him, particularly in the treatment of simple and natural subjects. He therefore sent to Grasse, where his elder brother apparently possessed a handsome house, for the dimensions of all the rooms and cabinets; then discussed with the artists the divisions of the walls, and fixed accordingly upon the size of the large oil-paintings, which were not to be framed but to be fastened upon the walls like pieces of tapestry. Forthwith the work began in earnest. Seekatz undertook country scenes, and succeeded admirably with his old men and children, who were copied directly from nature. His young men were not so successful, they were usually too thin, and his women erred in the opposite direction. For as his wife was a fat, good, but unpleasing little person, who presumably would not allow him to have any other model, the result was not attractive. He was also obliged to exceed the usual size of his figures. His trees were natural, but the foliage was too laboured. He was a pupil of Brinckmann, whose painting of easel pieces is not to be despised.

Schütz, the landscape painter, perhaps understood best what was required. He was thoroughly at home in the scenery of the Rhine, and could catch the sunny tone which lights it up at a favourable time of year. Besides, he had had experience of work on a large scale, and so was not obliged to sacrifice skilful handling of details and a due proportion of light and shade. The pictures which he produced were of a cheerful cast.

Trautmann *Rembrandtized* some resurrection miracles from the New Testament, and alongside of them set fire to villages and mills. He had a cabinet to himself, as I found from the designs of the rooms. Hirt painted good oak and beech forests. His cattle were praiseworthy. Juncker, accustomed to imitate the most elaborate Dutch artists, was least able to accommodate himself to this tapestry-work, but he condescended to ornament many compartments with flowers and fruits for a handsome price.

As I had known all these men from my earliest youth and had

often visited them in their studios, and as the Count besides liked to have me with him, I was present when suggestions were made, consultations held, and orders given, as well as when the pictures were sent home, and even ventured to speak my opinion freely when sketches and designs were handed in. Among amateurs, and still more at auctions, which I attended diligently, I had gained the reputation of being able to tell at once what any historical picture represented, whether taken from Biblical or profane history, or from mythology; and even if I did not always hit upon the meaning of allegorical pictures, there was seldom any one present who understood it better than I. I had often persuaded artists to represent this or that subject, and I now was delighted to make use of my advantages. I still remember writing an elaborate essay, in which I described twelve pictures representing the history of Joseph; some of them were executed.

After these achievements, which were certainly laudable in a boy, I will mention a slight disgrace which happened to me among this circle of artists. I was well acquainted with all the pictures which from time to time had been brought into that room. My youthful curiosity left nothing unseen or unexamined. One day I found a little black box behind the stove; I proceeded to investigate what was concealed in it, and slipped back the lid without long deliberation. The picture contained was certainly of a kind not usually exposed to view, and although I tried to shut it again immediately, I was not quick enough. The Count entered and caught me—"Who allowed you to open that box?" he asked, with his Royal Lieutenant manner. I had not much to say for myself, and he immediately pronounced my sentence in a very stern manner. "For a week," said he, "you are not to enter this room." I bowed and walked out. This order I obeyed most punctiliously, so that the good Seekatz, who was then at work in the room, was much annoyed, for he liked to have me about him; and, out of spite, I carried my obedience so far as to put down Seekatz's coffee, which I generally brought him, upon the threshold. He was thus obliged to leave his work and fetch it, which he took in such ill part that he almost stopped being friends with me.

It now seems necessary to explain in greater detail how I managed to make my way, under these circumstances, more or less easily, with the French language, without having ever learned it. Here, again, I was helped by a natural aptitude which enabled me to catch easily the sound of a language, its movement, accent, tone, and all other outward peculiarities. I knew many words from the Latin; Italian supplied still more; and by listening to servants and soldiers, sentries and visitors, I soon picked up so much that, if I could not join in conversation, I could at any rate understand single questions and answer them. All this, however, was trifling compared to the profit I derived from the theatre. My grandfather had given me a free ticket, which I used daily, with my father's disapproval, but with my mother's support. There I sat in the pit, before a foreign stage, and watched the movements and the expression both of gesture and speech the more narrowly as I understood little or nothing of what was being said, and therefore could only derive entertainment from the action and the intonation. I understood least of comedy, because it was spoken rapidly, and related to matters of everyday life, the phrases of which were unknown to me. Tragedy was not played so often, and the measured flow and rhythm of the alexandrines, the generality of the sentiments expressed, made it more intelligible to me in every way. It was not long before I took up Racine, which I found in my father's library, and declaimed the plays to myself, in theatrical style, as my organs of hearing and speech, with their intimate connection, had assimilated them, and this I did with considerable animation, without being able to understand a single connected speech. I even learned entire passages by rote, and repeated them like a parrot, which was the easier to me from having previously been in the habit of committing to memory passages from the Bible which are generally unintelligible to a child, and then reciting them in the tone of Protestant preachers. The versified French comedy was then much in vogue; the pieces of Destouches, Marivaux, and La Chaussée, were often produced, and I still remember distinctly many characteristic figures. Of those of Molière I recollect less. What made the greatest impression upon me was the *Hypermnestra* of Lemierre, which was a new piece, and therefore produced carefully and often repeated. The *Devin du Village*, *Rose et Colas*, *Annette et Lubin*, each left a very pleasing impression upon me. I can even now recall the youths and maidens decorated with ribands, and their movements. It was not long before the wish arose in me to explore the interior of the theatre, for which many opportunities were offered me. For as I did not always have patience to hear the whole of the plays, I often carried on all sorts of games with other children of my age in the corridors, and in warmer weather even outside the door. Often a handsome, lively boy joined us, who was connected with the stage, and whom I had seen in many small parts, though only incidentally. He could make himself understood better with me than with the rest, as I could turn my French to good account with him, and he attached himself to me the more readily because there was no boy of his age or his nationality at the theatre, or anywhere in the neighbourhood. We met at other times, as well as during the play, and even while the representations were going on he seldom left me in peace. He was a most delightful little braggart, chattered away charmingly and incessantly, and could tell so much of his adventures, quarrels, and other strange incidents, that he amused me extremely, and in four weeks I learned from him more of the language, and of the power of expressing myself in it, than would have been thought possible; so that no one knew how I had acquired the foreign tongue all at once, as if by inspiration.

In the very earliest days of our acquaintance he took me with him upon the stage, and in particular led me to the *foyers*, where the actors and actresses remained during the intervals and dressed and undressed. The premises were neither suitable nor convenient, for they had squeezed the theatre into a concert-room, so that there were no separate chambers for the actors behind the stage. A tolerably large ante-room, which had formerly served for card-parties, was now generally used by both sexes in common, who appeared to feel as little ashamed before each other as before us children, even if the strictest propriety were not observed in putting on or changing articles of dress. I had never seen anything of the kind before, and yet from habit, after repeated visits, I soon found it quite natural.

It was not long before a very peculiar interest of my own arose. Young Derones, for so I will call the boy whose acquaintance I kept up, was, apart from his boasting, a properly conducted and well-mannered boy. He introduced me to his sister, who was a few years older than we were, and a very pleasant, well-grown girl, of good figure, with brown complexion, black hair and eyes; her whole bearing had something quiet, even sad, about it. I tried to make myself agreeable to her in every way, but I could not attract her notice. Young girls think themselves far in advance of younger boys, and while their glances are directed towards young men, they assume the manner of an aunt towards the boy whose first affection is expended upon them.—With a younger brother of his I had no acquaintance.

Often, when their mother had gone to rehearsals, or was out visiting, we met at her house to play and amuse ourselves. I never went there without presenting the fair one with a flower, fruit, or some other little gift, which she always received very kindly, and thanked me most politely, but I never saw her sad look brighten, and found no trace of her having given me a further thought. At last I fancied I had discovered her secret. The boy showed me a pastel drawing of a handsome man, behind his mother's bed, draped with elegant silk curtains, remarking at the same time, with a sly look, that this was not really papa, but just the same as papa; and as he glorified this man, and told me many things in his circumstantial and ostentatious manner, I thought I might infer that the daughter belonged to the father, but the other two children to the intimate friend. I thus explained to myself her melancholy look, and only loved her all the more.

My liking for this girl helped me to put up with the extravagances of her brother, which sometimes surpassed all bounds. I had often to endure prolix accounts of his exploits, how he had already fought various duels, but without wishing to injure his opponent—all merely for the sake of honour. He had always contrived to disarm his adversary, and had then forgiven him; nay, he had such skill in knocking his opponent's arms out of his hands that he once caused himself great embarrassment by hitting the sword of his opponent into a high tree, so that it was not easy to recover it.

What much facilitated my visits to the theatre was that my free ticket, coming from the hands of the *Schultheiss*, gave me access to any of the seats, including those in the proscenium. This was very deep, after the French style, and had seats on either side. These seats were enclosed by a low railing, and were arranged in tiers behind one another in such a way that the front seats were but slightly raised above the stage. The whole was regarded as a place of special honour, and was generally used only by officers, although the nearness to the actors destroyed, I will not say all illusion, but, to a certain extent, all charm. I have even experienced and seen with my own eyes the usage, or abuse, of which Voltaire so much complains. It occurred when the house was very full, at such time as troops were passing through the town, and distinguished officers attempted to occupy this place of honour, which was generally already filled: then rows of benches and chairs would be placed in the proscenium on the stage itself, so that nothing remained for the heroes and heroines but to divulge their secret joys and sorrows in the very limited space between the uniforms and orders. I have even seen the *Hypermnestra* performed under such conditions.

The curtain did not fall between the acts; and another strange custom must be mentioned which struck me very much, as its inconsistency with art was to me, as a good German boy, quite intolerable. The theatre was considered the most sacred spot, and any disturbance occurring there would have been instantly resented as the greatest outrage upon the majesty of the public. Therefore in all comedies, two grenadiers stood with their arms grounded, in full view, at the two sides of the curtain at the back of the stage, and were witnesses of all that occurred in the bosom of the family. Since, as I said before, the curtain did not fall between the acts, two others, to the sound of music, relieved guard, by coming from the wings directly in front of the first, who retired with the same measured tread. Since such a practice was calculated to do away with all so-called illusion, it is the more surprising that it should obtain at a time when, in accordance with Diderot's principles and examples, the most *natural naturalness* was demanded upon the stage, and an absolute imitation of life was proposed as the proper aim of theatrical art. Tragedy, however, was absolved from any such military police-regulations, and the heroes of antiquity had the right to guard themselves; nevertheless, the same grenadiers stood close at hand in the wings.

I will also mention that I saw Diderot's "Father of a Family," and "The Philosophers" of Palissot, and still perfectly remember the figure of the philosopher in the latter piece, going upon all fours, and biting a raw head of lettuce.

All this theatrical variety could not, however, keep us children always in the theatre. In fine weather we played in front of it and in the vicinity, and committed all manner of absurdities, which, especially on Sundays and festivals, by no means corresponded to our personal appearance; for I and my comrades then appeared dressed as I described myself in the fairy tale, with my hat under my arm, and a little sword, the hilt of which was ornamented with a large silk knot. One day when we had been playing about, and Derones had joined us, he took it into his head to assert that I had insulted him, and must give him satisfaction. It is true I had no conception what the provocation was; but I accepted his challenge, and prepared to draw my sword. He, however, assured me that in such cases it was customary to go to a secluded spot, so as to settle the matter more conveniently. We therefore withdrew behind some barns, and placed ourselves in the proper position. The duel took place in a somewhat theatrical style, the blades clashed, and the thrusts fell wide of their mark; but in the heat of the combat the point of his sword became entangled in the ribbon knot at my hilt. This was pierced through, and he assured me that he had received the most complete satisfaction; then he embraced me, likewise theatrically, and we went to the nearest coffee-house to refresh ourselves with a glass of almond-milk after our mental agitation, and to knit all the more closely the former bond of friendship.

In this connection I will relate another adventure which also happened to me at the theatre, although at a later date. I was sitting very quietly in the pit with one of my playmates, watching with pleasure a *pas seul*, which was executed with much skill and grace by a pretty boy about our own age—the son of a French dancing-master who was passing through the city. After the fashion of dancers, he was dressed in a close-fitting doublet of red silk, which ended in a short full skirt, like a runner's tunic, reaching down to the knee. We had given our meed of applause to this young artist with the whole of the audience, when—I know not how—a moral reflection came into my head. I said to my companion, "How handsomely this boy is dressed, and how well he looks; who knows in how tattered a jacket he may sleep to-night!"—People were already on their feet, but the crowd prevented our moving. A woman who had sat beside me, and who was now standing close to me, chanced to be the mother of the young artist, and felt much hurt by my reflection. Unfortunately, she knew German enough to understand me, and spoke just as much as enabled her to scold. She abused me violently. Who was I, she would like to know, to have the right to doubt the family and respectability of this young man? At all events, she would be bound he was as good as I, and his talents might probably procure him a fortune, of which I could not even venture to dream. This moral lecture she read me in the crowd, and made those about me wonder whatever rudeness I could have committed. As I could neither excuse myself nor escape from her, I was really embarrassed, and when she paused for a moment, said without thinking, "Well! why make so much fuss?—to-day red, to-morrow dead."* These words seemed to strike the woman dumb. She stared at me, and moved away from me as soon as it was in any degree possible. I thought no more of my words; it was only some time afterwards that they recurred to me, when the boy, instead of continuing to perform, fell ill of a very dangerous malady. Whether he died or not, I cannot say.

Such premonitions in the shape of inopportune, or even unsuitable words, were held in repute even by the ancients, and it is very remarkable that the forms of belief and of superstition have remained unchanged among all peoples and in all periods.

From the first day of the occupation of our city, incessant diversion might be had, especially for children and young people. Plays and balls, parades, and the marching through of troops, drew our attention hither and thither. The numbers passing through were always on the increase, and the soldiers' life seemed to us a merry and attractive one.

The residence of the King's Lieutenant in our house procured us the advantage of gradually seeing all the distinguished members of the French army, and especially of inspecting at close quarters the commanders, whose names were already known to us by reputation. It was quite easy for us to look down from staircases and landings, as though they had been galleries, upon the generals who passed by. In particular I remember the PRINCE SOUBISE as a handsome, affable gentleman, but most distinctly of all the MARÉCHAL DE BROGLIO, who was a younger man, not tall, but well-built, lively, and quick, with intelligent eyes for what was passing around him.

He came frequently to the King's Lieutenant, and it was obvious that weighty matters were discussed. By the end of the first three months we were just beginning to get accustomed to having strangers quartered upon us, when a vague rumour was circulated that the Allies were on the march, and that Duke Ferdinand of Brunswick was coming to drive the French from the Maine. A poor opinion was held of the latter, as they had not been particularly successful in the war, and after the battle of Rossbach there seemed reason for despising them. Duke Ferdinand enjoyed the

---

* A German proverb, "Heute rot, morgen tot."

greatest confidence, and all who were Prussian in their sympathies awaited with eagerness their deliverance from the yoke hitherto borne. My father was in somewhat better spirits—my mother was apprehensive. She was wise enough to see that a slight present discomfort might easily be exchanged for a great disaster; for it was but too plain that the French would not advance to meet the Duke, but would wait to be attacked in the neighbourhood of the city. A defeat of the French, their flight, the defence of the city, if it were only to cover their retreat and to hold the bridge, a bombardment, a general pillage—all these possibilities presented themselves to the excited imagination, and were cause of anxiety to both parties. My mother, who could bear everything but suspense, imparted her fears to the Count through the interpreter. She received the usual answer in such cases: she might be quite easy, for there was nothing to fear, and should keep quiet and mention the matter to no one.

Many troops passed through the city; we learned that they had halted at Bergen. The coming and going, the riding and running constantly increased, and our house was in an uproar day and night. At this time I often saw Maréchal de Broglio, always cheerful, always the same in look and manner, and I was afterwards pleased to find the man, whose appearance had made such a good and lasting impression upon me, honourably mentioned in history.

Thus, after an unquiet Passion week, the Good Friday of 1759 arrived. A profound stillness announced the approaching storm. We children were forbidden to quit the house: my father could not rest, and went out. The battle began: I went up into the garret, where, though I could not see the country round, I could plainly hear the thunder of cannons and the volleying of musketry. After some hours we saw the first evidences of the battle in a line of wagons, in which the wounded, sadly mutilated, and groaning with pain, were slowly driven past us, to be taken to the convent of St. Mary, now transformed into a hospital. The compassion of the citizens was instantly called forth. Beer, wine, bread, and money were distributed to such as were in a condition to receive them. But when shortly afterwards wounded and captive Germans were seen in the train, pity knew no limits, and it seemed as if everyone were anxious to divest himself of all his goods and chattels to assist his suffering countrymen.

The prisoners, however, were an indication that the battle was going against the Allies. My father, whose party feelings made him quite certain that they would come off victorious, had the reckless temerity to go forth to meet the expected victors, without thinking that the defeated party must run over him in their flight. He first repaired to his garden outside the Friedberg Gate, where he found everything quiet and deserted; then he ventured on to the Bornheim Heath, where he soon descried various stragglers and camp followers, amusing themselves by shooting at the boundary-stones, so that the rebounding bullets whizzed about the head of the inquisitive wanderer. He therefore considered it more prudent to go back, and learned on enquiry—as the sound of firing might have convinced him—that all stood well for the French, and that there was no thought of retreating. Reaching home out of temper, the sight of his wounded and captured countrymen made him altogether lose his usual self-control. He, too, caused various donations to be given to the passers-by, but only Germans were to have them, which was not always practicable, as fate had packed together friend and foe in the same wagon.

My mother and we children, who had relied on the Count's word before this happened, and had therefore passed a tolerably quiet day, were highly rejoiced, and my mother was doubly reassured, for in the morning, when she consulted the oracle of her "Golden Treasury," by sticking a pin between the leaves, she had received a very consoling answer, both as regards the present and the future. We wished our father a similar faith and frame of mind; we flattered him as much as we could; we entreated him to have something to eat, as he had taken nothing all day; but he repulsed our caresses and all food, and betook himself to his chamber. Our joy, meanwhile, was untroubled; the encounter was at an end; the King's Lieutenant, who, contrary to his wont, had been on horseback to-day, at last returned home, where his presence was more necessary than ever. We sprang to meet him, kissed his hands, and testified our delight. This seemed to please him greatly. "Well," said he more kindly than usual, "I am glad also for your sakes, my dear children." He immediately ordered sweetmeats, sweet wine, in short, the best of everything to be given us, and went to his room, already surrounded by a crowd of persons, importuning him with demands and petitions.

We now enjoyed a delicious feast, pitied our poor father who would not partake of it, and pressed our mother to go and call him; but she, wiser than we, well knew how distasteful such gifts would be to him. In the meantime she had prepared supper, and would have liked to send some up to his room, but he never permitted such irregularities even in the most extreme cases; and after the sweet things were removed, we endeavoured to persuade him to come down into the ordinary dining-room. At last he unwillingly allowed himself to be persuaded, and we had no notion of the mischief which we were preparing for him and ourselves. The staircase ran through the whole house, past all the corridors. My father on his way down had to go directly past the Count's apartment. The hall outside his room was so full of people, that the Count, with a view to transacting various businesses at once, resolved to come out, and unfortunately this happened at the moment when my father was coming downstairs. The Count went up to him cheerfully, greeted him, and remarked, "You must congratulate yourselves and us that this dangerous affair has terminated so happily." "By no means!" replied my father in great wrath; "I wish they had driven you to the devil, even if I had had to go too." The Count paused for a moment, and then broke out in a rage—"You shall suffer for this," cried he; "you will find that you have not insulted the good cause and myself in this way for nothing!"

My father, meanwhile, had come down calmly, seated himself with us, seemed more cheerful than before, and begun to eat. We were glad of this, unconscious of the dangerous method in which he had unburdened his heart. Soon afterwards my mother was called out, and we longed to chatter to our father about the good things the Count had given us. Our mother did not return. At last the interpreter came in. At a hint from him we were sent to bed; it was already late, and we obeyed willingly. After sleeping quietly all night, we heard of the violent commotion which had perturbed the house the previous evening. The King's Lieutenant had instantly ordered my father to be taken to the guard-house. The subalterns knew very well that he was never to be contradicted; yet they had often earned thanks by delaying to execute his orders. The interpreter, whose presence of mind never forsook him, succeeded in impressing this point of view upon them. The tumult, moreover, was so great, that delay under the circumstances would be unnoticed and excusable. He had called out my mother, and put the aide-de-camp, as it were, into her hands, so that by prayers and representations she might effect a brief respite. He himself hurried to the Count, who with his great self-command had immediately retired into the inner room, and preferred that the most urgent business should wait a moment, rather than wreak the ill-humour that had been aroused in him on an innocent person, and give a decision derogatory to his dignity.

His own address to the Count, as well as the train of the whole conversation, were so often repeated to us by the fat interpreter, who prided himself not a little on the fortunate issue, that I can still reproduce it from memory.

The interpreter had ventured to open the cabinet and enter, an act which was strictly prohibited. "What do you want?" shouted the Count, angrily. "Out with you!—no one but St. Jean has a right to enter here."

"Well, suppose I am St. Jean for a moment," answered the interpreter.

"It would need a lively imagination to do that! Two of him would not make one such as you. Retire!"

"Count, you have received a great gift from heaven, and to that I appeal."

"You think to flatter me! Do not fancy you will succeed."

"You have the great gift, Count, of listening—even in moments of passion, in moments of anger—to the opinions of others."

"Well, well, it is precisely a question of opinions that we have before us—opinions to which I have listened too long. I know but too well that we are not liked here, and that these burghers look askance at us."

"Not all!"

"Very many. What! Do these citizens call themselves citizens of the Empire? They saw their Emperor elected and crowned, and when he is unjustly attacked and in danger of losing his dominions and surrendering to an usurper; when he fortunately finds faithful allies who sacrifice their blood and their wealth in his behalf—they will not bear the slight burden that falls to their share, towards humbling the enemy!"

"But you have long known these sentiments, and have tolerated them like a wise man; they are, besides, held only by a minority. A few, dazzled by the splendid qualities of the enemy, whom you yourself acknowledge to be an extraordinary man, a few only—as you are aware."

"Yes, indeed! I have known and tolerated it too long; otherwise this man would not have presumed to utter such insults to my face, at the most critical moment. Let them be as many as they please, they shall be punished in the person of this their audacious representative, and find out what they have to expect."

"Only delay, Count!"

"In some cases it is impossible to act too promptly."

"Only a slight delay, Count!"

"Neighbour, you think to lead me into a false step; you shall not succeed."

"I would neither lead you into a false step nor keep you from one; your resolution is just; it becomes the Frenchman and the King's Lieutenant; but consider that you are also Count Thorane!"

"He has nothing to say in this case."

"But the gallant man has a right to be heard."

"What would he say then?"

"King's Lieutenant," he would begin, "you have so long had patience with so many insignificant, disobliging, bungling men, if they did not go too far. This man certainly went very far; do but prevail upon yourself to be equally patient now, King's Lieutenant, and every one will praise and extol you for so doing."

"You know I can often endure your jests, but do not abuse my good-will. These people—are they completely blinded? Suppose we had lost the battle, what would have been their fate at this moment? We fight to the very gates, we shut up the city, we halt, we defend ourselves to cover our retreat over the bridge. Think you, the enemy would have stood with his hands before him? He throws grenades, and whatever he has at hand, and they set fire wherever possible. This householder—what would he have? Here, in these rooms, a bomb might have burst this minute, and another have followed it;—in these rooms, where I spared the cursed China wall-papers and inconvenienced myself by not nailing up my maps! They ought to have spent the whole day on their knees."

"How many have done so!"

"They ought to have prayed for a blessing on us, and to have gone out to meet the generals and officers with tokens of honour and joy, and the wearied soldiers with refreshments. Instead of this, the poison of party-spirit destroys the fairest and happiest moments of my life, won by so many anxieties and efforts."

"It is party-spirit; but you will only increase it by punishing this man. Those who think with him will proclaim you a tyrant and a barbarian:—they will consider him a martyr, who has suffered for the good cause; and even those of the other opinion, who are now his opponents, will see in him only their fellow-citizen, will pity him, and while they confess your justice, will yet feel that you have proceeded too severely."

"I have listened to you too long already,—now, away with you!"

"Only listen to this one word more! Remember this is the most unheard-of thing that could befall this man, this family. You have had no reason to be edified by the good-will of the master of the house; but the mistress has anticipated all your wishes, and the children have regarded you as their uncle. With this single blow, you will for ever destroy the peace and happiness of this dwelling. Indeed, I may say, that a bomb falling into the house, would not have occasioned greater desolation. I have so often admired your self-command, Count; give me on this occasion reason to adore you. A warrior is worthy of honour who considers himself a guest in the house of an enemy; but here there is no enemy, only a mistaken man. Prevail upon yourself, and you will acquire everlasting fame."

"That would be odd," replied the Count, with a smile.

"Merely natural," continued the interpreter; "I have not sent the wife and children to your feet, because I know you detest such scenes; but I will depict to you the gratitude of this wife and these children. I will depict them to you talking all their lives of the Battle of Bergen, and of your magnanimity on this day, relating it to their children, and children's children, and inspiring even strangers with their own interest for you: an act of this kind can never perish."

"But this does not appeal to my weak side, interpreter! About posthumous fame I am not in the habit of thinking; that is for others, not for me; but to do right at the moment, not to neglect my duty, not to prejudice my honour—that is my care. We have already had too many words; now go—and receive the thanks of the thankless, whom I spare."

The interpreter, surprised and moved by this unexpectedly favourable issue, could not restrain his tears, and would have kissed the Count's hands. The Count motioned him off, and said sternly and gravely, "You know I cannot bear such things." And with these words he went into the passage to attend to his pressing affairs, and hear the wants of the waiting crowd. So the matter was disposed of, and next morning we celebrated with the remnants of the yesterday's sweetmeats the passing of a disaster which had menaced us while we were happily asleep.

Whether the interpreter really spoke so wisely, or merely painted the scene in this way to himself, as one is apt to do after a virtuous and successful action, I will not decide; at least he never varied in repeating it. Suffice it to say, this day seemed to him both the most anxious and the most glorious in his life.

One little incident will show how the Count always rejected all false parade, never assumed a title which did not belong to him, and how witty he always was in his more cheerful moods.

A man of good family, who was one of the eccentric, solitary Frankforters, felt it necessary to complain of the quartering of the soldiers upon him. He came in person, and the interpreter proffered his services, but the other considered that he did not require them. He presented himself to the Count with a most gentlemanly bow, and said, "Your Excellency!" The Count returned the bow, as well as the "Excellency." Surprised by this mark of honour, and inferring that the title was too humble, he bowed more deeply, and said, "Monseigneur." "Sir," said the Count, quite seriously, "we will go no further, or else we might easily arrive at 'Your Majesty.'" The gentleman was extremely confused, and had not a word to say. The interpreter, standing at some distance, and cognizant of the whole proceeding, was spiteful enough not to move, but the Count continued with great sprightliness, "Well now, for example, sir, what is your name?" "Spangenberg," replied the other. "And mine," said the Count, "is Thorane. Spangenberg, what is your business with Thorane? Now, then, let us sit down; the matter shall be settled at once."

And the matter was settled at once, to the great satisfaction of the person I have here called Spangenberg, and the very same evening, in our family circle, the story was not only related by the malicious interpreter, but was acted with all the details and gestures.

After such disturbances, turmoil, and troubles, we soon returned to the security and thoughtlessness in which young people, especially, live from day to day, if it be at all possible. My passion for the French theatre grew with every performance. I did not miss a single evening, although, when I sat down with the family to supper after the play—often satisfied with scanty remains—I had to endure the invariable reproaches of my father, that theatres were useless, and would lead to nothing. In these cases I adduced all and every available argument used by apologists of the stage when they find themselves in a difficulty such as mine. Vice in prosperity and virtue in misfortune are in the end set right by poetical justice. I laid stress on those beautiful examples of misdeeds punished, *Miss Sara Sampson*, and *The Merchant of London;* but, on the other hand, I often came off worst when *Les Fourberies de Scapin*, and similar plays, appeared on the programme, and I was twitted with the delight taken by the public in the impostures of intriguing servants, and the successful escapades of dissolute youths. Neither side convinced the other, but my father was very soon reconciled to the theatre when he saw with what incredible rapidity I was acquiring the French language.

Men are so constituted that everybody is anxious to try his own hand at whatever he sees others doing, whether he has aptitude for it or not. I had soon covered the whole range of the French stage; several pieces were being given for the second and third times; all had passed before my eyes and mind, from the stateliest tragedy to the most frivolous afterpiece; and just as when a child I had presumed to imitate Terence, so now as a boy I did not fail, on much greater incitement, to copy the French forms to the best of my ability and inability. At that time some half-mythological, half-allegorical pieces in the taste of Piron were being acted; they had something of the nature of parody about them, and were very popular. These representations had a particular attraction for me: the little gold wings of a sprightly Mercury, the thunderbolt of a disguised Jupiter, an amorous Danaë, or whatever the name of the fair one visited by the gods might be, if indeed it were not a shepherdess or huntress to whom they stooped. And as figures of this kind, from *Ovid's Metamorphoses*, or the *Pantheon Mythicum* of Pomey, very often flitted through my head—I had soon put together a little play of the same kind in imagination, of which I only remember that the scene was rural, but at the same time king's daughters, princes, and gods appeared in it. Mercury, especially, was so vividly before my mind's eye, that I could almost swear to having actually seen him.

I presented my friend Derones with a very neat copy, made by myself, which he accepted very ceremoniously, and, with the manner of a real patron, glanced hastily over the manuscript, pointed out a few grammatical blunders, found some speeches too long, and finally promised to examine the work attentively and give his verdict when he had the requisite leisure. To my modest question, whether the piece could be performed, he assured me that it was not altogether impossible. In the theatre, he said, a great deal went by favour, and he would support me with all his heart: only the thing must be kept a secret; for he had himself once surprised the manager with a piece of his own, and it would certainly have been acted, if the authorship had not been discovered too soon. I promised him all possible secrecy; and already saw in my mind's eye the name of my piece posted up in large letters at the corners of the streets and squares.

Frivolous as my friend generally was, the opportunity of acting the part of master was only too attractive. He read the piece through with attention, and after sitting down with me to make some trivial alterations, in the course of the conversation turned the whole thing topsy-turvy, so that not one brick was left standing on another. He cancelled, added, took away one character, substituted another,—in short, proceeded with the wildest caprice in the world, so that my hair stood on end. My preconceived idea that he knew what he was talking about prevented my interfering; for he had often talked so much to me about the Three Unities of Aristotle, the regularity of the French drama, dramatic probability, the harmony of the verse, and all cognate subjects, that I was fain to regard him, not merely as well-informed, but backed up by reason. He abused the English and scorned the Germans; in short, he recited to me the same old dramatic theory which I have been obliged to hear repeated so often in my life.

Like the boy in the fable, I carried my mangled offspring home, and strove to restore it to life, but in vain. As, however, I did not wish to abandon it altogether, I had a fair copy made by our clerk from my first manuscript, with a few alterations, and this copy I presented to my father, with the result that for some time afterwards he let me eat my supper in peace on returning from the play.

This unsuccessful attempt had made me reflective, and I resolved now to study the sources of these theories, these laws, to which everyone appealed, but the truth of which I had begun to suspect, especially after the unmannerly conduct of my arrogant master. It was not difficult for me to do so, but entailed some hard reading. First I read Corneille's *Treatise on the Three Unities*, and discovered from it the form of drama which people desired, but the reason why they desired this form was by no means clear to me, and, worst of all, I became involved in yet greater confusion when I made myself acquainted with the disputes on the *Cid*, and read the prefaces in which Corneille and Racine are obliged to defend themselves against the critics and the public. Here at least I saw most plainly that no one knew what he was aiming at; that a piece like the *Cid*, which had achieved the noblest success, was actually to have been condemned at the command of an all-powerful cardinal; that Racine, the idol of the Frenchmen living in my day, who was now likewise my idol—(for I had come to know him well when Schöff von Olenschlager made us children act *Britannicus*, in which the part of Nero fell to me)—I saw that Racine, even in his own day, was unable to conciliate both amateurs and critics. Thus I became more perplexed than ever, and after tormenting myself a long time with these pros and cons, and the theoretical twaddle of the previous century, I cast away good and bad alike. I was the more resolute in throwing all this rubbish overboard, because I noticed that when authors of really excellent works began to discuss their own productions and to explain their methods, there was apt to be no little confusion in their attempts at self-defence, justification, or excuse. I hastened back again, therefore, to what the present day offered me, attended the theatre far more zealously, read more conscientiously and connectedly, so that I had the perseverance to work through the whole of Racine and Molière, and a great part of Corneille, at this time.

The King's lieutenant still lived in our house. He had made no change in his behaviour, especially towards us; but it was observable, and the interpreter made it still more evident to us, that he no longer discharged his duties with the same cheerfulness and zeal as at the outset, though always with the same rectitude and fidelity. His character and habits, which showed the Spaniard rather than the Frenchman; his caprices, which probably now and then affected his business transactions; his

569

refusal to accommodate himself to circumstances; his susceptibility to everything that touched his person or reputation—all
this together may have sometimes brough him into conflict with
his superiors. Added to this, he had been wounded in a duel,
which had arisen in the theatre, and it was deemed wrong that
the King's Lieutenant, himself chief of police, should have committed a punishable offence. All this, as has been said, may have
contributed to make him live in greater retirement, and now
and then perhaps to act with less energy.

Meanwhile, a considerable number of the pictures he had
ordered had been delivered. Count Thorane passed his leisure
hours in examining them; he had them nailed up in the aforesaid
gable-room, canvas after canvas, large and small, side by side, and,
from lack of space, even one over another, and then taken down
and rolled up. The works were constantly inspected anew; the
parts that were considered the most successful were a source of
ever fresh delight; but the wish that this or that had been differently done was also expressed.

This gave rise to a new and very singular operation. As one
artist excelled in figure-painting, another in the management of
perspective, a third in trees, a fourth in flowers, it occurred to
the Count that these talents might be combined in the paintings,
and perfect works produced by this method. A beginning was
made at once; for instance, some beautiful flocks were painted
into a finished landscape. But because there was not always an
appropriate space, and a few sheep more or less was no great
matter to the animal-painter, the most extensive landscape proved
in the end too confined. Then the figure-painter had to introduce
the shepherd, and some wayfarers; these, again, seemed to deprive
each other of air; and it was a wonder that they were not all
stifled, even in the most open country. It was never possible to
foresee what was to be the final result, and when the picture
was finished it gave no satisfaction. The artists were annoyed.
They had profited by their first commissions, but lost by these
supplementary labours, though the Count paid for these, too,
very liberally, and as the miscellaneous parts, promiscuously
introduced by several hands into one picture, failed of their
effect after all the trouble taken, in the end each one fancied
that his own work had been spoiled and destroyed by that of the
others; hence the artists were within a hair's-breadth of falling
out and becoming irreconcilable enemies. These alterations, or

rather additions, were made in the before-mentioned studio, where I remained quite alone with the artists; and I amused myself by selecting, particularly from the studies of animals, this or that individual or group, and proposing it for the foreground or the distance; and, either from conviction or kindness, my suggestions were frequently followed.

The participators in this business were, therefore, greatly discouraged, especially Seekatz, a reserved and very splenetic person, whose incomparably good spirits nevertheless made him the best of companions when among friends, but when at work, he liked to be left alone, lost in thought and free to do as he liked. This man, after tackling difficult tasks, and finishing them with the greatest diligence and the warmest love, of which he was always capable, was forced to travel repeatedly from Darmstadt to Frankfort, either to change something in his own pictures, or to add figures to those of others, or even to assist in having his pictures converted into motley jumbles by a third person. His ill-humour increased, his resistance became more decided, and it needed many efforts on our part to induce this friend, whose connection with us had recently become more intimate, to carry out the Count's wishes. I still remember that when the boxes were standing ready for packing all the pictures in the right order, so that on arriving at their place of destination the upholsterer might hang them at once, it was found that a trifling but indispensable bit of supplementary work was required, but Seekatz could not be induced to come over. He had, in fact, finally done his very best in a series of pictures to be placed over the doors, representing the four elements in the guise of children and youths copied from life, and had expended the greatest care, not only on the figures, but on the accessories. These pictures had been delivered and paid for, and he thought he had said good-bye to the business for ever; but now he was to come back again, in order to enlarge, by a few strokes of his brush, certain pictures which did not fulfil the required measurements. Some one else, he thought, could do it just as well; he had already set about a new piece of work; in short, he would not come. The time for sending off the pictures was at hand; they must also have time to dry; every delay was most awkward; and the Count, in despair, was about to have him fetched by military authority. We all wished to see the last of the pictures, and in the end were reduced to sending our friend the interpreter in a carriage to fetch the refractory subject, with wife and child. He was kindly received by the Count, well treated, and at last dismissed, loaded with presents.

After the pictures had been sent away, great peace reigned in the house. The gable-room in the roof was cleaned and given up to me; and my father, when he saw the boxes go, could not stifle the wish to send the Count after them. For much as the tastes of the Count coincided with his own, much as he must have rejoiced to see his principle of patronizing living artists so generously put into practice by a man richer than himself, much as it may have flattered him to see his collection the means of bringing so considerable a profit to a number of honest artists in hard times, he nevertheless felt such a repugnance to the foreign interloper in his house, that he could not think well of any of his doings. He thought painters ought to be employed, but not degraded to upholterers; one ought to be satisfied with the result of their conviction and ability, even if it did not please one altogether; and one ought not to be perpetually cavilling at and bargaining about it. In short, in spite of all the Count's own generous endeavours, there could, once for all, be no mutual understanding. My father only visited the Count's room when he was at table, and I can recall but one instance when the wish to see certain pictures in which Seekatz had surpassed himself had brought the whole household together: my father and the Count met and expressed a common pleasure in these works of art, which they could not take in each other.

Scarcely, therefore, had the house been cleared of the boxes and cases, than the plan for removing the Count, which had been initiated some time before, but afterwards interrupted, was resumed. We endeavoured to gain justice by representations, equity by entreaties, favour by influence, with the result that the billeting authorities came to the following decision: the Count was to change his lodgings, and our house, in consideration of the burden borne uninterruptedly day and night for several years, was to be exempt for the future from billeting. But, to furnish a plausible pretext, we were to take in lodgers on the first floor, which the Count had occupied, and thus make, as it were, a new quartering out of the question.

LITERARY ESSAYS

Literary Essays

SHAKESPEARE AD INFINITUM

(1813-16)

THERE has already been so much said about Shakespeare that it would seem as if there was nothing left to say; and yet it is the characteristic of genius ever to be stimulating other men's genius. In the present case I wish to consider Shakespeare from more than one point of view,—first as a poet in general, then in comparison with the classic and modern writers, and finally as a writer of poetic drama. I shall attempt to work out what the imitation of his art has meant to us, and what it can mean in the future. I shall express my agreement with what has been written by reiterating it, and express my dissent briefly and positively, without involving myself in conflict and contradiction. I proceed to the first topic.

I. SHAKESPEARE AS POET IN GENERAL

THE HIGHEST achievement possible to a man is the full consciousness of his own feelings and thoughts, for this gives him the means of knowing intimately the hearts of others. Now there are men who are born with a natural talent for this and who cultivate it by experience towards practical ends. From this talent springs the ability to profit in a higher sense by the world and its opportunities. Now the poet is born with the same talent, only he cultivates it not for his immediate worldly purposes but for a loftier spiritual and universal purpose. If we call Shakespeare one of the greatest poets, we mean that few have perceived the world as accurately as he, that few who have expressed their

Translated by Randolph Bourne

inner contemplation of it have given the reader deeper insight into its meaning and consciousness. It becomes for us completely transparent: we find ourselves at once in the most intimate touch with virtue and vice, greatness and meanness, nobility and infamy, and all this through the simplest of means. If we ask what these means are, it seems as if they were directed towards our visual apprehension. But we are mistaken; Shakespeare's works are not for the physical vision. I shall attempt to explain what I mean.

The eye, the most facile of our organs of receptivity, may well be called the clearest of the senses; but the inner sense is still clearer, and to it by means of words belongs the most sensitive and clear receptivity. This is particularly obvious when what we apprehend with the eye seems alien and unimpressive considered in and for itself. But Shakespeare speaks always to our inner sense. Through this, the picture-world of imagination becomes animated, and a complete effect results, of which we can give no reckoning. Precisely here lies the ground for the illusion that everything is taking place before our eyes. But if we study the works of Shakespeare enough, we find that they contain much more of spiritual truth than of spectacular action. He makes happen what can easily be conceived by the imagination, indeed what can be better imagined than seen. Hamlet's ghost, Macbeth's witches, many fearful incidents, get their value only through the power of the imagination, and many of the minor scenes get their force from the same source. In reading, all these things pass easily through our minds, and seem quite appropriate, whereas in representation on the stage they would strike us unfavorably and appear not only unpleasant but even disgusting.

Shakespeare gets his effect by means of the living word, and it is for this reason that one should hear him read, for then the attention is not distracted either by a too adequate or a too inadequate stage-setting. There is no higher or purer pleasure than to sit with closed eyes and hear a naturally expressive voice recite, not declaim, a play of Shakespeare's. According to the delineation of the characters we can picture to ourselves certain forms, but more particularly are we able by the succession of words and phrases to learn what is passing in their souls; the characters seem to have agreed to leave us in the dark, in doubt, about nothing. To that end conspire heroes and lackeys, gentlemen and slaves, kings and heralds; indeed even the subordinate characters are often more expressive in this way than the leading figures. Everything which in an affair of great importance breathes only secretly through the air, or lies hidden in the hearts of men, is here openly expressed. What the soul anxiously conceals and represses is here brought freely and abundantly to the light. We experience the truth of life,—how, we do not know!

Shakespeare associates himself with the World-Spirit; like it, he explores the world; from neither is anything hidden. But whereas it is the business of the World-Spirit to keep its secrets both before and after the event, it is the work of the poet to tell them, and take us into his confidence before the event or in the very action itself. The depraved man of power, the well-intentioned dullard, the passionate lover, the quiet scholar, all carry their heart in their hand, often contrary to verisimilitude. Every one is candid and loquacious. It is enough that the secret must out, and even the stones would publish it. The inanimate insists upon speaking; the elements, the phenomena of sky, earth and sea, thunder and lightning, wild animals, lift their voice, often apparently symbolically, but all joining in the revelation.

The whole civilized world too brings its treasures to Shakespeare; Art and Science, Commerce and Industry, all bear him their gifts. Shakespeare's poems are a great animated fair; and it is to his own country that he owes his riches.

For back of him is England, the sea-encircled and mist-covered country, whose enterprise reaches all the parts of the earth. The poet lives at a noble and important epoch, and presents all its glory and its deficiencies with great vivacity; indeed, he would hardly produce such an effect upon us were it not just his own life-epoch that he was representing. No one despised the outer costume of men more than he; but he understood well the inner man, and here all are similar. It is said that he has delineated the Romans with wonderful skill. I cannot see it. They are Englishmen to the bone; but they are human, thoroughly human, and thus the Roman toga presumably fits them. When one takes this into consideration, one finds his anachronisms entirely admirable; indeed, it is just his neglect of the outer form that makes his works so vital.

Enough of these slight words, which cannot begin to sound

the praises of Shakespeare. His friends and worshipers will have to add many a word to them. But one more remark:—it would be hard to find a poet each of whose works was more thoroughly pervaded by a definite and effective idea than his.

Thus *Coriolanus* is permeated by the idea of anger at the refusal of the lower classes to recognize the superiority of their betters. In *Julius Cæsar* everything hinges on the idea that the upper classes are not willing to see the highest place in the State occupied, since they wrongly imagine that they are able to act together. *Antony and Cleopatra* expresses with a thousand tongues the idea that pleasure and action are ever incompatible. And so one will ever find, in searching his works, new cause for astonishment and admiration.

II. Shakespeare Compared with the Ancients and the Moderns

The interests which vitalize Shakespeare's great genius are interests which centre in this world. For if prophecy and madness, dreams, omens, portents, fairies and gnomes, ghosts, imps, and conjurers introduce a magical element which so beautifully pervades his poems, yet these figures are in no way the basic elements of his works, but rest on a broad basis of the truth and fidelity of life, so that everything that comes from his pen seems to us genuine and sound. It has already been suggested that he belongs not so much to the poets of the modern era, which has been called "romantic," but much more to the "naturalistic" school, since his work is permeated with the reality of the present, and scarcely touches the emotions of unsatisfied desire, except at his highest points.

Disregarding this, however, he is, from a closer point of view, a decidedly modern poet, separated from the ancients by an enormous gulf, not perhaps with regard to his outer form, which is here beside our point, but with regard to his inner and most profound spirit.

Here let me say that it is not my idea to use the following terminology as exhaustive or exclusive; it is an attempt not so much to add another new antithesis to those already recognized, as to indicate that it is already contained in these. These are the antitheses:—

Ancient	Modern
Natural	Sentimental
Pagan	Christian
Classic	Romantic
Realistic	Idealistic
Necessity	Freedom
Duty (*sollen*)	Will (*wollen*)*

The greatest ills to which men are exposed, as well as the most numerous, arise from a certain inner conflict between duty and will, as well as between duty and its accomplishment, and desire and its accomplishment; and it is these conflicts which bring us so often into trouble in the course of our lives. Little difficulties, springing from a slight error which, though taking us by surprise, can be solved easily, give the clue to situations of comedy. The great difficulties, on the other hand, unresolved and unresolvable, give us tragedy.

Predominating in the old poems is the conflict between duty and performance, in the new between desire and accomplishment. Let us put this decided divergency among the other antitheses and see if it does not prove suggestive. In both epochs, I have said, there predominates now this side, now that; but since duty and desire are not radically separated in men's characters, both will be found together, even if one prevails and the other is subordinate. Duty is imposed upon men; "must" is a bitter pill. The Will man imposes upon himself; man's will is his kingdom of heaven. A long-continued obligation is burdensome, the inability to perform it even terrible; but a constant will is pleasurable, and with a firm will men can console themselves for their inability to accomplish their desire.

---

* "Goethe, in a thoughtful essay, *Shakespeare und kein Ende*, written many years later than his famous criticism of Hamlet in *Wilhelm Meister*, says that the distinction between the two [ancient and modern drama] is the difference between *sollen* and *wollen*, that is, between *must* and *would*. He means that in the Greek drama the catastrophe is foreordained by an inexorable Destiny, while the element of free will, and consequently choice, is the very axis of the modern. The definition is conveniently portable, but it has its limitations. Goethe's attention was too exclusively fixed on the fate tragedies of the Greeks, and upon Shakespeare among the moderns. In the Spanish drama, for example, custom, loyalty, honor, and religion are as imperative and as inevitable as doom. In the *Antigone*, on the other hand, the crisis lies in the character of the protagonist."— James Russell Lowell, *Shakespeare Once More.*

Johann Wolfgang von Goethe

Let us consider a game of cards as a kind of poem; it consists of both those elements. The form of the game, bound up with chance, plays here the rôle of necessity, just as the ancients knew it under the form of Fate; the will, bound up with the skill of the player, works in the other direction. In this sense I might call whist "classic." The form of play limits the operation of chance, and even of the will itself. I have to play, in company with definite partners and opponents, with the cards which come into my hand, make the best of a long series of chance plays, without being able to control or parry them. In Ombre and similar games, the contrary is the case. Here are many openings left for skill and daring. I can disavow the cards that fall to my hand, make them count in different ways, half or completely discard them, get help by luck, and in the play get the best advantage out of the worst cards. Thus this kind of game resembles perfectly the modern mode of thought and literature.

Ancient tragedy was based on inescapable necessity, which was only sharpened and accelerated by an opposing will. Here is the seat of all that is fearful in the oracles, the region in which Œdipus lords it over all. Less tragic appears necessity in the guise of duty in the "Antigone"; and in how many forms does it not appear! But all necessity is despotic, whether it belong to the realm of Reason, like custom and civil law, or to Nature, like the laws of Becoming, and Growing and Passing-away, of Life and of Death. Before all these we tremble, without realizing that it is the good of the *whole* that is aimed at The will, on the contrary, is free, appears free, and is advantageous to the *individual*. Thus the will is a flatterer, and takes possession of men as soon as they learn to recognize it. It is the god of the modern world. Dedicated to it, we are afraid of opposing doctrines, and here lies the crux of that eternal division which separates our art and thought from the ancients. Through the motive of Necessity, tragedy became mighty and strong; through the motive of Will, weak and feeble. Out of the latter arose the so-called Drama, in which dread Necessity is overcome and dissolved through the Will. But just because this comes to the aid of our weakness we feel moved when, after painful tension, we are at last a little encouraged and consoled.

As I turn now, after these preliminaries, to Shakespeare, I must express the hope that the reader himself will make the proper comparisons and applications. It is Shakespeare's unique distinction that he has combined in such remarkable fashion the old and the new. In his plays Will and Necessity struggle to maintain an equilibrium; both contend powerfully, yet always so that Will remains at a disadvantage.

No one has shown perhaps better than he the connection between Necessity and Will in the individual character. The person, considered as a character, is under a certain necessity; he is constrained, appointed to a certain particular line of action; but as a human being he has a will, which is unconfined and universal in its demands. Thus arises an inner conflict, and Shakespeare is superior to all other writers in the significance with which he endows this. But now an outer conflict may arise, and the individual through it may become so aroused that an insufficient will is raised through circumstance to the level of irremissible necessity. These motives I have referred to earlier in the case of Hamlet; but the motive is repeated constantly in Shakespeare,— Hamlet through the agency of the ghost; Macbeth through the witches, Hecate, and his wife; Brutus through his friends gets into a dilemma and situation to which they were not equal; even in Coriolanus the same motive is found. This Will, which reaches beyond the power of the individual, is decidedly modern. But since in Shakespeare it does not spring from within, but is developed through external circumstance, it becomes a sort of Necessity, and approaches the classical motive. For all the heroes of ancient poetry willed only what was possible to men, and from this arose that beautiful balance between Necessity, Will, and Accomplishment. Still their Necessity is a little too severe for it really to be able to please us, even though we may wonder at and admire it. A Necessity which more or less, or even completely, excludes human freedom does not chime with our views any longer. It is true that Shakespeare in his own way has approximated this, but in making this Necessity a moral necessity he has, to our pleasure and astonishment, united the spirit of the ancient and the modern worlds. If we are to learn anything from him, here is the point where we must study in his school. Instead of singing the praises of our Romanticism so exclusively, and sticking to it so uncritically,—our Romanticism, which need not be chidden or rejected,—and thus mistaking and obscuring its strong, solid practical aspect, we should rather attempt to make this great fusion between the old and the new, even though it does seem inconsistent and paradoxical; and all the more should we make the attempt, because a great and unique master, whom we value most highly, and, often without knowing why, give homage to above all others, has already most effectively accomplished this miracle. To be sure, he had the advantage of living in a true time of harvest, and of working in a vigorous Protestant country, where the madness of bigotry was silent for a time, so that freedom was given to a true child of nature, such as Shakespeare was, to develop religiously his own pure inner nature, without reference to any established religion.

The preceding words were written in the summer of 1813; I ask that the reader will not now find fault with me, but simply recall what was said above,—that this is merely an individual attempt to show how different poetic geniuses have tried to reconcile and resolve that tremendous antithesis which has appeared in their works in so many forms. To say more would be superfluous, since interest has been centred in this question for the past few years, and excellent explanations have been given us. Above all I wish to mention Blümner's highly valuable treatise, *On the Idea of Fate in the Tragedies of Æschylus*, and the excellent criticism of it in the supplement of the *Jenaische Literaturzeitung*. Therefore, I come without further comment to my third point, which relates immediately to the German theatre and to Schiller's efforts to establish it for the future.

III. Shakespeare as Playwright

When lovers of art wish to enjoy any work, they contemplate and delight in it as a whole, that is, they try to feel and apprehend the unity which the artist can bring to them. Whoever, on the other hand, wishes to judge such works theoretically, to assert some judgment about them, or instruct some one about them, must use his discriminating and analytic faculty. This we attempted to carry out when we discussed Shakespeare, first as poet in General, and then compared him with the ancient and modern poets. Now we intend to close the matter by considering him as a playwright, or poet of the theatre.

Shakespeare's fame and excellence belong to the history of poetry; but it is an injustice towards all playwrights of earlier and more recent times to give him his entire merit in the annals of the theatre.

A universally recognized talent may make of its capacities some use which is problematical. Not everything which the great do is done in the best fashion. So Shakespeare belongs by necessity in the annals of poetry; in the annals of the theatre he appears only by accident. Since we can honor him so unreservedly in the first case, it behooves us in the second to explain the conditions to which he had to accommodate himself, but not therefore to extol these conditions as either admirable or worthy of imitation.

We must distinguish closely-related poetic *genres*, however often they may be confused and merged together in actual treatment,—epic, dialogue, drama, play. *Epic* requires the verbal delivery to the crowd through the mouth of an individual; *dialogue*, conversation in a narrow circle, where the crowd may eventually listen; *drama*, conversation bound up with action, even if enacted only before the imagination; *play*, all three together, in so far as they appeal to the sense of vision, and can be embodied under certain conditions of personal presence and stage-setting.

Shakespeare's works are in this sense highly dramatic; by his treatment, his revelation of the inner life, he wins the reader; the theatrical demands appear to him unimportant, and so he takes it easy, and we, spiritually speaking, take it easy with him. We pass with him from place to place; our power of imagination provides all the episodes which he omits. We even feel grateful to him for arousing our imagination in so profitable a way. Since he exhibits everything in dramatic form, he renders easy the working of our imaginations; for with the "stage that signifies the world," we are more familiar than with the world itself, and we can read and hear the most fantastic things, and still imagine that they might pass before our eyes on the stage. This accounts for the frequently bungling dramatizations of favorite novels.

Strictly speaking, nothing is theatrical except what is immediately symbolical to the eye: an important action, that is, which signifies a still more important one. That Shakespeare knew how to attain this summit, that moment witnesses where the son and heir in *Henry IV* takes the crown from the side of the slumbering king, who lies sick unto death,—takes the crown and marches proudly away with it. But these are only moments, scattered jewels, separated by much that is untheatrical. Shakespeare's whole method finds in the stage itself something unwieldy and hostile. His great talent is that of a universal interpreter, or "epitomizer" (*Epitomator*), and since the poet in essence appears as universal interpreter of Nature, so we must recognize Shakespeare's great genius as lying in this realm; it would be only falsehood—and in no sense is this to his dishonor—were we to say that the stage was a worthy field for his genius. These limitations of the stage, however, have forced upon him certain limitations of his own. But he does not, like other poets, pick out disconnected materials for his separate works, but puts an idea at the centre, and to it relates the world and the universe. As he works over and boils down ancient and modern history, he can often make use of the material of old chronicles; indeed, he often adapts them word for word. With romances he does not deal so conscientiously, as *Hamlet* shows us. *Romeo and Juliet* is truer to the original; still he almost destroys the tragic content of it by his two comic characters, Mercutio and the old nurse, played apparently by two favorite actors, the nurse perhaps originally by a male performer. If one examines the construction of the piece carefully, however, one notices that these two figures, and what surrounds them, come in only as farcical interludes, and must be as unbearable to the minds of the lovers on the stage as they are to us.

But Shakespeare appears most remarkable when he revises and pieces together already existing plays. In *King John* and *Lear* we can make this comparison, for the older plays are extant. But in these cases, too, he turns out to be more of a poet than playwright.

In closing, let us proceed to the solution of the riddle. The primitiveness of the English stage has been brought to our attention by scholars. There is no trace in it of that striving after realism, which we have developed with the improvement of machinery and the art of perspective and costuming, and from which we should find it hard to turn back to that childlike beginning of the stage,—a scaffolding, where one saw little, where everything was *signified*, where the audience was content to assume a royal chamber behind a green curtain; and the trumpeter, who always blew his trumpet at a certain place, and all the rest of it. Who would be content to-day to put up with such a stage? But amid such surroundings, Shakespeare's plays were highly interesting stories, only told by several persons, who, in order to make somewhat more of an impression, had put on masks, and, when it was necessary, moved back and forth, entered and left the stage; but left to the spectator nevertheless the task of imagining at his pleasure Paradise and palaces on the empty stage.

How else then did Schroeder acquire the great distinction of bringing Shakespeare's plays to the German stage, except by the fact that he was the "epitomizer" of the "epitomizer"!

Schroeder confined himself exclusively to effect; everything else he discarded, even many necessary things, if they seemed to injure the effect which he wanted to produce on his country and his time. Thus by the omission, for instance, of the first scenes of *King Lear*, he annulled the character of the play. And he was right, for in this scene Lear seems so absurd that we are not able, in what follows, to ascribe to his daughters the entire guilt. We are sorry for the old man, but we do not feel real pity for him; and it is pity that Schroeder wishes to arouse, as well as abhorrence for the daughters, who are indeed unnatural, but not wholly blameworthy.

In the old play, which Shakespeare revised, this scene produces in the course of the action the loveliest effect. Lear flees to France; the daughters and the stepson, from romantic caprice, make a pilgrimage over the sea, and meet the old man, who does not recognize them. Here everything is sweet, where Shakespeare's loftier tragic genius has embittered us. A comparison of these plays will give the thoughtful reader ever fresh pleasure.

Many years ago the superstition crept into Germany that Shakespeare must be given literally word for word, even if actors and audience were murdered in the process. The attempts, occasioned by an excellent and exact translation, were nowhere successful, of which fact the painstaking and repeated endeavors of the stage at Weimar are the best witness. If we wish to see a Shakespearean play, we must take up again Schroeder's version; but the notion that in the staging of Shakespeare not an iota may be omitted, senseless as it is, one hears constantly repeated. If the defenders of this opinion maintain the upper hand, in a few years Shakespeare will be quite driven from the stage, which for that matter would be no great misfortune; for then the reader, whether he be solitary or sociable, will be able to get so much the purer pleasure out of him.

They have, however, with the idea of making an attempt along the lines of which we have spoken in detail above, revised *Romeo and Juliet* for the theatre at Weimar. The principles according to which this was done we shall develop before long, and it will perhaps become apparent why this version, whose staging is by no means difficult, although it must be handled artistically and carefully, did not take on the German stage. Attempts of a similar kind are going on, and perhaps something is preparing for the future, for frequent endeavors do not always show immediate effects.

BYRON'S *MANFRED*

(1820)

TO ME Byron's tragedy of *Manfred* was a wonderful phenomenon, touching me closely. This singular but highly gifted poet has absorbed my own *Faust* into himself, and, like a hypochondriac, drawn from it the strangest sort of nourishment. Those motives and ideas which suited his purposes he has made use of, but in his own original way, so that everything seems different; and for this reason I cannot wonder enough at his genius. This transformation affects the whole so intimately that highly interesting lectures could be given on the similarity and dissimilarity which his work bears to his pattern; but I do not deny that in the long run the dull glow of a boundless and profound despair becomes irksome to us. Yet in the dissatisfaction which one feels there are always interwoven both admiration and respect.

Thus we find in this tragedy quite uniquely the very quintessence of the feelings and passions of a remarkable genius, but a genius doomed from birth to suffering and anguish. The details of his life and the characteristics of his poetry hardly permit of a just and fair criticism. He has often enough confessed his anguish; he has repeatedly presented it in his verse, and it is difficult for any one not to feel real pity for the unbearable pain which he is forever working and gnawing over in his heart.

There are two women whose shadows follow him unceasingly, and who play a large rôle in his best-known works; one appears under the name Astarte, the other, without form or presence, simply as A Voice.

The following story is told of the tragic adventure which was his experience with the first. As a young, daring and highly attractive youth he won the love of a Florentine lady; her husband discovered it and murdered her. But the murderer was found dead that same night in the street, and there was nothing to throw suspicion upon a single soul. Lord Byron left Florence, but these apparitions haunted him throughout his whole life.

Translated by Randolph Bourne

This romantic event appears in his poems in countless allusions, as for example where he, probably brooding over his own tragedy, applies the sad story of the king of Sparta to his own case. The story is as follows: Pausanias, the Lacedæmonian general, having won fame in the important victory at Platæa, later through arrogance, stubbornness, and cruel treatment, loses the affection of the Greeks, and, on account of a secret understanding with the enemy, loses also the confidence of his countrymen. He thus brings blood-guiltiness upon his head, which pursues him to a miserable end. For while in command of the fleet of the Greek allies in the Black Sea, he falls violently in love with a girl of Byzantium. After a long struggle he wins her from her parents; she is to be brought to him in the night. Filled with shame, she requests the servants to put out the light; this is done, but groping about in the room, she knocks over the lamp-stand. Pausanias awakes suddenly from sleep, suspects murder, seizes his sword and kills his beloved. The horrible vision of this scene never leaves him afterwards, its shadow pursues him unceasingly, so that he appeals in vain to the gods and to necromancers for aid and absolution.

What a sick heart the poet must have who would seek out such a story from the ancient world, appropriate it to himself, and burden himself with its tragic image! This will explain the following monologue, so laden with gloom and the despair of life; we recommend it to all lovers of declamation for serious practice. Hamlet's monologue is here intensified. It will take considerable art especially to pick out the interpolations and yet keep the connection and the flow and smoothness of the whole. Besides it will be discovered that a certain vehement, even eccentric, expression is needed in order to do justice to the intention of the poet.

BYRON'S *DON JUAN*

(1821)

IN HESITATING some time ago to insert a passage from [Manzoni's] *Count Carmagnola*, a piece which is perhaps translatable, and in the present instance making the daring attempt to take up and discuss the untranslatable *Don Juan*, it may seem

Translated by Randolph Bourne

as if we are guilty of an inconsistency. We shall therefore point out the difference between the two cases. Manzoni is as yet but little known among us, and it is better that people should learn to know his merits first in their complete fullness, as they are presented only in the original; after that, a translation by one of our young poets would be decidedly in order. With Lord Byron's talent, on the other hand, we are sufficiently acquainted, and can neither help nor injure him by translation, for the originals are in the hands of all cultivated people.

Yet such an attempt, even if it were attempting the impossible, will always have a certain value. For if a false reflection does not exactly give back the original picture to us, yet it makes us attentive at least to the mirror itself and to its more or less perceptible defects.

Don Juan is a work of infinite genius, misanthropical with the bitterest inhumanity, yet sympathetic with the deepest intensity of tender feeling. And since we now know the author and esteem him, and do not wish him to be otherwise than he is, we enjoy thankfully what he dares with overgreat independence, indeed insolence, to bring before us. The technical treatment of the verse is quite in accord with the singular, reckless, unsparing content. The poet spares his language as little as he does his men, and as we examine it more closely we discover indeed that English poetry has a cultivated comic language which we Germans wholly lack.

The comic in German lies preëminently in the idea, less in the treatment or style. We admire Lichtenberg's abounding wealth; he has at his command a whole world of knowledge and relations to mix like a pack of cards and deal them out roguishly at pleasure. With Blumauer too, whose compositions in verse certainly possess the comic spirit, it is especially the sharp contrast between old and new, aristocrats and common people, the noble and the mean, that delights us. If we examine further we find that the German, in order to be amusing, steps back several centuries and has the luck to be peculiarly ingenuous and engaging only in doggerel rhyme.

In translating *Don Juan* there are many useful things to be learned from the Englishman. There is only one joke which we cannot imitate from him,—one that gets its effect by a singular and dubious accent in words which look quite differently on paper. The English linguist may judge how far the poet in this case has wantonly exceeded the proper limits.

It is only by chance that the verses inserted here happened to be translated, and they are now published not as a pattern but for their suggestiveness. All our talented translators ought to try their skill at least partly upon them; they will have to permit assonances and imperfect rhymes and who knows what besides. A certain laconic treatment will also be necessary, in order to give the full quality and significance of this audacious mischievousness. Only when something has been accomplished along these lines, can we discuss the subject further.

Possibly we may be reproached for spreading in translation such writings as these through Germany, thus making an honest, peaceful, decorous nation acquainted wtih the most immoral works that the art of poetry ever produced. But according to our way of thinking, these attempts at translation should not be intended for the press, but may serve as excellent practice for talented brains. Our poets may then discreetly apply and cultivate what they acquire in this way, for the pleasure and delight of their countrymen. No particular injury to morality is to be feared from the publication of such poems, since poets and authors would have to cast aside all restraint to be more corrupting than the papers of the present day.

AN ESSAY ON GRANITE

GRANITE is a species of rock that, since times immemorial, has aroused the interest of men; today this interest is more intense than ever. The ancients did not know it under this name. They called it syenite, from Syene, a region on the borders of Ethiopia. The immense masses of this stone inspired the Egyptians with the idea of creating immense works. Their kings erected granite obelisks to honor the sun; later they gave this rock the name of "Fireglow" because of its reddish speckled hue. Granite sphinxes, statues of Memnon, and columns are still admired by travelers; and even today, etched against the sky of powerless Rome, stands a crumbling obelisk which the omnipotent rulers of the ancient Empire once brought intact from a distant continent.

The moderns called this rock "granite" because of its grainy appearance, and in recent times it had to suffer a certain period

Translated by Norbert Guterman

of humiliation before it earned the respect in which it is now held by all naturalists. The immensity of the obelisks and the wondrous pattern of their grain led an Italian naturalist to believe that the Egyptians artificially solidified them out of a liquid mass.

But this opinion was quickly discarded, and the dignity of granite was definitively established by many careful observers. Every journey into hitherto unexplored mountains confirmed the fact that granite forms both the lowest and the highest layer, that this species of rock which began to be the object of close study and could be distinguished from other minerals, is the foundation of our earth upon which all the other varied layers rest. In the innermost bowels of the earth, it stands unshaken, its high ridges soaring, so that the all-enveloping waters never reached the peaks. This much we know about granite, and little more. Compounded mysteriously from known elements, its origin is no more traceable to fire than to water. Complex, yet simple, its variations are innumerable. The position and relation of its parts, its solidity, and its color, vary with every mountain range, and the masses of each range often differ from one step to another, and yet resemble each other. And so everyone who knows the charm that natural mysteries have for man will not be surprised that I have left my former field of observation and became passionately interested in this one. I do not fear the reproach that it must have been the spirit of contradiction which led me from the consideration and description of the human heart —that most recent, most varied, most mobile, most changeable, most disturbing part of creation—to the study of the oldest, firmest, deepest, most unshakable child of nature. For it will be readily granted that everything in nature is closely connected with everything else, and that the investigating mind does not willingly allow itself to be excluded from anything attainable. I, who have suffered and still suffer a great deal from the changes in men's dispositions, from my own volatility and that of others, should not be begrudged the sublime peace that is the gift of great gentle-tongued nature to those who approach her silently and alone. And let those who have an inkling of this peace follow me.

In this spirit I approach you, most ancient, most dignified monuments of time. Sitting on a high bare peak and surveying a broad landscape, I can say to myself: Here you are resting on a foundation that reaches down to the deepest parts of the earth;

not a recent layer, not piled-up fused ruins are interposed between you and the firm ground of the primal world; you do not, as in the fertile beautiful valleys, walk over an ever-fresh grave; these peaks have neither created anything living nor swallowed anything living; they are before all life and above all life. At this moment, when the inner attractive and motive forces of the earth are acting upon me directly, so to speak, when the influences of the sky come closer to me, I am attuned to higher meditations on nature, and since the human mind brings life to everything, a symbol stirs within me, so sublime that I must recognize it as valid. I look down this entirely naked peak where only a scanty patch of moss can be seen in the distance at the foot, and say to myself: So solitary as this is the man who longs to open his soul only to the most ancient, the most primordial, the deepest feelings of truth.

Yes, he can say to himself: Here on the most ancient, the eternal altar, built directly on the foundations of the world, I bring a sacrifice to the being of all beings. I feel the first, the profoundest beginnings of existence; I survey the world, its rugged and its gentle valleys, its distant fertile meadows; my soul rises above itself and above everything else, it longs for the nearer sky. But soon the burning sun brings back thirst and hunger, his human needs. He looks about for those valleys above which his mind had already soared; he envies the inhabitants of those fertile plains, rich in springs, who have built their happy dwellings on the ruins of other men's errors and opinions, who trample the dust of their forefathers, and peacefully gratify the modest needs of their days in a narrow circle. Prepared by these thoughts, the soul penetrates past centuries, evokes all the experiences of careful observers, all the anticipations of visionary minds. These peaks, I say to myself, rose steeper, more jagged, higher in the clouds, when this range still stood as a sea-surrounded island amid the ancient waters; around it soared the spirit that brooded on the waves; and in its vast womb higher mountains formed from the ruins of the primal hills, and the later and more distant mountains formed from their ruins and the remains of their inhabitants.—And now the moss begins first to grow, and the shell-protected creatures of the sea move more rarely, the water recedes, the higher mountains become green, everything begins to teem with life.

However, soon this life is faced with new scenes of destruction.

Johann Wolfgang von Goethe

In the distance, raging volcanoes rise that seem to threaten the end of the world; but the ground layer remains unshaken; on it I still safely rest while the people of the distant shores and islands are buried under the shifting soil. I return from this far-ranging meditation and gaze at the rocks themselves; their presence elevates and reassures my soul. I see their mass split by jagged seams, here straight, there leaning upwards, now traced sharply one over the other, now as though thrown over one another in a formless scrawl; and at first sight I might almost exclaim: Here nothing is in its ancient state; here everything is ruins, disorder, and destruction. We shall find this same opinion expressed if we withdraw from the living presence of these mountains, retire into the study, and open the books of our forefathers. One says that the primal rock is entirely whole, as if molded from *one* piece; another, that it was separated into layers and beds by sedimentary formations intersected by many tunnels running in all directions; still another, that these rocks do not form layers but whole masses, separated from each other without an apparent pattern. A different observer, on the contrary, says that he sometimes found sharply defined layers, and then, again, confusion. How can we harmonize all these contradictions and find a guiding thread to further observations?

This is what I at present propose to do; and even if my enterprise is not as successful as I wish and hope, yet my efforts will give others the opportunity to go further; for in observation even errors are useful, since they make one careful and give those who are keen sighted an opportunity to exercise their own vision. One word of warning might not be superfluous at this point, to foreigners if this essay should reach them, even more than to Germans—the observer must learn to distinguish this rock from others. The Italians still confuse a species of lava with small-grained granite, and the French call gneiss, leafy granite or secondary granite; indeed, even we Germans, who are otherwise so meticulous in matters of this kind, have quite recently confused what we call *Toteliegende*, a mineral fused from quartz and varieties of hornstone, and usually found under beds of slate, and, also, the gray wacke of the Harz, a more homogeneous mixture of quartz and slate fragments, with granite.

LETTERS

Letters

1. *To the Schönkopf Family in Leipzig*

Frankfort, October 1, 1768

YOUR SERVANT, Herr Schönkopf! How do you do, Madam? Good evening, young lady; Peterchen, good evening!

NB. You must imagine that I am approaching your little door. You, Herr Schönkopf, are sitting on the sofa near the warm stove, Madame in her corner behind the desk, Peter lies under the stove, and if Kätchen is sitting at my place near the window, let her rise and make room for the visitor. And now I shall begin to give you the news.

I have stayed away for a long time, haven't I? For five full weeks and more I have not seen you, I have not spoken to you —something that has not happened once in two and a half years, and that, alas, will happen often from now on. I'm sure you'd like to know how I've got along. Indeed, I can tell you—indifferently, quite indifferently.

Apropos, you will forgive me for not having said good-bye. I was in the neighborhood, I was already downstairs at the door, I saw the lamp burning, and went as far as the staircase, but I did not have the heart to walk up. For the last time,—how would I ever have walked down again!

And so I am doing now what I should have done then. I thank you for all the love and friendship you have so constantly given me, and that I shall never forget. I don't have to ask you to remember me; a thousand opportunities will arise on which you must think of a man who for two years and a half was a part of your family, who, it is true, may often have given you reasons for displeasure, but who, nevertheless, was always a good boy, and whom I hope you will often miss. At least I often miss you. —But I will pass over this, it is always a sad chapter for me. My

Translated by Norbert Guterman

trip was good and uneventful; I found everyone here in good health, except my grandfather. Although the side that was paralyzed by the stroke is fairly well recovered, he still has not regained the use of his tongue. I am doing as well as a man who wonders whether or not he is consumptive can be doing; however, I feel somewhat better, my cheeks are again growing fatter, and since I have here no girl or food worries to plague me, I hope to progress from day to day.

Listen to me, young lady! Has my agent recently delivered to you the little trifles that I sent you on account, and how did you like them? The other commissions are not forgotten, even though not all of them are executed. The neckerchief has been attended to with the greatest enthusiasm, and it will follow at the first opportunity; if you wish one of the enclosed color, you need only order it, and indicate what color you want on it. The fan is being made, it will have a flesh-color background, with vivid flowers. Are the shoes still holding out? Decide with your shoe-maker whether, if they are to be solidly painted, he can manage not to spoil them when he puts them together, and then send me your shoe model, and I'll paint them for you with whatever colors you wish, for it goes quickly. Whatever other things you need, time will take care of. Write to me when you want them, only before November first, for then I will write to you again and more; for I know, dear Herr Schönkopf, that you do not write yourself, but hurry Kätchen a little, so that I hear from you soon. Don't you think, Madam, that it would be unfair if I did not, at least once a month, receive a letter from the house where I have been a visitor every day until now? And if you do not write to me, it does not matter, on November first I will write again . . .

Adieu to all of you! Kätchen, if you don't write to me, you will see what will happen!

2. *To Johann Gottfried Herder in Bückeburg*

Frankfort, ca. October 1771

I AM FORCING myself to write to you while I am still under the first impression. Away, coat and collar! Your Niesewurz letter is worth three years of everyday experience. This is not an answer to it, for who could answer it?

My whole being is shaken, that you can imagine, my dear man! And it is still vibrating too profoundly to permit my pen to write steadily.

Apollo Belvedere, why do you show yourself in your nakedness, so that we must be ashamed of ours?

Spanish attire and Spanish paint!

Herder, Herder! Remain for *me*, what you are for me.

If I am destined to be your planet, I will be it, I will be it gladly, faithfully. A friendly moon to the earth.

However—do you not feel that I should rather be Mercury, the last, the smallest, rather, of the seven planets that revolve with you around *one* sun; or the first of the five satellites which move around Saturn.

Farewell, my dear man! I shall not let go of you. I shall not! Jacob wrestled with the angel of the Lord. I shall do the same even though I be stricken with lameness.

Tomorrow your Ossian shall be sent to you.

I would pay—to spend an hour with you now.

I have reread my letter, I must seal it at once. By tomorrow I would have decided not to send it.

3. *To Johann Georg Christian Kestner*

Frankfort, November 21, 1774

AT LAST I have your letter, Kestner! On a stranger's desk, in a painter's studio—for yesterday I began to paint in oils—I have your letter and I must say to you: Thanks! Thank you, my friend! You always do the right thing!—O I could fall on your neck, throw myself at Lotte's feet! One, one minute, and everything, everything would be erased, explained, everything that I could not disclose on reams of paper!—O ye of no faith! I would exclaim! O ye of little faith!—If you could feel one-thousandth part of what Werther means to a thousand hearts, you would not reckon what it has cost you.—Here, read a page and be sure to send it back to me, just as I now send you back your page. —You sent me Hennings' letter; he does not accuse me, he excuses me. Brother, beloved Kestner, if you will only be patient, your anxiety will be allayed. I would not, even if my very life were at stake, retract Werther, but trust me, trust in me. Your apprehensions, your complaints will fade away like phantoms of the night if only you are patient, and then—within one year, I promise you that whatever still may remain of suspicion, misinterpretation, etc. in the gossiping public, I will sweep away as a clean north wind sweeps away fog and vapor, just as though they were a herd of pigs.—Werther must—he must be! You don't feel him, you feel only *me* and *yourselves*, and that which

597

you call a blot on your scutcheon—and which, despite you, and others—is woven in . . . If I am still alive, it is to you that I owe it, therefore you are not Albert—and therefore—

Press Lotte's hand warmly for me, and tell her that, after all, to know that one's name is uttered with awe by a thousand hallowed lips is compensation for apprehensions that can hardly annoy anyone for long in this humdrum life where one is exposed to all sorts of gossiping old aunts.

If you behave well and don't plague me, I'll send you letters, utterances, sighs à la Werther, and if you have faith, be confident that everything will be well, and that gossip is nothing, and take to heart your philosopher's letter—I have kissed it—you do not realize how this man understands you, comforts you—and finds enough consolation in your and Lotte's worth for the misery that frightens you even in fiction. Lotte, farewell—Kestner, you —do love me—and don't plague me—

G.

Don't show anyone this note! Just you two! Otherwise, no one must see it.—Adieu, dears! Kestner, kiss your wife and my godfather for me.

And keep my promise in mind. I alone can *invent* what will put you completely outside all gossip, outside the little breath of suspicion. I have this in my power, but its' still too early! Give my cordial regards to your Hennings!

A young girl said to me yesterday: "I didn't know that Lotte was such a beautiful name! It sounds so perfect in Werther!" Another wrote recently: "For God's sake, I beg you, don't call me Lotte any more!—Lottchen or Lolo—as you wish—only not Lotte, until I am worthier of the name than I am.

O magic power of love and friendship!

Zimmermann's note soon. It is cold, I cannot look for it upstairs. It will be freezing today, adieu, my darlings!

4. To Charlotte von Stein

Weimar, February 23, 1776

How PEACEFUL and light my slumber was, how happily I rose and saluted the beautiful sun, with a free heart for the first time in two weeks, and how full of gratitude I am to you, angel of heaven, to whom I owe this. I must tell you this, you who alone of all women have aroused love in my heart, who make me happy. I shall have to wait till the masked ball before I see you again!

If I followed my heart—no I'll be good—I lie at your feet, I kiss your hands.

5. *To His Mother*

MY WISH at last to see you again has, until now, been thwarted by the circumstances in which I was obliged, more or less inevitably, to be here. But soon there may be an occasion, about which, however, I must ask you first of all to maintain the strictest secrecy. The Duke desires to enjoy the beautiful autumn season on the Rhine, I would go with him as well as Wedel, his chamberlain. We would visit you, stay for a few days in order to avoid the Fair celebrations, and then continue our journey by water. Then we would return and set up quarters in your house, and from there we would visit the neighborhood. Whether you take this prosaically or poetically, this is actually the dot on the i of your past life, and I would, for the first time, come back to my native land happy, in good health, and as honorably as possible. But because I should also like that, the wine having thrived so well on the hills of Samaria, we should also rejoice about it, I want only that you and Father should have open and feeling hearts to receive us, and to thank God that He lets you see your son again in his thirtieth year in this fashion. Since I have resisted all temptation to steal away from here and to surprise you, I want to enjoy this journey to my heart's content. I do not expect the impossible. God did not will that Father should enjoy the so ardently desired fruit that is now ripe. He spoiled his appetite, and let it be so. For my part I will ask him only to do what the mood of the moment may inspire in him. But I should like to see you very cheerful, and offer you the happiest day you have ever experienced. I have everything that a man can wish for, a life in which I daily practice and daily grow. I will come this time in good health, free from any consuming passion, without confusion, without dull pursuits, but like one beloved by God, who has accomplished the half of his life, and from past suffering hopes for much good for the future, and who has also preserved courage for future suffering; if I find you contented, I will return with pleasure to the toil and labor of the day that awaits me. Answer me fully, at once—in any event we shall arrive by the middle of September. More details, down to the minutest circumstances, I shall let you know as soon as I receive your answer to this. But keep it an unbreakable secret for the time being, also with regard to Father, Mercken, Bölling, etc.; our arrival must be a happy surprise to all. I count on you. Here, no one knows anything as yet.

How I have imagined our quarters and what we need, etc., all this will follow in my next letter, after you have told me your ideas.

6. *To Johann Kasper Lavater in Zürich*

Ostheim vor der Rhön, ca. September 20, 1780

THE DAILY task with which I am charged, and which is every day both easier and more difficult for me, requires my presence both in my waking and in my sleeping hours. This duty becomes more precious to me every day, and therein, and not in anything greater, do I wish to be equal to the greatest man. This desire, to raise as high in the air as possible the pyramid of my existence, whose foundation has been given to me, outweighs everything else, and hardly can be forgotten for a moment. I must not tarry, I am already far ahead in years, and perhaps fate will break me in the middle of my career, and the Babylonian tower will remain an unfinished stump. At least, it should be possible to say that it was boldly projected, and if I live, may my strength suffice for me to reach the summit, if God wills.

Also, the talisman of the beautiful love with which Charlotte von Stein perfumes my life is of great importance to me. She has inherited my love for my mother, sisters, and loved ones, and a bond has been woven which is like the bonds of nature.

Adieu, dearest friend, remain close to me in spirit! With the Dürers, who travel slowly because of the expense, will come flowers and bunches of herbs that I gather on the way. Let them see only few persons, and absolutely no aspiring writers; the rascals have always tried to go me one better and parrotted me, and made my style stink before the public.

Have I ever before quoted to you the phrase, *Individuum est ineffabile*, whence I deduce a world?

7. *To Karl Ludwig von Knebel*

Weimar, December 3, 1781

THAT YOU will smile at this new proof of my indefatigability, I could well imagine, but it is not a great virtue on my part. The need of my nature compels me to a multiple activity, and I would have to be equally industrious in order to live, were it in the most insignificant village or on a desert island. If there are things that don't suit my taste, I easily get over them because it is an article of my faith that only by steadfastness and loyalty in our present state can we merit and become capable of entering a higher state, be it a transient one in this world or an eternal one in the next. Of the emperor I think the same as you. If luck favors him and his genius does not desert him, he is destined to conquer much without a stroke of the sword.

8. *To Duke Karl Augustus*

Rome, March 17, 1788

YOUR FRIENDLY and cordial letter I make haste to answer with a happy: I am coming! Thus my hopes and wishes and my original purpose are fulfilled. I feel entirely the extent of your kindness, so my first and next expression of thanks will be absolute frankness. The delicacy which you show me bids me avoid all so-called delicacies, which, when closely examined, often seem pretentions.

I would gladly have offered my services in Italy to Madame Your Mother, if you had deemed it necessary and proper, although I realize that I would thereby have lost more than she could have gained by my presence. However, I believe that, because of the many preparations I made, I have not been quite useless in Italy to her, also.

This week goes by in a frenzy, I must swim with the current. Immediately after Easter Sunday I will make serious preparations for my departure. I am still expecting some things from Naples, I have to put in order all kinds of matters for myself and others, loosen many threads which have spun themselves this year and which, since your Mayence letter, have become rather securely knotted. Taking everything into account, I think I will be in Florence by the end of April. I will hasten to see the most remarkable treasures in this city, the work of Corregio in Parma, and then Milan, and then I should like to take the road home via Chiavenna and Chur, Lindau, Augsburg, and Nuremberg. I have already dispelled my mother's hope of seeing me on my way back, and have comforted her by promising to visit her on another occasion. Both in Rome and on the journey I will write diligently, and report on myself and my travels.

Since, after all this, I could reach home only by the middle of June, may I add one more request—that you grant me, after my arrival, and while I am present, the leave that you already granted me absent. My wish is: considering my singular and insurmountable disposition which made me, even in complete freedom and in the enjoyment of the most longed-for happiness, suffer many things, to find myself at your side, with your entourage, among them, to draw the balance sheet of my journey, and to conclude the mass of many memoirs and meditations on art in the three last volumes of my works. I may well say: in this solitude of a year and a half I have found myself again; but as what?—as an artist! Whatever else I still am, you will judge and use. In your continually active life you have more and more extended and sharpened that princely art which consists in knowing how people can be used, as I can clearly see from each of your letters; and I gladly submit to your judgment. Receive me as a guest, let me fill the whole measure of my existence at your side, and enjoy life. Thus my energy, like a now released and purified stream from a height, will be easily directed hither or thither according to your will. The plans that you have so far communicated to me in your letter are noble and honorable for me to the point of embarrassment. I can only say: Master, here I am, make of your slave whatever you will. Each place, each little place that you reserve for me will be to my liking, I will gladly come and go, sit down and rise . . .

9. *To Charlotte von Stein*

Weimar, February (?) 1789

IF YOU LIKE to hear this, I should gladly say to you that your reproaches, even though I am sensitive to them at the moment, do not leave in my heart any annoyance or grudge. I can answer *them*, too, and if you must tolerate many things in me, it is fair that I should suffer from you in return. It is also so much better if one settles accounts in a friendly way than trying to be like each other and parting ways if this does not succeed.

With you I can litigate least of all, because in any settlement with you I must remain your debtor. Moreover, when we reflect how much we have to bear from all people, we will rather excuse each other's faults. Farewell and love me! Occasionally you will again hear about the beautiful secrets.

10. *To Charlotte von Stein*

(Goethe has in the meantime met Christiane Vulpius.)

Weimar (Belvedere), June 1, 1789

I THANK YOU for the letter that you left behind, although it saddened me immediately in more than one way. I tarried with my answer because in such cases it is hard to be frank without hurting.

The extent of my love for you, how much I know my duty toward you and Fritz, I have proved by my return from Italy. I would still have been there if I had done what the duke wished; Herder went there; and since I did not foresee that I would be of any help to the hereditary prince, I had hardly anything in mind except you and Fritz.

What I left in Italy I don't want to repeat. You received my confidences about that in a quite unfriendly fashion.

Unfortunately, when I arrived, you were in a peculiar mood, and I frankly confess that the manner in which you received me, and the others took me, wounded me deeply. I saw Herder and the duchess leave, I left vacant a seat in the coach that was urgently pressed upon me, I stayed for the sake of my friends, just as I had come for your sake, and at the same moment I had to hear stubbornly repeated to me that I could have stayed away, that after all I am not interested in people, etc. And all that before there could be question of a relationship that seems to annoy you profoundly.

And what sort of relationship is this? Who gets the short end of it? Who boasts of the thrills that I don't begrudge the poor girl? The hours that I spend with her?

Ask Fritz, the Herders, everyone who is close to me, whether I am less interested in, less communicative with, less active on behalf of my friends than before. Whether I do not rather only now really belong to them and the set.

And it would be strange indeed for me to neglect you alone, my best and most intimate relationship.

How keenly I felt that it is still there when I once found you in a mood to talk with me about interesting things.

But I freely admit that I cannot bear the way you have treated me until now. When I was talkative, you closed my mouth; when I was communicative, you accused me of indifference; when I was active on behalf of my friends, you accused me of coldness and neglect. You have controlled each of my gestures and expressions, criticized my way of being, and always put me *mal à mon aise*. How could trust and frankness thrive when you drive me from you deliberately?

I should gladly add many other things if I did not fear that in your present temper it might offend rather than conciliate you.

Unfortunately, you have long since ignored my advice with regard to coffee, and adopted a diet that is extremely harmful to your health. It is not enough that it is already difficult mentally to overcome many impressions, you strengthen the hypochondriac, tormenting power of gloomy ideas by a physical means whose harmfulness you have known for some time, and which you avoided for a certain period out of love for me—and you felt well. May the cure and the journey agree well with you! I do not entirely give up the hope that you will recognize me again. Farewell! Fritz is contented and visits me faithfully. The prince feels energetic and cheerful.

11. *To Christiane Vulpius*

Camp before Verdun, September 2, 1792
YOU MUST, dear child, soon again have a little note from me. We have advanced further into France, the camp is now near Verdun. The city refused to surrender and so, last night, was bombarded. It is a terrible sight, and one would not wish to think that one has something one loves in it. Today it will surrender and the army will continue toward Paris. Everything is proceeding so fast that in all probability I will soon be with you again. It was a good thing that went soon. I am quite well, although I miss many comforts and especially my sweetheart. Keep loving me, take care of the house and the garden, greet Herr Meyer, kiss the little one, and eat your cabbage in peace. Don't worry about me. Good bye, I love you dearly. I'll bring you a little something from Paris that will be better than anything you can buy at the local shop. Take good care of yourself.

12. *To Schiller in Jena*

    (Goethe and Schiller had drawn closer after a conversation held in Jena in July. Schiller invited him to contribute to his periodical *Die Horen*, and wrote him the great letter of August 23, in which he interpreted Goethe's nature.)

Ettersburg, August 27, 1794
FOR MY BIRTHDAY, which falls this week, no gift could have been more agreeable to me than your letter in which you draw up the balance sheet of my existence with a friendly hand, and which stimulates me, by your interest, to a more diligent and more effective use of my energies.

    Enjoyment can be pure and benefit true, only if they are

mutual, and I am happy to tell you on this occasion all that I have gained from my conversation with you, how I date an epoch from those days, and how content I am to have proceeded on my way without special encouragement, for it now seems as though, after such an unexpected meeting, we were bound to continue our ways together. I have always appreciated the honest and so rare seriousness which is manifested in everything you have written and done, and now I have the right to claim that I have been acquainted by you yourself with the evolution of your ideas, especially in the recent years. Since we have clarified to each other the points we have now reached, we will henceforth be able to work in common without interruption.

I will communicate with pleasure all that is happening to me and in me. Since I feel quite acutely that my undertaking [the writing of Faust] far exceeds the measure of human strength and its earthly duration, I should like to deposit many things with you and thereby not only preserve, but also add life to them.

How greatly I will benefit from your interest, you will soon see for yourself when, upon closer acquaintance, you discover in me a kind of darkness and hesitation that I can never master, although I am always distinctly aware of them. However, there are many such phenomena in our human nature by which, nevertheless, we gladly let ourselves be ruled, if only it is not too tyrannical.

I hope soon to spend some time with you, and then we shall discuss many things.

Unfortunately, I gave Unger my novel [*Wilhelm Meister's Apprenticeship*] a few weeks before your invitation, and the first printed sheets are already in my hands. More than once, these days I have thought that it would have been very suitable for the magazine; it is the only work that I still have that is massive and that represents a kind of problem in composition, such as our good Germans like.

I will send you the First Book as soon as the galleys are together. The work was written so long ago that actually I am now only the publisher.

If any of my other ideas could be presented through this medium, we could easily agree about the most suitable form, and would not be deterred by the problem of carrying out our plans.

With best wishes, and remember me in your circle.

Johann Wolfgang von Goethe

13. To Schiller

Weimar, June 22, 1797

SINCE IT IS extremely necessary that I should give myself something to do in my present restless state, I have decided to take up my *Faust* and, if I could not complete it, at least to advance it considerably by breaking down the text that has been printed, and combining great chunks of it with material that is now ready or conceived; thus I would come closer to carrying out my plan which actually is only an idea. Now I have again undertaken this idea and its exposition, and I am fairly in agreement with myself. But I should like you to be so kind as to think over this matter some sleepless night, to present to me your suggestions regarding the whole, and thus like a true prophet to tell me and to interpret for me my own dreams.

Since the various parts of this poem, with regard to mood, can be treated differently once the spirit and tone of the whole are mastered, and since, moreover, the whole work is subjective, I can work on it at widely separate intervals, and so I am able to accomplish something also now.

Our study of ballads has once again led me to this path of vapor and fog, and under the present circumstances, I find it advisable to wander about on it for a time, in more than *one* sense.

The interesting part of my new epic project [*Novelle*] will probably also go up in the air in such a vapor of rimes and stanzas; for the time being I'll let it distil in me. For today, good bye.

14. To Karl Friedrich Zelter in Berlin

(On May 9, Schiller died; Goethe himself had been sick for many months.)

Weimar, June 1, 1805

SINCE I LAST wrote to you I have had few good days. I thought I would be lost myself, and now I have lost a friend, and in him, half my own existence. I really should begin a new mode of life; but there is no way of doing it in my age. Therefore I live from day to day and do whatever has to be done without thinking of further consequences.

In the meantime, because people try to get amusement even out of loss and misfortune, I am urged by our theater people and several others to celebrate his memory on the stage. Concerning this I wish to say nothing, except that I am not disinclined to do it, and now I want to ask you whether you would help me in this, and first of all, whether you would be kind enough to send me your motet, *Man Lives and Endures*, on which the *Musical Gazette* No. 27 reports, and whether you would compose some other pieces in the solemn style, or whether you would seek out and send me already composed musical pieces (I will tell you what kind I need) so that I may adapt proper words to them. As soon as I have your ideas on it, I will give you further details.

A cordial farewell, and let me hear from you soon!

15. *To Lili von Türckheim, née Schönemann, in Strassburg*
Weimar, December 14, 1807
YOUR PRECIOUS letter, my adored friend, came too late; your son sent it to me from Dresden. He had visited me without my knowing that it was he. I confused the two families similar in name, and thought he was of the other one. But even so, as a complete stranger to me, I liked him a great deal. The second time he came, a downpour of rain occurred most opportunely and kept him for a long time in my house. I reproached myself for not having invited him to stay for dinner, for I felt a true inclination to him. I have been impatiently waiting for the other announced visitor for a long time, but in vain. I should like to make up with this one what I failed with the other.

In conclusion permit me to say this—that it gave me infinite pleasure after such a long time once again to see a few lines by your dear hand, which I kiss a thousand times in memory of the days that I reckon among the happiest in my life. May you fare well and in peace after so many external sufferings and trials which came too late to us and which often give me occasion to think about your constancy and enduring greatness. Once again, farewell, and please remember me.

16. *To Zelter*

(Zelter had reported the suicide of his stepson; beginning with the following letter Goethe addressed his friend intimately, as "thou.")

Weimar, December 3, 1812
YOUR LETTER, my dear friend, which informs me of the great misfortune that has stricken your house, greatly oppressed me

and even laid me low, because it found me in the midst of very serious meditations about life; and I rose up again only thanks to yourself. Tested by the black touchstone of death you proved true, refined gold. How magnificent is a character so suffused with spirit and soul, and how noble must be a talent that rests on such a foundation.

Of the deed or misdeed itself, I cannot say anything. When a man is overpowered by *taedium vitae*, he can only be pitied, not cursed. That all the symptoms of this strange sickness, which is both natural and unnatural, once also ravaged my innermost being, Werther surely betrays. I know full well what resolution and effort it cost me at that time to escape from the waves of death, as well as how hard it was to save myself and recover from many later shipwrecks. And that is the way with all sailing and fishing adventures. After the storms of the night, one regains the shore; he who has been drenched dries himself, and the next morning, when the waves once again gleam in the splendid sun, the sea is again ready to be defied.

When one sees not only how people in general, and especially the youth, are given over to their lusts and passions, but also how the loftier and better part of them is diverted and distorted by the gross stupidities of the age, so that everything that ought to lead to bliss becomes their doom, not counting indescribable external pressure, one is not surprised at the war that the individual wages against himself and others. I feel strong enough to write a new Werther which will make people's hair stand on end even more than the first. Let me add one more remark. Most young people who sense a certain worth in themselves, demand of themselves more than is reasonable. Nevertheless, they are driven and compelled to this by the overwhelming environment. I know a half dozen such men who have certainly run aground, and who could not be helped even if it were possible to enlighten them about their true interest. No one can easily be convinced that reason and a firm will are given to us, to keep us away not only from evil, but also from an excess of good . . .

17. *To Karl Ludwig von Knebel*

Weimar, November 9, 1814

AMONG THE GOOD qualities that I acquired as a result of my last journey, the tolerance that I more than ever feel for the individual no doubt occupies first place. When one observes several hundred persons closely, and thousands from a distance, one must admit that in the end every one has enough to do to create for himself a condition, to preserve and further it; one cannot admonish anyone as to how he should go about it, for in the end it is left to him to decide how he can best help himself in ill fortune and behave in good fortune. Keeping this in mind, I have this time got along with the world happily, never asking of anyone more than he could and wanted to give, not offering him anything more than was proper to him, and cheerfully taking and giving whatever the day and the circumstances brought; and in this way I have never led anyone astray from his own mode of life. Convictions, moral conduct, habits, preferences, religion, everything seemed to me entirely in accord with the persons who expressed themselves before me, and I found the same thing also with regard to taste.

Everyone seeks and wishes that toward which he is naturally inclined. One wants to drink from a narrow-necked bottle, another from a flat plate, one likes his food raw, another cooked. And so, on this occasion, I also quite carefully filled my pots and bowls, my bottles and jugs, and indeed added many pieces to my kitchen battery. I feasted at the Homeric, as well as the Nibelung table, but I have never found anything more suitable to me personally than broad, deep, ever living Nature, the world of the Greek poets and sculptors.

The highest that fell to my lot are some bas reliefs from the Parthenon, Velletri's Pallas, the infinitely beautiful torso of a Venus; and then the head of a Venetian horse.

I can show reproductions of splendid gems; and I saw magnificent paintings, drawings, and copper engravings of the great Italian school.

This much for now. I am enclosing an outline of my travel chronology, which please send me back soon.

Vale fave.

18. *To August von Goethe*

Weimar, September 19, 1816

WITHOUT going into the particulars of the case, in which, as you tell me, you propose to stand surety, I must ask you, my dear son, carefully to consider the following.

When my blessed father gave me my portion of the estate, there was among the good teachings that he gave me at the same time, one which was like a commandment—that in his lifetime I should not stand surety for anyone, and that I should remember this warning also after his death.

For, he said, if you have cash, you may lend it to a friend even without great security. If you want to offer it as a gift, there is nothing to say against that, either; if you borrow, you will arrange matters so that you can pay interest and amortize the capital; but if you stand surety, you put yourself in a restless state, which is all the more painful because you must behave inactively, and even passively. No one easily gives a pledge unless he thinks he runs no risk; but once he has given the pledge, he feels very soon, especially in moments of worry, that he is threatened by an evil looming in the distance, which seems to him all the more fearful because he feels that he would not be equal to it if it came closer.

To risk one's life for a friend as for oneself, is praiseworthy, because it is a matter of one decisive moment; but to heap up anxiety for yourself for an indefinite time or perhaps for your whole life, and to undermine the security of your possessions at least in the imagination, is by no means advisable: for our physical condition and the course of life have many hypochondriac hours in store for us, and then worry brings forth all the phantoms that a cheerful day scares away.

Such was my father's attitude, and such my own has remained. In my life I have done a great deal, perhaps more than a fair amount, for others, forgetting myself and my own; I can tell you this without boasting since you already know much of it; but I have never stood surety, and you will not find such an act in my estate. Therefore have the old proverb before your eyes, and remember me!

19. *To Marianne von Willemer in Baden-Baden*

(Marianne's husband, Jacob von Willemer, had paid a surprise visit to Goethe on his way to Berlin in March 1819, but did not repeat the visit on his way back.)

Weimar, July 26, 1819

No, DEAREST MARIANNE, you shall not miss a word from me in Baden, since you again permit your dear lips to rule, and since you wish to break an ungratifying silence. Shall I say again that I considered you inseparable from the presence of the friend, and that, seeing his honest face, I vividly recalled everything that he so readily and nobly let us have. Although you were silent,

I had explained all sorts of things to myself; but the returning traveler avoided me, and I let matters rest there.

Now, since you say that you remember me and like to remember, hear doubly and triply the assurance that I cordially and unfailingly respond to each of your feelings. May this find you at a propitious hour and induce you to write a very long commentary on this short text. If I were Hudhud [probably the name of a dog] I would not run across your path, but straight to you. Not as messenger; you would have to receive me in a friendly way for my own sake. In conclusion, the pious loving wish

Eia! If we were there!

20. *To Zelter*

(On March 5 Zelter had lost his last son, Georg.)

Weimar, March 19, 1827

WHAT SHALL a friend answer in such a case. A like evil brought us most closely together, so that our union cannot be more intimate. The present misfortune leaves us as we are, and this is already a great deal.

The old fairy tale of the thousand thousand and one nights closing in, the Parcae tell it each other untiringly. To live long means to survive many, so sounds the empty *ritornello* of our vaudevillesque and wasted life story; the turn always comes again, it torments us and yet it again drives us to renewed and earnest striving.

My immediate entourage appears to me a convolution of Sibylline leaves; one after the other, consumed by the flames of life, it is dispersed in the air, lending higher value to the survivors from moment to moment. Let us continue to be active until, one before or after the other, we are summoned by the *Weltgeist* to return to the ether! May then the everlastingly living one not deny us new activities analogous to those in which we have already tested ourselves! If he then, in a fatherly way, also grants us the memory and continued feeling of the right and the good, of what we here already willed and accomplished, we shall certainly be caught all the sooner in the teeth of the world machinery.

The entelechian monad can preserve itself only in constant activity; if this activity becomes its second nature, it cannot lack an occupation for all eternity. Forgive these abstruse phases! but people have always lost themselves in such regions and attempted to communicate with the help of such expressions wherever reason did not suffice, and where they nevertheless refused to let unreason prevail. That you, in your grief, should still remember the book of art and antiquity, rejoices me greatly, because, even when faced with the greatest loss, we must immediately look about to see what remains to keep us alive and to be accomplished. How often in such cases have we tested our activity with new impatience, thus distracting ourselves and opening up the path to all solace!

21. *To Zelter*

> (On November 16 Goethe had received the news that his son had died in Rome on October 27.)

Weimar, November 21, 1830

NEMO ANTE OBITUM BEATUS is a proverb that figures in history, but that actually does not mean anything. It it were expressed with some exactness, it would run: "Expect trials till the end."

You have not lacked them, my good friend, nor have I, and it is as though fate were convinced that we are woven together not of nerves, veins, arteries, and other structures derived from them, but of wire.

Thank you for your kind letter! After all, once I had to give you such a message of grief as the greeting of hospitality. So let the matter rest as it is.

What is really curious and important in this trial is that all the burdens which I hoped soon—indeed, with the coming year— to take off myself and transfer to one younger than myself, I must now drag on myself and that they have even grown heavier.

At this point, only the great idea of duty can keep us erect. I have no worry except to move physically in equilibrium; everything else comes of itself. The body must, the spirit wills, and he who has prescribed the necessary path to his will need not think much.

I won't go farther, but I reserve for myself to progress from this point on occasion. My most heartfelt, most grateful greetings to all so loyally sympathizing with me.

22. *To Sulpiz Boisserée in Munich*

Weimar, March 22, 1831

ON THIS last page, I am induced, in seriousness and in jest, to conclude with something unusual.

No man can ward off religious feeling, but it is impossible for him to elaborate such a feeling in himself alone, therefore he seeks or makes proselytes.

The latter is not in my style, but the former I did faithfully, and beginning with the creation of the world, I have not found any religion which I could fully profess. But now, in my old age, I have learned about a sect of Hypsistarians, who, hemmed in between heathens, Jews, and Christians, declared that they valued, admired, and venerated the best and most perfect that came to their knowledge, and since it must be in close relation to the divinity, that they would worship it. That was joyous light coming to me from a dark age, for I felt that I had all my life intended to qualify as a Hypsistarian; but this is no little endeavor: for how does one come, within the limitations of one's individuality, to be aware of that which is most excellent?

At least let us not permit anyone to surpass us in friendship.

23. *To Wilhelm von Humboldt*

Weimar, March 17, 1832

AFTER A LONG involuntary interruption I begin as follows, and yet it is only on the spur of the moment. Animals are taught by their organs, said the ancients; I should like to add that this applies to men too, but that they have the advantage of teaching their organs in turn.

Every activity, hence every talent, requires the presence of an innate element, which operates of itself and unconsciously brings in its train the necessary predispositions, and which, for this reason, continues to operate irresistibly in such a way that, although it has its own inherent law, in the end it can proceed aimlessly.

The earlier a man realizes that there is a craft or an art that can help him systematically to enhance his natural dispositions, the happier he is; whatever he receives from outside, does no harm to his innate individuality. The best genius is that which absorbs and assimilates everything without doing the least violence to its fundamental destiny—that which we call character—but rather improving and enhancing it as far as possible.

At this point arise various connections between the conscious and the unconscious; imagine a musical talent that undertakes to compose an important score: consciousness and unconsciousness will be to one another as warp to weft—a simile that I like to use.

613

Johann Wolfgang von Goethe

Through training, instruction, contemplation, success, failure, advancement, hindrance, and ever more contemplation, the organs of man, in their instinctive, free activity, unite the acquired with the innate to produce a harmonious unity that astonishes the world.

These general remarks will serve as a brief answer to the question and as clarification of the page I am sending back.

More than sixty years have passed since the conception of Faust was clear before me, in my youth, and the whole sequence, in less detailed form. Now, I have always let the intention go by me gently, and I developed only the places that were individually most interesting to me, so that gaps remain in the second part, to be connected with the rest by a uniform interest. True, here came in the great difficulty of achieving, by sheer will and determination, that which actually should only be the work of spontaneously active nature. But it would be bad if this had not become possible after such a long, actively reflective life, and I am not deterred by the fact that it will be possible to distinguish between the older from the more recent, the later from the earlier, which we will leave to the future readers' favorable insight.

Of course it would give me infinite pleasure to dedicate and communicate, even in my lifetime, these very serious jests to my honored, by all means gratefully acknowledged, and widely scattered friends, as well as to hear their answers. But the times are really so absurd and confused that I am convinced that my earnest, persevering endeavors about this curious construction would be ill rewarded, and, driven on the beach, they would lie like a wreck in ruins, and, to begin with, will be buried under the enormous rubble of the hours. Confusing doctrines preaching confused action prevail in the world, and I have nothing more pressing to do than to enhance as much as possible that which is and remains in me, and to distil my peculiarities, just as you, my worthy friend, are doing it in your own fortress.

Therefore let me know something about your labors; as you know, Riemer devotes himself to the same or similar studies, and our evening conversations often lead us to the limits of the subject.

Forgive this delayed letter! Despite my seclusion, I rarely can find an hour where one likes to evoke these mysteries of life.

PROVERBS IN RHYME

Proverbs in Rhyme

TODAY will bring you naught
More than yesterday brought.

WHO AT BIRTH has ills endured,
He to hardship is inured.

HOWEVER CLEAR or simple be it,
Finder or doer alone may see it.

ACT NOW before the night
Blots out your light.

WHEN THE overburdened cries
"Even hope my lot denies'
There is solace, let it be heard—
The brotherly word.

WHY BEMOAN an enemy?
Would you have him, then, as friend
Whom every self that you can be
Will secretly offend?

WHEN GREAT DAYS come to the wise,
This is hard to bear numbly:
To be counselled by fools to wear
Their greatness humbly.

TO IGNORANCE the wise descend
When with the ignorant they contend.

Translated by Isidor Schneider

Johann Wolfgang von Goethe

To SEE the whole town at a time,
To the rooftop we must climb.

THANKSGIVING to Allah from my heart
For keeping suffering and knowledge apart.
How more grievous would diseases grow
If the ill knew what their doctors know!

ALL THIS RHAPSODY and chanting
Leave me overwhelmed and panting.
No one clubs the muse so hard
As the bard.

DAMMED MAY all these humans be!
They've driven me fair frantic.
Let me never, never see
Another human antic.
To themselves I leave all men—
To God or to the devil!
Yet show a human face again,
Again I crave the evil!

WHAT WILL NOT MIX don't let us press together.
I leave you free to choose your when and whether.
In turn leave me at peace; we'll never mix, we two,
I who was born antique, and you, so new!

To KNOW your powers, look in your mind;
Not from me starts your creation.
In my words you'd feel confined.
Go to God for inspiration.

IN THE MASTERS' WORKS I see my quits—
It's always more than I've believed.
Reviewing then my seven bits
I see what should have been achieved.

UNDER THE TONGUE's a good place to hide;
He who stays silent keeps care aside.

You ASK ME why stray? You want me back
Upon the comfortable beaten track.
I'll still veer off though you think it a waste;
I never wrote to please your taste.

ARTIST BLOW your horn a little.
Honors come with noise and spittle.
Praise before and blame today?
Neither matters while they pay.

TWO EPITAPHES

A GOOD and chipper lad was I
Then a full blooded youth and spry—
Good forecast of a man.
But love made claim and cost me dear,
Pursued by sorrow I reached here,
—And no further ran.

As A LAD, glum and suspicious,
As a youth, proud and capricious,
But of life never fearful.
So prove my gray years cheerful.
—On your tombstone will be seen,
"He in truth a man has been."

THE RIGHT is soon found
When God looks around.

IN THIS no paradox is said;
"Whom God misleads is well misled."

IF THE INFINITE you would stride,
Pace the Finite's every side.

THE SPARKLING WORDS, the words of glee
I hunted everywhere;
But grim days contented me—
I found the best words there.

Johann Wolfgang von Goethe

To HAVE the whole thing in your heart
You must con its every part.

AFTER KINGS have been to meeting
Bad news follows in their greeting.

YOU'VE MADE PATIENCE a habit? Say it loud,
Of that achievement, man, be proud!

No WELL DONE CHESTNUTS for your tongue to roll.
Too long they've roasted; now they're coal.

WHO NOTHING has walks light—you said it!—
But lighter still with a letter of credit.

"Is IT WELL and wisely done
Friend and foe alike to shun?
From all adults now I turn,
Grandsons are my sole concern.

WHAT MAN aspires to
He'll fulfill.
If God add health and strength
Unto his will.

No TRANSIENTS, we;
However we arrived, thus
To immortality
Nature summoned us.

How DO YOU bear so well
Arrogant, elbowing youth;
By being as unbearable,
Having as little ruth.

"YOU GET ON so well with people!
How do you plant your wedge?"
I acknowledge each man's talent
Though it set my teeth on edge.

THEY SAY, "It don't please me a bit,"
And think they are done with it.

WHEN, NOT BY our contriving
And after gainless striving
Comes unhoped success—
Grasp quickly the largesse.

THAT BRINGS ME no distress,
God's gift I don't disdain;
Should I feel any less
When a foe I gain?

"To SEE YOU praised gives them no pleasure.
Of their mind, in yours, there's not a dram."
If I could fit into their measure
I would not be the man I am.

CURSE AND MUTTER, rip each word,
That won't better your affair.
Solace? Solace is absurd;
Living, you must know despair.

MY GOOD DEEDS done, of them I see
Nothing, nothing, though a host.
The false thing that slipped from me,
That's ever with me like a ghost.

"SIR, this loud derisive song
Is your enemy's lampoon."
"Let them sing it loud and long,
For so it will die soon."

IF IN MY COURSE, I'd thought it worth
To wait until I got their blessing,
I'd have, today, no foot on earth.
To shine a bit, to hide their dearth,
See how they crowd me, watch them pressing!

WHO CANNOT SPARE a man a smile?
Yet some ask, "Is it worth my while?"

Johann Wolfgang von Goethe

IF YOU'D AVOID the serenades of crows,
Out of the steeple never stick your nose.

"AND HAVE YOU had due recompense?"
Fine feathered and singing like a lark
Flew my arrow all through heaven,
And somewhere found its mark.

MAY THE NEW YEAR bring you health and grace;
And on your aches and wounds a healing salve.
On a coarse pedestal a coarse stone place;
And stones over him let a scoundrel have.

THE GOOD THING in Time's gallery
That once was understood,
Someday another will come to see
And call it good.

"THE TARGETS of your bitter gall
Are all so distant, why?"
Whoever gave you senses, all
Spirit did deny.

"As IT TURNED OUT you came through well, no wound, no speck."
But whoever follows me, still will risk his neck.

MY LITTLE BUZZ, my bit of fame,
Should that give you rue?
If I weren't Goethe,
I still wouldn't be you.

"Is YOUR QUESTION really meant?
Are you serious when you say—?"
Be unconcerned about intent;
Opinions are questions anyway.

NOT WITH MEN concern yourselves
But matter; love it.
This rapid youth approaching, he'll
Make something of it.

In themselves the old
Are but a kind of freight;
I know that I'll stay young
As long as I create.
Whoever would stay young
On this his mind should set;
That if no children come
To something else beget.

THE HEIGHT of a road's perfections
Is to go right in all directions.

WOULD YOU LIVE the happy way,
Keep the past out of today.
Whatever your loss be not forlorn,
In each experience be reborn.
Ask every day what it requires,
It will refresh you with desires.
Take joy in everything you do,
What others try will then please you.
Admit no hatred to your breast;
To God you then can leave the rest.

SINCE YOU my verses shun,
Show me your creation.
In nothing it's begun,
Its ending is negation.
So let your stiff broom scratch,
There's nothing to repay.
On nothing it can catch,
Your nothing's in the way.

DON'T ASK ME for perfection, ready-made;
That, my friend, is the pedant's stock in trade.

"GIVE US A RULE to guide the people."
In peace
Keep tidy
Your little coops.
In war
Get along
With quartered troops.

Johann Wolfgang von Goethe

FOR GOODLY growth of heart and mind,
Lad, to this advice give heed.
Let the muse who speaks so kind,
Accompany but never lead.

ON NO MORE LAND than holds a root
An able hand will bring forth fruit.

AND IF his friends turn foul,
One needn't care
Whether in marble crypt
Or still in open air.
Let the living only
Of this be sure
That what he gives a friend
Will long endure.

THE DOCTOR then forgive;
He and his own must live;
Though it may not please,
His interest is disease.

EACH SUCH SCOUNDREL will at last
By another be undone.
Be you good and you will walk
Pointed at by none.

GET WISE to yourself, now trot
Out of that mucky groove!
There's more to earth than this spot—
Move!

PROVERBS IN PROSE

Proverbs in Prose

WE PEER SO eagerly into the future because we should like so much, by force of our unexpressed wishes, to direct in our favor the uncertain potentialities that hover in it.

No ONE would speak much in company if he realized how often he misunderstands others.

THE REASON why, in quoting others, we so often change their words, is that we have not understood them.

HE WHO HOLDS long discourse before others without offering any flattery arouses antipathy.

EVERY WORD that is uttered evokes the idea of its opposite.

CONTRADICTION and flattery both make poor conversation.

THE SENSUAL MAN laughs often when there is nothing to laugh at. Whatever it is that stirs him, it is his complacence that asserts itself.

WE SAY, "He will die soon," when a man, in doing something, departs from his customary ways.

WHAT IMPERFECTIONS may we preserve, even cultivate in ourselves? Such as tend to flatter rather than to hurt others.

WE OBTAIN no knowledge of people when they come to us; we must go to them in order to find out what they are really like.

Translated by Norbert Guterman

Johann Wolfgang von Goethe

WE TAKE everyone in life at the value he puts upon himself; but he must indeed put some value upon himself. We are more inclined to endure the people who are difficult than to bear with people who are insignificant.

WHAT WE CALL conduct and good manners is designed to achieve what otherwise only violence, or not even violence, can achieve.

THERE IS no outward token of graciousness that is not deeply rooted in the ethos. True education should transmit both the outward token and the inner root.

THERE IS a graciousness of the heart; it is related to love. It is the source of the most natural graciousness of outward conduct.

IN THE FACE of the great superiority of another person there is no means of safety but love.

IT IS a terrible thing when fools thrive at the expense of a superior man.

MEDIOCRITY has no greater consolation than the idea that men of genius are not immortal.

THE GREATEST MAN is always linked to his own century through some weakness.

FOOLS and intelligent people are equally harmless. It is half-fools and the half-intelligent who are the most dangerous.

THERE IS no safer way of avoiding the world than through art, and there is no safer way of being linked with the world than through art.

ART deals with the difficult and the good.

CERTAIN books seem to be written not to enlighten the reader but to inform him that the author has acquired knowledge of something.

DIFFICULTIES increase the nearer one comes to the goal.

628

To sow is not as difficult as to reap.

ART IS a serious business; it is most serious when it is concerned with lofty and sacred objects. But the artist stands above art and the object: he stands above art because he utilizes it for his purpose; he stands above the object because he deals with it in his own manner.

IN EVERY ARTIST there is a germ of recklessness without which talent is inconceivable; it becomes active particularly when a gifted man is subjected to attempts to shackle him and to hire and use him for limited purposes.

SEEING someone accomplishing arduous things with ease gives us an impression of witnessing the impossible.

THE GREATEST respect that an author can show his public consists in never offering what people expect but rather what he considers proper and useful at the given stage of his own development and that of his reader.

IT IS JUST before a thunderstorm that we see a last violent flurry of the dust that is soon to be laid for a long time.

THERE IS something in the nature of everyone that, were it openly manifested, would create displeasure.

HE WHO does not know foreign languages, knows nothing of his own.

THE CHIEF concern of the man of action is that he should be doing the right thing; whether what is right eventually comes to pass should not concern him.

NATURE demands an occasional numbing of the senses though not in sleep; hence man's delight in smoking tobacco, drinking spiritous liquors, taking opiates.

IF A MAN reflects upon his physical or moral condition, he usually finds himself to be ill.

Johann Wolfgang von Goethe

WHAT WE do not understand, we do not possess.

NOT EVERY person to whom a fruitful idea is consigned becomes productive; usually it arouses only a habitual train of thought.

THERE IS no vulgarity that, when expressed with grimaces, would not seem humorous.

No NATION wins a judgment unless it can judge itself. But it achieves this very advantageous position only very late.

MAN WOULD NOT be the noblest creature on earth if he were not too noble for earth.

IN OUR DAYS it is possible to produce works that are without significance though they are not bad:—they are without significance because they have no substance; they are not bad because their authors keep before them a general pattern derived from good models.

THE NOVEL is a subjective epopee in which the author avails himself of the privilege of treating the world in his own manner. Thus the question is only whether he has a manner; the rest will take care of itself.

THE HAPPIEST MAN is he who can join the end of his life with the beginning.

IN THESE TIMES no one should remain silent or yield; one must speak and be up and bestir oneself, not in order to conquer, but to hold one's ground—regardless of whether one belongs to the majority or the minority.

ONE MUST from time to time reiterate one's profession of faith, say what one approves and what one condemns; after all, the opposite camp does not omit doing this.

HE WHO does not set too high a value on himself has a greater value than he thinks.

LIFE, however mean it may appear, however readily it may seem to content itself with humdrum, everyday things, nevertheless continues secretly to cherish and to foster certain higher demands, and seeks means to fulfill them.

THE BEAUTIFUL is a manifestation of secret laws of nature; without the revelation of the beautiful these laws would have remained eternally hidden from us.

THE CHIEF features of our mores as evinced in our practical existence are ill-will and envy.

AN ENGLISH critic pays me the compliment of saying that I have "panoramic ability"—for which I am obliged to tender him most gracious thanks.

WHAT THE French call *tournure* is arrogance tempered to charm. This shows that the Germans cannot have *tournure;* their arrogance is hard and blunt, their charm gentle and humble; the two are mutually exclusive and cannot be combined.

THE GLORIOUS hymn, *Veni Creator Spiritus,* is actually a summons to genius; that is why it has tremendous appeal to men of intellect and energy.

WE ARE ALL so opinionated that we believe ourselves to be in the right, and thus it is possible to conceive of an extraordinary mind that not only errs but even takes delight in erring.

WE OFTEN SAY to ourselves that we should avoid multifarious activity—*polypragmosyne*—especially that the older one becomes, the less should one engage in new ventures. But it is easy to talk, easy to advise oneself and others. To grow older is a new venture in itself; all relationships change, and one must either desist from activity altogether or assume the new role deliberately and consciously.

MAN IS PLACED as a real being in the midst of a real world, and is endowed with organs of such sort that he is capable of recognizing and bringing out the actual, and in addition, the possible. All healthy persons are convinced of their existence and of an existing world about them. At the same time there is a blank area in the brain, that is, an area in which no object is imaged, just as there is a blind spot in the eye. If this spot becomes a matter of special note to an individual, if he becomes preoccupied with it, he falls prey to a mental illness, has intimations of things of another world, which are however actually not things, and have neither form nor outline; they have the quality of the nocturnal void that affrights, and of ghosts pursuing him who does not wrest himself free.

THE MAN of action is always unscrupulous; it is only the observer who has conscience.

IT MAKES a great difference whether the poet seeks the particular in relation to the universal or contemplates the universal in the particular. The first method gives rise to allegory, in which the particular functions only as an example, as an instance of the universal; but the second indeed represents the very nature of poetry, it expresses a particular without thought or reference to the universal. He who grasps this particular as a living essence also encompasses the universal without realizing it, or realizing it only later.

ACTUALLY one knows only when one knows little; with knowledge doubt increases.

AGAINST criticism we can neither protect nor defend ourselves; we must act in despite of it, and gradually it resigns itself to this.

THE GERMANS ought not to utter the word *Gemüt* for a period of thirty years; then *Gemüt* would gradually reappear. At present it means only condoning of weakness in oneself and in others.

MATERIAL is visible to everyone; meaning is discovered only by him who has something to add to material, and form is a closed secret to most persons.

TRANSLATORS are to be regarded as officious match-makers who speak to us in glowing terms of a half-veiled beauty: they arouse an irresistible longing for the original.

MASTERY is often taken for egoism.

632

IN TRUTH, it is a man's mistakes that make him amiable.

I CAN promise to be frank, I cannot promise to be impartial.

INGRATITUDE is always a form of weakness. I have never seen a capable man who showed himself ungrateful.

IF ONE were to undertake to study all the laws, one would really not have time to transgress them.

ALL INTELLIGENT thoughts have already been thought; what is necessary is only to try to think them again.

IT DOES NOT make a whit of difference whether one is of noble or humble birth—in either case one must sweat out one's human lot.

IT IS RARE that the middle course is followed in bringing about what is good and what is right; what we usually see is obstructive pedantry or overhasty brashness.

MICROSCOPES and telescopes merely confuse pure human understanding.

I AM SILENT on many things; for I do not like to confuse people and am well satisfied if they find pleasure in that which annoys me.

ALL EXCELLENT things oppress us for a moment because we do not feel equal to them; only if we subsequently assimilate them, joining them to our own intellectual and emotional energies, shall we love and value them.

WHAT IS the best government? That which teaches us to govern ourselves.

NOTHING is more terrible than ignorance in action.

THE FIRST and last thing demanded of genius is love of truth.

Johann Wolfgang von Goethe

MYSTERIES are not miracles.

How CAN a man come to know himself? Never through contemplation, but indeed through action. Try to do your duty, and you will know at once what you amount to.

BUT WHAT is your duty? The challenge of each day.

GRAND IDEAS and great conceit are always geared to bring about fearful misfortune.

MUSIC in the best sense has little need of novelty; indeed the older it is and the more one is accustomed to it, the more effective it is.

THE POET must rely on representation. Representation is at its highest when it competes with reality, that is, when the images contrived by the mind have such living quality that they appear immediately present to everyone. In its highest form poetry seems quite external; the more it withdraws into inner realms, the more it tends to fail.—That poetry which represents only an inner essence without embodying it in an outer life, and that poetry which does not suffuse the outer life with the inner essence, are the dying phases from which poetry passes into the prosaic everyday.

PIETY is not an end, rather it is a means for attaining the highest stage of civilization through the purest serenity of heart.

WHEN A MAN is old, he must do more than when he was young.

EVEN WHEN duty has been fulfilled, one is left with a sense of guilt because in one's own judgment one has never done enough.

FAULTS are recognized only by one lacking in love; therefore in order to recognize faults one must become unloving, but not more than the situation requires.

THERE ARE two peaceful powers: Right and Propriety.

THERE IS a sensitive empiricism that intimately identifies itself with the object and thereby becomes genuine theory. This enhancement of intellectual capacity belongs, however, to an age of advanced culture.

THERE ARE pedants who are at the same time rogues, and these are the very worst.

THE GERMANS, and they are not the only ones, possess the gift of making the sciences inaccessible.

MUSIC is either sacred or profane. The sacred is entirely in accord with the dignity of music, and in this aspect it exerts its greatest influence on life, which remains the same throughout all ages and epochs. Profane music should be consistently in a cheerful vein.

THE VIRTUE of art is perhaps most eminently manifested in music because in music there is no material element that must be subtracted. It is entirely form and meaning and enhances and ennobles everything it expresses.

THE MATHEMATICIAN is perfect only in so far as he is a perfect man, as he experiences the beauty of Truth; only then does he become thorough, transparent, circumspect, pure, clear, graceful and even elegant. All this is needed to be like Lagrange.

MATHEMATICS is, like dialectics, an organ of the higher inner sense; in practice it is an art like eloquence. For both nothing is value except form; content is immaterial to them. It makes no difference in mathematics whether it is pennies or guineas that are to be computed, and in rhetoric whether it is the true or the false that is being defended.

HERE, however, the crucial issue is the character of the individual who is pursuing such a vocation, practicing such an art. An incisive advocate in a just cause, a penetrating mathematician observing the firmament, appear equally godlike.

EVERYTHING that liberates the mind without giving us control over ourselves is ruinous.

A MAN does not get rid of what is his own, even if he throws it away.

MATHEMATICS has no capacity to do away with prejudice, to moderate obstinacy, to allay factionalism; it can do nothing in the realm of morality.

THERE ARE only two true religions—the first that quite formlessly recognizes and worships the element of the sacred that dwells in and around us; the other that recognizes and worships it in the most beautiful forms. All that lies between is idolatry.

WE HAVE the unswerving, thoroughly serious aspiration, which must be renewed every day, to grasp the word most closely corresponding with what we feel, behold, think, experience, imagine, and with what we perceive by reason.

TRIALS increase with the years.

ONE IS never deceived, one deceives oneself.

HENCE the mark of highest originality lies in the ability to develop a familiar idea so fruitfully that it would seem no one else would ever have discovered so much to be hidden in it.

THERE IS no patriotic art and no patriotic science. Both, like all that is lofty and good, belong to the whole world and can be furthered only by the general free interaction of all those living in a given time, with constant regard to that which is preserved and known to us of the past.

NOTHING in life except health and virtue is more valuable than knowledge and science; nor is anything as easy to attain and as cheaply to be bought: the entire labor consists in being tranquil, and the expenditure consists of time, which we cannot save without expending it.

WHEN WE praise someone, we imagine ourselves to be like him.

THE MOST original authors of modern times are original not because they produce something new but only because they are capable of saying things in such a way as though they had never before been said.

IT IS BETTER to do the most trivial thing in the world than to consider a half-hour to be trivial.

"NATURE conceals God." But not to everyone!

GOD, if we stand in a high place, is everything; if we stand in a low place, he is a complement to our wretchedness.

FAITH is love for the invisible, trust in the impossible, the improbable.

THE CHRISTIAN religion is an intended political revolution which having failed afterward became a moral revolution.

PERFECTION is the norm of heaven; to desire what is perfect is the norm of man.

WE NEVER NOTICE anyone except persons who make us suffer. In order to go about the world unnoticed, we would only need never to hurt anyone.

ALL LAWS are attempts to approximate the purposes of the moral order in the way of the world and of life.

THERE IS no situation that could not be ennobled through action or endurance.

IF GOD had purposed that mankind should live and act in truth, he would have had to arrange things differently.

MAN IS a product not only of what is innate, but also of what is acquired.

WE KNOW only those who cause us suffering.

DUTY means loving that which one makes imperative upon oneself.

IT IS BETTER that injustices should occur than that they should be removed in an unjust way. Therefore let everyone submit to the law.

637

Johann Wolfgang von Goethe

THE ROOT EVIL—everyone would like to be what he could be, and would like the rest to be nothing, indeed, not to be.

AN INDIVIDUAL shows his character most clearly when he speaks about a great man or about something extraordinary. This is a real touchstone.

OF MERIT we demand modesty; but we listen with complacence to those who immodestly minimize merit.

EGOTISTIC provincialism, which imagines itself to be a center.

HOW THE GERMANS have carried on to ward off what I have in any event done and accomplished—and are they not still doing the same? Had they let things go and proceeded, had they exploited my gains, they would have got farther than they have.

A PARROTED TRUTH loses its grace, but a parroted fallacy is quite repellent.

EVERYONE hears only what he understands.

A CORRECT ANSWER is like an affectionate kiss.

THAT WHICH is expressed orally must be dedicated to the present, to the moment; that which is written must be dedicated to distant times, to posterity.

IN THE WORK of destruction all false arguments avail, but not in the work of construction. What is not true, does not build.

ONE MUST have found a thing if one presumes to know where it lies.

LET NO ONE think that he has been awaited as the savior!

THE WHOLE of life consists of desiring and not accomplishing, and accomplishing what has not been desired.

IN THE SPHERE of natural science we are pantheists; in the sphere of poetry, polytheists; in the sphere of morality, monotheists.

LEGISLATORS or revolutionaries who promise both equality and liberty are visionaries or charlatans.

BEFORE THE REVOLUTION everything was aspiration; after it, everything changed to demand.

To RULE and to enjoy do not go together. To enjoy means to belong to oneself and others in carefree spirit; to rule means to benefit oneself and others, in the most serious sense.

To RULE is easy to learn, to govern is difficult to learn.

IN THE NEWSPAPERS everything official is stilted, the rest flat.

THE POWER of a language lies not in its rejection of what is foreign, but rather in its assimilation of what is foreign.

I CURSE all negative purism that forbids the use of a word in which another language has grasped a meaning more fully or more sensitively.

To BE AWARE in youth of the advantages of age, to preserve in age the advantages of youth, each of these is one and the same good fortune.

AN ACTIVE skepticism is one that ceaselessly strives to overcome itself in order to achieve a kind of relative certainty through systematic experience.

IF WISE MEN never erred, fools would have to despair.

THE GOOD FORTUNE of genius—to be born in an era of high aims.

TEXTBOOKS should be alluring; they become so only when they present the most animated and least forbidding aspects of knowledge and theory.

GREAT TALENTS are the noblest means of reconciliation.

Johann Wolfgang von Goethe

ACUMEN deserts intelligent men least when they are in the wrong.

WHAT KIND of a time is this when one must envy the dead and buried!

WITHIN AN EPOCH there is no point of vantage from which to survey the epoch.

WHEN A LEXICON can keep up with an author, he is worthless.

CANTILENA: perpetuating the fullness of love and every passionate joy.

IT IS SAID, indeed in praise of the artist, that he has everything within himself. If only I need never hear this again! Closely scrutinized, the productions of such a genius are for the most part reminiscences; he who has experiences will usually be able to demonstrate them specifically.

THINKING is more interesting than knowing, but not more interesting than contemplation.

THE ERA is advanced, but each individual nevertheless begins at the beginning.

DIALECTIC is the development of the spirit of contradiction, which has been given to man to enable him to recognize differences between things.

POEMS OF WISDOM

Poems of Wisdom

HOLY YEARNING*

TELL NO man, tell wise men only,
  For the world might count it madness,
Him I praise who thirsts for fire,
  Thirsts for death, and dies in gladness.

Thou wast got, and thou begattest
  In dewy love-nights long ago;
Now a stranger love shall seize thee
  When the quiet lamp burns low.

Thou art freed and lifted, taken
  From the shadow of our night,
Thou art drawn by some new passion
  Towards a nobler marriage-rite.

Distance cannot weight thee, soaring
  Where the far enchantment calls,
Till the moth, the starfire's lover,
  Drinks the light, and burns, and falls.

Die and grow! Until thou hearest
  What that word can say,
The world is dark and thou a wanderer
  Who has lost his way.

*Translated by F. Melian Stawell

Johann Wolfgang von Goethe

ONE AND ALL*

How YEARNS the solitary soul
To melt into the boundless whole,
 And find itself again in peace!
The blind desire, the impatient will,
The restless thoughts and plans are still;
 We yield ourselves—and wake in bliss.

World-Spirit, come, our spirits firing!
For evermore to thee aspiring,
 We but obey our nature's call.
Good angels feelingly persuade us,
And heaven-taught masters gently lead us
 To Him who made and maketh all.

To re-create the old creation,
All things work on in fast rotation,
 Lest aught grow fixed, and change resist;
And what was not shall spring to birth,
As purest sun, or painted earth.
 God's universe may know no rest.

It must go on, creating, changing,
Through endless shapes forever ranging;
 And rest we only *seem* to see.
Th' Eternal lives through all revolving;
For all must ever keep dissolving,
 Would it continue still to be.

PROEM**

IN THE NAME of Him who caused Himself to be,
Creating ever from eternity,
In His name who made faith and trust and love,
The strength of things and man's activity,
Oft-named and still unfathomed mystery:

---

*Translated by John S. Dwight
**Translated by F. Melian Stawell

644

Far as thy hearing holds, far as thy sight,
Thou findest only known shapes like to His,
And soon thy spirit's furthest fire-flight
Hath store enough of symbols, likenesses.
Thou art drawn onward, sped forth joyously,
And where thou wanderest path and place grow bright;
No more thou reckonest, Time is no more for thee,
Now every footstep is Infinity.

What were a God who stood outside the whole,
Spun at His ring and let it twirl alone?
Nay, He must move the whole world from within,
His heart in Nature's and her own in His,
So that what lives and moves and dwells in Him
Can never lose His spirit and His strength.

Within us also lies a universe:
And they do well who take the best they know
And call it God, their God, trust to Him so
All things in earth beneath and heaven above,
Whom they can fear, and, where it may be, love.

WANDERER'S CONSOLATION*

OF THE BASE and the mean
Let none complain
For whatever you say, it is seen
These always win.

With the bad they dominate
For their own high profit.
Within the right they penetrate
And get their will of it.

Stranger, will you then resist
Against such trouble?
Whirlwind and caked mud persist:
Let them drive and redouble.

Translated by Stephen Spender

Johann Wolfgang von Goethe

STABILITY IN CHANGE*

WERE this early blessing steady,
   Ah, but for a single hour!
But the lukewarm West already
   Shakes abroad a blossom-shower.
Does my heart the verdure flatter,
   As its first cool shade it throws?
Soon e'en that the storms will scatter,
   Wavering pale at Autumn's close.

Wouldst thou of the fruits be tasting?
   Haste thy portion soon to get;
Some to their decay are hasting,
   Others in the bud as yet.
All thy pleasant fields are ever
   Changing with each gush of rain:
Ah! and in the self-same river
   Dost thou never swim again.

Thou thyself! thou changest, fleest;—
   Rock-firm things that by thee rise,
Walls and palaces thou seest
   Constantly with different eyes.
Vanished is the lip, that sweetly
   Revelled in the melting kiss,
And the foot, that boldly, fleetly
   Scaled, goat-like, the precipice.

Hands that, of a frank, kind nature,
   Moved but blessings to bestow,
And the form's symmetric stature,—
   All is turned another now!
And in place of these departed,
   What to bear thy name is sent,
By us like a billow darted,
   And so speeds to the Element.

*Translated by N. L. Frothingham

Let the end and the beginning
    Draw together into one!
Swifter than what's round thee spinning,
    Thou thyself be flying on!
Thanks! the Muses' gracious giving
    Makes the Imperishable thine;
In thy breast the Substance living,
    In thy soul the Form divine.

TALISMANS*

1.

THE EAST belongs to God; the West
Gladly obeys His high behest;
Tropic heat, and Arctic cold,
His hand in peaceful bond doth hold.

2.

Only God is just; He sees
    What is good for each and all:
Call Him by what name you please,
    But praise His name, both great and small.

3.

Life's a labyrinth, whose plan
Thou canst not learn from wit of man;
But make God guide in all thy ways,
And He will lead thee through the maze.

4.

Two graces give our breathing worth,
To draw air in, then send it forth;
That with a power to cramp and tighten,
This to expand us, and to lighten;—
So wondrously our life unites
Mysterious play of opposites.
Then thank thou God when He confines thy way,
And thank Him too when He gives larger sway.

---

*Translated by J. S. Blackie

Johann Wolfgang von Goethe

THE REUNION*

CAN IT BE! of stars the star,
  Do I press thee to my heart?
In the night of distance far,
  What deep gulf, what bitter smart!
Yes, 'tis thou, indeed at last,
  Of my joys the partner dear!
Mindful, though, of sorrows past,
  I the present needs must fear.

When the still unfashioned earth
  Lay on God's eternal breast,
He ordained its hour of birth,
  With creative joy possessed.
Then a heavy sigh arose,
  When He spake the sentence:—"Be!"
And the All, with mighty throes,
  Burst into reality.

And when thus was born the light,
  Darkness near it feared to stay,
And the elements with might
  Fled on every side away;
Each on some far-distant trace,
  Each with visions wild employed,
Numb, in boundless realms of space,
  Harmony and feeling-void.

Dumb was all, all still and dead,
  For the first time, God alone!
Then He formed the morning-red,
  Which soon made its kindness known:
It unravelled from the waste,
  Bright and glowing harmony,
And once more with love was graced
  What contended formerly.

---

*Translated by E. A. Bowring

648

And with earnest, noble strife,
 Each its own peculiar sought;
Back to full, unbounded life,
 Sight and feeling soon were brought.
Wherefore, if 'tis done, explore
 How? why give the manner, name?
Allah need create no more,
 We his world ourselves can frame.

So, with morning pinions bright,
 To thy mouth was I impelled;
Stamped with thousand seals by night,
 Star-clear is the bond fast held,
Paragons on earth are we
 Both of grief and joy sublime,
And a second sentence:—"Be!"
 Parts us not a second time.

IT IS GOOD*

In Paradise while moonbeams play'd,
 Jehovah found, in slumber deep,
Adam fast sunk; He gently laid
 Eve near him,—she, too, fell asleep.
There lay they now, on earth's fair shrine,
God's two most beauteous thoughts divine.—
When this He saw, He cried: 'Tis Good!!!
And scarce could move from where He stood.

No wonder, that our joy's complete
While eye and eye responsive meet,
When this blest thought of rapture moves us—
That we're with him who truly loves us.
And if he cries: Good, let it be!
'Tis so for both, it seems to me.
Thou'rt clasp'd within these arms of mine,
Dearest of all God's thoughts divine!

---

*Translated by E. A. Bowring

Johann Wolfgang von Goethe

THE UNLIMITED*

THAT THOU can'st never end, doth make thee great,
And that thou ne'er beginnest, is thy fate.
Thy song is changeful as yon starry frame,
End and beginning evermore the same;
And what the middle bringeth, but contains
What was at first, and what at last remains.

Thou art of joy the true and minstrel-source,
From thee pours wave on wave with ceaseless force.
A mouth that's aye prepar'd to kiss,
    A breast whence flows a loving song,
A throat that finds no draught amiss,
    An open heart that knows no wrong.

And what though all the world should sink!
    Hafis, with thee, alone with thee
    Will I contend! joy, misery,
    The portion of us twain shall be!
Like thee to love, like thee to drink,—
    This be my pride,—this, life to me!

Now, Song, with thine own fire be sung,—
For thou art older, thou more young!

PRIMEVAL ORPHIC SAYINGS

DESTINY**

As ON the day that brought thee to this earth
The sun stood in conjunction with the stars,
So art thou fashioned by the heavenly laws
That mark thy ways and walk with thee from birth.
Thus art thou stamped: thyself thou canst not flee.
Thus spake the Sibyls, thus the Prophets spake.
Not vasty time nor any power can break
The living Form that grows eternally.

Translated by E. A. Bowring
**Translated by F. Melian Stawell and Nora Purtscher Wydenbruck*

NECESSITY*

Then is it once more as the stars decree,
Limit and law: and all our human will
Is but to want that which we know should be,
And wilfulness through will is shamed and still:
Our dearest, loveliest wish we drive away,
Our will, our whims the stern "Thou must" obey.
Our freedom's fancied; after many a year
We are more fast-bound than we ever were.

HOPE*

And yet these barriers and this cruel door
Set in the brazen wall can be unbarred
Though firm-set as old mountains iron-hard.
A spirit light, untamed, flies on before,
Out of the cloud, the mist, the dreary rain
She raises us, she gives us wings again.
You know her well: through all spheres will she find us—
One beat of wings—and ages lie behind us!

CHANCE*

Yet round about the iron barrier goes
A kindly wanderer, wandering with us.
You are not lone, you grow with other men
And live in action as another does.
The luck of life, once good, turns ill again:
A toy it is in an unending game,
And when the circle of the year is run
The lamp waits there for the reviving flame.

LOVE**

It comes at last. From heaven it falls, down-darting,
    Whither from ancient chaos up it flew;
Around it floats, now near, and then departing.
    It fans the brow and breast the Spring-day through:
Mournful though sweet, a saddened bliss imparting,
    Rousing vague longings for the Fair and True,
While most hearts fade away, unfixed, alone,
The noblest is devoted to the *One*.

*Translated by F. Melian Stawell and Nora Purtscher Wydenbruck
**Translated by James F. Clarke

Johann Wolfgang von Goethe

ZULEIKA*

Thou mayst choose a thousand forms to hide thee,
Yet, All-beloved, I shall know thee there;
Thou mayst take enchanted veils to shroud thee,
Yet, thou All-present, I shall feel thee near.

In the pure springing of the tall young cypress,
All-stateliest, I know thee well the while,
In the pure lakelet's limpid, laughing ripple,
Thou All-beguiler, I behold thy smile.

And when the fountain lifts her jet and opens,
All-playfullest, I gaze upon thy glee,
And when the cloud-forms change their changing fashion,
All-myriad-natured, I am sure of thee.

Gay in the meadow's flower-embroidered raiment,
All-starry-brightness, I can see thy face;
Where the light-handed ivy climbs and clusters,
All-clamberer, I catch thy eager grace.

When the new morning flames upon the mountains,
All-gladdener, gladly I welcome thee,
And when the pure sky arches out above us,
All-heart-enlarger, I know it breathes of thee.

If aught I learn by outward sense or inward,
All-learned teacher, I learn it all through thee,
And when I name the hundred names of Allah,
There echoes with each one a name for thee.

FROM HOW MANY ELEMENTS**

From how many elements
Should a proper song be nourished
For the layman's entertainment
And by the Master to be cherished?

---

*Translated by F. Melian Stawell
**Translated by Stephen Spender

652

Love, love above everything
Be our theme when we sing:
If through the whole song it ring
So much the better will it wing.

Then ruby of the wine must shine
And there must be glasses' chink:
The loveliest chaplet is the sign
Of those who love and those who drink.

Clash of arms we also claim
So that trumpets blare with glory
And when Fortune bursts in flame
Heroes be deified by victory.

Last, it's indispensable
That poetic hatred thrive:
What's ugly and insufferable
Unlike the lovely, make not live.

If the singer have the skill
To mix such elemental flesh,
Equal with Hafiz, then he will
Rejoice men ever and refresh.

ANACREON'S GRAVE*

WHERE the rose is fresh and blooming—where the vine and myrtle
    spring—
Where the turtle-dove is cooing—where the gay cicalas sing—
Whose may be the grave surrounded with such store of comely
    grace,
Like a God-created garden? 'Tis Anacreon's resting place.
Spring and summer and the autumn poured their gifts around the
    bard,
And, ere winter came to chill him, sound he slept beneath the
    sward.

---

*Translated by W. E. Aytoun

Johann Wolfgang von Goethe

TAKE MY LIFE*

TAKE my life in one big chunk,
Precisely as I lead it;
Others may sleep off their drunk,
Mine's on paper—read it.

IN LIVING AS IN WHAT YOU KNOW**

IN LIVING as in what you know
Be studious of the Way you go:
Then storm and current, when they pull you,
Will not ever overrule you.
Compass and pole-star, chronometer,
And sun and moon, these known, the quieter
Will be your joy when you fulfill
Your voyage, according to your skill.
Especially if there's nothing soil you
So the Way in a circle coil you;
Then, globe-encompasser, you'll find
The port your ship first left behind.

FROM FATHER**

FROM FATHER I have the stature
For earnest living without fail,
From mother this uncaring nature
This joy telling a tale.
Great-grandfather was the ladies' man
This spook walks, soon or late;
Great-grandmother loved jewels which can
Over limbs palpitate.
Are not the elements all here
To compose this complexity:
And what in the whole chap is there
Can claim originality?

Translated by Calvin Thomas
**Translated by Stephen Spender*

654

TO AMERICA*

AMERICA, you're better off than
Our continent, the old.
You have no castles which are fallen
No basalt to behold.
You're not disturbed within your inmost being
Right up till today's daily life
By useless remembering
And unrewarding strife.

Use well the present and good luck to you
And when your children begin writing poetry
Let them guard well in all they do
Against knight- robber- and ghost-story.

---

*Translated by Stephen Spender